Mineral Nutrients in Tropical Forest and Savanna Ecosystems

SPECIAL PUBLICATION NUMBER 9 OF THE
BRITISH ECOLOGICAL SOCIETY

EDITED BY

J. PROCTOR
School of Natural Sciences
University of Stirling

BLACKWELL SCIENTIFIC PUBLICATIONS

OXFORD LONDON EDINBURGH

BOSTON MELBOURNE

1989

First published 1989

Set by Times Graphics, Singapore
Printed and bound in Great Britain
at The University Press, Cambridge

DISTRIBUTORS

Marston Book Services Ltd
PO Box 87
Oxford OX2 0DT
(*Orders*: Tel. 0865 791155
         Fax. 0865 791927
         Telex. 837515)

USA
Publishers' Business Services
PO Box 147
Brookline Village
Massachusetts 02147
(*Orders*: Tel. (617) 524 7678)

Canada
Oxford University Press
70 Wynford Drive
Don Mills
Ontario M3C 1J9
(*Orders*: Tel. (416) 441 2941)

Australia
Blackwell Scientific Publications
(Australia) Pty Ltd
107 Barry Street
Carlton, Victoria 3053
(*Orders*: Tel. (03) 347 0300)

British Library
Cataloguing in Publication Data

Mineral nutrients in tropical forest and
   savanna ecosystems
   1. Tropical regions. Soils
   I. Proctor, J.   II. Series
   631.4′913
   ISBN 0-632-02559-X

Library of Congress
Cataloguing-in-Publication Data

Mineral nutrients in tropical forest and
   savanna ecosystems/edited by J. Proctor.
   (Special publication no. 9 of the British
   Ecological Society)
   Includes index.
   ISBN 0-632-02559-X
   1. Rain forest ecology. 2. Savanna
   ecology. 3. Mineral cycle
   (Biogeochemistry)—Tropics. 4. Plant–soil
   relationships—Tropics.   I. Proctor, J.
   II. Series.
   QK936.M56   1989
   574.5′2642—dc19

Contents

iii

Preface

The aim of this symposium was to assess current knowledge of the mineral nutrient factors which are important in tropical rain forests and for their management. Papers were read by agronomists, ecologists, geographers, hydrologists, plant physiologists and soil scientists. They each gave an interpretation of concepts and methods from the viewpoint of their own discipline and it is hoped that the book can be viewed as an integrated appraisal of the current state of knowledge in the field. It is intended that it be used by all students and researchers who are interested in tropical rain forests.

The papers are arranged thematically after the Introduction by T. C. Whitmore. The first group of papers deals with aspects of soils and hydrology. The second deals with ecological aspects of the mineral nutrition of lowland forests whilst the third discusses savannas. Two papers are included in a short section dealing with montane forests. An important area where mineral nutrition impinges on forest management is shifting cultivation. Several papers deal with this and extend the spectrum of the book to include the growth of crops on soils formerly under rain forest. This wider scope is essential in areas where integrated land-use management is practised as part of a conservation strategy. Finally, there is an overview section in which an experienced hydrologist, ecologist and soil scientist each give their thoughts on the subject.

I would like to thank the anonymous referees for their help. Dr E. Broadhead and later Professor C. H. Gimingham gave much support and good advice from the Publications Committee of the British Ecological Society (BES). Financial assistance for the Symposium was provided by the BES and the International Union of Biological Sciences. Dr M. Hadley is thanked for his help in arranging funding from the latter. Special thanks are due to Dr B. R. Trenbath for his help with the organization of the session on shifting cultivation and in the preparation of the papers from it for publication. Mrs M. Burnett of the University of Stirling provided flawless secretarial assistance at every stage of the Symposium and the production of this volume.

J. PROCTOR

Tropical forest nutrients, where do we stand?
A *tour de horizon*

T. C. WHITMORE

Department of Plant Sciences,
South Parks Road, Oxford OX1 3RB

SUMMARY

1 Conventional wisdom that rain forest ecosystems have most of their mineral nutrients in the above-ground biomass and have tight nutrient cycles is apparently frequently untrue. There are no studies of all nutrient pools and flows.
2 The biological processes which underly shifting agriculture are now well understood and are being utilized to devise more intensive farming systems based on it.
3 Soils under heath forests have similar total amounts of nutrients to those under other kinds of rain forest. These soils are very acid and easily degraded. Heath forests may suffer periodic drought. Fuller comparative studies of nutrition and hydrology are needed.
4 The zonation of forest formations on tropical mountains and their compression on low and outlying peaks is still unexplained. Adaptation to periodic drought or to oligotrophy have both been invoked. There may be no universal explanation.
5 Various correlations between species ranges and soils occur. Soil specificity is only one of many factors which contribute to the species richness of tropical rain forests.
6 Virgin rain forests are fast disappearing as a result of pressures for national development. For sustainable utilization to be possible, more information is needed on nutrients in first and later generation tree plantations, and in forests totally harvested for their biomass.

INTRODUCTION

The study of nutrients in natural tropical forests (reviewed by Proctor (1983, 1987)) has been based on insufficient good data and has been driven forward largely by the hope that it will shed light on some of the problems connected with these forests which forest ecologists find perennially fascinating.

While forest ecologists have been at work on forest nutrients there have been other studies in progress of which they are largely unaware. This Symposium brings together work on forest hydrology and a whole set of investigations into aspects of traditional farming systems in rain forest climates which have involved soil agronomists, anthropologists, chemists and geographers.

After a review I suggest directions in which it would be desirable to channel further effort. This paper is written with no special knowledge, and is a review from the outside of the important and complex discipline discussed at the Symposium. It attempts to 'see the wood' without getting lost amongst the 'trees'.

NUTRIENT POOLS AND CYCLES

The study of nutrient pools and transfers between them in tropical rain forests is important because of pressures either to utilize the forests for timber production or to convert them to forest plantations or agriculture.

Conventional wisdom

There are twin pillars of conventional wisdom. Firstly, there is the belief that all or most of the nutrients in tropical rain forest ecosystems are in the above-ground biomass. Secondly, it is widely held that these forests have closed and tight nutrient cycles with little or no leakage out of them. These ideas can be traced back to the 1930s when studies in East Africa purported to explain why tobacco crops failed on sites cleared of lush tropical forest in the Usambara hills (Richards (1952) gives a summary).

These are intuitively appealing ideas, but have been proved to be too simple and largely incorrect now that more data have been assembled. The twin myths are both now dismantled, although not everyone who talks and writes about tropical rain forests has realized.

Nutrient pools

There are many tropical rain forests which have a substantial proportion of the total ecosystem nutrients below ground, mostly in the soil within rooting depth. This is clearly shown in fig. 10.1 of Whitmore (1984a) and fig. 11.4 of Jordan (1985). A few forests do approach the old paradigm for some nutrients, notably the central Amazon forest analysed by Klinge (1976). Some forests have a substantial root biomass, and in the extreme case of some of the San Carlos, Venezuela, forests, below-ground biomass exceeds that above ground (Medina & Cuevas *this volume*). Jordan (1985) showed that in lowland forest ecosystems less calcium and potassium is retained in the soil in very wet compared with less wet climates due to differences in leaching, and pointed to similarities between tropical montane and temperate broadleaf forests.

Nutrient cycles

Comparison of the nutrients received by a forest from rainfall with the losses in stream water has shown that many forests are leaky, losing more than they receive (see table 3 in Proctor (1987)). The data are critically reviewed by Bruijnzeel (*this volume*). He points out that input in solution, which is always at very low concentrations, is very prone to overestimation because of contaminants, but this is compensated by aerosol input (e.g. in smoke from nearby shifting cultivators) which is seldom measured. If all studies are compared, Bruijnzeel finds there is a pattern, with export in stream water related to substrate lithology. The very infertile soils of South America have little leakage (Bruijnzeel *this volume*; Medina & Cuevas *this volume*), or even apparently a slight net increase (Poels 1987), whereas fertile soils have higher leakage. These conclusions are based on the measurement of input to and export from small catchments (which are assumed to be watertight) and depend on the assumption that all the nutrients are within the ecosystem. Many tropical soils are, however, very deep, with saprolite beyond the reach of plant roots as both Burnham (*this volume*) and Kellman (*this volume*) demonstrate. On such soils, nutrients may be weathered out of the saprolite and exported in streamflow, but never enter the ecosystem. Nutrient mass balance studies of catchments on deep soils may therefore be misinterpreted to indicate ecosystem nutrient leakage. Nevertheless, many tropical rain forests occur on hilly or mountainous terrain with continually rejuvenating soils in which surface erosion removes the topsoil and parent material enters the bottom of the rooting zone, where it weathers and releases nutrients. We can draw a contrast between such forests, which are widespread, for example, in Malaysia (e.g. Sarawak (Baillie & Ashton 1983)) and along the slopes of the Andes or Ruwenzori ranges, and others which grow on deep, ancient soils with no rejuvenation, such as the huge plains of Tertiary sediments of the central Amazon. On shallow and rejuvenating soils the whole solum is within the ecosystem. In addition, some deep tropical soils are periodically rejuvenated by additions of volcanic ash, for example those under lower montane forests in Ecuador and New Guinea studied by Grubb *et al.* (1963) and Edwards & Grubb (1977), respectively. In conclusion, although there undoubtedly are forested catchments which lose more nutrients than they gain, there are many others which leak nutrients.

Nutrient cycling within the ecosystem has also received attention. In his review Bruijnzeel (*this volume*) shows that rainfall throughfall measurements are commonly unrepresentative, and to a lesser extent stemflow measurements also. None of the several studies made of nutrient transfer in stemflow and through-flow are based on the rigorous sampling regime Bruijnzeel now shows to be essential. The problems in drawing generalizations on nutrient cycling from these studies are therefore very likely because the data are inadequate.

Forest floor and decomposers

Nutrients which reach the forest floor in solution or in litterfall are trapped by the root mat which is strongly mycorrhizal. Measurements of litterfall decomposition rates have aroused controversy. It was first thought that decomposition was rapid. Then as data accumulated it was realized that there were methodological problems; after allowing for these there is a spread of rates in both tropical and temperate forests with considerable overlap (Anderson & Swift 1983). Jordan (*this volume*) argues that if proper allowance is made for moisture, temperature and soil fertility then tropical decomposition rates are higher.

There are considerable differences in the composition of the soil macrofaunal decomposer community between tropical and temperate forests. In the lowland tropics termites are commonly held to be the main group of decomposers, but there have been very few studies to substantiate this. Termites also comminute soil (Burnham *this volume*) and some termites create local concentrations of nutrients which are preferentially colonized by seedlings of some tree species (see below). Opening a forest canopy alters the microclimate and may change the composition of the termite community.

It is probably the case that forest alteration which damages the forest floor, including the root mat, either physically or by exposure to the open, changes and usually impairs the ability of the forest to trap and cycle nutrients and also to regenerate its canopy. An important aspect of sustainable management of tropical rain forests is, it appears, to minimize damage to the forest floor.

Discussion

There have been no studies of all pools and flows. For example, the studies of Proctor *et al.* (1983) in Gunung Mulu National Park, Sarawak contained no destructive sampling and so omitted biomass nutrients and the New Guinea montane forest study of Edwards and Grubb (1977) omitted streamflow. There may be systematic differences between forest nutrients in rejuvenating soils and those in other soils in which the saprolite is uncoupled from the ecosystem. The oligotrophic ecosystems studied in detail in Amazonia probably represent one end of the spectrum in this respect.

MYCORRHIZAS

One recent development in the analysis of forest ecosystem nutrients has been the realization of the probably important role of mycorrhizas in various ways (Alexander *this volume*). Their role in nutrient trapping in the root mat at San Carlos (Medina & Cuevas *this volume*) led to the now discredited direct nutrient cycling hypothesis (Janos 1983; Alexander *this volume*). They sometimes play a role in species–site relationships (e.g. in Korup (Gartlan *et al.* 1986), see below). We do not yet know their significance in forest recovery after disturbance.

SHIFTING AGRICULTURE

The old view of colonial days that shifting agriculture is a destructive and primitive form of farming only persists in a few places, sometimes as part of a government's policy to 'improve' 'backward' tribespeople. It is, however, only able to support about seven people per square kilometre because of the large fraction of the area under bush fallow at any one time. Under pressure from increasing populations, and sometimes also from a government's desire to convert unproductive bush fallow areas to cash-generating use, fallow periods are often curtailed. This destroys the biological basis of the system, the fallow period is no longer of sufficient length to restore fertility, and the system breaks down. Geographers and anthropologists have now uncovered many examples of the subtlety of shifting agriculturalists, for example in New Guinea and north-east Kalimantan (Bayliss-Smith & Feacham 1977; Kartawinata *et al.* 1981). A body of data from all parts of the tropics documents recovery of above-ground ecosystem nutrients during the fallow period. Shifting agriculture is now widely recognized as a sustainable low-input system well suited to infertile tropical soils prone to strong leaching and erosion. Many of its facets have been closely analysed as can be seen from the eight papers in this volume devoted to it. Soil chemists have analysed changes in the soil after forest clearance (e.g. Mueller-Harvey, Juo & Wild *this volume*; Robertson *this volume*; Sibanda & Young *this volume*). Nutrient uptake by crops, weeds and bush fallow shrubs and trees has been studied (e.g. Lambert & Arnason *this volume*; Nakano & Syahbuddin *this volume*). It has been shown that farmers themselves adapt to changing circumstances by introducing cash crops (e.g. Juo & Kang *this volume*) and by modifying rotations and mixtures (e.g. Ramakrishnan *this volume*). Trees as 'nutrient pumps' are believed to be an important biological component of shifting agriculture. This property is exploited in the mixed cultivation of trees and herbaceous crops. For example, 'alley-cropping', in which rows of trees and crops alternate, has been closely investigated at IITA in Nigeria; systems stable (so far for 10 years or more) on non-acidic alfisols have been developed; however, as yet no trees have been discovered which are suitable for alley-cropping on the far more extensive acid soils (Juo & Kang *this volume*). Some tree and weed species concentrate certain plant mineral nutrients in their above-ground parts. In north-east India Ramakrishnan (*this volume*) and colleagues have found that the introduced vigorous weedy climber *Mikania cordata* concentrates potassium. After a few years of fallow it is shaded out and the same role is taken over by the bamboo *Dendrocalamus hamiltonianus*. The bush fallow period in north-east India has been successfully shortened by planting *Alnus nepalensis* which fixes nitrogen, and which can sustain repeated coppicing (Ramakrishnan *this volume*).

The mixed cultivation of trees and food crops is currently fashionable with development agencies, and the term 'agroforestry' has been coined. Both shifting agriculture and agroforestry are here to stay. Both are being developed in some places by the activities of farmers themselves (Juo & Kang *this volume*; Ramakrishnan *this volume*). Outsiders can facilitate development. Many of the problems are the concerns of soil science, agronomy and socio-economics which are outside the expertise of forest ecologists. Foresters of the Oxford Forestry Institute are introducing to cultivation new species and new ecotypes of already cultivated species (e.g. *Gliricidia sepium, Leucaena leucocephala*) which are likely to be useful in mixed cropping systems.

HEATH FORESTS

These are the forests of distinctive structure and physiognomy which grow on podzolized quartz sands (residual soils, sandy alluvium or old beach terraces). They are extensive in South America, where they are called *caatinga Amazonian* or *campina*, and in west Malaysia, but are virtually absent from Africa, except for small coastal areas of Cameroon (Newbery *et al.* 1986), Gabon and Ivory Coast. Some detailed studies have been carried out.

In Borneo heath forests are called *kerangas*, which in the Iban language means land which will not grow rice, and it is widely believed that the soil is extremely infertile. In fact, all the analyses published so far show that soil nutrients are not less abundant under virgin heath forest (see Fig. 1), and so on this point also conventional wisdom is wrong. These soils are, however, unusually acid, even by tropical standards (pH *c.* 3.5) (see Fig. 1), and unadapted species, including crops, may suffer toxicity from hydrogen ions or possibly from phenols (Proctor *et al.* 1983). Heath forest soils also degrade very quickly once the forest has been removed. Humus (which may be abundant) oxidizes, clay leaches down the profile (Riswan 1982) and the remaining bleached quartz sand gets very hot when exposed to the sun. These are truly fragile sites.

Explanations for the distinctive structure and physiognomy of heath forests have been sought in both nutrient poverty and in periodic water shortage. In a recent review Vitousek & Sanford (1986) compared foliar and fine litterfall nutrients of various rain forests, and showed that nitrogen and phosphorus appear to cycle less in heath forests than in other lowland forests, even though (above and Fig. 1) amounts in the soil are not unusually low. At both San Carlos in Venezuela (Bongers, Engelen & Klinge 1985) and in Sarawak (Brünig 1969; Baillie 1972, 1976) short periods of water shortage occurred in the heath forests studied which were very wet for most of the time. I have argued elsewhere that the special structural and physiognomic features of these forests are adaptations to minimize heat load during dry periods (Whitmore 1984a), and Medina, Sobrado & Herrera (1978) demonstrated this effect for one of the heath forest types at San Carlos.

In Sarawak there is a range of low to tall heath forests whose floristics and structure have been well described by Brünig (1974). The relative importance of oligotrophy and drought in determining the distinctive features of this forest formation would be illuminated by comprehensive studies of water balance over a prolonged period and of ecosystem nutrient pools and cycles in samples of this range of heath forests. As yet there has been no detailed investigation of an apparently similar and often contiguous kind of forest found in Sarawak, called

---

FIG. 1. Soil analyses of various tropical rain forests in Asia, America and Africa and in adjacent forests at Mulu, Sarawak (heath forests represented as solid circles). Data are from the surface horizon 0–2 (5) cm and are taken from Proctor *et al.* (1983), tables 7 and 10 (exchangeable bases and cation exchange capacity (CEC) in m-equiv. 100 g^{-1}; phosphorus in $\mu g\ g^{-1}$).

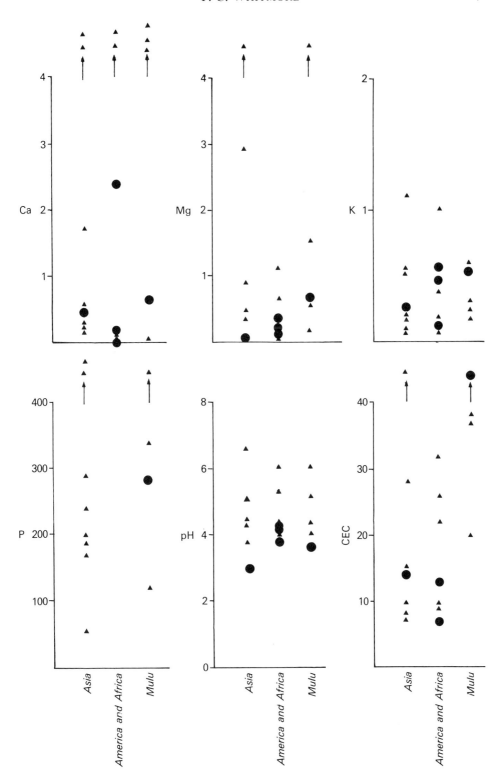

kerapah, which experiences periodic waterlogging. This is a further example where hydrologists and forest ecologists need to collaborate.

MONTANE FORESTS

One question which has puzzled and irritated scientists is why forests change with increasing elevation on tropical mountains. There is a change in forest structure and physiognomy with increasing elevation, notably a decrease in stature and biomass plus a change to scleromorphic microphylls. As a consequence, the same sequence of forest formations can be recognized on wet mountains throughout the tropics. Moreover, the zones are always extended on large cordilleras in comparison with small outlying mountains, the so-called *Massenerhebung* effect.

There are similarities in structure and physiognomy between upper montane rain forest and heath forest (as well as with some kinds of peat swamp forest) and in Malaysia a few species occur in more than one of these formations.

The zonation and compression of forest formations on mountains have attracted much study. As with heath forest, either periodic water shortage or nutrient shortage have been suggested to be responsible. Other factors, e.g. wind, also play a role in some cases. Upper montane rain forest occurs above the lower level of persistent cloud. Even so, many (if not all) mountain tops may suffer occasional water shortage in exceptionally clear weather spells. Leaching of nutrients from ridge crests or their immobilization in peat (which is often formed in mist-sodden forests) could cause oligotrophy. Heaney & Proctor (*this volume*) show that available nitrogen in the soil and nitrogen concentration in litterfall diminish with elevation on Volcán Barva, Costa Rica. Vitousek & Sanford (1986) suggested, from foliar nutrient and fine litterfall studies, that compared with lowland forests, nitrogen cycles less in montane forests.

As in heath forests, periodic water shortage has to be tolerated even if it is rare, and much of the structure and physiognomy of upper montane forest which makes it look so similar to heath forest may be similarly adapted to reduce heat load and minimize water loss in rare dry periods. Long-term studies of the complete water balance spanning one of the rare drought periods are needed before the role of water balance can be assessed, plus a detailed ecophysiological study of, for example, leaf temperature. Studies of leaf water relations in a Malayan upper montane rain forest have shown that few of the handful of species investigated are able to control water loss in desiccating conditions (Buckley, Corlett & Grubb 1980).

Tanner *et al.* (1988) increased the girth growth of upper montane forest trees in Jamaica by large annual additions of both nitrogen and phosphorus for 4 years. They concluded that for at least a few common tree species in the forest type studied these nutrients are limiting. However, in order to demonstrate that upper montane forest occurs as a result of low soil nutrients, it would be necessary to show that nutrient addition leads to its replacement by lower montane forest with its completely different suite of structural and physiognomic characteristics, not simply that girth growth is enhanced.

Studies of the forests of the small island Rakata of the Krakatau group could provide illumination on this intractable question (Bush 1986). The island is 735 m high. The forests are floristically the same from sea-level to summit, but become stunted upwards. During the study period of only a few weeks the mountain top had frequent cloud and was cooler. Water deficiency is more likely at low elevations. Soils are similar at all elevations and show no evidence of leaching. The forests of Rakata provide an opportunity to study the same species in the various environments which occur up a mountain. This removes one of the usual difficulties, i.e. not only structure and physiognomy but also flora change with elevation. For example, trees of different species naturally attain different heights, which complicates the ecophysiological analysis of zonation.

I suspect that there is no single universal set of causes of forest zonation and its compression on wet tropical mountains. Zonation itself may differ in ecophysiologically important details; for example, some Sumatran mountains have mesophyllous upper montane forest (Whitten *et al.* 1984). To penetrate these perplexing questions further will require prolonged and detailed analysis of both hydrology and mineral nutrition.

SPECIES RICHNESS

The desire to account for high species richness has been another driving force of tropical forest ecology. By contrast with the montane forest conundrum it has proved somewhat tractable. Some tropical forests are extremely rich with over 200 species ≥ 10 cm ha^{-1}. We now realize that there are many contributing factors (Whitmore 1984a, b). Here we are only concerned with those related to soils and soil nutrients.

Any discussion of species richness must specify the spatial scale (Whittaker 1972). At a coarse level there are floristic differences between forest formations on contrasting soil types, for example between peat swamp, heath and lowland evergreen rain forest. At a finer level, some species have different topographic preferences within a formation which are also likely to reflect differences in soil; this was first shown by Ashton (1964) at Andulau, Brunei.

Correlation of species distribution with soil becomes more equivocal once these two levels of variation have been removed. The question is partly whether numerous species co-exist by fine partitioning of the physical habitat between themselves. Can we demonstrate close correlations between species occurrence and soil chemical or physical properties?

A recent study at Korup, Cameroon showed a strong correlation between soils of low phosphorus (≤ 5 μg g^{-1}) available in the wet season and species of leguminous trees of tribes Amherstiae and Detarieae of the Caesalpinioideae, which are unusual in the family in having ectotrophic mycorrhiza, and therefore probably have enhanced phosphorus-trapping capacity compared with other trees (Gartlan *et al.* 1986). As the authors point out, although there is clear species segregation according to soil phosphorus, this niche has only been divided into two at Korup.

In another study which addressed this question sample plots were enumerated throughout Sarawak on a wide range of soils. As Burnham (*this volume*) points out these are shallow soils in which the saprolite is within the rooting zone, although these sedimentary rocks are, in fact, very low in plant nutrients. From an analysis of the sample plots, Ashton (1977) proposed that at total soil phosphorus concentrations below 200 μg g^{-1} spatial variation in species composition can be related to soil mineral nutrients rather than to differences in phytogeographic history, for example. Baillie & Ashton (1983) examined the subset of plots on sedimentary rock and discovered a correlation between plot floristics and available magnesium. Recently, Baillie (*this volume*) has found available magnesium to be the major soil difference between two adjacent vegetation types in Belize and explains these unexpected discoveries in terms of an influence on phosphorus uptake.

The many investigations carried out to unravel species–site correlations within tropical rain forest (initially and most thoroughly in west Malaysian dipterocarp forests; reviewed in Whitmore (1984a)) have led most rain forest ecologists to believe that it is very unlikely that physically different sites exist for all the hundred or more tree species which can co-exist on a single hectare. Species may differ in other aspects of their ecology, e.g. seedling shade tolerance, and it may well be that rare species can co-exist with identical ecology because they seldom or never meet.

Seedling establishment is perhaps the most important single phase of the forest growth cycle for the control of species composition. It is therefore of great interest that at San Carlos, Venezuela 'vigorous crops of tree seedlings sprouted from several abandoned termitaria' and soil analysis showed significantly increased concentration of nutrients in termitaria (Salick, Herrera & Jordan 1983). The leaf cutter ant *Atta* likewise concentrated nutrients in Venezuela under a rain forest on an oxisol (Haines 1983). These discoveries seem to warrant further study and bring me to my final section.

FUTURE STUDIES

Tropical rain forests are rapidly disappearing. Scientists of our generation are living through the stage when there cease to be huge, continuous tracts. Increasingly, the remaining forests persist only as isolated fragments. The tide of national development will not be reversed.

I strongly believe that we have a duty to focus our work on problems which make possible the sustained use of land in the humid tropics. This makes it more feasible for a nation to leave parts of its forest untouched. Otherwise, without the knowledge to do better, forests will be destroyed for nothing and wastelands will be created.

There are two directions where I believe more basic research in tropical forest nutrients is needed to underpin and contribute to sound national development.

Forest plantations

'There is no such thing as a free lunch'. The growth and harvesting of plantation trees inevitably removes some of the ecosystem nutrients. Ultimately the system runs down. Although much is involved in addition to nutrient pools, scientists need to unravel, and to develop an understanding of, ecosystem processes so that plantations can be made to work. The research by Russell at Jari (see Sanchez *et al.* (1985)), for example, shows that under *Gmelina* biomass phosphorus and calcium actually increase, but this unexpected result might be an artefact of the sampling system employed. More study is needed of nutrients under second and later generation plantations (Lundgren 1980).

On central Javanese lower montane andosols *Pinus merkusii* (but not the more valuable *Agathis dammara*) can be grown and harvested without lowering ecosystem nutrients (Bruijnzeel 1984; Bruijnzeel & Wiersum 1985).

Is there perhaps a systematic difference in the nutrient economy between plantations on non-rejuvenating and rejuvenating soils, i.e. broadly between plains and hills?

Forests for biomass

In some parts of the humid tropics rain forest is utilized for fuel wood, for example in Brazil to smelt iron, fuel power stations or dry bauxite. In three places in dryland rain forest, Gogol (Papua New Guinea), Bajo Calima (Colombia) and Sipitang (Sabah), most of the above-ground biomass is being harvested for wood chips for paper making. Mangrove forests in Malaysia and India are also being used as a source of cellulose.

We have little concrete knowledge about the sustainability of these extraction systems which are so far all at the first rotation. Concern should focus on nutrients. There are nutrient additions from the atmosphere everywhere; however, the inputs from the soil are more site specific. Would biomass productivity of the regrowth forest and ecosystem nutrient levels be usefully enhanced if power station ash were returned as fertilizer, or if the bark was stripped off and left behind in the forest? Is there enough weathering of parent material to maintain adequate ecosystem nutrient levels on hilly sites with rejuvenating soil? Can total biomass extraction be practised on hills without catastrophic erosion?

CONCLUSION

The study of tropical forest nutrients has progressed, as do other subjects, by the collection of data, interspersed by attempts to seek generalities. Progress in this field has been hampered because some of the early generalizations were extremely plausible and became fixed beliefs. The rapid advances of the past decade or so have overthrown these fixed beliefs, and have also led to the rapid supersedence of successive attempts at generalization as the diversity and complexity of nutrient pools and cycles have been progressively revealed. Progress has also come from more applied scientists seeking to investigate how shifting agriculture works as a sustainable system. I believe that more collaboration between different specialists working together is badly needed. Furthermore, comparative studies of different forest ecosystems will prove to be useful in the explanation of the intricacies of the ecosystems and will provide a basis for sound generalizations. Above all, I believe that we have a responsibility to address those scientific questions which underpin the utilization of tropical rain forests and the sites they occupy. We owe this to the future.

REFERENCES

Anderson, J.M. & Swift, M.J. (1983). Decomposition in tropical rain forests. *Tropical Rain Forest: Ecology and Management* (Ed. by S.L. Sutton, T.C. Whitmore & A.C. Chadwick), pp. 287–309. Blackwell Scientific Publications, Oxford.

Ashton, P.S. (1964). *Ecological Studies in the Mixed Dipterocarp Forests of Brunei State. Oxford Forestry Memoirs 25.* Oxford University Press, Oxford.

Ashton, P.S. (1977). A contribution of rain forest research to evolutionary theory. *Annals of the Missouri Botanical Garden*, **64**, 694–705.

Baillie, I.C. (1972). *Further Studies on the Occurrence of Drought in Sarawak. Soil Survey Report F7.* Forest Department, Kuching.

Baillie, I.C. (1976). Further studies on drought in Sarawak, East Malaysia. *Journal of Tropical Geography*, **43**, 20–29.

Baillie, I.C. & Ashton, P.S. (1983). Some soil aspects of the nutrient cycle in mixed dipterocarp forests in Sarawak. *Tropical Rain Forest: Ecology and Management* (Ed. by S.L. Sutton, T.C. Whitmore & A.C. Chadwick), pp. 347–356. Blackwell Scientific Publications, Oxford.

Bayliss-Smith, T.P. & Feacham, R.G. (Eds.) (1977). *Subsistence and Survival. Rural Ecology in the Pacific.* Academic Press, London.

Bongers, F., Engelen, D. & Klinge, H. (1985). Phytomass structure of natural plant communities on spodosols in southern Venezuela: the Bana woodland. *Vegetatio*, **63**, 13–34.

Bruijnzeel, L.A. (1984). Immobilization of nutrients in plantation forests of *Pinus merkusii* and *Agathis dammara* growing on volcanic soils in central Java, Indonesia. *International Conference on Soils and Nutrition of Perennial Crops* (Ed. by E. Pusparajah & Tachib), pp. 19–29. Malayan Soil Science Society, Kuala Lumpur.

Bruijnzeel, L.A. & Wiersum, K.F. (1985). A nutrient balance sheet for *Agathis dammara* Warb. plantation forest under various management conditions in central Java, Indonesia. *Forest Ecology and Management*, **10**, 195–208.

Brünig, E.F. (1969). On the seasonality of drought in the lowlands of Sarawak (Borneo). *Erdkunde*, **23**, 127–133.

Brünig, E.F. (1974). *Ecological Studies in the Kerangas Forests of Sarawak and Brunei.* Borneo Literature Bureau, Kuching.

Buckley, R.C., Corlett, R.T. & Grubb, P.J. (1980). Are the xeromorphic trees of upper montane rain forests drought resistant? *Biotropica*, **12**, 124–136.

Bush, M. (1986). Some effects of physical processes on the redevelopment of the forests of Krakatau. *The Krakatau Centenary Expedition Final Report* (Ed. by M. Bush, P. Jones & K. Richards), pp. 57–76. Department of Geography, University of Hull.

Edwards, P.J. & Grubb, P.J. (1977). Studies of mineral cycling in a montane rain forest in New Guinea. I. The distribution of organic matter in the vegetation and soil. *Journal of Ecology*, **65**, 943–969.

Gartlan, J.S., Newbery, D. McC, Thomas, D. & Waterman, P.G. (1986). The influence of topography and soil phosphorus on the vegetation of Korup Forest Reserve, Cameroun. *Vegetatio*, **65**, 131–148.

Grubb, P.J., Lloyd, J.R., Pennington, T.D. & Whitmore, T.C. (1963). A comparison of montane and lowland rain forest in Ecuador. I. The forest structure, physiognomy and floristics. *Journal of Ecology*, **51**, 567–601.

Haines, B. (1983). Leafcutting ants bleed mineral elements out of rainforest in southern Venezuela. *Tropical Ecology*, **24**, 85–93.

Janos, D.P. (1983). Tropical mycorrhizas, nutrient cycles and plant growth. *Tropical Rain Forest: Ecology and Management* (Ed. by S.L. Sutton, T.C. Whitmore & A.C. Chadwick), pp. 327–345. Blackwell Scientific Publications, Oxford.

Jordan, C.F. (1985). *Nutrient Cycling in Tropical Forest Ecosystems*. Wiley, Chichester.

Kartawinata, K., Adisoemarto, S., Riswan, S. & Vaydan, A.P. (1981). The impact of man on a tropical forest in Indonesia. *Ambio*, **10**, 115–119.

Klinge, H. (1976). Bilanzierung von Hauptnahrstoffen im Ökosystem tropischer regenwald (Manaus) — vorlaufige daten. *Biogeographica*, **7**, 59–76.

Lundgren, B. (1980). *Plantation Forestry in Tropical Countries*. Swedish University, Agricultural Sciences.

Medina, E., Sobrado, M. & Herrera, R. (1978). Significance of leaf orientation for leaf temperature in an Amazonian sclerophyll vegetation. *Radiation and Environmental Biophysics*, **15**, 131–140.

Newbery, D. McC, Gartlan, J.S., McKay, D.B. & Waterman, P.G. (1986). The influence of soil phosphorus on the vegetation of Douala-Edea forest-reserve, Cameroun. *Vegetatio*, **65**, 149–162.

Poels, R.L.H. (1987). *Soils, Water and Nutrients in a Forest Ecosystem in Surinam*. Doctoral Thesis, Agricultural University, Wageningen, The Netherlands.

Proctor, J. (1983). Mineral nutrients in tropical forests. *Progress in Physical Geography*, **7**, 422–431.

Proctor, J. (1987). Nutrient cycling in primary and old secondary rain forests. *Applied Geography*, **7**, 135–152.

Proctor, J., Anderson, J.M., Chai, P. & Vallack, H.W. (1983). Ecological studies in four contrasting rain forests in Gunung Mulu National Park, Sarawak. I. Forest environment. *Journal of Ecology*, **71**, 237–260.

Richards, P.W. (1952). *The Tropical Rain Forest*. Cambridge University Press, Cambridge.

Riswan, S. (1982). *Ecological Studies on Primary, Secondary and Experimentally Cleared Mixed Dipterocarp Forest and Kerangas Forest in East Kalimantan, Indonesia*. PhD Thesis, Aberdeen University, U.K.

Salick, J., Herrera, R. & Jordan, C. (1983). Termitaria: nutrient patchiness in nutrient-deficient rain forests. *Biotropica*, **15**, 1–7.

Sanchez, P.A., Palm, C.A., Davey, C.B., Szott, L.T. & Russell, C.E. (1985). Trees as soil improvers in the humid tropics? *Attributes of Trees as Crop Plants* (Ed. by M.G.R. Cannell & J.E. Jackson), pp. 327–58. Institute of Terrestrial Ecology, Natural Environment Research Council, Monks Wood, U.K.

Tanner, E.V.J., Kapos, V., Freskos, S., Healey, J.R. & Theobald, A.M. (1988). Nitrogen and phosphorus fertilization of Jamaican montane forest trees. *Journal of Tropical Ecology*, (in press).

Vitousek, P.M. & Sanford, R.L. (1986). Nutrient cycling in moist tropical forest. *Annual Review of Ecology and Systematics*, **17**, 137–168.

Whitmore, T.C. (1984a). *Tropical Rain Forests of the Far East*, 2nd edn. Clarendon Press, Oxford.

Whitmore, T.C. (1984b). Plant species diversity in tropical rain forests. *Biology International Special Issue*, **6**, 5–7.

Whittaker, R.H. (1972). Evolution and measurement of species diversity. *Taxon*, **21**, 213–251.

Whitten, A.J., Damanik, S.J., Anwas, J. & Hisyam, N. (1984). *The Ecology of Sumatra*. Gadjah Mada University Press, Yogyakarta, Indonesia.

Soil characteristics and classification in relation to the mineral nutrition of tropical wooded ecosystems

I. C. BAILLIE

Department of Geography, Polytechnic of North London,
383, Holloway Road, London N7 8DB

SUMMARY

1 Mineral weathering contributes nutrients to some tropical wooded ecosystems in small but important quantities. Ecosystems where weathering sources are non-existent or inaccessible develop highly efficient nutrient cycling and retention mechanisms.

2 Comparison between broadleaf forest and lowland pine savanna on two different geological substrates in coastal Belize shows that their soils differ for a wide range of morphological, hydrological and chemical characteristics. It is not possible to select any one soil factor as the most important. Total concentrations of nutrients show as marked differences between the soils of the two communities as exchangeable and available forms.

3 Floristic variation in the mixed dipterocarp forest of Sarawak is associated with soil conditions, especially those related to parent materials. Variations in total, rather than available, nutrients appear to be more associated with forest variation.

4 The modern international soil classification systems differentiate the main soils of tropical forest areas mainly on clay illuviation and exchangeable base status. They tend to ignore or relegate more lithogenic properties, such as total concentrations of nutrients.

5 Tropical forest ecologists need to explicitly and routinely take account of parent materials and lithologically derived variation in soils wherever possible.

INTRODUCTION

Wooded ecosystems in the tropics tend to be efficient in nutrient conservation. They accumulate nutrients in the biomass, and have a high degree of internal cycling with limited extraneous transfers (Jordan 1985). Within this broad generalization, it is possible to distinguish, from a pedological viewpoint, two types of nutrient cycle. The first is less self-contained and has losses to the atmosphere, surface water and groundwater. These losses are more or less offset by gains from rainwater and aerosols (Kellman & Carty 1986) and from mineral weathering in the soil and upper parts of the saprolite. Roots in ecosystems with this type of cycle penetrate to the zone of weathering and are not concentrated near the surface.

15

The second type of cycle occurs where there is no nutrient input from weathering. This type is more efficient and is virtually leak-proof for much of the time. Any losses are made good entirely from atmospheric inputs. The nutrients absorbed by roots in this kind of cycle are almost wholly derived from litter decomposition and infiltrating surface water. The roots tend to be highly concentrated in the surface layers of the soil.

These two types of cycle correspond to the coupled and uncoupled models of Burnham (*this volume*) and represent the extremes of a spectrum rather than clearly defined groups. The distinction is clear for extreme cases; however, many tropical wooded ecosystems are probably intermediate with small, intermittent, but important inputs from weathering. Because different nutrients have their own pathways and functions, it is an over-simplification to place ecosystems on a simple univariate weathering input cline from eutrophic to oligotrophic. Weathering may contribute for some nutrients, but not at all for others (Vitousek & Sanford 1986).

Factors which influence the nature and scale of weathering inputs include successional status, site stability, climate and season, but soil characteristics appear to be the main determinants. Only if there is no accessible source of nutrients from weathering will the more closed and parsimonious type of cycle operate. Examples of closed cycles arising in the virtually complete absence of any near-surface zone of weathering include the *caatinga* forests of the Amazon basin (Stark & Jordan 1978) and the heath forests of Malaysia (Brünig 1974). These grow on humus podzols developed on highly quartzose parent materials. There may also be cases where a source of weathering-derived nutrients is rendered inaccessible by soil morphological features such as poor subsoil drainage or a mechanical impedance to root penetration. Many soils in the Mountain Pine Ridge savanna of Belize appear to exemplify this kind of situation. Kellman & Sanmugadas (1985) found that the weathering of the underlying granite contributes significantly to the dissolved load of the streams and rivers of the area. However, the nutrients released by this weathering are not taken up by the savanna, which has a very efficient closed cycle with a high concentration of surface roots. In this case the barriers to deep rooting and tapping of the weathering nutrients seem to be imperfect drainage and a very dense and firm consistency in the mottled clay subsoils.

There have been a number of studies in which it has been shown that soil drainage determines spatial variation in the forest (Ashton 1976; Lescure & Boulet 1985; Liebermann *et al.* 1985). In some of these poor drainage may prevent deep rooting into weathering zones below shallow water tables. However, poor drainage need not always give rise to closed nutrient cycles. Where poor drainage is topogenic and is associated with periodic flooding, the inaccessibility of nutrients from weathering can be offset by their importation in floodwaters (e.g. Proctor *et al.* 1983).

As well as determining the general type of nutrient cycle, soil characteristics can affect their internal workings. In systems with weathering inputs, the nature of the parent material, its rate of weathering, the type and rate of nutrient release and its depth of placement in the soil profile are important. There are also soil effects on the working of closed cycles. In his study of such cycles in the Mountain Pine Ridge savanna of Belize, Kellman (1985) concluded that soil texture and mineralogy are major influences particularly on the ecosystem's ability to retain nutrients against deep leaching.

The concentrations, pools and fluxes of nutrients in the biotic components of wooded ecosystems vary widely in space and time. They are influenced by the accumulation and translocations within individual plants in periods of stagnation and surges of growth (Primack *et al.* 1985; Tanner 1985), by the floristic diversity of mature forest (Whitmore 1984), and by the additional nutrient diversity resulting from gap formation and successional status (e.g. Vitousek & Denslow 1986). This leads to considerable sampling problems in nutrient characterization of biotic components. However, if only an overview of the nutrient status of the ecosystem is required, the less variable nutrient contents of soils can be used as a sampling-efficient general indicator. Foliar analyses have sometimes, but not invariably, been found to be satisfactory for this purpose (Vitousek & Sanford 1986).

Whatever the purpose of soil nutrient characterization the choice of methods of nutrient extraction is problematical. The conventional pedological and agronomic methods of soil analysis tend to extract and emphasize the nutrients that are immediately available for plant uptake and which tend to be very variable in time and space. However, many nutrients held in less immediately available forms, and that have to be extracted by more drastic analytical methods, may contribute to the nutrient supply of long-lived trees. This point is further discussed by Wild (*this volume*). The selection of ecologically meaningful measures of soil nutrient status and other soil characteristics is examined in examples from Belize and Borneo. In both cases the soil properties assumed to be important influences on the nutrient cycles are those associated with the floristic and structural variation in the communities.

FOREST AND SAVANNA IN COASTAL BELIZE

The example from Belize compares the soils of two nearby ecosystems, one (under forest) with an input from weathering and the other (under savanna) without.

The coastal plain of the northern part of Toledo district, Belize, has an annual rainfall of about 2500–3000 mm and a dry season of 3–4 months. The natural vegetation for most of the area is evergreen or semi-deciduous broadleaf forest of high diversity and stature, often with many cohune palms (*Orbignya cohune* (Mart.) Dahlgren ex Standley). This forest is found on rolling–undulating terrain over a range of clastic sedimentary rocks of Tertiary age. These include sandstones, conglomerates and calcareous shales, but mudstones and siltstones predominate (King *et al.* 1986).

There are also large areas of savanna, known locally as Pine Ridge. This is the low altitude equivalent of the Mountain Pine Ridge savanna, the ecology of which is fairly well known (Kellman 1979, 1985; Kellman & Miyanashi 1982; Kellman & Sanmugadas 1985; Kellman & Carty 1986). The coastal Pine Ridge is a more or less open savanna, the tree flora of which is dominated by *Pinus caribaea* Moret. There are also broadleaved species such as *Byrsonima crassifolia* L. DC. and *Quercus oleoides* Cham. & Schlecht. In moister areas there are clumps of the palmetto, *Paurotis wrightii* (Griseb. & Wendl.) Britt. (Anderson & Fralish 1975). *Trachypogon* spp. are prominent in the grasses. The pine savanna is found on unconsolidated deposits of a large, low angle, alluvial fan of Pleistocene age (Wright *et al.* 1959; King *et al.* 1986). There are broad belts of broadleaf gallery forest where the fan has been dissected by major rivers and overlain by recent alluvium. The association of lowland pine savanna with unconsolidated Pleistocene deposits has been noted elsewhere in the Caribbean area (e.g. Beard 1953; Parsons 1955; Sarmiento 1983).

The soils were examined and sampled at five sites in each of the two ecosystems during a recent survey of land resources (King *et al.* 1986). The two sets of parent materials have given rise to soils with very different morphological, chemical and hydrological characteristics.

The savanna soils have sharply differentiated textural and consistence profiles. The surface horizons are very dark coloured, coarse or medium textured and have a friable, open consistence. They are underlain by bright yellowish horizons, again light textured and friable. There is then often a thin, very sandy or silty horizon which is light grey, very loose and contains a high concentration of tree roots, often running horizontally. This horizon can be found at depths between 30 and 90 cm. It abruptly overlies a deep, brightly mottled red, yellow and white subsoil. This is of finer texture and of much denser and firmer consistence than the overlying horizons. It is virtually devoid of roots, and is clearly a barrier to downward rooting (Kellman & Sanmugadas 1985). The increase in clay content with depth (subsoil clay/topsoil clay quotients range from 1.28–16.0; median 2.3) is partly due to argilluviation, as indicated by some coatings of clay deposited on subsoil structure faces. However, the weathering of clay minerals in the upper horizons by the alternation of free iron between its ferric and ferrous states (Muller & Bocquier 1986) and the lateral export of clay by surface wash and throughflow may also contribute to the textural contrast.

The soils under the broadleaf forest are derived from mudstone and have generally finer textures. Like the savanna soils they tend to become finer textured, more compact and more mottled with depth, but these differences are less pronounced and the changes are gradual rather than abrupt. The colour changes are also less marked, with lighter coloured topsoils and with reddish-yellowish-brownish matrix colours predominating throughout the subsoil. Roots are found throughout the solum, with some penetrating right through the fairly compact subsoil to the underlying weathering rock, especially in shallower profiles. The subsoil clay/topsoil clay quotients range from 0.64–2.76 (median 1.03).

The differences in topography, profile morphology and root distribution between the two groups of soils confirm earlier suggestions that the two ecosystems have different soil moisture regimes, despite being under the same atmospheric climate (Beard 1953). The coarse-textured and shallow rooting zone in the savanna soil is likely to be saturated for fairly long periods in the wet season because of the impermeable subsoils and gentle slopes. In the dry season the lack of clay and depth reduces the available moisture capacity and renders the savanna liable to moisture stress. The broadleaf forest is less subject to these alternating extremes of anaerobic conditions and moisture stress. The difference in soil moisture regimes may also contribute to the frequency of dry season fires in the savanna and their rarity in the forest.

The compact and impermeable subsoils also constrain the nutrient supply to the savanna vegetation. The underlying Pleistocene sediments contain some weatherable primary minerals (Lietzke & Whiteside 1981), and nutrients are probably being released by their weathering. However, the lack of deep rooting precludes their uptake by the savanna, which seems to operate a closed, near-surface type of nutrient cycle, although there may be some tapping of soil reserves during periods of sustained growth in the absence of fire (Kellman 1979; Kellman & Carty 1986). In contrast, nutrients released by weathering of the underlying Tertiary sedimentary rocks would appear to be available to the deep-rooting broadleaf forest, allowing for substantial accumulation of nutrients in the aerial biomass (Arnason, Lambert & Gale 1984).

However, the presumed difference in nutrient cycles cannot be wholly attributed to the morphological and rooting differences. There are also large differences in the nutrient concentrations between the two groups of soils. This can be seen in the comparison of the ranges and medians of soil nutrient concentrations (Table 1). The forest soils have higher concentrations of most nutrients especially total magnesium, manganese and zinc. For exchangeable calcium and magnesium and for total exchangeable bases (TEB), the forest ranges are higher in the topsoils, but overlap with the savanna group for the subsoils. These differences are complemented by the higher extractable aluminium and percentage aluminium saturation of the exchange complex, and lower pH values in the savanna soils. Concentrations of nickel and copper and both total and available concentrations of phosphorus are higher in the forest soils, but the ranges for these nutrients overlap in both topsoils and subsoils. The only elements which do not show distinct differences are potassium, both exchangeable and total, and total chromium. The topsoil organic carbon concentrations confirm the colour evidence that the savanna soils have more surface organic matter. The higher C : N ratios suggest that the organic matter in the savanna topsoil is decomposing more slowly than that under forest. The clay contents confirm that the textural contrasts under savanna are greater than under forest.

Apart from noting the marked differences in magnesium concentrations between the two sets of soils, the individual nutrients are of less interest here. Rather it is the indication that the edaphic environments of the two ecosystems

TABLE 1. Medians (with ranges in parentheses) of chemical characteristics and percentage clay of pine savanna and broadleaf forest soils in southern Belize ($n = 5$) (from King et al. (1986))

	Topsoil (A1, 0–10/15 cm)				Subsoil (Bt, c. 50 cm)			
	Pine savanna		Broadleaf forest		Pine savanna		Broadleaf forest	
pH (log units)	5.2	(4.8–5.3)	5.8	(5.4–6.2)	5.3	(5.2–5.5)	5.9	(5.1–6.9)
Organic C (%)	3.40	(1.11–5.65)	2.49	(1.74–3.41)	0.24	(0.04–0.32)	0.39	(0.14–0.69)
N_{total} (%)	0.23	(0.09–0.45)	0.24	(0.21–0.38)	0.04	(0.02–0.05)	0.05	(0.02–0.09)
C : N ratio	13	(11–16)	9	(8–12)	6	(2–8)	7	(5–8)
P_{total} (mg kg^{-1})	110	(50–210)	210	(90–360)	60	(40–100)	120	(50–140)
K_{total} (mg kg^{-1})	1100	(500–5200)	2750	(800–4500)	1900	(750–15050)	3350	(2050–11400)
Mg_{total} (mg kg^{-1})	1050	(250–1450)	7350	(1650–11250)	2000	(650–3950)	16300	(4450–21650)
Cu_{total} (mg kg^{-1})	10	(0–30)	40	(10–50)	20	(10–40)	60	(40–90)
Cr_{total} (mg kg^{-1})	240	(10–400)	380	(270–530)	110	(20–240)	130	(130–170)
Mn_{total} (mg kg^{-1})	30	(20–80)	1000	(20–1100)	30	(20–30)	600	(50–1050)
Ni_{total} (mg kg^{-1})	10	(0–90)	160	(30–170)	50	(10–140)	220	(90–260)
Zn_{total} (mg kg^{-1})	10	(0–30)	50	(30–60)	30	(20–30)	60	(40–70)
Available P (mg kg^{-1})	2	(2)	3	(2–4)	2	(1–3)	3	(2–3)
$K_{exchangeable}$ (m-equiv. kg^{-1})	0.00	(0.00–0.02)	0.02	(0.01–0.03)	0.00	(0.00–0.02)	0.02	(0.00–0.04)
$Ca_{exchangeable}$ (m-equiv. kg^{-1})	0.04	(0.00–0.13)	0.94	(0.28–1.80)	0.02	(0.00–0.58)	1.06	(0.04–1.59)
$Mg_{exchangeable}$ (m-equiv. kg^{-1})	0.03	(0.01–0.13)	0.32	(0.18–0.50)	0.07	(0.04–0.47)	0.63	(0.22–1.44)
TEB (m-equiv. kg^{-1})	0.05	(0.02–0.30)	1.45	(0.48–2.24)	0.10	(0.02–1.09)	2.08	(0.28–3.09)
$Al_{exchangeable}$ (m-equiv. kg^{-1})	0.22	(0.13–0.45)	0.02	(0.00–0.03)	0.15	(0.10–0.47)	0.23	(0.03–1.10)
Al saturation (%)	76	(53–90)	2	(0–6)	71	(19–80)	10	(1–80)
Clay (%)	20	(4–47)	28	(22–39)	59	(44–67)	29	(14–68)

differ morphologically, hydrologically and chemically; and that it is not possible to select any one soil property as being the critical determinant of the distribution of the two ecosystems. As far as nutrients are concerned, the morphological and hydrological constraints on accessibility may be as important as the size of the soil pools. As useful measures of these pools, total concentrations appear to give as clear indications as exchangeable or available concentrations.

The multivariate differences between the two sets of soils derive from the differences between the parent materials. The close spatial association found between the vegetation and geological boundaries in the area confirms the ecological importance of lithogenic soil properties.

VARIATION IN BORNEAN DIPTEROCARP FORESTS

The mixed dipterocarp forest (MDF) is the most extensive type of natural vegetation in Borneo. It covers much of the rugged terrain that comprises most of the island, even at low altitudes. It grows on soils derived from a wide range of all but the most siliceous rocks. The soils are mostly shallow, with weathering rock usually found at less than 2 m depth. Most of the soils show an increase in clay content and compaction with depth. These features do not usually prevent root ramification into the subsoil, and some roots penetrate the underlying weathering rock (Baillie & Mamit 1983). Moisture balance studies show that the MDF needs to exploit the whole depth of the relatively shallow soil profiles in order to minimize moisture stress in occasional droughts (Brünig 1969; Baillie 1976).

There are some similarities between the soils of the MDF and those under the Belizean broadleaf forest. In general, the Bornean subsoils are slightly less mottled and have less impeded drainage. The Bornean soils are more acid and deficient in exchangeable bases (cf. Baillie & Ashton (1983) and King et al. (1986)). Like the broadleaf forest in Belize, the MDF has a slightly open nutrient cycle with some inputs from weathering. It is of interest that geophagous colobine monkeys in Bornean dipterocarp forests prefer subsoil material, as exposed in termitaria, to topsoils in their attempts to supplement their nutrient intake (Davies & Baillie 1988).

A number of studies have indicated that floristic and structural variations in the MDF are at least partly determined by edaphic conditions. Ashton (1964) found consistent floristically defined forest types within the MDF, the distributions of which were more or less associated with variations in soils and their parent materials. Austin, Greig-Smith & Ashton (1972) found drainage characteristics to be the main determinant of the floristic variation in the MDF in Brunei. When the sampling range was extended in Sarawak, lithogenic properties such as total nutrient concentration, especially of phosphorus, were found to be more influential (Baillie & Ashton 1983). The distribution of individual species within the MDF in Sarawak also shows some evidence of edaphic influence, especially of lithogenic properties such as texture and total nutrient concentrations (Baillie et al. 1987). As in Belize, magnesium figures prominently. On the whole the concentrations of the more immediately accessible nutrients (e.g. exchangeable bases or available phosphorus) appear to be relatively unimportant as floristic determinants (Baillie & Ashton 1983). This may be due to their high measured spatial and assumed temporal variabilities (Baillie & Ahmed 1984 & 1985).

SOIL CLASSIFICATION

The edaphic effects on the more subtle variation within the MDF are less pronounced than those distinguishing the distinctive Belizean ecosystems. Nonetheless, there are a number of common features. These include the multiplicity and multidimensionality of potential edaphic determinants, and the apparent importance of the concentrations of total nutrients and other lithogenic characteristics.

Vitousek & Sanford (1986) were able to use the higher levels of the Soil Taxonomy to distinguish broad classes of soil fertility in their review of nutrient cycling in moist tropical forests. However, the tropical ecologist wishing to take particular account of lithogenic soil characteristics is generally poorly served by the modern international soil classification systems.

The most influential of these is the Soil Taxonomy of the United States Soil Conservation Service (Soil Survey Staff 1975). This is a general purpose classification and is not specifically designed for ecological purposes. It is a monothetic divisive system in which the descending taxa are differentiated on a succession of limited criteria. Such a procedure is unavoidable on practical grounds, but has fundamental weaknesses when applied to multivariate and continuous phenomena like soils (Webster 1968; Fitzpatrick 1986).

In this system most non-swamp soils of humid tropical lowlands qualify as Oxisols, Ultisols, Alfisols or related immature soils (Inceptisols). These are differentiated at the highest (order) level on the properties of the main subsoil horizon, which is designated as 'diagnostic' and which is usually found between 25 and 125 cm. Ecologically this is possibly the least interesting part of the profile, as it excludes both the main zone of biological nutrient cycling in the top-soil, and the weathering zone. For tropical forests its main function is likely to be as a reservoir of moisture (Lietzke & Weber 1981).

The properties of the diagnostic horizons used to differentiate these orders are dominance by oxidic minerals, illuvial clay and exchangeable base saturation. Neither of the last pair are wholly satisfactory criteria. Many humid tropical soils have increases in clay content with depth. However, the relative contributions from clay enrichment from above (argilluviation), preferential erosion of clays by surface wash and shallow throughflow, and *in situ* hydrolysis of topsoil clay minerals are variable and debatable (e.g. Brinkman 1970; Andriesse 1975; Bleeker 1983; Muller 1983; Tessens 1984). The use of base saturation as a criterion suffers from the fact that many of the earlier data are unsatisfactory.

Calculation of base saturation percentage requires estimation of the cation exchange capacity (CEC) as the divisor. CEC used to be measured at pH 7, or even pH 8.2, several units above those prevailing in the field. This gave over-estimates of CEC and hence artificially low values for base saturation (Juo & Pleysier 1980; Grove, Fowler & Sumner 1982). Moreover, the more heavily weighted differentiae are ecologically unsatisfactory because they lay insufficient emphasis on the morphology of the whole profile, the concentrations of total nutrients and other lithogenic properties. An example of the workings of the system can be seen in Table 2 which shows the classification of pine savanna and broadleaf forest soils in the Belize study (Lietzke & Whiteside 1981; King *et al.* 1986). The differentiae include superfluous information on climate and location, but nothing on parent materials.

TABLE 2. Soil taxonomy classification of typical pine savanna and broadleaf forest soils in coastal Belize

Pine savanna

Classification	Umbric	A1b	–	aqu	–	ult
Meaning	Low exchangeable base status and dark coloured topsoil	Thin, pale, sandy or silty subsoil horizon abruptly over finer texture		Impeded drainage		Illuvial clay and low exchangeable base status in diagnostic horizon

Broadleaf forest

Classification	Ochr	–	aquic	Trop	–	ud	–	ult
Meaning	Lighter coloured topsoil		Slightly impeded drainage	Tropical location		Humid climate		Illuvial clay and low exchangeable base status in diagnostic horizon

The authors of the Legend of the Soil Map of the World (FAO/UNESCO 1974) acknowledge their conceptual debt to the Seventh Approximation (Soil Survey Staff 1960), an earlier version of the Soil Taxonomy. The FAO Legend therefore suffers from some of the ecological defects of Soil Taxonomy, such as the prominence given to illuvial clay and exchangeable base status. In humid tropical regions the Ferralsol, Acrisol, Luvisol and Nitisol units each cover a wide range of edaphic and ecological conditions. However, there are also some high level units which are defined more in terms of whole-profile morphology (e.g. Planosols) and others which make explicit reference to parent material (e.g. Andosols and Rendzinas). The FAO system more clearly distinguishes the two groups of Belizean soils at the highest level. Most of the pine savanna soils qualify as Dystric Planosols, whilst the broadleaf forest soils are mostly Acrisols.

CONCLUSION

Pedogenesis by deep leaching and deep weathering (Burnham *this volume*) operates over large areas of the humid tropics. It is particularly prevalent in conditions of tectonic and geomorphological stability in shield areas of plate interiors. In such areas, the identification and differentiation of deeply weathered parent materials is difficult. It is often impracticable to incorporate lithogenic characteristics into working classifications for pedological and soil survey work.

There are, however, extensive areas, especially along plate margins, where tectonic and geomorphological activity is high. In these areas there are large tracts of shallower soils, in which identification of parent materials is easier.

Whether easily identifiable or not, soil parent materials are too important to be ignored by tropical ecologists. It is suggested that they should qualify their soil designations with some indication of parent materials, wherever these can be determined. The degree of lithological differentiation will depend on the area, purpose and opportunity. In many cases very broad distinctions, e.g. 'granite' 'basaltic colluvium' etc. may suffice. In others finer subdivisions, e.g. between calcitic and dolomitic limestones, or according to clay mineralogy, may be necessary.

ACKNOWLEDGEMENTS

I thank Dr M. Holder, Dr R. B. King and Mr A. C. S. Wright for their contributions to the Belizean material, Mr A. J. Smyth, formerly Director of the Land Resources Development Centre, for permission to use it, many former colleagues in the Department of Forestry for their contributions to the Sarawak studies and anonymous referees for comments on the manuscript. The Belizean soil analyses were carried out at the Tropical Soils Analysis Unit, Reading, under the supervision of Dr R. Baker.

REFERENCES

Anderson, R.C. & Fralish, J.E. (1975). An investigation of palmetto, *Paurotis wrightii* (Griesb. & Wendl.) Britt., communities in Belize, Central America. *Turrialba*, **25**, 37–44.

Andriesse, J.P. (1975). *Characteristics and Formation of so-called Red–Yellow Podzolic Soils in the Humid Tropics (Sarawak-Malaysia). Communication 66*. Royal Tropical Institute, Amsterdam.

Arnason, J.T., Lambert, J.D. & Gale, J. (1984). Mineral cycling in a tropical palm forest. *Plant and Soil*, **79**, 211–215.

Ashton, P.S. (1964). *Ecological Studies in the Mixed Dipterocarp Forests of Brunei State. Oxford Forestry Memoirs 25*. Oxford University Press, Oxford.

Ashton, P.S. (1976). Mixed dipterocarp forest and its variation with habitat: a re-evaluation of Pasoh. *Malayan Forester*, **39**, 56–72.

Austin, M.P., Greig-Smith, P. & Ashton, P.S. (1972). The application of quantitative methods to vegetation survey III. A re-examination of rain forest data from Brunei. *Journal of Ecology*, **60**, 305–324.

Baillie, I.C. (1976). Further studies on drought in Sarawak, East Malaysia. *Journal of Tropical Geography*, **43**, 20–29.

Baillie, I.C. & Ahmed, M.I. (1984; 1985). The variability of Red Yellow Podzolic soils under mixed dipterocarp forest in Sarawak, Malaysia. *Malaysian Journal of Tropical Geography*, 9, 1–13; 10, 87.

Baillie, I.C. & Ashton, P.S. (1983). Some soil aspects of the nutrient cycle of mixed dipterocarp forest in Sarawak. *Tropical Rain Forest: Ecology and Management* (Ed. by S.L. Sutton, T.C. Whitmore & A.C. Chadwick), pp. 347–356. Blackwell Scientific Publications, Oxford.

Baillie, I.C., Ashton, P.S., Court, M.N., Anderson, J.A.R., Fitzpatrick, E.A. & Tinsley, J. (1987). Site characteristics and the distribution of tree species in mixed dipterocarp forest on Tertiary sediments in Central Sarawak, Malaysia. *Journal of Tropical Ecology*, 3, 201–220.

Baillie, I.C. & Mamit, J.D. (1983). Observations on rooting in mixed dipterocarp forest, Central Sarawak. *Malayan Forester*, 46, 369–374.

Beard, J.S. (1953). The savanna vegetation of northern tropical America. *Ecological Monographs*, 23, 149–215.

Bleeker, P. (1983). *Soils of Papua New Guinea*. Australian National University Press, Canberra.

Brinkman, R. (1970). Ferrolysis, a hydromorphic soil forming process. *Geoderma*, 3, 199–206.

Brünig, E.F.W. (1969). On the seasonality of droughts in the lowlands of Sarawak (Borneo). *Erdkunde*, 23, 127–133.

Brünig, E.F.W. (1974). *Ecological Studies in the Kerangas Forests of Sarawak and Brunei*. Borneo Literature Bureau, Kuching, Malaysia.

Davies, A.G. & Baillie, I.C. (1988). Soil-eating by red-leaf monkeys (*Presbytis rubicunda*) in Sabah, northern Borneo. *Biotropica*, 20, 252–258.

FAO/UNESCO (1974). *Soil Map of the World. Volume I Legend*. UNESCO, Paris.

Fitzpatrick, E.A. (1986). A comparison of Soil Taxonomy with Fitzpatrick's system of soil designation and classification. *Ciencia del Suelo*, 4, 193–207.

Grove, J.H., Fowler, C.S. & Sumner, M.E. (1982). Determination of charge characteristics of selected acid soils. *Soil Science Society of America Journal*, 46, 32–38.

Jordan, C.F. (1985). *Nutrient Cycling in Tropical Forest Ecosystems*. Wiley, Chichester.

Juo, A.S.R. & Pleysier, J.L. (1980). A new method for rapid determination of effective cation exchange capacity and exchangeable cations in highly weathered soils. *Research Briefs*, 1, 5–6. International Institute for Tropical Agriculture, Ibadan, Nigeria.

Kellman, M. (1979). Soil enrichment by neotropical savanna trees. *Journal of Ecology*, 67, 565–577.

Kellman, M. (1985). Nutrient retention by savanna ecosystems: III. Response to artificial loading. *Journal of Ecology*, 73, 963–972.

Kellman, M. & Carty, A. (1986). Magnitude of nutrient influxes from atmospheric sources to a Central American *Pinus caribaea* woodland. *Journal of Applied Ecology*, 23, 211–226.

Kellman, M. & Miyanashi, K. (1982). Forest seedling establishment in neotropical savannas: observations and experiments in the Mountain Pine Ridge savanna, Belize. *Journal of Biogeography*, 9, 193–206.

Kellman, M. & Sanmugadas, K. (1985). Nutrient retention by savanna ecosystems: I. Retention in the absence of fire. *Journal of Ecology*, 73, 935–951.

King, R.B., Baillie, I.C., Bissett, P.G., Grimble, R.J., Johnson, M.S. & Silva, G.L. (1986). *Land Resource Survey of Toledo District, Belize. Report P 177*. Overseas Development Administration, Tolworth, U.K.

Lescure, J.P. & Boulet, R. (1985). Relationships between soil and vegetation in tropical rainforest in French Guiana. *Biotropica*, 17, 155–164.

Liebermann, M., Liebermann, D., Hartshorn, G.S. & Peralta, R. (1985). Small scale altitudinal variation in lowland wet tropical forest vegetation. *Journal of Ecology*, 73, 505–516.

Lietzke, D.A. & Weber, R.S. (1981). The importance of Cr horizons in soil classification and interpretation. *Soil Science Society of America Journal*, 45, 593–599.

Lietzke, D.A. & Whiteside, E.P. (1981). Characterisation and classification of some Belizean soils. *Soil Science Society of America Journal*, 45, 378–385.

Muller, J.-P. (1983). Micro-organisation of loose ferrallitic materials in the Cameroons. *Soil Micromorphology* (Ed. by P. Bullock & C.P. Murphy), pp. 655–666. AB Academic, Berkhamstead.

Muller, J.-P. & Bocquier, G. (1986). Dissolution of kaolinites and accumulation of iron oxides in lateritic ferruginous nodules: mineralogical and micro-structural transformations. *Geoderma*, **37**, 113–136.

Parsons, J.J. (1955). The miskito pine savanna of Nicaragua and Honduras. *Annals of the American Association of Geographers*, **45**, 36–63.

Primack, R.B., Ashton, P.S., Chai, P. & Lee, H.S. (1985). Growth rates and population structure of Moraceae trees in Sarawak, East Malaysia. *Ecology*, **66**, 577–588.

Proctor, J., Anderson, J.M., Fogden, S.C.L. & Vallack, H.W. (1983). Ecological studies in four contrasting lowland rain forests in Gunung Mulu National Park, Sarawak. II. Litterfall, litter standing crop and preliminary observations on herbivory. *Journal of Ecology*, **71**, 261–284.

Sarmiento, G. (1983). The savannas of tropical America. *Ecosystems of the World, 13, Tropical Savannas* (Ed. by F. Bourliere), pp. 245–288. Elsevier, Amsterdam.

Soil Survey Staff (1960). *Soil Classification, A Comprehensive System, 7th Approximation*. Soil Conservation Service, U.S. Department of Agriculture, Washington DC.

Soil Survey Staff (1975). *Soil Taxonomy: A Basic System of Soil Classification for Making and Interpreting Soil Surveys. Agriculture Handbook 436*. U.S. Department of Agriculture, Washington DC.

Stark, N.M. & Jordan, C.F. (1978). Nutrient retention by the root mat of an Amazonian rain forest. *Ecology*, **59**, 434–437.

Tanner, E.V.J. (1985). Jamaican montane forests: nutrient capital and cost of growth. *Journal of Ecology*, **73**, 553–568.

Tessens, E. (1984). Clay migration in upland soils of Malaysia. *Journal of Soil Science*, **35**, 615–624.

Vitousek, P.M. & Denslow, J.S. (1986). Nitrogen and phosphorus availability in treefall gaps of a lowland tropical rainforest. *Journal of Ecology*, **74**, 1167–1178.

Vitousek, P.M. & Sanford, R.L. Jr. (1986). Nutrient cycling in moist tropical forest. *Annual Review of Ecology and Systematics*, **17**, 137–167.

Webster, R. (1968). Fundamental objections to the 7th Approximation. *Journal of Soil Science*, **19**, 354–366.

Whitmore, T.C. (1984). *Tropical Rain Forests of the Far East*, 2nd edn. Oxford University Press, Oxford.

Wright, A.C.S., Romney, D.H., Arbuckle, R.H. & Vial, V.E. (1959). *Land in British Honduras: Report of the British Honduras Land Use Survey Team*. Colonial Office, London.

Pedological processes and nutrient supply from parent material in tropical soils

C. P. BURNHAM

Environment Section, Wye College (University of London),
Ashford, Kent TN25 5AH

SUMMARY

1 Tropical forests may have a 'closed' nutrient cycle in which nutrients from weathering parent material do not reach the biosphere in significant quantities, or an 'open' cycle in which such weathering makes a contribution to the biosphere.

2 Closed cycles are favoured by: great depth of weathering (>2 m); unrootable compact or waterlogged layers in the subsoil; strong leaching, such that nutrient elements are largely removed from weathering rock before it is sufficiently disintegrated to be penetrated by roots; alluvial or colluvial parent materials, very strongly weathered, leached and perhaps cemented in an earlier cycle of soil formation; and parent material which, although weathering within rooting depth, has a low content of nutrient elements even when fresh.

3 Open cycles are favoured by: seasonally dry climates in which soils are shallow because of weak weathering and leaching and in which faunal activity and/or rooting extends to large depths; and tectonically active areas in which soils are shallow because of persistent severe truncation by erosion or by landslips (often triggered by earthquakes) or in which soils are enriched by additions of volcanic ash or alluvium containing unweathered minerals.

INTRODUCTION

In many temperate regions different geological parent materials give obviously different soils which bear woodland of different species composition. In the humid tropics similar differences are often not evident. Schimper (1903) noted that 'in constantly humid districts the rain forest, without apparently exhibiting any essential difference, extends over the most varied kinds of soil'. Richards (1961) remarked on the uniformity of soil and (rain forest) vegetation in Africa, where in Ivory Coast Lemée (1961) noted little difference in the forest developed on two contrasting materials: a base-poor granite with an abnormally low content of ferromagnesian minerals, and a base-rich amphibolite. At Pasoh in Malaya, Wong & Whitmore (1970) found no sign that species groups were correlated with the three distinct soil types present. In a more extensive study Whitmore (1973) enumerated sample plots totalling 676 ha representing 10 000 km^2 of lowland forest in Ulu Kelantan, Malaya, partly underlain by granite and partly by sedimentary rocks. The different parent materials were accompanied by differences in soil profiles and in topography, but nearly all tree species were found on

27

both parent materials on which, moreover, the more obvious trees were present in equal abundance. In Sarawak, Newbery & Proctor (1984) found no association between soils and vegetation differences within Dipterocarp forest in the Gunung Mulu National Park.

However, other studies have shown variation in forest with soil differences. Davis & Richards (1933, 1934) described very different forest types in the lowlands of Guyana, noting that 'the correspondence of vegetation and soil type in this area is in general very exact' (Richards 1961). Ashton (1964) contended that in Brunei, soil differences produced notable effects within lowland forest, and Austin, Ashton & Greig-Smith (1972) reaffirmed that 'contrary to some claims, variation in the species composition of trees in tropical lowland rain forest on sites of similar topography is associated with variation in soils'. Baillie & Ashton (1983) also found that factors related to soil fertility led to differences in mixed dipterocarp forest in Sarawak.

A model which accounts for these contrasting results is needed. Jordan & Herrera (1981) and Jordan (1985) argue for a distinction between chemically fertile (eutrophic) and infertile (oligotrophic) soils. This is obviously fruitful in some cases, but in others it does not work well, e.g. in explaining the differences between the four sites in Gunung Mulu National Park, Sarawak (Proctor *et al.* 1983). Here the important soil differences may be physical rather than chemical. However, it also does not explain the absence of differences associated with 'base-rich' and 'base-poor' parent materials reported by Lemée (1961), nor why (as noted already by Schimper in 1903) 'the differentiation in the flora and in the ecological features of the vegetation, arising from differences in the constitution of the soil, is much more pronounced in the periodically dry districts than in the constantly humid ones'.

Another model involves making a distinction between 'open' and 'closed' nutrient cycling systems as does Baillie (*this volume*).

In an 'open' system there is an input of nutrients from the weathering of parent material, usually roughly balanced by losses, e.g. by leaching. In this case the nutrients in the parent material are an important factor in soil fertility. In a 'closed' system inputs of nutrients are negligible except from the atmosphere, and fertility can only be maintained by efficient cycling so that leaching losses do not exceed the atmospheric inputs. In this case the nature of the substratum matters little. Probably the first full exposition of this situation was given by Hardy (1935), who pointed out that in Caribbean soils exposed to high rainfall most of the soil nutrients are contained in the upper 15 cm of soil. 'The nutrient status diminishes rapidly below the six-inch (15 cm) level and plant roots become much less plentiful, although some may penetrate to the six-foot (183 cm) depth. Circulation of nutrients is maintained in forest lands and orchards through leaf fall, but soil deterioration rapidly ensues when the trees are felled and the land is exposed to erosion and leaching, or subjected to continuous cropping'. Hardy showed that these conditions could occur in red earths on various parent materials, in red soils with mottled subsoils on shale and in podzolized soils on sandstone. However, he contrasted such soils with others well supplied with weatherable minerals from materials like alluvium incorporating recent volcanic ash, which were well able to sustain continuous cropping—in present terminology the 'open' system.

The idea of the closed system was given its classical form by Walter (1936, 1971), who drew on experience in Africa and the Amazon Basin to explain the apparent contradiction between low soil nutrient content and vigorous growth. In his later account we read (pp. 91–93): 'A natural virgin forest, in which there is no exploitation by man, is a self sustained closed system, including the soil . . . there is a continuous cycle of matter. The amount of nutrients in the soil at any one time is practically zero. If there were a slow but continuous leaching of soil nutrients virgin forest would degrade gradually'. He explained that the nutrient capital 'accumulated gradually during the period when weathering had not yet penetrated too deeply and when roots were still in contact with the undecomposed rock . . . in the more distant past in most tropical areas'. Walter hardly mentions the accession of nutrients from the atmosphere which nearly equal or exceed losses in 'closed' systems (Jordan 1985, p. 25), thus offering a possibility of slow regeneration of a nutrient stock. Conversely, a large excess of leaching loss over atmospheric input would be evidence for an 'open' system.

This paper concentrates on the third factor, the supply of nutrients from soil parent materials, and explores the processes which may hinder or promote this. Circumstances are suggested in which 'open' or 'closed' systems may be expected.

The relevant processes are those which increase soil depth or impede rooting and those which can bring soil material to the surface, either continually or episodically, and their relative effect.

FACTORS IMPEDING THE SUPPLY OF NUTRIENTS FROM PARENT MATERIAL TO THE BIOSPHERE

Intense weathering

In the tropical lowlands temperatures are constantly high, with a typical mean annual temperature of between 20 °C and 26 °C. Van't Hoff (1884) stated that, for every 10 °C rise in temperature, there is a twofold to threefold increase in the speed of a chemical reaction. This suggests a general fourfold increase in the speed of chemical weathering between cool temperate and tropical lowland climates. Actual rates are high, although variable (Colman & Dethier 1986). Bockheim (1980) verified that solum thickness, depth of oxidation and clay content in the B horizon—all related to weathering—are positively correlated with mean annual temperature. However, even in the tropics chemical weathering takes a considerable time. Equally important, therefore, to the development of deep soils is the lack of very cold periods during the Pleistocene, so that soil formation has been uninterrupted by the massive disturbance associated with glacial and periglacial episodes. Climatic changes have occurred, mainly affecting

Nutrient supply from soil parent material

TABLE 1. Exchangeable bases at a depth of 0.8–1.0 m (or nearly) in soils of Peninsular Malaysia (Burnham 1978)

Parent material	Exchangeable bases (m-equiv. 100 g^{-1})				
	Ca	Mg	K	Na	Total
Deep sedentary soils (2–20 m deep)					
Shale	0.19	0.08	0.20	0.24	0.82
Shale	0.42	0.02	0.14	0.11	0.94
Granite	0.40	0.02	0.06	0.10	0.58
Granite	0.27	0.02	0.18	0.16	0.63
Quartz diorite	0.24	0.05	0.21	0.12	0.62
Basalt	0.20	0.04	0.12	0.14	0.72
Serpentine	0.30	0.38	0.33	0.16	1.21
Limestone	0.42	0.11	0.24	0.22	0.99
Shallow sedentary soil (1.5 m deep)					
Limestone	12.54	0.75	0.36	0.21	13.86
Alluvial soils (material mainly granitic)					
Recent alluvium (small stream)	1.09	0.06	0.25	0.22	1.62
Recent alluvium (large river)	0.69	0.06	0.22	0.14	1.11
Old alluvium (terrace)	0.20	0.03	0.11	0.11	0.45

rainfall, but in equatorial regions, weathering has been continually assisted by leaching which removes base cations and silica to the rivers (Bishop 1973; Brinkmann 1985). Indeed leaching is more effective at high temperatures, because the viscosity of water falls and infiltration into soil increases with temperature rise (Shanan & Tadmor 1979).

Intense weathering results in subsoils composed almost entirely of kaolinitic clay, quartz and sesquioxides in some combination, having low cation retention and often high phosphate fixation. Actual nutrient cation contents are low, and vary little with parent material (Table 1). Since the whole weathering mantle is poor, transported materials such as alluvium tend also to be low in nutrients. Thus where soils are rarely dry, plants are not well rewarded for deep rooting, and the 'closed' nutrient cycle is more likely to result.

Great soil depth

In the humid tropics weathering reaches great depths. Taking soils on granite or granite gneiss as an example, Owens & Watson (1979) described a profile 6.88 m deep in Zimbabwe in a rainfall of 920 mm (7 dry months). In Cameroon with 1450–1700 mm (2–3 dry months), 10–30 m is the typical range (Vallerie 1973). In Peninsular Malaysia with 2000–4000 mm (no dry months), 5–30 m is typical (Ledgerwood 1963). Eswaran & Bin (1978) chose a profile 19 m deep as representative. Even in North Carolina in the subtropics (mean annual temperature 15° C; rainfall 1200 mm) Calvert, Buol & Weed (1980) chose a profile 5.2 m deep as typical. In Scotland, in contrast, stones or boulders of fresh granite are found at or near the surface.

On sandstones, Fauck (1974) noted that B horizons 6–8 m thick were found in West Africa under a rainfall of between 900 and 1800 mm, with a gradual transition to parent material below that. In Britain 1 m would be unusually thick.

Summarizing much other information, it may be concluded that in the humid tropics unweathered material is found within 2 m of the surface only in restricted areas, often associated with recent volcanic or tectonic activity, e.g. Sabah (Paton 1963; Acres *et al.* 1975).

Where shallow soils occur the content of cations varies significantly with parent material (Table 2). When in Brunei and Sarawak, Baillie & Ashton (1983) found that forest composition varied notably with soils; these were generally less than 1.0 m and almost always less than 2.0 m deep. They noted that 'the soils differ from those in many tropical rain forest areas in being neither extremely weathered nor extremely deep'. Some roots then penetrate the underlying weathered rock (Baillie & Mamit 1983). The cation content of shallow soils is not necessarily high, indeed very base-poor shales and sandstones are common in Sabah and in Sarawak, e.g. under dipterocarp forest on Gunung Mulu (Proctor *et al.* 1983; Whitmore 1984). Where they are deeper, the nutrient differences between soils on different parent materials tend to disappear in Sabah as in Malaya (Table 2).

TABLE 2. Exchangeable bases at a depth of 0.1–0.4 m in the Semporna Peninsula, Sabah (Paton 1963)

Parent material	Exchangeable bases (m-equiv. 100 g^{-1})				
	Ca	Mg	K	Na	Total
Shallow sedentary soils (around 0.4 m deep)					
Sandstone & shale	0.16	0.09	0.05	0.06	0.36
Limestone	52.35	1.27	0.26	0.13	54.01
Andesitic agglomerate	26.30	2.70	0.17	4.03	33.20
Serpentine	36.35	11.40	0.02	0.42	48.19
Basalt	5.67	8.53	0.06	0.42	14.66
Deep sedentary soils (>5 m deep)					
Basalt	0.59	0.51	0.12	0.09	1.29
Sandstone & shale	0.16	0.62	0.12	0.09	0.99

Rainfall is important, as rapid weathering is favoured by the continual removal of soluble products (Latham 1980). In general, where the mean annual rainfall is below 1000 mm, soils are less weathered (retaining some 2 : 1 clay minerals), have a moderate to high base content and do not average more than about 2 m in depth (Duchaufour 1983). There are exceptions on old surfaces and on loose, base-poor materials, but the 'closed' state is not typical of drier climates.

Inaccessible locus of release of bases by weathering

The studies of humid tropical weathering of granite mentioned above show that several metres of saprolite (rotten rock) normally intervene between the soil layers proper (themselves several metres thick) and fresh rock. Saprolite retains the structure of the original rock, but only the more resistant minerals such as quartz (and sometimes muscovite) remain intact, the remainder being converted to clay minerals (usually kaolinite and/or halloysite) and sesquioxides, mostly gibbsite. There is usually a sharp boundary ('weathering front') between the saprolite and nearly fresh rock. Indeed thin sections sometimes show a large felspar crystal fresh at one end and converted to gibbsite at the other. However, even very near to the weathering front, saprolite has a very similar low pH and low base content to subsoil layers much nearer the surface (Table 3). Most of the content of base cations in the parent rock has already disappeared.

TABLE 3. Weathering of granite at Ulu Gombak, 25 km north-east of Kuala Lumpur, Peninsular Malaysia (Burnham 1978)

Depth (m)	Clay (%)	Ca	Na	K	Mg	Total	pH_{H_2O}
		Exchangeable bases (m-equiv. $100\ g^{-1}$)					
3.00	40.4	0.27	0.14	0.23	0.04	0.68	5.1
		Mottled saprolite underlies soil at 3.65 m					
8.00	30.1	0.11	0.12	0.15	0.06	0.44	4.5
		Saprolite consists of about equal parts of quartz, gibbsite and kaolinite with a trace of mica					
9.95	4.3	0.13	0.11	0.24	0.06	0.54	4.8
10.00+		Fresh granite, just beginning to alter to gibbsite and kaolinite. Abrasion pH about 8.0 when fully fresh					

Unfortunately, few studies of weathering have included chemical analyses of the transition from completely fresh to slightly weathered rock. This is where most of the calcium and a significant proportion of other base cations and silica are lost. Calvert *et al.* (1980) found that the calcium content of granite gneiss in North Carolina fell from 1.61% to less than 0.01% before the rock was sufficiently weakened to break with a hammer! Magnesium and sodium were less completely depleted, and potassium not at all. On an equal volume basis more than half the silica was lost at this stage with the formation of gibbsite and a lesser amount of halloysite. The pH of a suspension of crushed rock was 7.9 when completely fresh, but fell to 5.3 when still apparently fresh and to between 4.1 and 4.5 when weathered but still not readily breakable. This base depletion took place at a depth of about 5 m, but even if the overlying saprolite and soil layers had been much thinner, no root could have intercepted any significant proportion of these ions.

The leached bases must find their way by joint fissures into rivers. Thus the calculation of nutrient uptake by roots from a balance between atmospheric inputs and losses in river water, as quoted by Whitmore (1984, p. 104) from Kenworthy (1971), is unsound. Such 'balances' differ enormously, as Jordan (1985, p. 25) remarks, 'due to the nature of the parent rock'.

Barriers to rooting in the subsoil

Unrootable layers often occur in tropical and subtropical subsoils. Dense horizons may develop within saprolite, and are considered to be serious limitations to rooting if within 1.8 m of the surface (Lietzke & Weber 1981). Some compact and normally unrootable layers have the hardening property characteristic of plinthite (Soil Survey Staff 1975). In climates with even a short dry season a plinthite layer may harden irreversibly to ironstone, but plinthite which hardens occurs in only about 2% of tropical soils (Moorman & van Wambeke 1978). Ironstone is more often formed in the uppermost part of weathering parent material by vertical or lateral migration, and may seal it against root penetration. Any layer, compact or not, which is waterlogged for much of the year is likely to be a barrier to roots (Baillie *this volume*).

PROCESSES WHEREBY CONSTITUENTS PRODUCED BY WEATHERING REACH THE BIOSPHERE

Six processes seem worthy of consideration: uptake by roots; disturbance of soil by tree fall; bioturbation by burrowing organisms (e.g. termites, earthworms); colluvial movements (soil erosion); landslides; lateral (downslope) leaching. The effect of these processes and the depth to which they operate is of obvious importance.

Uptake by roots

Root biomass is very variable (Jordan 1985) and rooting depth is difficult to determine. Particularly in humid climates and especially on nutrient-poor soils (Stark & Jordan 1978), most forest trees concentrate nearly all their roots in the uppermost 0.3 m of the soil (Kerfoot 1963), but the density falls exponentially and a few roots are found at a much greater depth. Odum & Pigeon (1970) collected information on root density by depth in a number of well-drained tropical forest soils and found that roots became fewer than 500 per m^2 of vertical surface at depths ranging from 0.22 to 0.70 m. In Malayan rain forest, roots are usually few and small below 0.75 m and rare below 1.50 m, presumably because deep rooting is not needed to obtain moisture. It is not likely that these few fine roots exploring base-depleted soil play any considerable part in nutrient supply. In Sarawak (Baillie & Mamit 1983), on a shallow soil with an average depth to weathering rock of 1.05 m, the mean rooting depth was 1.77 m and a few roots of

Shorea and *Dryobalanops* reached below 3.0 m. These trees obviously explore weathering rocks, but to little effect as these are base-poor sandstones and shales. On other parent materials similar rooting habits would presumably support a relatively 'open' nutrient cycle.

In seasonally dry climates deeper roots are needed to obtain water, and may play some part in nutrient supply (Nye & Greenland 1960). Humbel (1974) studied the porosity and seasonal water content of soils in Cameroon under moist forest with a dry season of 2–3 months and under savanna or dry forest with a dry season of 6 months. In the moist forest roots diminished considerably below 0.4 m and even the surface roots did not dry the soil out to wilting point during the dry season. Under savanna roots dried the soil in the dry season to wilting point to a depth of 0.8 m, and had some drying effect to 1.8 m. Under dry forest considerable rooting apparently reached 2.0 m.

Tree fall

In a natural forest trees are sometimes felled by the wind, and this may create hummocks and hollows (Whitmore 1984). However, the 'root plate' of soil dragged up by the tree is seldom more than 0.3 m in thickness, and so only nutrient-poor immediate subsoil is brought up (Vitousek & Denslow 1986).

Bioturbation

In temperate forest there are no termites and only a small minority of earthworms ingest soil (although these may be very important). In the tropics earthworms frequently ingest soil (Lavelle 1983). Some Nigerian earthworm casts are huge (100 mm or more in height). In Malaysia most topsoils under lowland rain forest contain some earthworm casts, but their role is less than that of termites. Earthworm channels typically reach a depth of 0.6–0.8 m in Malaya. Earthworms predominate in some montane soils because they are more tolerant of cool and moist environments than termites.

Termites are highly important soil organisms in the tropical lowlands (Lee & Wood 1971). Mound-building termites bring up fine earth from a considerable depth, and are particularly abundant in seasonally dry climates. When the mounds degrade, a surface layer is formed almost free from coarse particles. Several estimates of the rate of formation of this layer have been made, ranging from 0.025 mm per year (Nye 1955), through 0.04–0.12 mm (Pomeroy 1976) to 0.75–1.0 mm (Lepage 1984). The last estimate is related to a plateau in Ivory Coast, capped by lateritic ironstone and covered with only 0.1–0.3 m depth of loose soil, in an area of mean annual rainfall of 1100 mm with a dry season of 8 months and a vegetation of savanna and dry forest. The especially rapid accumulation was attributed to the regular destruction of termite colonies by predators, following which an 8 m^3 mound took 20 or 25 years to degrade.

It is noteworthy that the material of termite mounds is enriched in bases, especially calcium (Hesse 1955; Watson 1962; Lee 1987). Some termites cultivate 'fungus gardens' (Wood 1978). The 'combs' on which the fungus is grown often occur within mounds; however, *Microtermes* which is common in Malaya makes them in bun-shaped cavities in the subsoil to a depth of 1.2 m, locally 1.5 m. Linking these chambers, and also under and around termite mounds, there is a network of galleries (Darlington 1982). It is obvious that these galleries greatly increase soil permeability and that in constructing them, termites move an immense amount of mineral soil (Maldague 1964). In Para state, Brazil (FAO/UNESCO 1971), termite activity makes some soils under tropical rain forest loose and porous to a depth of 1.3 m.

Together with earthworms, termites mix the upper part of the soil profile so that thin layers which form slowly, such as the Eb and Bt horizons produced by lessivage (downwashing of clay particles) or the Ea and Bs horizons of an incipient podzol, have no chance to differentiate. The latter only appear in montane soils in Malaysia where termites are absent (Burnham 1978). Similarly, material arriving at the surface as dust, volcanic ash or colluvium is 'stirred in' by termites. Detailed microscope work may be needed to demonstrate its existence, as when Burnham (1978) showed grains of volcanic glass in a strongly termite-worked soil near Raub in Malaya. Discrete layers of volcanic ash usually occur in Malaya only where protected from termite mixing by waterlogging or overlying alluvium (Stauffer 1973). Ash contamination could explain a high content of silt and fine sand, especially of the 20–50 μm fraction, which reached 37.7% in the 0–150 mm layer, and also an unusually large (and highly pH-dependent) cation exchange capacity for a soil otherwise dominated by kaolinite. Since the ash is some 400 km from its probable source in northern Sumatra and microscopic studies are rare, such admixture could be widespread, and of significance in nutrient supply.

An interesting parallel is provided by Edwards & Grubb (1982) who sought to explain exceptionally fertile soils in New Guinea with an abnormally high content of organic carbon and nitrogen to more than 1 m. They suggested that the soil profile was built up from numerous moderate falls of volcanic ash, and deep mixing by earthworms. The profile showed no sign of stratification, even though six distinct ash showers, datable within the last 10 000 years, were interbedded with peat on Mt. Wilhelm only 25 km away (Hope 1976).

Termites are not found on high mountains (Collins 1983), but in seasonally dry climates they are very important. In the humid part of Cameroon (Humbel 1974) all biological activity diminishes considerably below 0.4 m, but where there is a long dry season termites have a large effect on porosity to a depth of 1.5 m or slightly more.

Fölster, Moshrefi & Ojenuga (1971) studied ferrallitic pedogenesis on metamorphic rocks in southern Nigeria under transition forest with a mean annual rainfall of 1200–1500 mm and 3½ months of dry season. They found a surface 'zoogenous cover', typically about 1 m thick, but with a maximum of 1.2 m, in which the fabric of weathered rock (saprolite) had been homogenized by roots and soil fauna (mostly termites) to a uniform reddish brown, brown or yellowish brown colour. In the zoogenous cover, material coarser than 1 mm in diameter tended to be lacking, apart from concretions thoroughly detached from the matrix.

An overall estimate of biological activity can be obtained from the organic matter content. Like root density this tends to fall exponentially with depth. Bennema (1974) plotted the logarithm of percentage carbon with depth for several Brazilian oxisols (ferrallitic soils) and found this fell linearly to a depth between 1.0 m and 2.0 m, at which it was about 0.3–0.4%, and then there was an inflection to a much steeper fall. A similar effect is seen in temperate soils at about 0.8 m. This is possibly the best overall measure of the depth to which biological activity reaches, although a little fine humus may be washed down mechanically.

A fair general conclusion appears to be that roots and soil fauna are active in tropical forest soils to about 1.5 m, but where there is a long dry season a safer limiting depth is about 2.0 m. Within this depth faunal activity provides many paths for recycling, but layers beyond it remain virtually unaffected.

Colluvial movement

In tropical soils it is common to find a relatively homogeneous layer, often about 1 m thick, underlain by a layer of stones (vein quartz, ironstone, etc.), known as a 'stone line', under which there may be a sharp transition to a contrasting layer. The homogenized layer may be the work of termites, but is often due to the accumulation of eroded material from upslope ('colluvium'). This relates to an episode of severe soil erosion, followed by a period of stability, as expounded by Butler (1959) in Australia. Pedological studies in Puerto Rico (Beinroth 1981) have shown that differences in soil profiles and properties can often be explained by colluvial covers of different ages and depths, which overlie saprolite at a sharp boundary representing a marked discontinuity in soil formation. Such discontinuities are common in the tropics and are not always marked by a stone line (Eswaran & Sys 1979).

Runoff moves surface soil and much of this is redeposited on the soil surface downslope. Rates of erosion in undisturbed tropical forest are not particularly high (Mitchell 1957), and only locally, e.g. in areas of rapid tectonic uplift, is little-weathered material involved.

Landslips

Fieldwork along the road cutting up Gunung Ulu Kali in Malaya (Whitmore & Burnham 1969) revealed an intricate variation in soil depth (especially depth to granite saprolite) largely due to a mosaic of old landslip scars on slopes of 20°–30°

or more. It appeared that under primary forest landslips were more important than soil erosion in effecting soil rejuvenation in this mountainous area. Day (1980) also noted a high frequency of landslides on very steep slopes in Gunung Mulu National Park, Sarawak. The parent material there was somewhat metamorphosed shale. It seems agreed by all authors, e.g. K. E. Clare & D. Newill (unpublished), that weathered schists and shales are especially liable to slips, because the material is laminated and fissured and impermeable except along the fissures. On argillaceous materials landslips occur on slopes over 10°; on most other materials a slope of the order of 20° is required.

In areas of tectonic activity, such as New Guinea and Central America, landslides are often triggered by earthquakes (Garwood, Janos & Brokaw 1979). In 1976 landslides caused by earthquakes removed soil and all vegetation from 12% of a region in Panama extending to more than 450 km^2 (Garwood 1984). However, any steep slope is vulnerable, for the high infiltration capacity of most tropical forest soils which reduces erosion also provides penetrating water to lubricate mass movements (De Ploey & Cruz 1979).

Unlike bioturbation and root activity, landslides are episodic in their effect. They can 'rejuvenate' soil profiles and bring less weathered materials to the surface. Landslips in Malaya quite often involve incompletely weathered material, including large corestones of fresh granite.

Lateral leaching

Lateral movement of constituents in solution from high parts of the landscape to lower places is an important feature of tropical pedogenesis involving silica (e.g. Fauck 1974; Millot, Bocquier & Paquet 1976) and iron (e.g. Ambrosi, Nahon & Herbillon 1986). Bases are transported and appear in rivers (Kenworthy 1971; Bishop 1973) and to a limited extent in alluvium (see Table 3). However, in Malaya there is very little evidence that the enrichment of soils with nutrients by 'flushing' on the lower parts of slopes is significant, as it often is in Britain. One can only conclude that the lateral movement of bases takes place at great depth along the interface of weathered and fresh rock or actually along fissures within the parent material.

In summary, it may be concluded that, apart from occasional landslips, no process in soils of the humid tropics will bring up significant amounts of plant nutrients from a depth of more than 1.5–2.0 m.

CONCLUSION

'Closed' cycles may be expected when there is little replenishment of nutrients from parent materials. This occurs where the original concentration of nutrients is very low or where strongly weathered and leached soils are more than 1.5–2.0 m deep or contain a subsoil barrier to rooting.

Relatively 'open' cycles prevail in dry climates where leaching is comparatively weak and in humid climates where soils are shallower than 1.5–2.0 m to a nutrient-rich substratum. This is commonly the case in tectonically active areas where rapid uplift is balanced by strong erosion and by landslips. The role of landslips in drastic soil profile truncation has probably been undervalued, especially in areas where argillaceous strata outcrop on slopes or where earthquakes are prevalent. Garwood *et al.* (1979) calculated that landslides affected between 8 and 16% of an earthquake-liable area in New Guinea in a century and between 41 and 89% in 500 years, a short period in terms of chemical weathering (Colman & Dethier 1986). In a less seismically active area in Panama between 4 and 10% was affected in 500 years, still a significant proportion.

Open cycles are also favoured by a supply of volcanic ash or alluvium from an area where little-weathered material is being eroded.

Nutrient cycling studies have often been conducted in sites where the parent material is of uncertain relevance or is inaccessible to sampling in an unweathered state. This paper may assist the interpretation of these hard-won results.

REFERENCES

Acres, B.D., Bower, R.P., Burrough, P.A., Folland, C.J., Kalsi, M.S., Thomas, P.E. & Wright, P.S. (1975). Soil profile descriptions. Appendix 1. *The Soils of Sabah, Vol. 5. References and Appendices. Land Resource Study 20.* Land Resources Division, Surbiton, U.K.

Ambrosi, J.P., Nahon, D. & Herbillon, A.J. (1986). The epigenic replacement of kaolinite by hematite in laterite-petrographic evidence and the mechanisms involved. *Geoderma*, 37, 283–294.

Ashton, P.S. (1964). *Ecological Studies in the Mixed Dipterocarp Forests of Brunei State. Oxford Forestry Memoirs 25.* Oxford University Press, Oxford.

Austin, M.P., Ashton, P.S. & Greig-Smith, P. (1972). The application of quantitative methods of vegetation survey III. A re-examination of rain forest data from Brunei. *Journal of Ecology*, 60, 305–324.

Baillie, I.C. & Ashton, P.S. (1983). Some soil aspects of the nutrient cycle in mixed dipterocarp forests in Sarawak. *Tropical Rain Forest: Ecology and Management* (Ed. by S.L. Sutton, T.C. Whitmore & A.C. Chadwick), pp. 347–356. Blackwell Scientific Publications, Oxford.

Baillie, I.C. & Mamit, J.D. (1983). Observations on rooting in mixed dipterocarp forest, Central Sarawak. *Malayan Forester*, 46, 369–374.

Beinroth, F.H. (1981). Some highly weatherd soils of Puerto Rico. I. Morphology, formation and classification. *Geoderma*, 27, 1–74.

Bennema, J. (1974). Organic carbon profiles in Oxisols. *Pédologie*, 24, 119–146.

Bishop, J.E. (1973). *Limnology of a Small Tropical River.* Junk, The Hague.

Bockheim, J.G. (1980). Solution and use of chronofunctions in studying soil development. *Geoderma*, 24, 71–85.

Brinkmann, W.L.F. (1985). Studies on hydrobiogeochemistry of a tropical lowland forest system. *Geo Journal*, 11, 89–101.

Burnham, C.P. (1978). *Soil formation and its variation with altitude in Malaya and western Sabah.* PhD Thesis, Wye College, University of London.

Butler, B.E. (1959). *Periodic Phenomena in Landscapes as a Basis for Soil Studies. Soil Publication 14.* CSIRO, Australia.

Calvert, C.S., Buol, S.W. & Weed, S.B. (1980). Mineralogical characteristics and transformations of a vertical rock–saprolite–soil sequence in the North Carolina Piedmont. *Soil Science Society of America Journal*, 44, 1096–1112.

Collins, N.M. (1983). Termite populations and their role in litter removal in Malaysian rain forests. *Tropical Rain Forest: Ecology and Management* (Ed. by S.L. Sutton, T.C. Whitmore & A.C. Chadwick), pp. 311–326. Blackwell Scientific Publications, Oxford.

Colman, S.M. & Dethier, D.P. (1986). *Rates of Chemical Weathering of Rocks and Minerals.* Academic Press, Orlando.

Darlington, J.P.E.C. (1982). The underground passages and storage pits used in foraging by a nest of the termite *Macrotermes michaelseni* in Kajiado, Kenya. *Journal of Zoology*, 198, 237–247.

Davis, T.A.W. & Richards, P.W. (1933). The vegetation of Moraballi Creek, British Guiana: an ecological study of a limited area of tropical rain forest. Part I. *Journal of Ecology*, 21, 350–384.

Davis, T.A.W. & Richards, P.W. (1934). The vegetation of Moraballi Creek, British Guiana: an ecological study of a limited area of tropical rain forest. Part II. *Journal of Ecology*, 22, 106–155.

Day, M.J. (1980). Symposium on the geomorphology of the Mulu hills. II. Landslides in the Gunung Mulu National Park. *Geographical Journal*, 146, 7–13.

De Ploey, J. & Cruz, O. (1979). Landslides in the Serra Do Mar, Brazil. *Catena*, 6, 111–121.

Duchaufour, P. (1983). *Pédologie 1. Pédogenèse et classification*, 2nd edn. Masson, Paris.

Edwards, P.J. & Grubb, P.J. (1982). Studies of mineral cycling in a montane rain forest in New Guinea IV. Soil characteristics and the division of mineral elements between the vegetation and soil. *Journal of Ecology*, 70, 649–666.

Eswaran, H. & Bin, W.C. (1978). A study of a deep weathering profile on granite in Peninsular Malaysia. *Soil Science Society of America Journal*, 42, 144–158.

Eswaran, H. & Sys, C. (1979). Argillic horizon in low activity clay soils: formation and significance to classification. *Pédologie*, 29, 175–190.

FAO/UNESCO (1971). *Soil Map of the World 1: 5000000 Vol. IV South America.* UNESCO, Paris.

Fauck, R. (1974). Les facteurs et les mécanismes de la pédogenèse dans les sols rouges et jaunes ferrallitiques sur sables et grès en Afrique. *Cahiers ORSTOM Série Pédologie*, 12, 9–72.

Fölster, H., Moshrefi, N. & Ojenuga, A.G. (1971). Ferrallitic pedogenesis on metamorphic rocks, S.W. Nigeria. *Pédologie*, 21, 95–124.

Garwood, N.C. (1984). Revegetation of earthquake-caused landslides in Panama. *Tropical Rain Forest: the Leeds Symposium* (Ed. by A.C. Chadwick & S.L. Sutton), p. 302. Leeds Philosophical and Literary Society, Leeds.

Garwood, N.C., Janos, D.P. & Brokaw, N. (1979). Earthquake-caused landslides: a major disturbance to tropical forests. *Science*, 205, 997–999.

Hardy, F. (1935). Some aspects of tropical soils. *Transactions of the 3rd International Congress of Soil Science (Oxford)*, 2, 150–163.

Hesse, P.R. (1955). A chemical and physical study of the soils of termite mounds in East Africa. *Journal of Ecology*, 43, 449–461.

Hope, G.S. (1976). The vegetation history of Mt. Wilhelm, Papua New Guinea. *Journal of Ecology*, 64, 627–663.

Humbel, F.X. (1974). La compacité de sols ferrallitiques du Cameroun: une zonalité dans ce milieu en relation avec la dessiccation saisonnière. *Cahiers ORSTOM Série Pédologie*, 12, 73–101.

Jordan, C.F. (1985). *Nutrient Cycling in Tropical Forest Ecosystems.* Wiley, Chichester.

Jordan, C. & Herrera, R. (1981). Tropical rain forests: are nutrients really critical? *American Naturalist*, 117, 167–180.

Kenworthy, J.B. (1971). Water and nutrient cycling in a tropical rain forest. *The Water Relations of Malesian Forests* (Ed. by J.R. Flenley), pp. 49–65. Miscellaneous Series No. 11, Department of Geography, University of Hull, U.K.

Kerfoot, O. (1963). The root systems of tropical forest trees. *Empire Forestry Review*, 42, 19–26.

Latham, M. (1980). Ferralisation in an oceanian tropical environment. *Proceedings Conference on Classification and Management of Tropical Soils, 1977* (Ed. by K.T. Joseph), pp. 20–26. Malaysian Society of Soil Science, Kuala Lumpur.

Lavelle, P. (1983). The structure of earthworm communities. *Earthworm Ecology from Darwin to Vermiculture* (Ed. by J.E. Satchell), pp. 449–466. Chapman and Hall, London.

Ledgerwood, E. (1963). Some notes on the humid tropical weathering of granite and associated rocks in the Cameron Highlands area, Federation of Malaya. *Geological Survey Professional Paper*, E-63, 1–6.

Lee, K.E. (1987). Termites, micro–organisms, soil organic matter and soil processes. *Transactions of the 13th Congress of the International Society of Soil Science*, **5**, 167–174.

Lee, K.E. & Wood, T.G. (1971). *Termites and Soils.* Academic Press, London.

Lemée, G. (1961). Effets des caractères du sol sur la localisation de la végétation en zones équatoriales et tropicales humides. *Proceedings of the Symposium on Tropical Soils and Vegetation, Abijan*, pp. 25–39. UNESCO, Paris.

Lepage, M. (1984). Distribution, density and evolution of *Macrotermes bellicosus* nests (Isoptera: Macrotermitinae) in the north–east of Ivory Coast. *Journal of Animal Ecology*, **53**, 107–117.

Lietzke, D.A. & Weber, R.S. (1981). The importance of Cr horizons in soil classification and interpretation. *Soil Science Society of America Journal*, **45**, 593–599.

Maldague, M.E. (1964). Importance des populations de termites dans les sols equatoriaux. *Transactions of the 8th International Congress of Soil Science (Bucharest)*, **3**, 743–751.

Millot, G., Bocquier, G. & Paquet, H. (1976). Geochimie et paysages tropicaux. *La Recherche*, **65**, 236–244.

Mitchell, B.A. (1957). A note on land erosion in the Cameron Highlands. *Malayan Forester*, **20**, 30–32.

Moorman, F.R. & van Wambeke, A. (1978). The soils of the lowland rainy tropical climates: their inherent limitations for food production and related climatic restraints. *11th Congress of the International Society of Soil Science (Edmonton, Canada). Plenary Session Papers*, **2**, 272–291.

Newbery, D.M. & Proctor, J. (1984). Ecological studies in four contrasting lowland rain forests in Gunung Mulu National Park, Sarawak. IV. Associations between tree distribution and soil factors. *Journal of Ecology*, **72**, 475–493.

Nye, P.H. (1955). Some soil–forming processes in the humid tropics. IV. The action of the soil fauna. *Journal of Soil Science*, **6**, 73–83.

Nye, P.H. & Greenland, D.J. (1960). *The Soil Under Shifting Cultivation. Technical Communication 51.* Commonwealth Bureau of Soil Science, Harpenden, U.K.

Odum, H.T. & Pigeon, R.F. (Eds.) (1970). *A Tropical Rain Forest.* Division of Technical Information, U.S. Atomic Energy Commission, Washington DC.

Owens, L.B. & Watson, J.P. (1979). Rate of weathering and soil formation on granite in Rhodesia. *Soil Science Society of America Journal*, **43**, 160–166.

Paton, T.R. (1963). *A Reconnaissance Soil Survey of the Semporna Peninsula, North Borneo. Department of Technical Cooperation Colonial Research Studies 36.* HMSO, London.

Pomeroy, D.E. (1976). Some effects of mound–building termites on soils in Uganda. *Journal of Soil Science*, **27**, 377–394.

Proctor, J., Anderson, J.M., Chai, P. & Vallack, H.W. (1983). Ecological studies in four contrasting rain forests in Gunung Mulu National Park, Sarawak. I. Forest environment. *Journal of Ecology*, **71**, 237–260.

Richards, P.W. (1961). The types of vegetation of the humid tropics in relation to the soil. *Proceedings of the Symposium on Tropical Soils and Vegetation, Abijan*, pp. 15–23. UNESCO, Paris.

Schimper, A.F.W. (1903). *Plant-geography upon a Physiological Basis.* Oxford University Press, Oxford.

Shanan, L. & Tadmor, N.H. (1979). *Microcatchment Systems for Arid Zone Development.* Israel Ministry of Agriculture, Rehovot.

Soil Survey Staff (1975). *Soil Taxonomy. Agriculture Handbook 436.* U.S. Department of Agriculture, Washington DC.

Stark, N.M. & Jordan, C.F. (1978). Nutrient retention by the root mat of an Amazonian rain forest. *Ecology*, **59**, 434–437.

Stauffer, P.H. (1973). Late Pleistocene age indicated for volcanic ash in West Malaysia. *Geological Society of Malaysia Newsletter*, **40**, 1–3.

Vallerie, M. (1973). Contribution à l'étude des sols du centre sud Cameroun. *Travaux et Documents de l'ORSTOM*, **29**, 112 pp.

Van't Hoff, J.H. (1884). *Études de Dynamique Chimique.* Frederik Muller, Amsterdam.

Vitousek, P.M. & Denslow, J.S. (1986). Nitrogen and phosphorus availability in tree fall gaps of a lowland tropical rain forest. *Journal of Ecology*, **74**, 1167–1178.

Walter, H. (1936). Nährstoffgehalt des Bodens und natürliche Waldbestände. *Forstliche Wochensch-rift Silva*, **24**, 201–205, 209–213.

Walter, H. (1971). *Ecology of Tropical and Subtropical Vegetation*. Oliver & Boyd, Edinburgh.

Watson, J.P. (1962). The soil below a termite mound. *Journal of Soil Science*, **13**, 46–51.

Whitmore, T.C. (1973). Frequency and habitat of tree species in the rain forest of Ulu Kelantan. *Singapore Gardens Bulletin*, **26**, 195–210.

Whitmore, T.C. (1984). *Tropical Rain Forests of the Far East*, 2nd edn. Clarendon Press, Oxford.

Whitmore, T.C. & Burnham, C.P. (1969). The altitudinal sequence of forests and soils on granite near Kuala Lumpur. *Malayan Nature Journal*, **22**, 99–118.

Wong, Y.K. & Whitmore, T.C. (1970). On the influence of soil properties on species distribution in a Malayan lowland dipterocarp rain forest. *Malayan Forester*, **33**, 42–54.

Wood, T.G. (1978). Food and feeding habits of termites. *Production Ecology of Ants and Termites* (Ed. by M.V. Brian), pp. 55–80. Cambridge University Press, Cambridge.

Variations in soil nutrients in relation to soil moisture status in a tropical forested ecosystem

S. NORTCLIFF* AND J. B. THORNES**

*Department of Soil Science, University of Reading,
Reading RG1 5AQ, and
**Department of Geography, University of Bristol,
Bristol BS8 1SS

SUMMARY

1 Following from the results of earlier hydrological studies in Reserva Ducke, Amazonas, a bi-phasic system of soil macropores and micropores is proposed.

2 Such a bi-phasic system may result in macropore water flowing rapidly through the system, with consequent short residence times and low solute concentrations.

3 For the drier season of 1978 the bi-phasic system is confirmed by analysis of the mean volumes yielded in ceramic cup samplers extracted at a range of soil moisture states.

4 Analysis of soil solute samples extracted across the range of soil moisture states confirms the contrast between solute concentrations in macropores and those in mesopores and micropores.

5 Implications for plant nutrient supplies in tropical forested ecosystems are discussed.

INTRODUCTION

The pathways of nutrients in all forest ecosystems are largely determined by the flows of water through the system. The general structure of these pathways is quite well known as a result of the prolonged study of forest hydrology (see, for example, the early work of Bates & Henry (1928)), intensive studies of forest nutrient cycling (e.g. Likens & Bormann 1975; Jordan 1985) and many hundreds of local small-scale studies, including those in and around Manaus (e.g. Brinkmann & Santos 1973; Stark & Holley 1975; Nortcliff & Thornes 1978; Brinkmann 1983). This paper adds to the growing bank of data, but has a more general purpose, to identify the effects of a bi-phasic soil pore water system on the nutrient pathways in the soil.

In 1978 we hypothesized that the forest latosols (Oxisols) of Reserva Ducke consisted of two systems, one dominated by macropores, through which water drained rapidly and had a short residence time, and the other dominated by micropores, through which the water drained slowly and hence exhibited a longer residence time. We argued (Nortcliff & Thornes 1978) and demonstrated

(Nortcliff, Thornes & Waylen 1979) that in the wet season rapid drainage occurred through the macropore system, leading to an almost instantaneous response of hillslope subsurface flow (Nortcliff & Thornes 1981), saturated floodplain storage and almost immediate floodplain overland flow (Nortcliff & Thornes 1984). We concluded that there was a nesting of soil water and solute systems, of which the macropore–micropore system was the lowest, the horizon to horizon contrasts an intermediate stage, and the slope–floodplain system the highest in the context of the Reserva Ducke systems considered. We expected that floodplain overland flow in virtually all periods would be characterized by low solute concentrations, whereas water with longer residence times in the system would be characterized by relatively high solute concentrations. Implicit in this idea is the questioning of stream-runoff quality as an indicator of closed or open forest nutrient cycles. By evaluating river water quality, one is largely confirming that it is rapidly draining, low-residence time water which moves along pathways with low cation exchange status, if the hypothesized model is correct. It does not mean that the usual exchange processes are not occurring within the micropore system. In describing the nesting of systems above, we have extended this analogy to include position in the soil profile and in the hillslope catena. Throughput of water will be higher lower down the profile and at lower zones in the hillslope in accordance with hydrological laws and this should be reflected in variations in solute concentrations.

Since 1978 the recognition of the bi-phasic nature of soil water drainage has become widespread (e.g. Beven & Germann 1981; Philip 1986). This also implies a fairly rapid response through the macropore system and a much slower response through the micropore system for most, if not all, soils and the consequent limitations of the Darcian approach to water and solute transfer. Moreover, detailed studies of soil microstructure in the Reserva Ducke soils (Chauvel, Soubies & Melfi 1983) have confirmed the existence of a strongly bi-phasic pore structure. We describe and interpret an experiment designed to test if the solute concentrations in the two systems are different and assess the significance of this difference in the overall nutrient cycling of bi-phasic soils.

If we assume that a bi-phasic structure exists, then the lower residence times of the macropore system should be reflected in lower solute concentrations and vice versa. To test this, solutes have to be extracted from the two systems and compared. We have done this by sampling soil solutes extracted at different conditions of soil tension.

STUDY SITES

The study was located in the catchment of the Barro Branco, a small tropical forest stream with a catchment area of *c*. 1.5 km², above the experimental site within the National Forest Reserve, Reserva Ducke (2°57′S, 59°57′W). The Reserve is situated 26 km east of Manaus on the Manaus–Itacoatiara road. A full description of the site is given in Nortcliff & Thornes (1981).

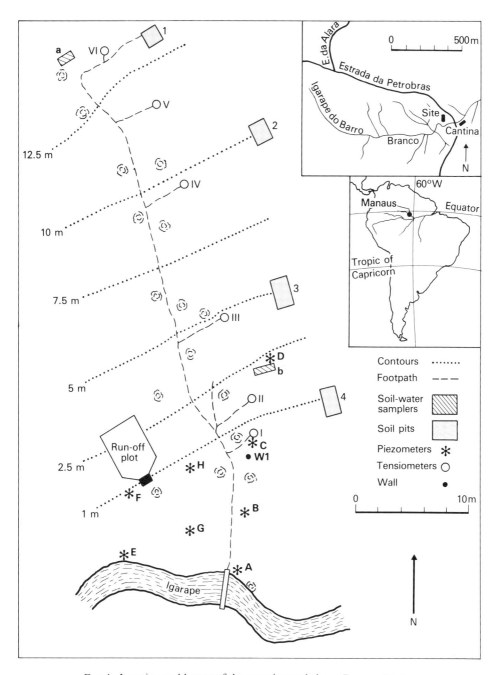

FIG. 1. Location and layout of the experimental site at Reserva Ducke.

The soils found on the experimental site were examined in a series of soil pits shown in Fig. 1. Pits 2, 3 and 4 correspond broadly with those described by Brinkmann & Santos (1973) as yellow latosols. In the terminology of Soil Taxonomy (Soil Survey Staff 1975) they are Oxisols, probably plinthic haplorthox, being composed predominantly of kaolinitic clays and quartz, with few weatherable minerals and hardened plinthitic nodules within a narrow band (20–40 cm thick) at depth (between 90 and 160 cm) within the profile. Hughes (1980) has considered these soils in the context of a weathering sequence with reference to soils from other tropical regions, concluding that these soils are from weathering zone 4 in the middle of the sequence, with soils from Quilichao, Colombia (zones 1 and 2) and Nigerian Basement Complex (zones 2 and 3) earlier (less weathered) in the sequence, and soils from the Brazilian Cerrado (zones 5, 6 and 7) more weathered.

Soil pit 1 is located at the foot of the slope towards the back of the floodplain and has characteristics which distinguish it from the slope soils. The parent material appears to be white sands with some finer material and a thin veneer of oxisolic material at the surface. The soil shows distinctive gleyic features and during examination in the wet season the pit filled rapidly with water.

A summary of results from the laboratory analyses for soil pits 2, 3 and 4 is given schematically in Fig. 2. The distinctive features of these soils are as follows. There is a very thin litter layer (*c.* 1 cm) consisting of fresh litter and partially decomposed leaves with abundant fungal growth and numerous fine fibrous red roots throughout. This overlies a thin (8–15 cm) A horizon, consisting of a dense root mat with abundant fine fibrous roots and common large woody roots, often lying parallel to the surface. Below the A horizon roots are present but are far less numerous and are either fine or very fine fibrous roots or very large (5–20 cm) woody roots. Below are inorganic horizons (B_{21}, B_{22} and B_3) with diffuse boundaries between 40 and 70 cm and 90 and 130 cm. There is little textural change down the profile, the major changes being in colour and the occurrence of plinthitic nodules in B_3, and only very low organic carbon contents in the mineral soil from 0.52% C in the 0–20 cm layer to 0.09% in the 120–140 cm layer. There is, however, an important change in the dry bulk density, which is closely related to the decrease in saturated hydraulic conductivity. Table 1 gives particle size distribution details for the slope pits (2, 3 and 4) showing a high degree of similarity between the soils. An interesting feature is the relatively low percentage of silt size (60-2 μm) particles. Low silt content is often used as an indicator of intensive weathering (e.g. Van Wambeke 1967). Even these low percentages of silt (and possibly fine sand) may be an overestimate due to the presence of very stable microaggregates, which proved very difficult to disperse. In the field, stable aggregations of fine material are common and are referred to as 'pseudosands'; Van Wambeke (1974) reported similar features for African ferralsols. The occurrence of these very stable aggregates may account for the high porosity of these soils. Detailed analysis of the clay fraction shows it to be predominantly kaolinitic with only traces of other clays.

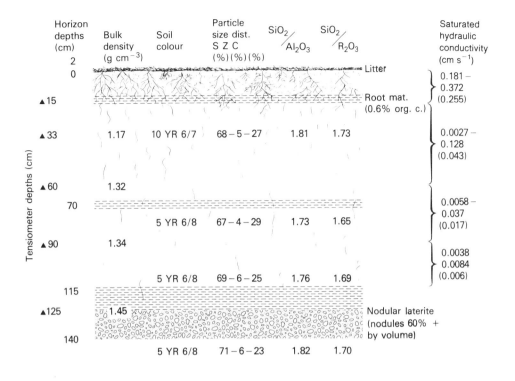

===== Merging boundaries

FIG. 2. Schematic soil profile, with summary of selected soil characteristics averaged for the sampled profiles at the experimental site, Reserva Ducke: bulk density (g cm^{-3}), moist soil colour (Munsell notation—Hue, Value, Chroma), particle size distribution (sand %—S; silt %—Z; clay %—C), molar ratios (SiO$_2$/Al$_2$O$_3$ and SiO$_2$/R$_2$O$_3$) and saturated hydraulic conductivities (cm s^{-1}).

TABLE 1. Particle size distributions and organic carbon at selected depths in soil pits 2, 3 and 4 at the experimental site, Reserva Ducke, Amazonas, Brazil

	2000–200 μm (%)	200–60 μm (%)	60–2 μm (%)	<2 μm (%)	Organic C (%)
Depths					
Pit 2 40 cm	53	21	4	22	0.45
80 cm	48	24	4	24	0.19
120 cm	53	20	4	23	0.11
160 cm	56	22	5	17	0.13
Pit 3 40 cm	40	28	7	25	0.55
80 cm	41	26	5	28	0.16
120 cm	43	25	5	27	0.10
Pit 4 40 cm	35	28	6	31	0.45
80 cm	37	26	6	31	0.20
120 cm	37	26	9	28	0.13

Average bulk densities and saturated hydraulic conductivities are shown in Fig. 2. The hydraulic conductivities were determined using a falling head permeameter with cores taken using a 7.5-cm diameter corer. Although the permeameter results cover a wide range of values there is broad agreement with rates derived from infiltration measurements and wetting front movements.

The temperature and precipitation regimes were studied by Ribeiro (1976). For the period 1965–1973, the range of temperatures was from 14.3 to 37 °C; the average daily maximum was about 33 °C. The total annual rainfall had an average over this period of 2468 mm; the wettest months were March (average 339 mm) and April (average 315 mm) and the driest was September (average 89 mm). The data for the present paper were collected and analysed in 1977 (wet season, March, April and May) and 1978 (wet season, January; dry season, August and September). Rainfall totals in the three observation periods are given in Table 2.

TABLE 2. Rainfall at Reserva Ducke, Amazonas, Brazil in the three observation periods, with the mean values for 1965–1973 in parentheses

Period 1		
1977 March	364 mm	(339 mm)
April	351 mm	(315 mm)
May	166 mm	(295 mm)
Period 2		
1978 January	240 mm	(285 mm)
Period 3		
1978 August	42 mm	(99 mm)
September	105 mm	(89 mm)

MATERIALS AND METHODS

The experimental design follows that of Nortcliff & Thornes (1981), comprising a small hillslope section from the channel to the top of the slope and onto the flat interfluve (Fig. 1). The slope was divided into six approximately equal segments, with instrumentation in each. In the first period of study tensiometers were located at five sample depths within each of the slope segments. Ceramic cup samplers (with ceramic cups of 4.2 cm outside diameter and 6.5 cm in length) (Hansen & Harris 1975; Silkworth & Grigal 1981) were installed at two sites: by tensiometer II near the foot of the slope and by tensiometer VI at the junction of the slope and the flat interfluve. At each location, soil water samples were taken on a regular basis at four depths: 23, 33, 63 and 103 cm below the surface. The samplers were evacuated to a suction of -60 kPa and left for 180 min before the water samples were extracted. Following the convention of Greenland (1977), at a suction of -60 kPa only pores with an equivalent diameter of <50 μm will be water-filled. Furthermore, Greenland suggests that pores remaining water-filled at this suction will be residual pores, and that transmission pores (>50 μm equivalent diameter) will be emptied at tensions between 0 and -6 kPa, and storage pores (<50 to 0.5 μm equivalent diameter) will be emptied at soil tensions between -6 and -60 kPa. Marshall (1959) suggests a similar cut-off, but with macropores defined as water-filled at tensions greater than -10 kPa. In general, two sets of samples were collected per day.

In January 1978 soil samplers were installed within each of the segments, with cups at 15, 30, 60, 90 and 120 cm. In the third period, August and September 1978, a much drier period, the spatial sampling design was as in January 1978. The samplers were evacuated to a suction of -60 kPa and water samples were taken after periods ranging from 48 to 120 h. This proved the most satisfactory water sampling scheme, and there were few cases where the process of equilibration of the sampler and the surrounding soil water had not been achieved. The samples were analysed using a Perkin–Elmer atomic absorption spectrophotometer, following the procedures outlined in Black (1965).

RESULTS

Sample volumes and sources

We comment first on the quantities sampled and their relation to the soil suction. The flow of water to plant roots is complicated (Tinker 1976; Nye & Tinker 1977). The point sampler can be regarded as analagous to a root in which, as used here, there is a constant boundary potential of -60 kPa, a constant 'root length' of the ceramic cup and a constant root radius. In these circumstances the amount absorbed by the cup will be a direct function of the difference between the mean soil suction and the stress applied to the ceramic cup (Lang & Gardner 1970). To some extent this will be a function of the time elapsed, at least in the initial transient stage. It is suggested that the maximum rates should be of the order of 1 cm^3 cm^{-2} day^{-1} which, in our case, should yield inflow rates of about 90 cm^3 day^{-1} at a maximum. To simplify and generalize the model we have expressed, for each sampler, the mean volume obtained from a large number of observations, standardized for the length of the sampling cylinder, to accommodate relative changes in the boundary suction on uptake of water (v_*) against the mean soil tension (φ) during the period over which the water was sampled (see Fig. 3). The result is a reverse S-shaped curve. As expected there is an upper limit to the absorption rate which occurs close to zero tension and this remains more or less constant at v_* approximately equal to 0.55 even at positive pressures. From a mean suction of -10 kPa (corresponding to the macropore 'cut-off' of Marshall (1959)), the curve falls steeply and then levels off at about $v_* = 0.04$, even at relatively high suctions. We interpret this as indicating a sharp separation between 'gravitational' and 'non-gravitational' drainage, and between macropore and micropore drainage. It seems logical therefore, in terms of our hypothesis, to look at the composition of samples on either side of the -10 kPa ambient soil-tension boundary.

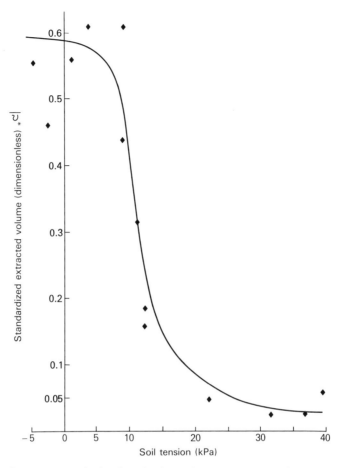

FIG. 3. Curve of mean standardized collected solute volume (v_*) plotted against mean soil tension (φ) for different locations at the experimental site during the dry season of 1978.

Soil solution

The hypothesis was tested in two ways. In the first experiment we performed paired t-tests between samples taken during the dry season of 1978 at tensions of less than and greater than -10 kPa. These are summarized in Table 3. In all cases the differences between the mean concentrations (mg l^{-1}) are significant ($p < 0.05$), supporting the hypothesis.

In the second test we clustered the full 1978 dry season data set for all four cations using Ward's grouping algorithm (Ward 1963), with each set of cation data standardized to zero mean and unit variance. With such a large data set (165 points) numerous groups were produced in the early stages of the analysis, but eventually four distinct groups were identified (Fig. 4). The number of group

TABLE 3. Summary of comparisons of soil solution composition for soil water extracted during the three sample periods from sample points on the experimental site, when the ambient tensions at the sample points were above and below -10 kPa. All differences in ion concentrations in solutions extracted at different water tensions are significant ($p < 0.05$)

Ion	n	>-10 kPa Mean	S.D.	n	<-10 kPa Mean	S.D.
Ca^{2+}	59	0.079	0.098	106	0.163	0.129
Mg^{2+}	59	0.260	0.230	106	0.331	0.211
K^+	59	0.777	0.760	106	1.239	0.801
Na^+	58	1.604	1.096	106	2.538	1.492

members, means and standard deviations for soil tension and each cation are given in Table 4. Group A is distinct from the remaining three groups, with the lowest mean concentrations in soil solution samples for all measured cations. In addition, group A has the lowest mean tension at -14 kPa. Although this is not coincident with the -10 kPa cut-off previously chosen, it does provide further general support for the hypothesis. The separation of the remaining three groups is chiefly with respect to the concentrations of potassium and sodium, the

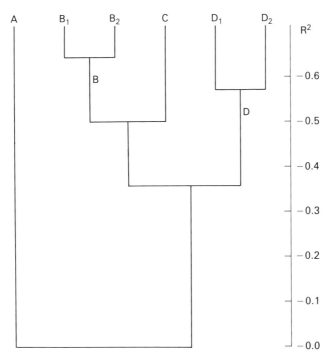

FIG. 4. Plot showing hierarchical grouping of soil solution data for 165 samples collected during the dry season of 1978 using Ward's grouping algorithm (Ward 1963). Four groups are distinguished. R^2 indicates the proportion of the variance accounted for by the clusters.

TABLE 4. Summary of soil solution compositions for the four groups identified using Ward's grouping algorithm

Group	n	Mean tension ($-$kPa) $\bar{x}$	Mean tension ($-$kPa) S.D.	Ca^{2+}(mg l^{-1}) $\bar{x}$	Ca^{2+}(mg l^{-1}) S.D.	Mg^{2+} (mg l^{-1}) $\bar{x}$	Mg^{2+} (mg l^{-1}) S.D.	K^+ (mg l^{-1}) $\bar{x}$	K^+ (mg l^{-1}) S.D.	Na^+ (mg l^{-1}) $\bar{x}$	Na^+ (mg l^{-1}) S.D.
A	73	14	18.6	0.04	0.05	0.16	0.08	0.74	0.61	1.33	0.60
B	51	28	16.4	0.26	0.11	0.33	0.11	1.04	0.40	2.14	0.65
C	33	28	16.7	0.12	0.08	0.45	0.16	1.78	0.67	3.17	0.85
D	8	16	10.0	0.20	0.12	0.82	0.49	2.90	1.54	6.53	1.99

concentrations increasing from group B, through C to D. All three groups have higher average tensions than group A, with the smallest group, D, consisting of a small number of near-surface samples taken at the beginning of the sample period, having tensions closest to those of group A.

DISCUSSION

The results broadly confirm the hypothesis of a bi-phasic system of soil water within the soils studied, and show that there are marked solute concentration differences between the two phases, with water in the macropores generally having lower concentrations of the four cations than water in the mesopores and micropores.

As stated above the outflow from the system in terms of flow to groundwater stores, and subsequently as streamflow, will to a large degree consist of water flowing rapidly through the macropore system of a saturated soil, and consequently we would expect this water to have low solute concentrations. This water may not represent the nutrient status of the whole system, but rather is a reflection of the status of the rapidly emptying and filling macropore system. In contrast, most water held in mesopores and micropores will be available to plants, will have longer residence times and probably higher solute concentrations, but will contribute a relatively small amount to groundwater recharge and streamflow at both peak flow and base flow conditions. Therefore, interpretations of the nutrient status of the soil system (e.g. Sioli 1975) from the analysis of river waters draining that system seem inappropriate, both for the reasons presented in this paper and the previously discussed geomorphological division of hillslope and floodplain. Thus the conclusions that exceptionally low concentrations of solutes in river waters indicate exceptionally impoverished soils may be invalid. Table 5 gives comparative data for rainfall, streamflow and soil solution concentrations for the four cations studied at this site for wet (March, April and May 1977 and January 1978) and dry (August and September 1978) seasons. The contrasts between seasons are not clear, probably as a result of the considerable variability in soil moisture conditions during the two periods and also across the slope, with water sampled at a range of tensions (and hence from macropore, mesopore and micropore systems). There is, however, a sharp contrast between the three sets of water samples, with the stream water samples

TABLE 5. Comparisons of solute concentrations in rainfall, soil solutions and streamflow for wet and dry seasons at Reserva Ducke, 1977 and 1978 (Nortcliff & Thornes 1978 and unpublished)

Source	Season	Ca^{2+} (mg l^{-1})	Mg^{2+} (mg l^{-1})	K^+ (mg l^{-1})	Na^+ (mg l^{-1})
Rainfall	Wet	0.32	0.20	1.33	0.42
	Dry	0.15	0.05	0.97	0.55
Soil solution	Wet	0.24	0.32	0.95	1.84
	Dry	0.13	0.30	1.15	2.20
Streamflow	Wet	0.01	0.03	0.06	0.19
	Dry	0.00	0.04	0.09	0.34

showing the lowest concentrations, lower indeed than the incoming open site rainfall. Where there is a more marked seasonality in the environmental conditions, with prolonged wet and dry seasons, it is anticipated that the soil solute concentrations will show strong seasonal contrasts. In the wet season the macropores will be frequently filled and emptied, and the bulk of the soil water will be of low concentration. In contrast, we would expect the soil solution water during the dry season to have a higher proportion of mesopore and micropore water and therefore to have higher solute concentrations.

In terms of plant nutrient supply the water extracted in this analysis was held at tensions between 0 and -60 kPa, all water readily available to plants. This further emphasizes the need to consider more than the rapidly draining 'macropore' water when assessments of the system's plant nutrient supply are required. Whilst there may be a 'direct nutrient supply' system with a nearly closed cycle as suggested by Jordan & Kline (1972), it seems very probable that the soil system will hold nutrients within the soil solution which are readily available to plants. This nutrient store can only be determined by examining the solute concentrations of macropores, mesopores and micropores. Analysis of only the water flowing from the system will give an unsatisfactory indication of the potential supplies of plant nutrients.

ACKNOWLEDGEMENTS

The authors gratefully acknowledge the help they have received from several persons and institutions whilst carrying out this research. The work was sponsored in the first year by the Royal Society and in the second year by the Organization of American States Regional Scientific and Technological Development Program. In the field logistic support was provided by the Instituto Nacional de Pesquisas da Amazonia, Manaus, and the Max Planck Institute of Limnology.

REFERENCES

Bates, C.G. & Henry, A.J. (1928). Forest and stream flow experiments at Wagon Wheel Gap, Colorado. *Monthly Weather Review*, Supplement **30**.

Beven, K. & Germann, P. (1981). Water flow in macropores. II. A combined flow model. *Journal of Soil Science*, **32**, 15–29.

Black, C.A. (Ed.) (1965). *Methods of Soil Analysis: Part 1.* American Society of Agronomy, Madison.

Brinkmann, W.L.F. (1983). Nutrient balance of a central Amazonian rainforest: comparisons of natural and man–managed systems. *Hydrology of Humid Tropical Regions* (Ed. by R. Keller), pp. 153–163. International Association of Scientific Hydrologists, Publication No. 140.

Brinkmann, W.L.F. & Santos, A. (1973). Natural waters in Amazonia. VI. Soluble calcium properties. *Acta Amazonica,* **3**, 55–61.

Chauvel, A., Soubies, F. & Melfi, A. (1983). Ferrallitic soils from Brazil: formation and evolution of structure. *Sciences Géologiques Mémoires,* **72**, 37–46.

Greenland, D.J. (1977). Soil damage by intensive arable cultivation: temporary or permanent? *Philosophical Transactions of the Royal Society, London, Series B,* **281**, 193–208.

Hansen, E.A. & Harris, A.R. (1975). Validity of soil water samples collected with porous ceramic cups. *Soil Science Society of America Proceedings,* **39**, 528–536.

Hughes, J.C. (1980). Crystallinity of kaolin minerals and their weathering sequence in some soils from Nigeria, Brazil and Colombia. *Geoderma,* **24**, 317–325.

Jordan, C.F. (1985). *Nutrient Cycling in Tropical Forest Ecosystems.* Wiley, Chichester.

Jordan, C.F. & Kline, J.R. (1972). Mineral cycling: some basic concepts and their application to tropical rainforests. *Annual Review of Ecology and Systematics,* **3**, 33–51.

Lang, A.R.G. & Gardner, W.R. (1970). Limitations to water flux from soils to plants. *Journal of Agronomy,* **62**, 693–695.

Likens, G.E. & Bormann, F.H. (1975). An experimental approach to New England landscapes. *Coupling of Land and Water Systems—Ecological Studies 10* (Ed. by A.D. Hasler), pp. 7–29. Springer, New York.

Marshall T.J. (1959). *Relations Between Water and Soil. Technical Communication 50.* Commonwealth Bureau of Soils, Harpenden, U.K.

Nortcliff, S. & Thornes, J.B. (1978). Water and cation movement in a tropical rainforest environment I. Objectives, experimental design and preliminary results. *Acta Amazonica,* **8**, 245–258.

Nortcliff, S. & Thornes, J.B. (1981). Seasonal variations in the hydrology of a small forested catchment near Manaus, Amazonas, and the implications for its management. *Tropical Agricultural Hydrology* (Ed. by R. Lal & E.W. Russell), pp. 37–57. Wiley, Chichester.

Nortcliff, S. & Thornes, J.B. (1984). Floodplain response of a small tropical stream. *Catchment Experiments in Fluvial Hydrology* (Ed. by T.P. Burt & D.E. Walling), pp. 73–85. Geo-Abstracts, Norwich.

Nortcliff, S., Thornes, J.B. & Waylen, M.J. (1979). Tropical forest systems: a hydrological approach. *Amazoniana,* **6**, 557–567.

Nye, P.H. & Tinker, P.B. (1977). *Solute Movement in the Soil–Root System.* Blackwell Scientific Publications, Oxford.

Philip, J.R. (1986). Steady infiltration from spheroidal cavities in isotropic and anisotropic soils. *Water Resources Research,* **22**, 1874–1880.

Ribeiro, M. de N.G. (1976). Aspectos climatologicos de Manaus. *Acta Amazonica,* **6**, 229–233.

Silkworth, D.R. & Grigal, D.F. (1981). Field comparison of soil solution samplers. *Soil Science Society of America Journal,* **45**, 440–442.

Sioli, H. (1975). Amazon tributaries and drainage basins. *Coupling of Land and Water Systems, Ecological Studies 10* (Ed. by A.D. Hasler), pp. 199–213. Springer, New York.

Soil Survey Staff (1975). *Soil Taxonomy. Agriculture Handbook 436.* U.S. Department of Agriculture, Washington DC.

Stark, N. & Holley, C. (1975). Final report on studies of nutrient cycling on white and black water areas in Amazonia. *Acta Amazonica,* **5**, 51–76.

Tinker, P.B. (1976). Transport of water to plant roots in soil. *Philosophical Transactions of the Royal Society, London, Series B,* **273**, 445–461.

Van Wambeke, A. (1967). Recent developments in the classification of soils in the tropics. *Soil Science,* **104**, 309–313.

Van Wambeke, A. (1974). *Management Properties of Ferralsols. Food and Agriculture Organisation Soils Bulletin 23.* FAO, Rome.

Ward, J.H. (1963). Hierarchical grouping to optimise an objective function. *Journal of the American Statistical Association,* **58**, 236–244.

Nitrification and denitrification in humid tropical ecosystems: potential controls on nitrogen retention

G. P. ROBERTSON
W. K. Kellogg Biological Station and Department of Crop and Soil Sciences, Michigan State University, Hickory Corners, MI 49060–9516, USA

SUMMARY

1 Nitrification is an important microbial process in humid tropical ecosystems because of its effects on potentials for nitrogen loss via nitrate leaching and denitrification and on the hydrogen ion cycle. Nitrification rates in humid tropical soils vary markedly among different forest types but in general appear to increase following disturbance. Proximal controls on nitrifiers include ammonium and oxygen; other major controls (water, temperature, net nitrogen mineralization, plant uptake, cation exchange capacity (CEC), respiration rates and aggregate structure) operate chiefly through their effects on the availability of ammonium and oxygen. There are a number of more distal controls, particularly plant community structure (the composition and physical stature of the plant community), which can be greatly influenced by human activity.

2 Denitrification has been less extensively studied in the humid tropics. A priori predictions suggest that denitrification rates ought to be high in the humid tropics as long as nitrate is available: soils tend to be highly aggregated and are often moist, resulting in low O_2 diffusion potentials, and carbon inputs from primary producers tend to be high. Recent results from *in situ* studies suggest that denitrification trends among rain forest sites may be similar to those for nitrification: high where nitrogen mineralization is high and low where nitrogen mineralization is low. Thus denitrification tends to be lowest in mid-successional sites where nitrate availability limits denitrifier activity.

3 Nitrification and denitrification can both lead to high nitrogen losses after vegetation clearing: denitrification directly and nitrification via its effects on nitrate leaching and denitrification potentials. Additionally, both processes may play an important role in the maintenance of soil exchange properties following disturbance. Nitrification, by producing hydrogen ions, will tend to force the soil exchange system to a net positive charge (to a net anion exchange capacity) and denitrification, by consuming some of the H^+ ions produced by nitrifiers, will tend to restore negative charges. Feedbacks in the system following disturbance may tend to make soil pH equilibrate near the soil's point of zero charge, a pH at which exchangeable ions are held only loosely against leaching from the rooting zone.

INTRODUCTION

Nitrification and denitrification are two of the potentially most important regulators of nitrogen retention in tropical rain forests. In temperate forests, nitrification can play a central role with respect to nitrogen loss from these systems (Fig. 1). When nitrification is low, mineral nitrogen stays in the ammonium form which tends to be conserved by cation exchange processes and by plant and microbial uptake. When nitrification is high, however, mineral nitrogen becomes more susceptible to loss because nitrate ions are not preferentially utilized and thereby immobilized by most microbial heterotrophs, are not held against leaching on cation exchange sites, and are available for gaseous loss via denitrification. Denitrification, the microbial reduction of nitrate to nitrogen gas in oxygen-depleted microsites in soil, can be a major pathway for nitrogen loss in some temperate zone forests (Melillo *et al.* 1983; Robertson & Tiedje 1984).

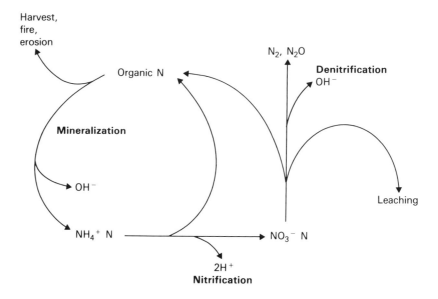

FIG. 1. Major potential pathways of nitrogen loss in a hypothetical terrestrial ecosystem.

In the humid tropics the influence of nitrification and denitrification on nitrogen loss may differ in at least three ways from that in temperate regions. First, because soils in humid tropical systems are often highly weathered with variable-charge clays predominant (Uehara & Gillman 1981; Sollins, Robertson & Uehara 1988), the soil charge system may under certain circumstances effectively switch polarity so that nitrate rather than ammonium is conserved on exchange sites. Thus nitrifiers in such soils may help to conserve mineral nitrogen as nitrate, particularly at depth (Matson *et al.* 1987).

Second, denitrification may be an especially important sink for available nitrogen in the humid tropics. As discussed later, soil O_2 potential is a major proximal control on denitrification in soil. Because soil moisture in the humid tropics is often high and because primary productivity and consequently decomposition also tend to be high in rain forests, soil oxygen diffusion can be inhibited at the same time that oxygen demands are great. This means that a large proportion of microsites in these soils may be anaerobic and hence favourable sites for denitrification. In addition, where the availability of nitrate is enhanced, as it may be in soils with a net anion exchange capacity, denitrification rates may be further elevated.

Third, and perhaps specific to humid tropical forests, nitrifiers and denitrifiers may regulate the charge status of these soils through their net effect on the H^+ ion cycle. In soils dominated by variable-charge clays, charge capacities are driven by the protonation and deprotonation of variable-charge surfaces (Uehara & Gillman 1981); because variable-charge soils typically are only weakly buffered, biological processes which (like nitrification) produce H^+ ions may reduce cation exchange capacity (CEC) and enhance anion exchange capacity (AEC). On the other hand, biological processes such as denitrification which consume H^+ ions may increase CEC at the expense of AEC. These changes may have important implications for overall ion retention.

In the sections that follow, I give an overview of nitrification and denitrification in humid tropical ecosystems, with a particular emphasis on the factors controlling these processes. In addition, I present a discussion of how these processes fit into the larger ecosystem, and the consequent potentials for system-wide effects.

NITRIFICATION

Nitrification in humid tropical soils has been studied extensively since early surveys of nitrifier numbers in West African forest soils (e.g. Laudelout & DuBois 1951; Dommergues 1952; Berlier, Dabin & Leneuf 1956; Jacquemin & Berlier 1956). Together with studies of soil nitrate concentrations under different vegetation types following clearing (e.g. Diamond 1937; Greenland 1958), results suggested that nitrification rates differed substantially among forest types and tended to increase temporarily after vegetation clearing. As early as 1950, for example, Vine (1953) had documented enhanced concentrations of soil nitrate following primary forest clearing and had noted that these concentrations tended to fall off after 8–10 years of cultivation.

Results from recent work using more direct measures of nitrification in tropical forest soils do not contradict these early findings. Using soil incubation and ^{15}N techniques Matson *et al.* (1987) found that nitrification rates in a premontane (650 m elevation) secondary rain forest in Central America were substantially increased for the first 6 months following secondary forest clearing, after which rates returned to levels close to those in uncut plots. Robertson &

Sollins (1987) documented nitrification increases following the clearing of 20-year-old secondary lowland vegetation on a Costa Rican Oxic Dystropept soil (Fig. 2). In this experiment cleared plots were kept vegetation-free throughout the 1-year experiment and nitrification rates remained high for the entire period.

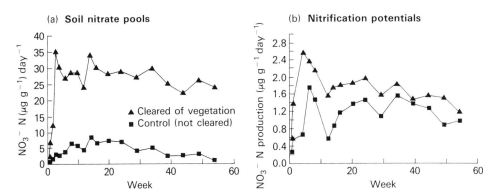

FIG. 2. Nitrate accumulation (a) and nitrification potentials (b) in a site cleared of secondary vegetation at a lowland rain forest site in Central America (from Robertson & Sollins (1987)).

Higher nitrification rates early in rain forest successions are typically followed by rates lower than those in either early or old-growth forest. Working in a subtropical rain forest sere in Australia, Lamb (1980) found lower nitrification rates in a 10-year-old site than in four older sites. Robertson (1984) found lower nitrification in the three early sites along a five-site sere in Costa Rica (Fig. 3).

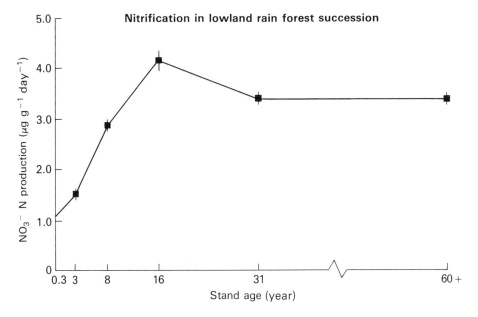

FIG. 3. Nitrification rates along a lowland tropical rain forest sere (from Robertson (1984)).

Such patterns of nitrification in succession are consistent with the hypothesis (Gorham, Vitousek & Reiners 1979) that in many types of seres soil nitrogen turnover should be high mainly very early and relatively late in succession when plant biomass accumulation, and therefore net plant nitrogen immobilization, is low. As discussed below, such trends have important implications for the effects of tropical deforestation on global nitrogen cycle processes such as nitrous oxide accumulation in the upper atmosphere.

Although nitrification trends in tropical rain forest succession appear to be consistent across a wide variety of forest types, undisturbed forests nevertheless differ widely in their extent of nitrification. Reports of nitrification in soils from intact primary rain forest range from <0.1 to >6 μg g^{-1} day^{-1} NO$_3^-$–N (deRham 1970; Tanner 1977; Lamb 1980; Vitousek et al. 1983; Chandler 1985; Robertson 1984). Although this wide range may to some extent be an artefact of different incubation techniques, both Montagnini & Buschbacher (1988) and Vitousek & Matson (1988) reported equally wide ranges in two surveys in which identical techniques were employed across a broad range of sites. Vitousek & Matson (1988) in a survey of nitrogen turnover in nine old-growth tropical forests in several different geographic regions documented rates that showed a more than fivefold difference between sites (Table 1), and Montagnini & Buschbacher (1988) documented rates among three Amazonian and Costa Rican sites that differed more than tenfold (Table 2).

TABLE 1. Net nitrification and nitrogen mineralization in nine old-growth tropical rain forest sites sampled on a single date within each site; values ($\pm$ S.E.) based on 10-day incubations of fresh soil (from Vitousek & Matson (1988)) (na = no S.E. available)

Site	Nitrification (μg g^{-1} day^{-1} N)	N mineralization (μg g^{-1} day^{-1} N)
Costa Rica (lowland forest)		
Residual soil	2.5 (0.3)	3.9 (0.5)
Old alluvial soil	1.8 (0.8)	2.7 (0.03)
Panama (semi-deciduous forest)		
Basalt	1.2 (0.1)	1.2 (0.2)
Sedimentary	1.6 (0.1)	1.6 (0.2)
Brazil (lowland forest)		
Oxisol	2.2 (0.3)	1.9 (0.3)
Oxisol/Ultisol	1.5 (0.1)	1.4 (0.2)
Psamment	0.6 (0.1)	0.8 (0.1)
Hawaii (montane forest)		
>1000-year-old Andept	0.0 (0.05)	0.1 (0.04)
>4000-year-old Andept	0.5 (na)	0.5 (na)

TABLE 2. Comparison of nitrogen mineralization and nitrification rates in soils from old-growth forests of San Carlos de Rio Negro, south-west Venezuela, and La Selva, north-east Costa Rica (from Montagnini & Buschbacher (1988))

	pH	Nitrification (μg g^{-1} day^{-1})	N mineralization (μg g^{-1} day^{-1})
San Carlos, Oxisol	3.3	0.50	0.47
San Carlos, Ultisol	3.5	0.12	0.06
La Selva, Inceptisol	5.3	3.43	3.43

Understanding the mechanisms underlying these differences in nitrification rates requires an understanding of the potential controls on nitrification in rain forest soils. As shown in Fig. 4, two main factors regulate nitrification at a fundamental, cellular level in most soils: ammonium ions and oxygen. All other important factors exert their influence mainly by affecting the ways in which ammonium and oxygen interact with individual cells. Soil moisture, for example, influences nitrification chiefly by controlling the diffusion of ammonium ions and oxygen through water films to the individual nitrifiers. Temperature (climate) influences nitrification mainly by its direct effects on processes affecting ammonium availability (mineralization/immobilization and ammonium ion diffusion), by its direct effects on the availability of O_2 (respiration and O_2 diffusion), and by its longer term effects on plant community structure and soil type.

Figure 4 shows the five major scales at which nitrification can be regulated in rain forest soils, ranging from the most proximal (ammonium and oxygen availability) to the most distal (climate, soil type and disturbance). This approach emphasizes indirect effects and explicitly identifies those factors operating at several different levels. A major secondary factor controlling nitrification through its influence on ammonium ions, for example, is the balance between nitrogen mineralization and immobilization. Nitrifiers are well-known to be poor competitors for ammonium in soil (Jones & Richards 1977; Schmidt 1982): where the available soil organic matter fraction has a high C : N ratio, microbial heterotrophs will readily immobilize NH_4^+ ions in solution, leaving little for nitrifiers. In temperate zone forests this immobilization can account for significant nitrogen retention in the system following clearcutting (Vitousek & Matson 1984); it may partly explain the low nitrification early on in some rain forest seres in which woody slash does not completely burn or is left on site (e.g. Robertson 1984). A more important mechanism retaining ammonium in many rain forest soils following clearing is plant uptake, however. Robertson & Rosswall (1986) estimated from literature reviews that early successional rain forest (0–20 years old) in West Africa removed an average 229 kg ha^{-1} year^{-1} N from the soil solution; of this around 114 kg N year^{-1} was incorporated into standing biomass. Although mature forests were estimated to take up an equivalent amount of nitrogen — 211 kg ha^{-1} year^{-1} — less than 1 kg ha^{-1} year^{-1} appeared to be retained via biomass accretion. This implies that in primary rain forests a much higher proportion of the system's nitrogen is circulating through the soil solution and available to nitrifiers, and partly explains the enhanced rates of nitrification late in many rain forest successions.

A fourth secondary control on nitrification via effects on ammonium availability in rain forest soils (Fig. 4) is the cation exchange capacity (CEC) of the soil. Those soils with a higher CEC will tend to retain NH_4^+ ions against leaching, thereby enhancing their availability to nitrifiers provided that there is little competition from plants and microbial heterotrophs and that sufficient moisture is available for the ions to diffuse.

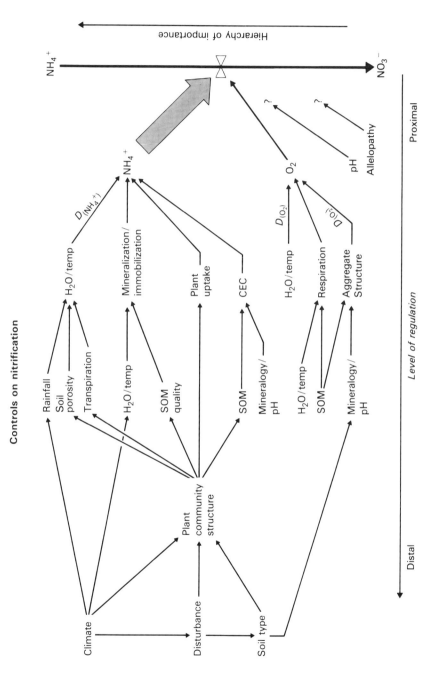

FIG. 4. A schematic diagram of the major factors regulating nitrification in rain forest soils (adapted from Tiedje (1987)). $D_{(NH_4)}$ and $D_{(O_2)}$ refer to the diffusion of NH_4^+ ions and O_2 to the nitrifiers.

At the tertiary level, factors that affect ammonium availability through their effects on water flow include rainfall, soil porosity, and transpiration, each in turn affected mainly by the composition and structure of the plant community. The chief factors that affect ammonium availability through effects on net nitrogen mineralization include water and soil organic matter (SOM) quality, which are also directly affected by plant community structure, as is plant uptake and the effect of SOM on soil CEC. Soil mineralogy and, in variable-charge soils, soil pH, interact with SOM to control soil CEC.

Secondary controls on nitrification via effects on oxygen availability include soil moisture (as mentioned above), respiration, and soil aggregate structure. Respiration in many soils can be high; Singh & Gupta (1977) reported oxygen consumption rates of more than 70 mmol O_2 cm^{-2} h^{-1} as a result of root and microbial respiration, rates that can exceed oxygen supply especially where soil moisture impedes diffusion. Soil aggregation can further impede oxygen availability by providing an additional diffusion barrier for microbes within aggregates. Tertiary level controls on oxygen availability include the effects of water and soil organic matter on respiration and of soil organic matter and mineralogy/pH interactions on aggregate structure.

The central role of plant community structure (the composition and physical stature of the plant community) in controlling nitrification at a distal level can be seen from its position in Fig. 4. Through effects on soil porosity, on the amount of water extracted from the soil, on soil organic matter inputs and quality, and on ammonium uptake, community structure exerts a major indirect influence on nitrification rates. Changes in plant community structure brought about by long-term changes in climate or soil type or by direct human influence in the short term may greatly alter nitrification rates, mainly through effects on factors which influence the supply of NH_4^+ ions and oxygen to nitrifiers. Knowledge about these factors and their interactions should allow us to predict and to some extent to manage many aspects of the response of nitrifiers to disturbance and to major differences in plant community types.

Both soil pH and allelopathy are included in Fig. 4 as potential proximal regulators of nitrification in the humid tropics. However, neither have been shown to influence nitrification directly in unamended soils. Active nitrification is known to occur in a variety of soils at pH values of less than 4.0 (Robertson 1982; Schmidt 1982), and recent attempts to document allelochemical inhibition of nitrifiers *in situ* in rain forest soils have met with little success (Chandler 1985).

DENITRIFICATION

Less is known about denitrification than about any other major part of the nitrogen cycle in humid tropical ecosystems. This is largely due to the difficulty of measuring nitrogen gas fluxes in soil: available methods are technically difficult, laborious, provide results that can be difficult to interpret, and require instru-

mentation which is not easily transported or maintained in rain forest environments.

Controls on denitrification in tropical rain forests (Fig. 5) are similar to
controls in temperate region ecosystems (Groffman *et al.* 1988). Oxygen, carbon,
and NO_3^- ions regulate denitrification at the most proximal, cellular level. Of
these, oxygen dominates. Denitrification is an anaerobic process that occurs only
in the absence of oxygen (Tiedje 1988); in soils this appears to occur mainly in
soil organic matter particles and soil aggregates, microenvironments where high
respiratory demand can exceed the supply of oxygen slowly diffusing through the
surrounding water film.

NO_3^- ions are an important proximal control on denitrification where the
demand for them by plants is high or where their production via nitrification is
low. Available carbon, too, can be limiting because most denitrifiers are
heterotrophs that rely on organic carbon for the donor electron. Although the
effect of carbon on denitrifiers is more likely to be indirect via the effects of carbon on oxygen availability, direct effects are potentially important in soils with
high concentrations of NO_3^- ions such as fertilized agricultural sites and very
recently cleared or perhaps late successional rain forest.

Although denitrification has rarely been measured in humid tropical ecosystems, one might predict that rates should be high in uncut forests (Greenland
1956): variable-charge soils tend to exhibit strong aggregate structure, soils in
these regions are rarely dry, and they tend to have high carbon inputs from high
primary productivity. This suggests that oxygen-stressed microsites with adequate carbon may be relatively plentiful in many rain forest soils, and in those
where nitrification is high, nitrate will be available and denitrification high.

This has been shown in at least one lowland rain forest region in Central
America. Robertson & Tiedje (1988) measured denitrification in four primary
forest sites in Costa Rica using the acetylene inhibition technique on intact soil
cores. Over a 14-month period, average rates extrapolated to an annual flux of
7.6–21 kg ha^{-1} year^{-1} N gas in the primary forest site, up to four times greater
than rates in nearby mid-successional sites (*c.* 15 years from primary forest
cutting and 5 years since last grazed; Fig. 6). Rates of denitrification in early
successional sites cleared several weeks prior to first measurements were even
higher than rates in the most active primary forest site (Fig. 6), although these
high rates did not persist for more than a few months.

It was suggested from the results of a nitrate amendment experiment (Table 2)
that low rates in mid-successional sites were the result of low nitrate availability.
Nitrate added as sodium nitrate to soil cores from the primary forest sites had no
appreciable effect on denitrification in these cores, whereas nitrate added to cores
from the two mid-successional sites significantly stimulated denitrification. Such
results suggest that denitrification rates in humid tropical forests will parallel
nitrification trends fairly closely; however, until denitrification rates are measured elsewhere it will be difficult to generalize. At only one additional site has

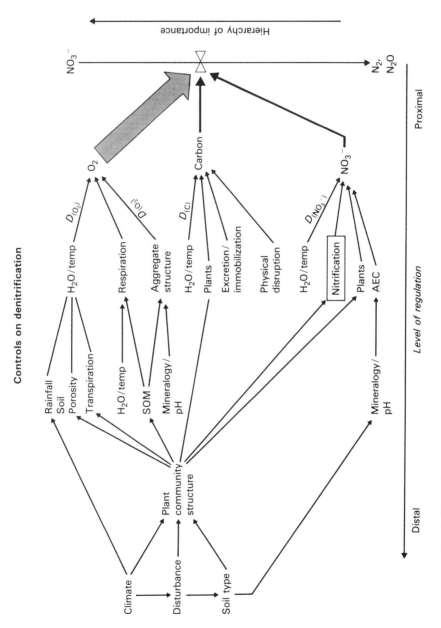

FIG. 5. Major factors controlling denitrification in rain forest soils (after Groffman *et al.* (1988), Tiedje (1987)). $D_{(C)}$, $D_{(NO_3^-)}$ and $D_{(O_2)}$ refer to the diffusion of C, NO_3^- and O_2 to the denitrifiers.

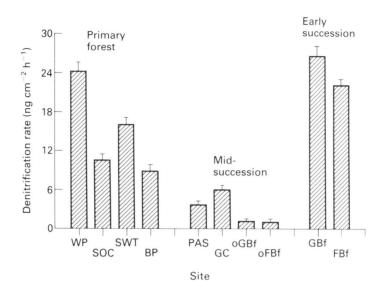

FIG. 6. Mean denitrification rates ($N_2 + N_2O$ production) in lowland rain forest sites at La Selva, north-east Costa Rica, at different stages of secondary succession. Primary forest sites have never been cut; early succession sites were recently cleared of mid-successional growth. Two mid-successional sites (oGBf and oFBf) had been cut over a year earlier and maintained vegetation-free. Vertical bars show the S.E. (from Robertson & Tiedje (1988)).

denitrification been measured *in situ*. Matson *et al.* (1987) quantified rates of denitrification in a premontane (650 m elevation) rain forest cleared of secondary vegetation and also found that rates immediately following clearing were high; later trends, however, were masked by high within-site variability.

ECOSYSTEM-LEVEL INTEGRATION

At the ecosystem level, both nitrification and denitrification can have important consequences for overall site fertility and for the recovery of fertility following disturbance. Indirect evidence suggests that phosphorus rather than nitrogen most commonly limits productivity in late successional tropical rain forests (Vitousek 1984; Vitousek & Sanford 1986); however, loss of nitrogen rather than phosphorus availability may more persistently affect productivity in many cleared and early successional systems, including agricultural ones (Brady 1982; Sanchez *et al.* 1982; FAO 1974). Consequently, the effects of nitrification and denitrification on nitrogen availability at a rain forest site may be particularly important in early to mid-successional stages.

In addition to effects on nitrogen availability early in secondary succession, nitrification and denitrification may play a critical role in maintaining the availability of other nutrients in the rooting zone during this period. As noted earlier, in variable-charge soils cation exchange capacity is largely dependent on the protonation and deprotonation of soil mineral surfaces. Because nitrification can play a large role in the H^+ budget of a site, and because nitrification generally increases following rain forest clearing (see above), it has the potential to alter the soil charge system significantly following disturbance. Specifically, nitrification following clearing may produce sufficient H^+ to drive soil pH close to or below the point of zero charge (PZC), the pH at which the soil has very little capacity to hold exchangeable ions in the rooting zone. Denitrification will tend to counteract this tendency, especially if it is also stimulated by disturbance: denitrifiers effectively consume the H^+ produced by nitrifiers when they denitrify NO_3^- ions to an uncharged nitrogen gas species. Thus if nitrification and denitrification are in balance following disturbance, soil pH will remain unchanged as long as other parts of the H^+ cycle remain unchanged.

Recent evidence suggests that at least under some circumstances the system does not stay in balance and soil pH can decline sharply following clearing with nitrifiers largely responsible for this decline. Robertson & Sollins (1987), in a field experiment on an Oxic humitropept soil in Costa Rica, found a soil pH drop of *c.* 0.5 units in the 2 weeks following vegetation removal on their site. The resulting pH, around pH 3.9, was almost 0.2 pH units below the soil's PZC and was lower than soil pH measured in a weak KCl solution for months following clearing (Sollins *this volume*), implying a correspondingly large drop in CEC in this soil for the period (Uehara & Gillman 1981). Subsequent laboratory experiments with similar soils strongly suggested that nitrification was the principal cause of the pH drop: in incubations in which nitrifiers were experimentally inhibited with 10 Pa acetylene (Berg, Klemedtsson & Rosswall 1982), soil pH did not drop (Fig. 7). Such results indicate the presence of a charge system in these soils that can be under biological control, and implicate nitrifiers as the principal agents of this control.

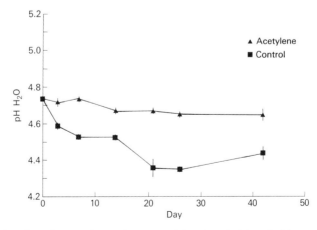

FIG. 7. Changes in soil pH in an Oxic Humitropept soil incubated with and without nitrification inhibited by 10 Pa acetylene. Vertical bars show the S.E. ($n = 5$) (from Robertson & Sollins (1987)).

If denitrifiers are stimulated by added nitrate in soils from disturbed systems (Table 3), and if nitrate pools increase on disturbance due to both increased nitrification and the development of significant anion exchange, then denitrifiers could help to keep soil pH from dropping below the soil's PZC. Specifically, as pH drops below PZC and greater quantities of NO_3^- ions are held in the upper soil horizons because of increasing anion exchange capacity, denitrifiers may respond to this increased nitrate pool by reducing additional quantities of NO_3^- and concomitantly consuming H^+; this could have the effect of slowing or even reversing the downward pH shift, effectively equilibrating soil pH close to soil PZC, since as pH begins to rise above the PZC denitrification will again fall off as the availability of NO_3^- ions declines from the loss of anion exchange capacity.

At present such a model is hypothetical, although it suggests feedback loops in the system that might be manipulated to sustain site fertility following clearing and conversion to agriculture. Clearly such indirect relationships in the system must be clarified if we are to manage humid tropical systems effectively.

TABLE 3. Response of denitrifiers in intact soil cores from primary forest and mid-successional (c. 20 years since clearing from primary forest) sites at La Selva, Costa Rica, to added water and water + nitrate. Cores were assayed for nitrate response after an initial no-amendment denitrification assay. Values are means ($\pm$S.E.) of ten cores; asterisks indicate significant differences between treatments ($p < 0.05$) (from Robertson & Tiedje (1988))

Site and soil type	Water	Water + nitrate
	N_2O–N (mg cm^{-2} h^{-1})	
Primary forest		
WP (Andic Humitropept)	87.7 (5.4)	77.2 (4.4)
SOC (Andic Humitropept)	111.0 (5.1)	91.6 (5.2)
BP (Andic Dystropept)	12.3 (3.9)	12.7 (0.9)
SWT (Typic Humitropept)	49.0 (4.0)	38.1 (9.0)
Mid-successional sites		
PAS (Andic Dystropept)	2.7 (1.5)	9.0 (2.2)*
GC (Oxic Dystropept)	0.2 (1.4)	148.0 (5.4)*

ACKNOWLEDGEMENTS

I thank E. Hidalgo and B. Paniagua for field and laboratory help with the nitrification and denitrification assays reported for La Selva, Costa Rica. P. A. Matson, F. Montagnini, J. Proctor, P. Sollins and P. M. Vitousek kindly reviewed an earlier draft of the manuscript and made many helpful comments. Financial support was provided by the US National Science Foundation. Contribution No. 613 of the W. K. Kellogg Biological Station.

REFERENCES

Berg, P., Klemedtsson, L. & Rosswall, T. (1982). Inhibitory effect of low partial pressures of acetylene on nitrification. *Soil Biology and Biochemistry*, **14**, 301–303.

Berlier, Y., Dabin B. & Leneuf, N. (1956). Physical, chemical and microbiological comparison of forest and savannah soils on the Tertiary sands of the lower Ivory Coast. *Transactions of the 5th International Congress of Soil Science*, **E**, 499–502.

Brady, N.C. (1982). Chemistry and the world food supply. *Science,* 218, 847–853.

Chandler, G. (1985). Mineralization and nitrification in three Malaysian forest soils. *Soil Biology and Biochemistry,* 17, 347–353.

deRham, P. (1970). L'azote dans quelques forêts, savanes et terrains de culture d'Afrique tropicale humide. *Veröffentlichungen des Geobotanischen Institutes der Eidgenössische Technische Hochschule, Stiftung Rübel in Zurich,* 45.

Diamond, W.E. de B. (1937). Fluctuations in nitrogen content of some Nigerian soils. *Empire Journal of Experimental Agriculture,* 5, 264–280.

Dommergues, Y. (1952). L'analyse microbiologique des sols tropicaux acides. *Mémoires de l'Institut Scientifique de Madagascar, Serie D,* 4, 169–181.

FAO (1974). *Fertilizers, the First Decade: a Summary of Results Achieved Between 1961 and 1971.* FAO, Rome.

Gorham, E., Vitousek, P.M. & Reiners, W.A. (1979). The regulation of chemical budgets over the course of terrestrial ecosystem succession. *Annual Review of Ecology and Systematics,* 10, 53–88.

Greenland, D.J. (1956). Is aerobic denitrification important in tropical soils? *Transactions of the 6th International Congress of Soil Science,* B, 765–769.

Greenland, D.J. (1958). Nitrate fluctuations in tropical soils. *Journal of Agricultural Science,* 50, 82–92.

Groffman, P.M., Tiedje, J.M., Robertson, G.P. & Christensen, S. (1988). Denitrification at different temporal and geographical scales: proximal and distal controls. *Advances in Nitrogen Cycling in Agricultural Ecosystems* (Ed. by J.R. Wilson), pp. 174–192. Commonwealth Agricultural Bureaux, Perth, Australia. In press.

Jacquemin, H. & Berlier, Y. (1956). Evolution du pouvoir nitrifiant d'un sol de basse Côte d'Ivoire sous l'action du climat et de la végétation. *Transactions of the 6th International Congress of Soil Science,* 3, 343–347.

Jones, J.M. & Richards, B.N. (1977). Effect of reforestation on turnover of N-15 labelled ammonium plus nitrate in relation to changes in soil microflora. *Soil Biology and Biochemistry,* 9, 383–392.

Lamb, D. (1980). Soil nitrogen mineralisation in a secondary rainforest succession. *Oecologia,* 47, 257–263.

Laudelout, H. & DuBois, H.M. (1951). Microbiologie des sols lateritiques de l'Uele. *Publication de l'Institut Nationale. Etude Agronome Congo Belge (INEAC) Series Scientifique,* 50, 1–36.

Matson, P.A. Vitousek, P.M., Ewel, J.J., Mazzarino, M.J. & Robertson, G.P. (1987). Nitrogen transformations following tropical forest felling and burning on a volcanic soil. *Ecology,* 68, 491–502.

Montagnini, F. & Buschbacher, R. (1988). Nitrification rates in two undisturbed tropical rain forests and three slash-and-burn sites of the Venezuelan Amazon. *Biotropica,* 21, 9–14.

Robertson, G.P. (1982). Nitrification in forested ecosystems. *Philosophical Transactions of the Royal Society of London, Series B,* 296, 445–457.

Robertson, G.P. (1984). Nitrification and nitrogen mineralization in a lowland rainforest succession in Costa Rica, Central America. *Oecologia,* 61, 99–104.

Robertson, G.P. & Rosswall, T. (1986). Nitrogen in West Africa: the regional cycle. *Ecological Monographs,* 56, 43–72.

Robertson, G.P. & Sollins, P. (1987). Biological control of soil charge chemistry in a humid tropical ecosystem in Costa Rica, Central America. *Ecological Society of America Bulletin,* 68, 46.

Robertson, G.P. & Tiedje, J.M. (1988). Denitrification in a lowland tropical rain forest. *Nature,* 336, 756–759.

Sanchez, P.A., Bandy, D.E., Villachica, J.H. & Nicholaides, J.J. (1982). Amazon basin soils: management for continuous crop production. *Science,* 216, 821–827.

Schmidt, E.L. (1982). Nitrification in soil. *Nitrogen in Agricultural Soils* (Ed. by F.J. Stevenson), pp. 253–288. *Agronomy Monographs 22.* American Society of Agronomy, Madison.

Singh, J.S. & Gupta, S.R. (1977). Plant decomposition and soil respiration in terrestrial ecosystems. *Botanical Review,* 43, 449–528.

Sollins, P., Robertson, G.P. & Uehara, G. (1988). Nutrient mobility in variable- and permanent-charge soils. *Biogeochemistry,* 6, 181–199.

Tanner, E.V.J. (1977). Four montane rainforests of Jamaica: a quantitative characterization of the floristics, the soils and the foliar mineral levels, and a discussion of the interrelations. *Journal of Ecology*, **65**, 883–918.

Tiedje, J.M. (1987). Ecology of denitrification and dissimilatory nitrate reduction to ammonium. *Environmental Microbiology of Anaerobes* (Ed. by A.J.B. Zehnder), pp. 179–244. Wiley, New York.

Uehara, G. & Gillman, G. (1981). *The Mineralogy, Chemistry, and Physics of Tropical Soils with Variable Charge Clays.* Westview Press, Boulder, Colorado.

Vine, H. (1953). Experiments on the maintenance of soil fertility at Ibadan, Nigeria. *Empire Journal of Experimental Agriculture*, **21**, 65–85.

Vitousek, P.M. (1984). Litterfall, nutrient cycling, and nutrient limitation in tropical forests. *Ecology*, **65**, 285–298.

Vitousek, P.M. & Matson, P.A. (1984). Mechanisms of nitrogen retention in forest ecosystems: a field experiment. *Science*, **225**, 51–52.

Vitousek, P.M. & Matson, P.A. (1988). Nitrogen transformations in a range of tropical forest soils. *Soil Biology and Biochemistry*, **20**, 361–367

Vitousek, P.M. & Sanford, R.L. (1986). Nutrient cycling in moist tropical forest. *Annual Review of Ecology and Systematics*, **17**, 137–168.

Vitousek, P.M., Van Cleve, K., Balakrishnan, N. & Mueller-Dombois, D. (1983). Soil development and nitrogen turnover in montane rainforest soils on Hawaii. *Biotropica*, **15**, 269–274.

The effect of humus acids and soil heating on the availability of phosphate in oxide-rich tropical soils

H. M. SIBANDA* AND S. D. YOUNG**

*Department of Soil Science, University of Reading,
Reading RG1 5AQ*

SUMMARY

1 The effects of fulvic acid (FA) and humic acid (HA) on phosphate adsorption by goethite, gibbsite and selected Zimbabwean soils were studied. In addition, the implications of soil heating for phosphate adsorption, humus destruction and the growth of sorghum were investigated.

2 It was found that FA competed with phosphate more strongly than HA for adsorption sites and that such competition was more effective on gibbsite than on goethite. The effect of pH on the competitive ability of the organic ligands reflected the difference in proton buffering characteristics of the humus acids and phosphate: phosphate adsorption was reduced to the greatest extent on acid soils (pH 3.5–5.0).

3 Heating HA caused a disproportionately high loss of carboxyl (COOH) groups relative to the bulk molecule. At 200 °C less than 15% HA was lost, but 45–50% of the COOH groups were destroyed. Pre-heating soil thus caused a rise in phosphate adsorption capacity, which again was ameliorated by addition of FA or HA.

4 Sorghum growth and its uptake of phosphate were both enhanced by the mineralization of soil organic matter (SOM) caused by soil heating. However, heated soils benefited the most from the addition of HA, reflecting their increased phosphate adsorption capacity. There was some evidence that the effects of HA on plant growth were longer lived than the results of the flush of phosphate arising from the destruction of SOM.

INTRODUCTION

In soils, such as oxisols and ultisols, with high concentrations of iron and aluminium oxides, phosphate adsorption is of great agronomic importance (Juo & Fox 1977; Borgaard 1983). Humus, in this context, may assume a dual role

---

*Present address: GTZ/ARDA PPU, Box 151, Masvingo, Zimbabwe.
**Present address: Nottingham University School of Agriculture, Sutton Bonington, Loughborough LE12 5RD.

both as a source of phosphate and as an organic acid which competes for phosphate adsorption sites and may reduce phosphate fixation (Dalton, Russell & Sieling 1952). It is therefore important to know the likely effects on phosphate availability that arise from the destruction of soil organic matter (SOM).

Soil heating may result from grassland or forest fires, the burning of vegetation to aid land clearance, or 'soil burning' for fertilizer as in the Ethiopian *guie* process (Sertsu & Sanchez 1978). During vegetation clearance, temperatures of only 40–80 °C prevail in the topsoil; however, if large quantities of woody material are present then 600–700 °C may be reached and the effects can penetrate up to 60 cm (Laudelot 1964). Grassland fires can cause soil temperatures of greater than 500 °C in the top 5 cm for short times (Cook 1939) and the interiors of burning soil heaps (*guie* system) reach similar temperatures (Sertsu & Sanchez 1978).

There are various reports on the effects of elevated soil temperatures, including both enhancement and depression of crop yield. Generally, there is an increase in available phosphate (Nye & Greenland 1960), but yield reductions have also been reported, even following temperatures as low as 200 °C (Kang & Sajjapongse 1980; Kitur & Frye 1983). It is likely that the amount of vegetation burnt relative to the amount of SOM destroyed, the temperatures reached, and the mineralogy of the soil all affect the result of burning.

The purpose of this study is to investigate the mechanism of adsorption competition between humus acids and phosphate and thereby determine which soil types are most vulnerable to the adverse effects resulting from loss of SOM. In addition, the influence of soil burning on humus, phosphate adsorption and the growth of sorghum (*Sorghum vulgare*) is studied directly.

MATERIALS AND METHODS

Humic acid (HA) was extracted by the method of Schnitzer & Khan (1972) from soil of the Sonning series (acid brown earth under a deciduous woodland). After dialysis against acid and distilled water, the HA had an ash content of 3.8%. Fulvic acid (FA) was extracted by the method of Schnitzer (1982) from a coniferous woodland podzol Bh horizon from a site at Penny Hill near Bracknell, Berkshire, UK. The FA was purified by ultra-filtration with a molecular exclusion limit of 500 dalton and by treatment with H^+-resin, giving a final ash content of 1.56%. The carboxyl contents of the unheated HA and FA were estimated at 2.36 and 7.61 mmol g^{-1} respectively, as measured by titration according to Wilson & Kinney (1977). Goethite and gibbsite were synthesized by the method of Hingston, Posner & Quirk (1972) and kept in distilled water suspensions at concentrations of 34.0 and 21.7 mg cm^{-3}, respectively. The surface areas, measured by N_2 adsorption, were 96.2 m^2 g^{-1} for goethite and 38.2 m^2 g^{-1} for gibbsite. Soils used in phosphate adsorption studies were from the Salisbury (Harare) 5E.2 and the Marandellas (Marondera) 7G.2 series (described by Thompson (1965)) of Zimbabwe. The samples were taken from the top 20 cm during the dry season from sites which were both uncultivated and un-fertilized: Salisbury 5E.2 (17°05'S, 31°01'E); Marandellas 7G.2 (18°9'S, 31°30'E).

Measurement of soil characteristics

'Alkaline-extractable' organic matter (SOM_{NaOH}) was isolated by extracting the soil with 0.2 M NaOH and flocculating the soluble organic fraction with barium chloride. After centrifuging and drying the precipitate, organic carbon was determined by combustion in a high temperature induction (LECO) furnace and gravimetric measurement of evolved CO_2 collected on soda asbestos; it was assumed that organic matter contained 58% carbon.

The amount of iron oxide and aluminium hydroxide in each soil was determined by extraction of iron with sodium dithionite (Olson & Ellis 1962) and of aluminium with Tamm's reagent (Russell 1973).

Phosphate adsorption isotherms

Phosphate adsorption on goethite, gibbsite and soil which had been pre-treated with either FA or HA was studied. Humic or fulvic acid was added, from stock solutions, at the rates of 0, 11.8, 47.1 and 88.2% (w/w) in the case of goethite, at 0, 9.4, 28.1 and 46.9% (w/w) in the case of gibbsite and at 0, 0.4, 1.6 and 3.0% (w/w) in the case of soils. The initial phosphate (KH_2PO_4) concentrations for each adsorption isotherm were 0, 0.5, 1.5, 3 and 4.5 μg P cm^{-3} for goethite, 0, 1, 2, 3 and 4 μg P cm^{-3} for gibbsite and 0, 3, 6, 10 and 15 μg P cm^{-3} for soils with a background electrolyte of 0.1 M NaCl in a final volume of 30 cm^3. Solid : solution ratios of 1 : 882, 1 : 691 and 1 : 30 (w/v) were used for goethite, gibbsite and the soils, respectively. High phosphate adsorption isotherms were also conducted for the two oxides, at initial concentrations of 0, 5, 10, 15, 20, 30 and 50 μg P cm^{-3}.

After addition of FA or HA, oxide and phosphate solution, the pH of each suspension was adjusted with either NaOH or HCl and equilibration times, with continuous shaking, of 48 h (oxides) and 5 days (soils) were allowed. After equilibration the suspensions were centrifuged at 10 000 rpm for goethite, 13 000 rpm for gibbsite and 3000 rpm in the case of soils.

In order to determine phosphate by the method of Murphy & Riley (1962) in the supernatant solutions, HA had to be precipitated by the addition of 0.5 cm^3 of concentrated HCl to 10 cm^3 of the supernatant liquid and separated by centrifugation to give an almost clear solution. It was found that no inorganic phosphate was precipitated with the HA and that no hydrolysis of the HA (and hence possible release of phosphate) took place in the cold acid. In samples containing FA, the soluble organic matter was destroyed by wet digestion and a correction factor was used to allow for the phosphate release from the FA.

Proton buffer powers of FA, HA and H_3PO_4

The proton buffer powers of the three acids studied were measured by titration, in 0.1 M NaCl, with NaOH. Thus for two sequential pH values, '*a*' and '*b*' on the titration curve

$$\text{Buffer power} = \frac{\triangle\alpha \times 100}{\triangle\text{pH}} = \frac{|\alpha_a - \alpha_b|}{|\text{pH}_a - \text{pH}_b|} \times 100$$

where α is the degree of dissociation of the acid.

The buffer power was then expressed graphically as a function of the average pH value, i.e. $(\text{pH}_a + \text{pH}_b)/2$

Phosphate adsorption 'envelopes'

An adsorption envelope demonstrates either (a) the relative adsorption from a fixed initial adsorbate concentration or (b) the maximum adsorption capacity of a solid, as a function of pH. The former procedure was adopted here for both goethite and gibbsite, in the presence of 47% and 29% HA, respectively. All other experimental details are as described for phosphate adsorption isotherms; initial phosphate concentrations used were 4.5 μg P cm^{-3} for goethite and 13.0 μg P cm^{-3} for gibbsite.

Soil heating

A muffle furnace was used to heat the following: soil samples used in phosphate adsorption studies at 200, 400 and 600 °C for 6 h; soil used in the pot experiment at 350 °C; humic acid (for carboxyl analysis) at 100, 150, 200, 300, 350, 400, 500 and 600 °C.

Sorghum pot experiment

Soil of the Salisbury 5E.2 series was used to study the effect of soil heating and humic acid addition on phosphate uptake by sorghum. The soil treatments used included two HA concentrations (0 and 1%), two heat treatments (25 and 350 °C for 6 h) and four phosphate $(\text{Ca}(\text{H}_2\text{PO}_4)_2)$ concentrations (0, 40, 80 and 120 μg P g^{-1} soil). There were two replicates of each treatment.

Humic acid, in a 2000 μg cm^{-3} stock solution at the pH of the soil (pH 5.15), was added to 300 g soil with 600 g acid washed sand. These were mixed and incubated for 5 days in a glasshouse maintained between 25 and 30 °C. Phosphate $(\text{Ca}(\text{H}_2\text{PO}_4)_2)$ was then added from a stock solution of 2000 μg P cm^{-3}. The moisture content of the soil with sand mixture was raised to 25% with a solution containing 96 μg K cm^{-3} (KNO_3) and 100 μg N cm^{-3} $(\text{Ca}(\text{NO}_3)_2)$. Molybdenum

$((NH_4)_2MoO_4)$ was also applied, at a concentration of 0.25 μg Mo g^{-1}. The soils were then potted in 10 cm $\times$ 20 cm cylindrical containers.

After a further 48 h incubation, four seeds of sorghum (cultivar BR 64) were planted in each pot and watering continued with the nitrogen and potassium solutions until 96 μg K g^{-1} and 100 μg N g^{-1} had been applied; thereafter distilled water was used. Two days after germination the seedlings were thinned to two per pot and after 6 weeks the plant tops were harvested and oven dried at 80 °C for 4 days before analysis for total dry matter and phosphate uptake.

After harvest, a second crop was planted following removal of roots by sieving. No phosphate was added but a further 96 μg K g^{-1} and 100 μg N g^{-1} were applied and after 6 weeks the plants were harvested and processed as above.

RESULTS

The percentages of total organic matter, alkali-soluble organic matter, iron oxide and aluminium hydroxide in the two Zimbabwean soils studied are shown in Table 1. The alkali-soluble SOM content (FA + HA) of the soils was around 60% of the total SOM content.

TABLE 1. Percentage organic matter (SOM) and oxides in two Zimbabwean soils

Soil	SOM_{total} (%)	SOM_{NaOH} (%)	$\dfrac{SOM_{NaOH}}{SOM_{total}}$ (%)	Fe oxide (%)	Al hydroxide (%)
Salisbury 5E.2	3.28	1.94	59	14.61	0.44
Marandellas 7G.2	1.74	1.16	67	2.78	0.32

Three levels of FA or HA addition to the soils and to the synthetic oxides (goethite and gibbsite) were used to study the effects of humus acid on phosphate adsorption. Additions to the pure oxides were designed to cover the range of soil treatments when these were expressed as a percentage of the soil oxide content.

Competition between phosphate and humus acids

It was found that phosphate adsorption decreased with increasing humus acid concentration and that FA was considerably more effective than HA in this respect. The competitive ability of both organic acids was greater on gibbsite than on goethite and enhanced at lower pH values in all cases. Two examples of phosphate adsorption isotherms displaying competition by humus acids are shown in Figs. 1 and 2. Phosphate adsorption on goethite at pH 7 was only slightly affected by the presence of HA, while adsorption on gibbsite at pH 4 was dramatically reduced by FA. The competitive power of the organic acids fell between these two extremes under all other experimental conditions (i.e. pH 4, 5, 6 and 7 for both oxides and with both humus acids).

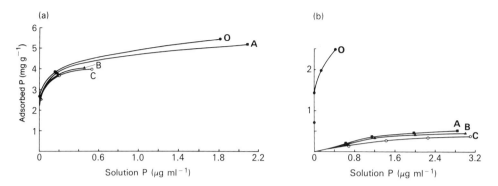

FIG. 1. (a) Phosphate adsorption isotherms on goethite at pH 7 and at four HA concentrations (see Table 2): O = 0%; A = 11.8%; B = 47.1%; C = 88.2%. (b) Phosphate adsorption isotherms on gibbsite at pH 4 and at four FA concentrations (see Table 2): O = 0%; A = 9.4%; B = 28.1%; C = 46.9%.

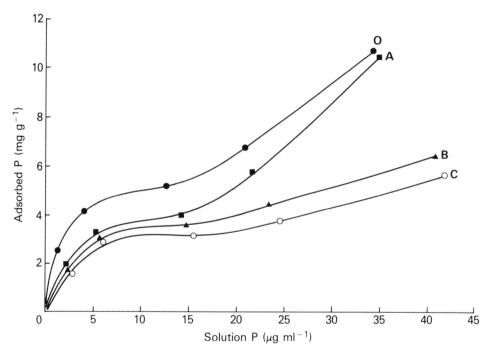

FIG. 2. Phosphate adsorption isotherms on gibbsite at pH 7 and at four HA concentrations (see Table 2) (high phosphate concentration): O = 0%; A = 9.4%; B = 28.1%: C = 46.9%.

Effect of adsorption surface

The competitive ability of HA and FA was apparently greater on gibbsite than on goethite. This may be partly because of the lower phosphate adsorption capacity of gibbsite (approximately 30% that of goethite) which was only partially compensated for by the use of lower concentrations of organic acid (Table 2). However, making allowance for this by comparing lower concentrations of FA and HA on gibbsite with high levels on goethite, both humus acids still apparently displaced phosphate more effectively on gibbsite. In addition, a study of the effect of increasing phosphate concentrations to exceptionally high levels (up to $40 \mu g$ P cm^{-3} at equilibrium) showed that while the competitive ability of HA was negligible at pH 7 on goethite it remained high on gibbsite (Fig. 2).

TABLE 2. Humic/fulvic acid treatments as a percentage of total mass of soil or oxide

| Soil or oxide | O | HA/FA treatment | | |
		A	B	C
Salisbury 5E.2	0	0.4	1.6	3.0
Marandellas 7G.2	0	0.4	1.6	3.0
Goethite	0	11.8	47.1	88.2
Gibbsite	0	9.4	28.1	46.9

Differences between humic and fulvic acids

Fulvic acid displayed a greater competitive power than humic acid in all cases. This is probably the result of a higher carboxyl group density in FA (7.61 mmol g^{-1}) compared with HA (2.36 mmol g^{-1}), assuming that adsorption involves Fe–OOC and Al–OOC linkages (Parfitt, Farmer & Russell 1977). Struthers & Sieling (1950) also found that pure organic acids with short chain lengths and high COOH densities were most effective in bonding with iron and aluminium in the presence of phosphate.

The effect of pH

The adsorption isotherms showed that both humus acids reduced phosphate adsorption to a greater extent at lower pH. This suggests that FA and HA are better able to compete with phosphate for adsorption sites under acid conditions. Without invoking a specific mechanism, it is well recognized that the adsorption of anions by oxides is enhanced at pH values where the adsorbing anion possesses a high proton buffer power (Hingston et al. 1972; Mott 1981). Figure 3 shows the variation in buffer power of HA and phosphoric acid (H_3PO_4) with pH, together with phosphate adsorption envelopes on gibbsite and goethite. Clearly, the pH range 3–5 where the buffer power of HA is highest relative to phosphate (Fig. 3(a)) also corresponds to conditions in which phosphate adsorption on gibbsite and goethite is suppressed to the greatest extent in the presence of the organic acid (Figs. 3(b) and 3(c)). It is purely coincidence that HA exhibits its highest buffer power around the pH of lowest buffer power for phosphoric acid, midway between the first and second dissociation steps of H_3PO_4 ($pK_1 = 2.1$; $pK_2 = 7.2$).

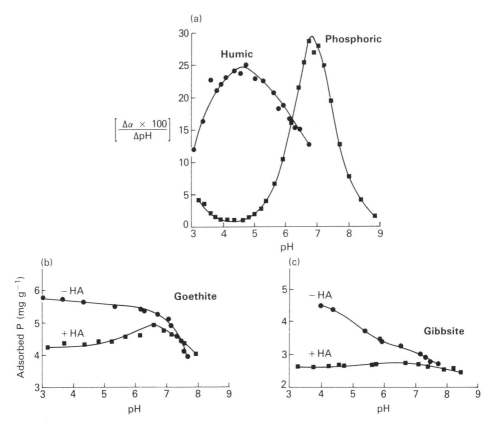

FIG. 3. (a) The variation in buffer power ($\Delta\alpha \times 100$ /ΔpH) with pH for humic and phosphoric acids. (b) Phosphate adsorption envelopes on goethite at two HA concentrations: $+$HA $= 47\%$; $-$HA $= 0\%$. (c) Phosphate adsorption envelopes on gibbsite at two HA concentrations: $+$HA $= 29\%$; $-$HA $= 0\%$.

Competition on soils

An example of phosphate adsorption on the Marandellas soil, in the presence of FA, is shown in Fig. 4. As for the oxides, both the strength of adsorption and the maximum adsorption capacity for phosphate were reduced by FA. In addition, the FA released native phosphate from the soil in agronomically important quantities (equilibrium concentration $= 0.05$–0.5 μg P cm^{-3}). On both soils the effect of HA was less than that of FA, particularly in the release of native phosphate.

The effect of heating on phosphate adsorption

Heating the Salisbury soil to 200, 400 and 600 °C resulted in a progressive increase in phosphate adsorption capacity (Fig. 5). It is likely that at 200 °C there are no substantial mineralogical changes (Sertsu & Sanchez 1978), so that the

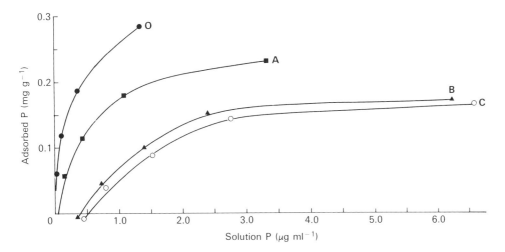

FIG. 4. Phosphate adsorption isotherms on the Marandellas 7G.2 soil series at four FA concentrations (see Table 2): O = 0%; A = 0.4%; B = 1.6%; C = 3.0%.

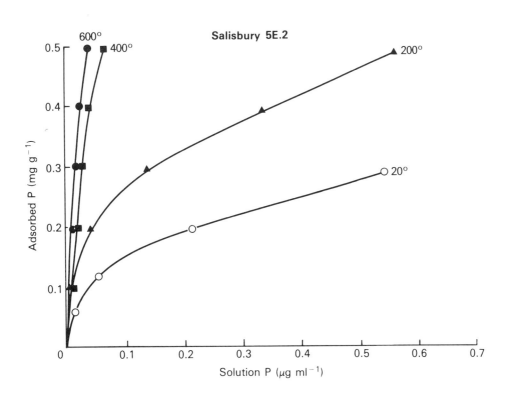

FIG. 5. Phosphate adsorption isotherms on the Salisbury 5E.2 soil series following soil heating to 20, 200, 400 and 600 °C.

increase in phosphate adsorption is largely the result of sites being freed by the destruction of organic matter (approximately 10% of SOM in this case). By this means, phosphate adsorption was consistently increased to 1.7–1.8 times that of the unheated soil. Heating to 400 °C ensures virtually complete destruction of all SOM and produces a variety of mineralogical changes such as the transformation of goethite to disordered haematite structures. A very large increase in adsorption strength resulted from temperatures of 400 and 600 °C. It was particularly noticeable that there was no net release of native phosphate into solution as a result of heating, suggesting that the increase in adsorption capacity more than compensated for mineralization of organic phosphate at all temperatures. As expected, HA and FA substantially reduced phosphate adsorption by the heated soils in all cases.

Although only 10% SOM was lost by heating to 200 °C, the substantial increase in phosphate adsorption can be explained by examination of the effects of temperature on HA (Fig. 6). At 200 °C less than 15% of the total mass of HA is lost, but 45–50% of COOH groups are oxidized to CO_2.

Thus a small loss of SOM, such as is found following vegetation burning, may substantially increase phosphate adsorption because of preferential loss of COOH groups on humus.

The effect of heating and HA addition on the growth of sorghum

A summary of the results from the sorghum pot experiment is shown in Table 3; yield and phosphate uptake quotients for '+HA/−HA' and 'heated/unheated' are given to isolate the effects of HA addition and soil heating. Heating the soil to 350 °C resulted in an increase in both the yield and phosphate uptake by the sorghum shoots. Thus, although the soil phosphate adsorption capacity was increased by the heat treatment, the increase in labile phosphate was apparently large enough to overcome this. However, although the plants were only six weeks old when harvested, the yield and phosphate uptake ratios (heated : unheated) declined sharply in the second growth, suggesting either that the flush of labile phosphate was virtually exhausted or that immobilization of mineralized phosphate had occurred. The effect of the HA was less than that of heating, but always greater when the soil had been heated, reflecting the greater phosphate adsorption capacity of the heated soil.

The benefits of HA are apparently longer lived than those of phosphate mineralization as shown by the consistency of the +HA : −HA ratios over the two growths. This may reflect the difference between a long-term effect caused by HA-bonding to phosphate adsorption surfaces and a fairly short-term benefit resulting from organic phosphate release.

DISCUSSION

It is clear that humus acids can benefit the phosphate nutrition of vegetation in oxide-rich tropical soils through competition (with phosphate ions) for adsorp-

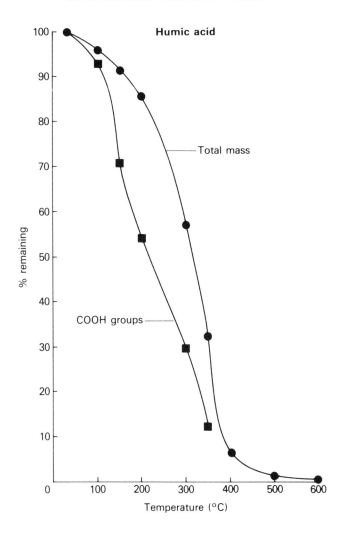

FIG. 6. The percentage weight and carboxyl loss of HA following heating.

tion sites. Our results indicate that such benefits will be greater in gibbsitic rather than iron-rich soils and in conditions of low pH (3.5–5.0) because of the contrasting proton buffer characteristics of humus and phosphoric acids. The latter finding is particularly important as it is acid soils which tend to possess the highest concentration of free iron and aluminium oxides and the highest phosphate adsorption capacity. Thus tropical oxisols may undergo considerable reductions in fertility because of organic matter losses resulting from bush clearance and cultivation operations.

The destruction of soil organic matter by heating also increases the phosphate adsorption capacity of soils. Even temperatures less than 200 °C, which cause only slight destruction of humus, may significantly affect phosphate adsorption because of preferential oxidation of humic carboxyl (COOH) groups. This may

TABLE 3. Effect of HA and soil heating on the growth and phosphate uptake of sorghum shoots grown for 6 weeks. Values for yield and phosphate uptake are averages of four phosphate treatments (0, 40, 80, 120 μg phosphate g^{-1} soil)

	First growth					
	Yield (g/pot)		Heated	Phosphate uptake (mg/pot)		Heated
	Unheated	Heated	Unheated	Unheated	Heated	Unheated
−HA	0.68	1.87	2.8	0.70	3.07	4.4
+HA	0.75	2.62	3.5	0.70	4.20	6.0
+HA/−HA	1.1	1.4		1.0	1.4	

	Second growth					
	Yield (g/pot)		Heated	Phosphate uptake (mg/pot)		Heated
	Unheated	Heated	Unheated	Unheated	Heated	Unheated
−HA	1.29	2.15	1.7	0.98	1.37	1.4
+HA	1.41	2.53	1.8	1.29	1.90	1.5
+HA/−HA	1.1	1.2		1.3	1.4	

explain yield decreases observed after heating soil to fairly low temperatures, e.g. 200 °C (Kang & Sajjapongse 1980) and 135–175 °C (Wilson 1914). However, the destruction of humus and vegetation also results in considerable organic phosphate mineralization, and yield increases following such operations are well documented (Nye & Greenland 1960). Both factors are likely to affect plant growth in heated soils. Thus growth of sorghum is enhanced by soil heating, but the plants grown on pre-heated soil benefit most from the addition of HA, reflecting the amelioration of a higher phosphate adsorption capacity by the organic acid. It is likely that processes such as phosphate depletion by plants and immobilization within the soil mean that the benefits of soil heating are relatively short lived. By contrast, the time required to re-establish a normal humus content may be considerably greater.

REFERENCES

Borgaard, O.K. (1983). The influence of iron oxides on phosphate adsorption by soils. *Journal of Soil Science*, **34**, 333–342.

Cook, L. (1939). A contribution to our information on grass burning. *South African Journal of Science*, **36**, 270–282.

Dalton, J.D., Russell, G.C. & Sieling, D.H. (1952). Effect of organic matter on phosphate availability. *Soil Science*, **73**, 173–177.

Hingston, F., Posner, A.M. & Quirk, J.P. (1972). Anion adsorption by goethite and gibbsite. I. The role of the proton in determining adsorption envelopes. *Journal of Soil Science*, **23**, 177–192.

Juo, A.S.R. & Fox, R.L. (1977). Phosphate sorption characteristics of some benchmark soils of West Africa. *Soil Science*, **124**, 370–376.

Kang, B.T. & Sajjapongse, A. (1980). Effect of heating on properties of soils from Southern Nigeria and growth of rice. *Plant and Soil*, **55**, 85–95.

Kitur, B.K. & Frye, W.W. (1983). Effects of heating on soil chemical properties and growth and nutrient composition of corn and millet. *Soil Science Society of America Journal*, **47**, 91–94.

Laudelot, H. (1964). *Dynamics of Tropical Soils in Relation to their Fallowing Techniques*. FAO, Rome.

Mott, C.J.B. (1981). Anion and ligand exchange. *The Chemistry of Soil Processes* (Ed. by D.J. Greenland & M.H.B. Hayes), pp. 179–219. Wiley, Chichester.

Murphy, J. & Riley, J.P. (1962). A modified single solution method for the determination of phosphate in natural waters. *Analytica Chimica Acta*, **27**, 31–36.

Nye, P. & Greenland, D.J. (1960). *The Soil Under Shifting Cultivation. Technical Communication 51.* Commonwealth Agriculture Bureau, Harpenden, U.K.

Olson, R.V. & Ellis, R. (1982). Iron. *Methods of Soil Analysis, Part 2* (Ed. by A.L. Page. R.H. Miller & D.R. Keeney), pp. 311–312. American Society of Agronomy, Wisconsin.

Parfitt, R.L., Farmer, V.C. & Russell, J.D. (1977). Adsorption on hydrous oxides. III. Fulvic acid and humic acid on goethite, gibbsite and imogolite. *Journal of Soil Science*, **28**, 289–296.

Russell, E.W. (Ed.) (1973). *Soil Conditions and Plant Growth.* Longman, London.

Schnitzer, M. (1982). Organic matter characterization. *Methods of Soil Analysis, Part 2* (Ed. by A.L. Page, R.H. Miller & D.R. Keeney), pp. 582–584. American Society of Agronomy, Wisconsin.

Schnitzer, M. & Khan, S.U. (1972). *Humic Substances in the Environment.* Marcel Dekker, New York.

Sertsu, S.M. & Sanchez, P.A. (1978). Effect of heating on some changes in soil properties in relation to an Ethiopian land management practice. *Soil Science Society of America Journal*, **42**, 940–944.

Struthers, P.H. & Sieling, D.H. (1950). Effect of organic anions on phosphate precipitation by iron and aluminium as influenced by pH. *Soil Science*, **69**, 205–213.

Thompson, J.G. (1965). The soils of Rhodesia and their classification. *Rhodesia Agricultural Journal Technical Bulletin*, **6**.

Wilson, D.E. & Kinney, P. (1977). Effects of polymeric charge variations on the proton–metal ion equilibria of humic materials. *Limnology and Oceanography*, **22**, 281–289.

Wilson, G.W. (1914). Studies of plant growth in heated soils. *Biochemistry Bulletin*, **3**, 202–209.

Factors affecting nutrient cycling in tropical soils

P. SOLLINS

School of Forestry and Environmental Studies,
Yale University, New Haven, CT 06511, USA

SUMMARY

1 Soil type determines many aspects of nutrient cycling and transformation. Once soil type is known, information on mineralogy, organic matter content, climate and charge chemistry can often be inferred, all of which strongly influence nutrient cycling patterns.

2 Soils of the tropics (and elsewhere) divide into two major types, variable-charge and permanent-charge, with differences that affect nutrient cycling processes.

3 Differences in soil structure affect nutrient retention capacity. In soils with a bi-phasic water flow regime, water flows mainly along preferred paths, through macropores and between aggregates, largely bypassing the soil matrix. Such soils thus resist leaching.

4 In weathered tropical soils, stable aggregation is caused in large part by low electric charge on clay particle surfaces. Thus as weathering decreases a soil's ability to retain ions on exchange sites, it may increase its ability to resist leaching.

INTRODUCTION

Soils are highly diverse in their composition and structure, and therefore in their nutrient cycling and transformation processes. As a result, soil classification is a prerequisite for efficient study of nutrient cycling mechanisms and patterns. Much of the power of soil science can be brought to bear on nutrient cycling questions if we know the classification of a soil. The Soil Taxonomy (Soil Survey Staff 1975), for example, incorporates extensive information on soil mineralogy, organic matter content and charge chemistry, all of which are fundamental to an understanding of nutrient dynamics (Uehara & Gillman 1981; Gillman 1984; Sollins, Robertson & Uehara 1988). Other variables, such as soil structure, are not so well reflected in the Soil Taxonomy but also strongly affect nutrient cycling processes.

The above caveats are perhaps nowhere more true than in the tropics where soil diversity can be extreme. Three factors of soil chemistry and structure in particular affect nutrient cycling patterns in tropical soils: charge chemistry (variable versus permanent charge), the extent to which the soil water flow regime is bi-phasic, and the degree of soil weathering. The last of these is obvious and needs little elaboration. The other two are discussed here, mainly with respect to the forest soils of the humid tropics. The principles should apply, however, to agricultural soils of the tropics as well as to many temperate-zone soils.

85

PERMANENT- VERSUS VARIABLE-CHARGE SOILS

If we consider only the moist portions of the world, soils can be divided broadly into two types based on major differences in charge chemistry, with attendant effects on nutrient mobility. In the first type, the electric charge on clay particles results from substitution of ions of lower valence for ions of a higher valence within the crystal structure. The resulting charge deficit is permanent in the sense that it is a structural feature of the clay particle and persists irrespective of changing conditions such as soil pH and soil solution composition. Most of the permanent charge in soils resides on surfaces of layer-silicate clays, mainly the 2 : 1 layer-silicates (illite, vermiculite and smectite) and the 2 : 2 clays (chlorite). The 1 : 1 clays (kaolinite) contain a small amount of permanent charge on their planar surfaces.

In the second type of soils, the electric charge is variable instead of permanent and results from protonation and deprotonation of surface hydroxyl groups (Parfitt 1980; Uehara & Gillman 1981; Gillman 1984). Surface hydroxyls occur at the edges of 1 : 1 layer-silicate clays (such as kaolinite), on less ordered aluminosilicates (such as halloysite), on very poorly ordered aluminosilicates (allophane and imogolite), on crystalline hydroxides of aluminium (gibbsite) and iron (goethite, haematite) and on organic matter. Deprotonation of these surface hydroxyls gives negative surface charge and thus cation exchange capacity (CEC); protonation gives anion exchange capacity (AEC) (Fig. 1). In addition, clay surface hydroxyls are readily replaced by phosphate ligands; thus the same clay mineralogy that gives rise to variable charge results also in phosphate sorption (Mott 1981). Overall, the amount of variable-charge (v-c) (hydroxylated) surface correlates well with phosphate sorption capacity. High-surface-area allophanic soils, such as Andepts, sorb the most phosphate, oxidic soils sorb somewhat less, kaolinite- and halloysite-dominated soils sorb intermediate amounts, and the permanent-charge (p-c) soils sorb the least (Sanchez 1976).

Although all soils contain both p-c and v-c surfaces, many soils are dominated by only one of these two charge systems. Variable-charge soils are more common in the tropics than in the temperate zone because v-c minerals develop most rapidly under warm humid conditions. However, not all tropical soils are dominated by v-c constituents; both p-c and v-c constituents occur to at least some extent in all soils, and large areas of the tropics are occupied by nearly pure p-c soils (Sanchez 1976). Moreover, variable charge is not restricted to highly weathered soils but is a feature of some extremely young soils as well — mainly those derived from volcanic parent materials. Such materials weather, at least in moist climates, to allophane, a gel-like amorphous mineral of extremely high surface area that contains only variable charge (Wada 1977).

The concept of a point of zero charge (PZC) is critical to understanding the nutrient dynamics of v-c soils. The PZC is the pH at which the soil is electrically neutral; CEC and AEC balance when the pH is at the PZC, and total charge (sum of absolute value of negative and positive) is at a minimum (Fig. 1). Sollins *et al.*

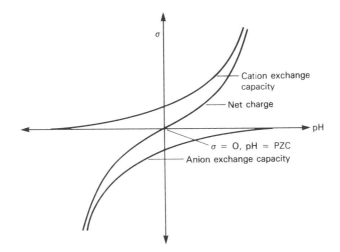

FIG. 1. Effect of pH on cation and anion exchange capacity and net surface charge of a variable-charge material (Sollins, Robertson & Uehara 1988). σ = net surface charge, PZC = point of zero charge.

(1988), reviewing interactions between biological processes and nutrient mobility in v-c and p-c soils, concluded that interactions are potentially more complex in the former.

1 In v-c soils, any process that affects either soil pH or soil PZC will alter surface charge and thus ion exchange capacity and mobility; in p-c soils, surface charge is relatively unaffected by soil solution composition. Variables that affect PZC include the amount of soil organic matter and the amount of adsorbed oxyanions such as sulphate, phosphate or silicate (Uehara & Gillman 1981; Gillman 1984).

2 Only v-c soils ever develop significant AEC. Thus nitrate is retained in significant amounts only by v-c soils, and then only deep in the soil where the lack of organic matter results in a high PZC.

3 Soil pH affects soil structure more in v-c than in p-c soils (see below).

A vegetation-removal experiment at La Selva, Costa Rica illustrates the extent to which changes in soil pH can affect soil charge properties (Sollins *et al.* 1988). Soil at this site is a highly weathered Oxic Dystropept with a PZC near 4.0 (0–15 cm depth). Several weeks after the vegetation was cleared, soil pH dropped markedly (Fig. 2), probably because of nitrification (Robertson *this volume*). (It should be noted that the cut vegetation was carried off the site. Had it been burned on the site, pH would probably have risen, at least initially.) The lowest pH (3.8) was below the measured PZC suggesting that AEC exceeded CEC, which, if true, would mean that nitrate was less mobile than ammonium, the reverse of the situation in most soils from which our knowledge of nitrogen dynamics is derived. Studies of ecosystem response to disturbance and management thus need to take into account the possibility of large and rapid changes in soil pH with large attendant effects on nutrient retention and mobility.

Because of the fundamental differences between v-c and p-c soils, methods of soil analysis need to be tailored to the soil type. Some procedures appropriate for p-c soils give erroneous results when applied to v-c soils. For example, a standard method for measuring CEC in p-c soils, namely M ammonium acetate at pH 7, markedly overestimates the CEC of v-c soils (Sanchez 1976; Uehara & Gillman 1981). Air-drying, a common procedure with many soils, may be generally undesirable for v-c soils of the humid tropics, as it can alter exchange acidity (Westfall, Moodie & Cheng 1973), CEC (Thomas, Parfitt & Smart 1974; Gillman & Murtha 1983) and phosphorus sorption (Barrow & Shaw 1980). Effects of air-drying on other soil properties are to be expected. The phosphate sorption capacity of v-c soils also imposes limitations on experimental design; for example, bioassays for phosphorus limitation require that the phosphorus be added uniformly throughout the soil volume, which can be very difficult in strongly phosphate-sorbing soils. In general, however, an understanding of the soil's chemistry allows appropriate methods to be chosen.

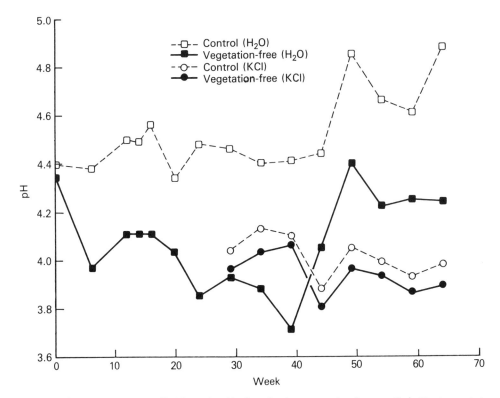

FIG. 2. Soil pH_{H_2O} and pH_{KCl} (0–15 cm depth) after clearing vegetation from an Oxic Dystropept at La Selva, Costa Rica (Sollins *et al.* 1988). The dry season began about week 16 and ended about week 39. pH_{KCl} was not measured until week 30.

EFFECTS OF SOIL STRUCTURE ON LEACHING

Like soil charge chemistry, soil physical structure also differs markedly among soil types with important effects on nutrient cycling. Two important soil physical properties for nutrient cycling are aggregation (both extent and stability) and macroporosity — the volume of pores that are too large to retain water against gravity. Aggregation can vary markedly among soils, accounting for approximately 0% to more than 70% of the <2 mm fraction (Fig. 3; Churchman & Tate 1986). Some aspects of aggregation are taken into account in the Soil Taxonomy

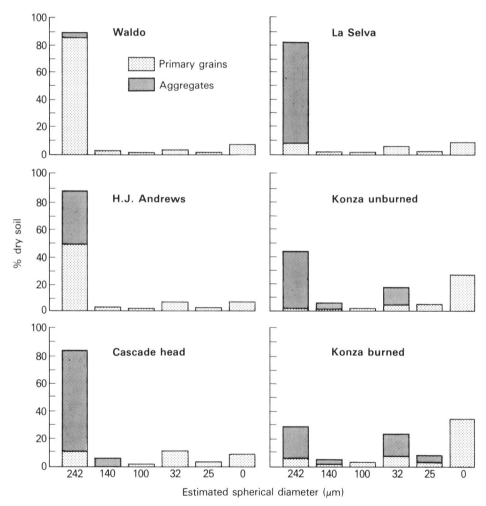

FIG. 3. Extent of aggregation in five soils from temperate and tropical zones (Strickland *et al.* 1988). Waldo, Florida: Ultic Haplaquod; La Selva, Costa Rica: Oxic Dystropept (upper alluvial terrace); H. J. Andrews, Oregon: Andic Haplumbrept; Konza Prairie, Kansas: Pachic Argiustoll; Cascade Head, Oregon: Typic Dystrandept.

because aggregation is controlled in part by soil mineralogy and organic matter content, both of which are important, at least implicitly, as taxonomic criteria. Macroporosity, however, is not used as a taxonomic criterion, probably because it can change rapidly with vegetation type and with agronomic practices such as tillage. Macropores take the form of cracks, animal burrows and holes left behind after coarse roots decay (Aubertin 1971; Trudgill, Pickles & Smettem 1983; Field, Parker & Powell 1984). They appear to be more evident in soils under forest or other perennial vegetation, perhaps because woody roots leave large channels behind as they decay, and because burrowing animals are more abundant and active than in cultivated soils.

The importance of aggregation and macroporosity to nutrient cycling is that both produce what is called a bi-phasic water flow regime in which water flows mainly between aggregates and through macropores rather than through the soil matrix (Van Genuchten & Wierenga 1976; Thomas & Phillips 1979; Beven & Germann 1981, 1982; White 1985; Van Genuchten & Dalton 1986). The water in the fine pores of the soil matrix remains immobile relative to the 'channellized' or 'macropore' flow, and solute exchange between the immobile and mobile phases can be very slow.

Three broad effects of a bi-phasic water flow regime on nutrient cycling are to be expected. The simplest effect is on erosion; a well-developed bi-phasic water flow regime virtually precludes overland flow and therefore erosion and attendant nutrient loss.

In addition, the slow solute transfer from immobile to mobile phase may serve to retard leaching. For example, Wild (1972) partly attributed slow nitrate leaching under bare fallow to channellized water flow. Nortcliff & Thornes (1978) have suggested that macropore flow might account for slow rates of cation leaching from some Brazilian Ultisols. Sollins & Radulovich (1988) studied effects of soil structure on nutrient retention in a highly aggregated Oxic Dystropept (mentioned earlier) under grass and secondary forest at La Selva, Costa Rica. They used dye stain patterns to assess the amount of macropore (channellized) flow and breakthrough curves to judge the importance of the bi-phasic water flow regime in controlling nutrient retention. They found that water flowed preferentially through very small regions of the soils often following decayed-root channels and cracks (Fig. 4). Breakthrough curves indicated very slow exchange between the mobile and immobile phases, and thus a strong tendency for the soil to resist leaching. McVoy (1985) and Seyfried & Rao (1987), working with a less weathered Typic Dystropept under forest vegetation at Turrialba, Costa Rica, reported a somewhat less pronounced effect of chanellized flow on nutrient retention.

Lastly, slow solute exchange between immobile and mobile phases implies not only slow solute loss from the soil matrix, but slow solute entry as well. For example, bi-phasic water flow has been shown to retard sorption of fertilizers and pesticides by soil (thus increasing the potential for groundwater pollution) and to increase the amount of water needed to desalinate soil (Thomas & Phillips 1979;

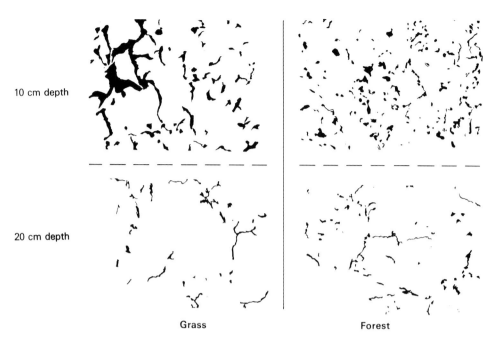

10 cm depth

20 cm depth

Grass   Forest

FIG. 4. Typical staining patterns resulting from field application of rhodamine-B. Patterns are for 40 × 50 cm areas of soil under grass and forest at 10 and 20 cm depths (Sollins & Radulovich 1988).

Bouma 1981; White 1985). In forest ecosystems, slow solute entry implies that solutes leached from foliage and litter should move rapidly through the soil and not be retained in the soil matrix. If true, one might expect rooting to be most concentrated in the litter layer at sites where bi-phasic flow is most pronounced.

Bi-phasic water flow regimes are to be expected especially in Oxisols, and in oxic subgroups of Ultisols and Inceptisols. This is because many such soils are highly aggregated simply because of low net charge, which decreases repulsive forces between clay particles (Uehara & Gillman 1981; Sollins *et al.* 1988). Thus as weathering decreases a soil's capacity to retain ions on exchange sites, it may increase its capacity to resist leaching. However, bi-phasic water regimes are not restricted to weathered soils. Many allophanic soils are well aggregated (Churchman & Tate 1986), have bi-modal pore size distributions (Tsuji, Watanabe & Sakai 1975), and thus might be expected to have a bi-phasic flow regime.

Effects of vegetation type and agronomic practice on macroporosity deserve increased attention. Forest soils support abundant animal activity and turnover of woody roots, which should replenish continually the supply of macropores. Conversion from forest to pasture eliminates woody roots and presumably decreases macroporosity. Cultivation may decrease macroporosity even more, although even cultivated soils may have extensive macroporosity below the plough layer (White 1985). The overall effect could be to decrease the soil's ability to resist leaching. A relationship might therefore be expected between bi-phasic water flow and the remarkable productivity of tropical forests on highly weathered soils, as well as the marked decreases in productivity that have sometimes occurred after conversion to agriculture (Jordan 1985; Ewel 1986; Vitousek & Sanford 1986).

Hand-in-hand with aggregation and a bi-phasic water flow regime goes a large amount of very fine pore space. As a result, soils of the humid tropics that are well aggregated and highly weathered retain large amounts of plant-available water, yet drain freely. Such soils are highly productive if problems of nutrition and low pH can be overcome. Extensive fine pore space can also be a disadvantage, however, in that the fine pores may become anaerobic and support high levels of denitrification. For example, the very well aggregated, highly weathered soils at La Selva, Costa Rica, have yielded some of the highest denitrification rates yet reported for unfertilized soils (Robertson & Tiedje 1988).

Methods for quantifying soil structure show little trend towards standardization. Some recent studies have emphasized differences in macro-aggregation, that is aggregates greater than 250 μm (e.g. Elliott 1986), but it seems likely that effects important to water flow and microbial activity involve aggregation at a finer scale as well (Tisdall & Oades 1982; Strickland *et al.* 1988). Air-drying of samples may create artefacts. For example, soils that are normally moist throughout much of the year (udic moisture regime) can show marked and largely irreversible changes in microstructure during air-drying compared with soils that dry thoroughly each year (ustic moisture regime) (Fig. 5). The effects of air-drying need to be carefully evaluated before routine measurement of soil structure is begun.

CONCLUSION

Early nutrient cycling studies of terrestrial ecosystems focused heavily on circulation of nutrients through the vegetation and back to the forest floor. As part of this, litterfall was monitored at literally hundreds of sites (Cole & Rapp 1981; Vitousek 1984). Attention shifted later to litter decomposition and nutrient release, but the soil was often excluded from such ecosystem-level studies of nutrient cycling. Soil science remained a discipline apart from the nutrient cycling work, even though it dealt directly with mechanisms of nutrient exchange and transfer. This trend continues to a certain extent even today. Better integration of soil science and ecosystem nutrient cycling studies offers exciting possibilities for rapidly improving our ability to predict nutrient availability across a wide range of vegetation types and management systems.

ACKNOWLEDGEMENTS

This research was supported by NSF grants BSR 83-17198 and BSR 86-05047 to the Organization for Tropical Studies, Duke University, BSR 84-18708 to Oregon State University, and by the Tropical Resources Institute, Yale University. Contributions by Eugenia Hidalgo and Michael Huston to the work at La Selva, Costa Rica, are gratefully acknowledged.

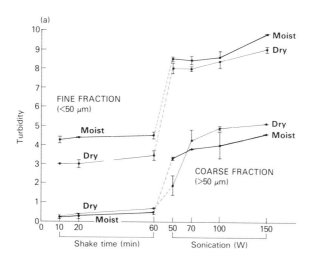

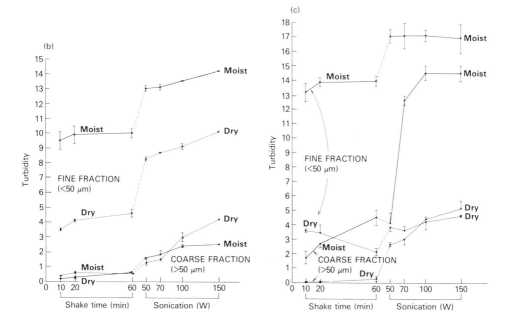

FIG. 5. Effect of air-drying (35 °C, 24 h) on aggregation and aggregate stability in soils from ustic, xeric and udic moisture regimes. Composite samples (0–15 cm depth) were wet-sieved (50 μm); both fractions were brought to 100 ml volume, shaken or sonicated (5 min) as shown, allowed to settle for 5 min, then assayed for turbidity (expressed as a ratio of light absorption (%) to dry weight of the soil fraction). (a) Pachic Argiustoll from Colorado Plains Experimental Reserve, Colorado; (b) Andic Haplumbrept from H. J. Andrews Experimental Forest, Oregon; (c) Oxic Dystropept from upper alluvial terrace at La Selva, Costa Rica.

REFERENCES

Aubertin, G.M. (1971). Nature and extent of macropores in forest soils and their influence on subsurface water movement. *US Forest Service Research Paper NE,* **192.**

Barrow, N.J. & Shaw, T.C. (1980). Effect of drying soil on the measurement of phosphate adsorption. *Communications in Soil Science and Plant Analysis,* **11,** 347–353.

Beven, K. & Germann, P.F. (1981). Water flow in soil macropores II. A combined flow model. *Journal of Soil Science,* **32,** 15–29.

Beven, K. & Germann, P.F. (1982). Macropores and water flow in soil. *Water Resources Research,* **18,** 1311–1325.

Bouma, J. (1981). Soil morphology and preferential flow along macropores. *Agricultural Water Management,* **3,** 235–250.

Churchman, G.J. & Tate, K.R. (1986). Aggregation of clay in different types of New Zealand soils. *Geoderma,* **37,** 207–220.

Cole, D.W. & Rapp, M. (1981). Elemental cycling in forest ecosystems. *Dynamic Properties of Forest Ecosystems* (Ed. by D.E. Reichle), pp. 341–409. Cambridge University Press, Cambridge.

Elliott, E.T. (1986). Aggregate structure and carbon, nitrogen, and phosphorus in native and cultivated soils. *Soil Science Society of America Journal,* **50,** 627–633.

Ewel, J.J. (1986). Designing agricultural ecosystems for the humid tropics. *Annual Review of Ecology and Systematics,* **17,** 245–271.

Field, J.A., Parker, J.C. & Powell, N.L. (1984). Comparison of field- and laboratory-measured and predicted hydraulic properties of a soil with macropores. *Soil Science,* **138,** 385–396.

Gillman, G.P. (1984). Using variable charge characteristics to understand the exchangeable cation status of oxic soils. *Australian Journal of Soil Research,* **22,** 71–80.

Gillman, G.P. & Murtha, G.G. (1983). Effects of sample handling on some chemical properties of soils from high rainfall coastal north Queensland. *Australian Journal of Soil Research,* **21,** 67–72.

Jordan, C. (1985). *Nutrient Cycling in Tropical Forest Ecosystems.* Wiley, Chichester.

McVoy, C.W. (1985). *Water and solute movement in an aggregated tropical soil: use of iodide and dyes for a morphological characterization.* M.S. Thesis, University of Florida, Gainesville.

Mott, C.J.B. (1981). Anion and ligand exchange. *The Chemistry of Soil Processes* (Ed. by D.J. Greenland & M.H.B. Hayes), pp. 179–219. Wiley, Chichester.

Nortcliff, S. & Thornes, J.B. (1978). Water and cation movement in a tropical rainforest environment. I. Objectives, experimental design and preliminary results. *Acta Amazonica,* **8,** 245–258.

Parfitt, R.L. (1980). Chemical properties of variable charge soils. *Soils with Variable Charge* (Ed. by B.K.G. Theng), pp. 167–194. New Zealand Society of Soil Science, Lower Hutt.

Robertson, G.P. & Tiedje, J.M. (1988). Deforestation alters denitrification in a lowland tropical rain forest. *Nature,* **336,** 756–759.

Sanchez, P.A. (1976). *Properties and Management of Soils in the Tropics.* Wiley, New York.

Seyfried, M.S. & Rao, P.S.C. (1987). Solute transport in undisturbed columns of an aggregated tropical soil. *Soil Science Society of America Journal,* **51,** 1434–1444.

Soil Survey Staff (1975). *Soil Taxonomy: a Basic System of Soil Classification for Making and Interpreting Soil Surveys. Agriculture Handbook 436.* U.S. Department of Agriculture, Washington DC.

Sollins, P. & Radulovich, R. (1988). Effects of soil physical structure on solute transport in a weathered tropical soil. *Soil Science Society of America Journal,* **52,** 1168–1173.

Sollins, P., Robertson, G.P. & Uehara, G. (1988). Nutrient mobility in variable- and permanent-charge soils. *Biogeochemistry,* **6,** 181–199.

Strickland, T.C., Sollins, P., Schimel, D.S. & Kerle, E.A. (1988). Aggregation and aggregate stability in forest and range soils. *Soil Science Society of America Journal,* **52,** 829–833.

Thomas, A.D., Parfitt, R.L. & Smart, R. St. C. (1974). The effect of drying on chemical properties of some Papua New Guinea soils. *Communications in Soil Science and Plant Analysis,* **5,** 165–172.

Thomas, G.W. & Phillips, R.E. (1979). Consequences of water movement in macropores. *Journal of Environmental Quality,* **8,** 149–152.

Tisdall, J.M. & Oades, J.M. (1982). Organic matter and water-stable aggregates in soils. *Journal of Soil Science,* **33,** 141–163.

Trudgill, S.T., Pickles, A.M. & Smettem, K.R.J. (1983). Soil water residence time and solute uptake. 2. Dye tracing and preferential flow predictions. *Journal of Hydrology,* **62,** 279–285.

Tsuji, G.Y., Watanabe, R.T. & Sakai, S. (1975). Influence of soil microstructure on water characteristics of selected Hawaiian soils. *Soil Science Society of America Proceedings,* **39,** 28–33.

Uehara, G. & Gillman, G. (1981). *The Mineralogy, Chemistry, and Physics of Tropical Soils with Variable Charge Clays.* Westview Press, Boulder.

Van Genuchten, M.T. & Dalton, F.N. (1986). Models for simulating salt movement in aggregated field soils. *Geoderma,* **38,** 165–183.

Van Genuchten, M.T. & Wierenga, P.J. (1976). Mass transfer studies in sorbing porous media I. Analytical solutions. *Soil Science Society of America Journal,* **40,** 473–480.

Vitousek, P.M. (1984). Litterfall, nutrient cycling, and nutrient limitation in tropical forests. *Ecology,* **65,** 285–298.

Vitousek, P.M. & Sanford, R. (1986). Nutrient cycling in moist tropical forests. *Annual Review of Ecology and Systematics,* **17,** 137–167.

Wada, K. (1977). Allophane and imogolite. *Minerals in Soil Environments* (Ed. by J.B. Dixon & S.B. Weed), pp. 603–638. Soil Science Society of America, Madison.

Westfall, D.G., Moodie, C.D. & Cheng, H.H. (1973). Effects of drying and wetting on extractable aluminum in strongly acid soils and in aluminum-saturated clays. *Geoderma,* **9,** 5–13.

White, R.E. (1985). The influence of macropores on the transport of dissolved and suspended matter through soil. *Advances in Soil Science,* **3,** 95–120.

Wild, A. (1972). Nitrate leaching under bare fallow at a site in northern Nigeria. *Journal of Soil Science,* **23,** 315–324.

Mineral nutrients in some Botswana savanna types

W. H. O. ERNST* AND D. J. TOLSMA**

*Biological Laboratory, Department of Ecology and Ecotoxicology,
Free University, PO Box 7161, 1007 MC Amsterdam. The Netherlands, and
**Department of Biology, University of Botswana,
Private Bag 0022, Gaborone, Botswana

SUMMARY

1 Several aspects of the mineral nutrition of a range of savanna types in Botswana were investigated.

2 The accumulation and allocation of nutrients in plants varied with species and were modified by soil properties and exposure to light.

3 Leaf litter of trees was found to modify the nutrient concentration in the top-soil.

4 Leaf nitrogen concentration of tree-parasitic Loranthaceae was higher on leguminous tree species compared with non-leguminous species. Loranthaceae on Combretaceae hosts had high concentrations of iron and manganese.

5 Fruits and seeds were important sinks for nutrients in tree and shrub species.

6 Annual nutrient loss by leaves, flowers and fruits of savanna species in Botswana varied from 4.0 to 85.7% of the total above-ground pool of nutrients.

7 Heavy grazing by cattle substantially reduced the amount of nutrients in the herb and grass layer of savanna species in Botswana.

8 Fuelwood harvesting and bush fencing caused a reduction in the size of the nutrient pool because of the removal of twigs and branches with high nutrient concentrations.

INTRODUCTION

Plant nutrition and the cycling of nutrients have received less attention in woody savannas than in tropical forests (Proctor 1984; Mott et al. 1985). In Africa, savanna species composition is being changed by several types of disturbance: overgrazing by cattle (Gammon & Roberts 1978; Skarpe 1986; Tolsma, Ernst & Verweij 1987), which sometimes leads to bush encroachment (van Vegten 1983), frequent burning (Skarpe 1980; Trollope 1982), intensive firewood consumption (Kgathi 1984), and the planting of exotic trees, especially *Eucalyptus* species (Tietema 1985; Bernhard-Reversat 1986, 1987). These changes may greatly influence the nutrient cycles. The effects of soil type on the floristic composition of savanna have long been recognized (Cole 1963; Wild & Fernandez 1968; Cole

& Brown 1976; Werger & Coetzee 1978; Huntley 1982; Huntley & Morris 1982), but the differences in nutrient cycling associated with different soil types are largely unknown except for the soils with high concentrations of copper, lead, nickel and zinc (Cole 1971; Ernst 1972; Cole & Le Roex 1978; Wild 1978). Information on the impact of mycorrhiza on the nutrient uptake (Högberg 1982, *this volume*) and on the reproductive effort of trees (Tolsma *et al.* 1987) is scarce. Large mammalian herbivores not only affect energy flow (Korn 1987), but they strongly affect floristic composition (Smart, Hatton & Spence 1985) and thus savanna nutrient cycles.

The aim of this study is to present results on some important aspects of nutrient cycles in some Botswana savanna types. The species nomenclature in this paper is taken from Turrill & Milne-Redhead (1952–1974), Field (1976) and Coates Palgrave (1984).

Study areas

The studies were made near Gaborone in Botswana (Fig. 1) where there is a mean annual rainfall of 537 mm year^{-1}, which varies greatly from year to year. During the investigation period (1977–1987) annual rainfall varied from 400 to 850 mm. The studies were made in the following savanna types (Timberlake 1980) (Fig. 1):

1 Mochudi (24°24′S, 26°15′E). *Terminalia sericea-Combretum zeyheri* tree and shrub savanna on coarse sandy soil with isolated trees and shrubs of *Boscia albitrunca, B. foetida, Combretum zeyheri, Grewia retinervis* and *Terminalia sericea*. The very open herb layer (Fig. 2(b)) is made up by the dominant *Dipcadi glaucum* (Liliaceae) together with *Cynodon dactylon, Harpagophytum zeyheri, Indigofera circinnata, Portulaca kermesina, Tragus berteronianus* and *Tribulus terrestris.*

2 Dikeletsane (24°20′S, 26°31′E). Eastern broadleaved tree savanna (Fig. 2(a)) with *Acacia fleckii* and *Terminalia sericea* intermingled with *Acacia erubescens* tree savanna on a coarse arenosol (Tolsma, Ernst & Verweij 1987).

3 Kumakwane (24°39′S, 25°36′E). *Croton gratissimus*-savanna woodland with *Combretum apiculatum, C. molle, Pappea capensis* and *Ximenia americana* on a lithosol over rocky iron-enriched outcrops.

4 Gaborone (24°40′S, 25°56′E). *Acacia erubescens* tree savanna on ferruginous loamy arenosol at the campus of the University of Botswana (Tolsma *et al.* 1987).

5 Morwa Forest (24°25′S, 26°05′E). *Acacia tortilis* riverine tree savanna on loamy soils with additional *A. mellifera*.

6 Modipane (24°38′S, 26°10′E). *Acacia tenuispina* shrub savanna on black-cracking-clay soil (cotton clay).

FIG. 1. Vegetation map of south-eastern Botswana showing the six study sites (from Timberlake (1980)).

METHODS

Sampling

Soils

Soil cores (10–30 cm depth) were taken 2 weeks after the first rain had fallen in November 1986. Each soil sample consisted of three subsamples; three samples per site were taken from under the sampled plants. To test the impact of tree species on the chemical composition of topsoils at the Dikeletsane site, soil samples (0–30 cm depth) were taken 1 m distant from the bole and outside of the tree canopy on bare ground (generally 5 m away from all trees) on 17 and 18

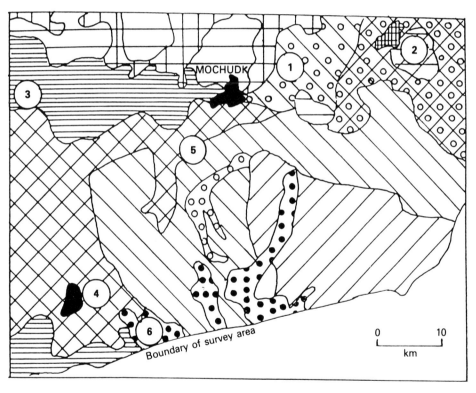

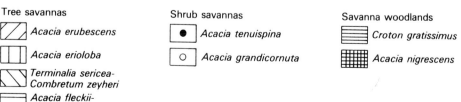

Tree savannas

▨	*Acacia erubescens*
▥	*Acacia erioloba*
◸	*Terminalia sericea-Combretum zeyheri*
▤	*Acacia fleckii-Terminalia sericea*

Shrub savannas

●	*Acacia tenuispina*
○	*Acacia grandicornuta*

Savanna woodlands

▦	*Croton gratissimus*
▦	*Acacia nigrescens*

Fig. 2. (a) Summer aspect of broadleaved savanna with *Terminalia sericea* on a loamy arenosol in the cattle-free zone near Gaborone in Botswana (note the good grass cover) (photograph by W. H. O. Ernst). (b) Heavily grazed broadleaved savanna with shrubby *Terminalia sericea*, the predominant bulbous *Dipcadi glaucum* and the annual herb *Tribulus terrestris* at the Mochudi site in Botswana (note the scarcity of grasses) (photograph by W. H. O. Ernst).

February 1983. There were three samples per tree and at least three trees per species and microsite.

For an analysis of the effects of fire, the upper 5 cm of the soil under burnt and unburnt plants of *Boscia foetida* and *Eragrostis rigidior* were sampled at the Gaborone site nearly 20 days after burning.

Plants

In order to investigate the relationship between soil chemistry and nutrient composition of plant species, randomly sampled leaves of plants were taken in the first part of November 1986. Because of the strong seasonal variation in nutrient concentrations in savanna plants, leaves of all species were taken within a week of each other where site effects were to be studied. The sampling procedure for trees followed that described earlier (Tolsma *et al.* 1987). For the herbs and grasses ten plants were taken at random, by cutting them just above the soil surface and washing them with deionized water to remove contamination by soil particles.

The impact of the tree canopy shadow of *Acacia tortilis* on the nutrient concentrations of the grasses *Panicum maximum* and *Eragrostis rigidior* was studied at the Gaborone site. Leaves of grasses were collected on four transects at right angles to each other from the bole to the open savanna at the end of the rainy season on 4 February 1983.

Leaves of burnt and unburnt plants of *Boscia foetida* and *Eragrostis rigidior* were sampled at the Gaborone site 3 weeks after burning on 14 September 1983.

Leaves of parasitic Loranthaceae and of their host trees (from branches adjacent to the parasite) were collected on 3 and 9 November 1986. For analysing the effect of tree regrowth after cutting boles, leaves were collected from regrown branches 1 year after cutting and from control uncut trees in the experimental plots at Morwa Forest on 20 November 1985. The allocation of nutrients to the different above-ground parts (bole, branches, twigs, leaves, flowers and fruits) was analysed from single trees, which were cut just above the soil surface. The fresh weights of boles, branches and twigs were measured in the field, and dry weights were determined from dried subsamples.

The allocation of nutrients during fruit development was analysed in 1-m long twigs. From each tree three twigs in the flowering state and fruiting stage were randomly chosen and separated into leaves, inflorescences and wood. The abortion of inflorescences was analysed by marking twigs and registering the shedding of inflorescences every 2 days. For analysing the production of fruits of *Combretum apiculatum*, *Combretum zeyheri* and *Terminalia sericea* 20 in-florescences in full flower were collected and the number of flowers per inflorescence was counted. At the time of fruit maturity, 20 infructescences of at least three trees per species were collected and the number of fruits and the seeds per fruit were recorded.

The impact of cattle on the savanna ecosystem in south-eastern Botswana was studied in three adjacent areas from the site near Mochudi. A nearly ungrazed area at the Gaborone site with a mixed *Eragrostis rigidior/Panicum maximum* field layer was selected as a reference area. The history of the areas has been followed by aerial photographs taken in 1950, 1963 and 1975 (van Vegten 1981) and by annual field inspection between 1980 and 1985. In each area the above-ground biomass of ten 1 m × 1 m plots was harvested on 20 November 1985.

Chemical analysis

Soils

For an evaluation of the immediately-available chemical elements, 10 g of dry soil were soaked with 25 ml water for 2 h and the filtrate was analysed by atomic absorption spectrophotometry after acidification with 0.1 M HCl (water-soluble fraction). Due to the low concentration of organic material and calcium, plant-available phosphorus was determined after extraction with water (1 : 50, w/w) for 12 h (Scheffer & Schachtschabel 1982). For the exchangeable form of the chemical elements, soil samples were soaked with 25 ml 1 M ammonium acetate for 2 h, filtered, acidified, and analysed in the same way as the water-soluble fraction. Carbon and nitrogen were analysed by burning the soil sample with pure oxygen and separating the gaseous compounds by column chromatography (Kirsten 1979). pH was measured after addition of 25 ml H_2O to 10 g dry soil followed by soaking for 2 h.

Plants

After drying at 90 °C for 24 h, plant material was wet-ashed (concentrated $HNO_3 : HClO_4$, 7 : 1, v/v). Soil and plant materials were analysed for potassium and sodium by emission spectrophotometry, and for calcium, copper, iron, magnesium, manganese and zinc by atomic absorption spectrophotometry (calcium and magnesium after addition of lanthanum nitrate (1% v/v)). Phosphorus was determined by spectrophotometry after formation of a blue ascorbic acid–phosphorus complex (Chen, Toribara & Warner 1956), and nitrogen was analysed by column chromatography after burning with oxygen (Merz 1970).

RESULTS

Abiotic factors and leaf nutrients

Soil–plant relationships

The pH of the soils varied between 6.0 ± 0.5 and 6.9 ± 1.0; the C : N ratio was between 10.0 and 15.3 (Table 1). From the soils of the six research sites, the black-cracking-clay soil from Modipane supporting the *Acacia tenuispina* shrub

TABLE 1. pH (log units) and the mean concentrations (mmol kg^{-1} dry soil) ($\pm$ S.E.) of total carbon and nitrogen, water-soluble phosphorus, ammonium-acetate-exchangeable potassium, sodium, calcium, magnesium and zinc and water-soluble iron in the soils (10–30 cm depth) at the savanna research sites in south-eastern Botswana ($n = 3$ for the Gaborone site, $n = 9$ for all other sites)

Site	pH$_{H_2O}$	C	N	P	K	Na	Ca	Mg	Mn	Zn	Fe
Mochudi	6.4	260	19.8	0.16	4.51	0.54	9.03	2.75	0.07	0.010	0.15
	±0.5	±58	±4.9	±0.03	±0.45	±0.08	±1.87	±0.61	±0.021	±0.002	±0.02
Dikeletsane	6.9	1110	118.0	0.27	4.22	0.32	5.35	3.69	0.07	0.030	3.94
	±1.0	±192	±11.9	±0.04	±0.26	±0.03	±0.07	±0.03	±0.0	±0.10	±1.09
Kumakwane	6.3	549	64.2	0.60	3.28	1.12	5.57	1.98	0.527	0.013	5.51
	±0.3	±42	±14.3	±0.10	±0.27	±0.09	±0.49	±0.34	±0.072	±0.003	±0.89
Gaborone	6.0	4280	457.0	0.37	5.50	0.49	8.87	7.38	0.040	0.012	2.50
	±0.5	±417	±40.0	±0.07	±0.19	±0.31	±1.63	±1.55	±0.011	±0.003	±0.69
Morwa	6.9	1700	142.0	0.14	4.20	0.38	10.34	2.33	0.187	0.002	0.10
	±0.6	±109	±10.0	±0.10	±0.30	±0.12	±1.71	±0.72	±0.035	±0.001	±0.01
Modipane	6.6	833	80.0	0.52	12.70	0.93	79.80	48.00	0.062	0.001	0.025
	±0.3	±78	±11.8	±0.13	±1.4	±0.23	±4.31	±3.52	±0.004	±0.001	±0.01

savanna had the highest ammonium-acetate-exchangeable concentrations of calcium, magnesium, potassium and sodium and one of the lowest of iron and zinc. The soils at Dikeletsane and Kumakwane were rich in iron and the latter also in manganese. The three other soils had unremarkable exchangeable nutrient concentrations.

A comparison of the same plant species growing on a lithosol at Kumakwane, on a coarse arenosol at Dikeletsane and on a black-cracking-clay soil at Modipane revealed that the main differences in leaf nutrient concentrations were those of iron and manganese which were the highest in plants on the lithosol. The concentrations of other nutrients varied with species (Table 2). Although the black-cracking-clay soil had the highest concentration of exchangeable calcium, the dicotyledonous species had a relatively low foliar calcium concentration on this soil and showed differences with species, e.g. the leaves of the herb *Tribulus terrestris* had twice to seven times the calcium concentration of those of *Acacia erubescens* and *Dichrostachys cinerea*.

The restrictions of the small tree *Croton gratissimus* to manganese-enriched soils and of the shrub *Acacia tenuispina* to black-cracking-clay soils rich in calcium, magnesium, potassium and sodium seem to be examples of a high demand, or a high sensitivity, to the micronutrients iron, manganese and zinc.

Because of litterfall and species-specific accumulation of nutrients in leaves (Tolsma *et al.* 1987), plant species influence the soil chemistry beneath the tree canopy (Table 3). A comparison of the upper soil layer (0–30 cm) beneath and outside the canopy of *Acacia* species and *Dichrostachys cinerea* revealed that the concentrations of exchangeable calcium and potassium were significantly increased under *A. erubescens* and *A. karroo*. Litter of *A. tortilis* had no effect on soil chemistry and that of *D. cinerea* increased the potassium concentration of the topsoil.

TABLE 2. The mean nutrient concentrations ($\pm$S.E.) (μmol g^{-1} dry wt.) in leaves (harvested between 6 and 11 November 1986) of several plant species growing on the coarse Kalahari sand near Dikeletsane, the iron-enriched rocky outcrops near Kumakwane, and on black-cracking-clay soil near Modipane in Botswana ($n = 3$ for trees and shrubs, $n = 10$ for grasses and herbs)

	P	K	Ca	Mg	Fe	Mn
Grasses						
Eragrostis rigidior						
Dikeletsane	24.4±6.5	329±52	572±235	138±2	2.26±0.77	1.00±0.14
Kumakwane	49.5±9.2	479±116	274±48	45±4	13.4±4.6	3.87±0.33
Tragus berteronianus						
Dikeletsane	16.0±2.8	291±10	238±51	85±1	21.8±1.5	0.34±0.02
Kumakwane	30.0±1.7	522±35	150±17	99±9	62.3±7.6	1.67±0.58
Herb						
Tribulus terrestris						
Dikeletsane	33.4±1.5	742±14	880±10	240±10	6.1±0.7	1.36±0.01
Kumakwane	57.1±4.0	522±7	993±15	125±8	21.2±2.4	2.08±0.05
Modipane	43.9±2.7	487±22	422±7	161±12	13.9±1.3	1.05±0.04
Trees						
Acacia erubescens						
Dikeletsane	30.7±1.4	273±11	762±17	151±3	1.7±0.1	1.12±0.05
Kumakwane	24.9±1.0	196±10	376±24	206±10	7.8±0.5	3.68±0.11
Modipane	29.0±2.7	243±25	272±22	130±5	1.3±0.1	0.39±0.01
Dichrostachys cinerea						
Dikeletsane	32.7±0.8	414±20	469±23	133±1	5.0±0.1	0.80±0.13
Kumakwane	29.9±3.4	446±13	383±16	141±6	15.8±1.7	1.30±0.20
Modipane	33.4±1.2	327±17	334±15	110±3	3.8±0.2	0.68±0.05
Acacia tenuispina						
Modipane	57.6±0.9	330±18	579±45	122±5	1.8±0.1	0.25±0.03
Croton gratissimus						
Kumakwane	35.5±1.0	338±22	489±21	132±13	6.70±1.10	22.3±0.66

Light and nutrition

One of the palatable grasses of the savanna in Botswana is *Panicum maximum*, which is sensitive to full sunlight (Humphreys 1981). To exclude the above-mentioned effect of tree litter on soil nutrients, we selected sites with *Acacia tortilis* (whose litter did not affect soil chemistry) to test the effect of light on plant nutrition in the field. An analysis of the nutrient concentrations of green leaves of *P. maximum* collected at different distances from the tree *Acacia tortilis*, growing in the ungrazed (by cattle) Gaborone site (Table 4), showed that calcium, magnesium and zinc decreased in the leaves and manganese increased with increasing distance from the tree. The concentrations of potassium and phosphorus did not vary with distance from the tree despite a decreasing biomass of *P. maximum* from the tree to the open.

TABLE 3. Ammonium-acetate-exchangeable potassium, calcium and magnesium (μmol kg^{-1} dry soil) (a) beneath the canopy (1 m distant from bole); (b) outside the canopy (5 m away from canopy) of the *Acacia* species and *Dichrostachys cinerea*; and quotient of beneath to outside the canopy (a)/(b) in the tree savanna at Dikeletsane in Botswana (mean ± S.E.; $n = 9$ per species and canopy; sampling on 17 and 18 February 1983)

	A. erubescens	A. karroo	A. tortilis	D. cinerea
K				
(a)	6.33 ± 1.71	7.97 ± 3.92	2.91 ± 1.49	5.10 ± 0.86
(b)	3.25 ± 0.69	2.34 ± 0.62	2.67 ± 0.95	3.22 ± 0.81
(a)/(b)	2.03 ± 0.77	4.50 ± 1.99	1.03 ± 0.23	1.73 ± 0.84
Ca				
(a)	6.19 ± 1.64	8.53 ± 1.83	10.75 ± 2.66	4.87 ± 1.18
(b)	4.41 ± 1.14	7.25 ± 3.94	11.12 ± 0.52	4.45 ± 1.40
(a)/(b)	1.41 ± 0.16	1.45 ± 0.18	0.97 ± 0.24	1.12 ± 0.14
Mg				
(a)	4.02 ± 1.43	7.31 ± 2.07	7.96 ± 1.14	3.36 ± 0.90
(b)	3.13 ± 0.97	5.41 ± 3.46	8.63 ± 0.93	3.28 ± 1.10
(a)/(b)	1.28 ± 0.26	1.90 ± 1.26	0.95 ± 0.20	1.04 ± 0.09

TABLE 4. Mean nutrient concentrations (±S.E.) (μmol g^{-1} dry wt.) of leaves of the grass *Panicum maximum* collected at four distances from the bole of *Acacia tortilis* on 4 February 1983 at the Gaborone site (the crown of the tree had a radius of 3.75 m; $n = 3$)

Distance (cm)	P	K	Ca	Mg	Mn	Zn
55	48.6 ± 4.5	986 ± 26	152 ± 0	103 ± 2	0.76 ± 0.01	0.41 ± 0.01
115	45.3 ± 3.1	1045 ±10	157 ± 5	94 ± 2	0.93 ± 0.01	0.38 ± 0.05
190	51.9 ± 1.9	962 ± 10	149 ± 1	87 ± 1	1.17 ± 0.01	0.36 ± 0.06
295	48.5 ± 1.2	1001 ± 35	130 ± 4	85 ± 1	1.32 ± 0.03	0.34 ± 0.02

Nutrients after burning

In the savanna areas of Botswana, fire had widely been used (up to the early 1980s) to combat shrub encroachment and to favour the development and maintenance of a grassland vegetation by killing seedlings and juveniles of woody plants (Skarpe 1980; W.H.O. Ernst, unpublished). The soil analysis of burnt and unburnt plots showed a rise in pH from 4.4 ± 0.2 in unburnt plots to 5.2 ± 0.3 in burnt plots, probably due to the formation of oxides or carbonates. In the upper 5 cm of the soil the concentrations of phosphorus, potassium, calcium and magnesium increased in the burnt plots (Table 5). As generally recognized, volatile elements such as nitrogen can be lost by fire. However, carbon increased from 0.46 ± 0.07% in the unburnt site to 0.56 ± 0.17% in the burnt site because of the deposition of charcoal on the soil surface.

In the frequently browsed perennial leaves of the tree *Boscia foetida* concentrations of nitrogen, phosphorus, potassium and zinc increased after fire,

TABLE 5. Mean concentrations (±S.E.) (µmol kg^{-1} dry wt.) of total nitrogen, water-soluble phosphorus, exchangeable potassium, calcium, magnesium, manganese and zinc and water-soluble iron in the topsoil (0–5 cm) and total concentrations of the same elements in leaves of burnt and unburnt *Boscia foetida* and *Eragrostis rigidior* at the Gaborone site nearly 20 days after burning in late August 1983 (sampling was carried out on 14 September 1983; n = 5 per site per plant species)

	N	P	K	Ca	Mg	Fe	Mn	Zn
Soil								
Burnt	400 ± 32	0.39 ± 0.12	8.17 ± 0.81	23.1 ± 2.4	12.0 ± 1.0	3.8 ± 0.5	0.08 ± 0.04	0.05 ± 0.01
Unburnt	520 ± 40	0.31 ± 0.03	6.20 ± 0.29	9.3 ± 1.8	7.9 ± 2.0	3.5 ± 0.8	0.05 ± 0.01	0.04 ± 0.01
Leaves								
Boscia foetida								
Burnt	3010 ± 500	56 ± 2	279 ± 12	202 ± 13	124 ± 4	1.9 ± 0.4	3.4 ± 0.4	0.65 ± 0.04
Unburnt	1930 ± 116	15 ± 1	76 ± 4	541 ± 23	219 ± 8	3.7 ± 0.1	5.0 ± 0.1	0.50 ± 0.12
Eragrostis rigidior								
Burnt	321 ± 2	62 ± 1	405 ± 10	544 ± 38	201 ± 5	22.0 ± 5.3	1.0 ± 0.1	2.55 ± 0.15
Unburnt	709 ± 28	8 ± 1	82 ± 11	148 ± 5	35 ± 1	9.5 ± 0.1	1.4 ± 0.2	1.48 ± 0.22

but those of calcium, iron, magnesium and manganese decreased. The regrowth of grasses showed, at least in the short term, an increased concentration of magnesium, phosphorus and potassium in young leaves (Table 5). Tainton & Mentis (1984) reported an increase in the protein concentration of new grass leaves shortly after burning; the nitrogen concentration of *Eragrostis rigidior*, however, showed the opposite trend (Table 5), and is more in accordance with soil nitrogen losses due to fire.

Biotic factors and leaf nutrients

Species-specific accumulation and grazing

The well-known differences between species in the uptake and accumulation of nutrients are of importance when the composition of vegetation is changed by management, e.g. overgrazing or tree-felling. One of the obvious changes in all savanna types in south-eastern Botswana has been the replacement of palatable fodder grasses, e.g. *Eragrostis superba*, *Panicum maximum* and *Setaria verticillata*, by unpalatable perennial grasses, e.g. *Cynodon dactylon*, *Eragrostis rigidior* and *Rhyncelytrium repens*, and the annual weeds *Tragus berteronianus* and *Tribulus terrestris*. At the same time, spiny shrubs and trees such as *Acacia tortilis*, *Commiphora pyracanthoides* and *Ximenia caffra* have replaced spineless *Boscia* spp., *Cadaba termitaria*, *Combretum* spp. and *Grewia flava*. The data in Table 6 show a general trend that less preferred species contain higher concentrations of phosphorus and potassium than palatable species. It has been shown that plant species which are avoided by cattle contain poisonous compounds, such as alkaloids in *Datura stramonium* (Waller & Nowacki 1978), sapogenines in *Tribulus terrestris* (Tomowa & Gjulemetova 1978) or unidentified toxins in *Dipcadi glaucum* (Vahrmeijer 1981), and high concentrations of nitrogen, potassium and phosphorus. The effect of selective grazing on the nutrient composition of the standing crop and on nutrient cycling is just becoming apparent.

Parasitism by Loranthaceae

A sink affecting nutrients in trees is the parasitism by Loranthaceae. The concentrations of nutrients varied between parasitic species and within the same species on different hosts (Table 7) as observed for Loranthaceae in miombo woodland by Baumeister & Ernst (1978). The nitrogen concentrations of Loranthaceae parasitizing non-leguminous trees (*Combretum zeyheri*, *Rhus marlothii* and *Terminalia sericea*) exceeded those of their hosts. Those Loranthaceae growing on the leguminous trees *Acacia fleckii*, *A. mellifera* and *Dichrostachys cinerea* had leaf nitrogen concentrations lower than those of their hosts. Another interesting result was the high concentration of iron and manganese in those

TABLE 6. Mean nutrient concentrations (±S.E.) (μmol g^{-1} dry wt.) in leaves of several trees, shrubs and grasses, preferred to different extents by cattle. Samples were taken at the Dikeletsane site on 11 November 1986 ($n = 3$ for shrubs and trees, $n = 10$ for grasses and herbs)

	N	P	K	Ca	Mg	Fe	Mn
Palatable species							
Boscia albitrunca	2520	18	110	200	58	9.7	3.30
	±124	±3	±10	±13	±7	±6.1	±0.41
Cadaba termitaria	3760	28	1100	394	144	12.8	1.31
	±210	±4	±90	±44	±3	±1.2	±0.20
Grewia flava	1970	33	277	620	160	3.2	0.95
	±115	±4	±3	±82	±42	±0.7	±0.26
Panicum maximum	1520	62	930	180	95	2.6	1.04
	±90	±4	±140	±27	±16	±0.8	±0.23
Less-preferred species							
Acacia tortilis	1890	48	490	290	120	1.8	0.56
	±257	±2	±63	±103	±7	±0.3	±0.05
Commiphora	1650	46	480	720	190	1.5	0.59
pyracanthoides	±120	±7	±27	±35	±20	±0.5	±0.07
Cynodon dactylon	2040	44	420	215	63	8.01	1.74
	±200	±1	±20	±20	±2	±1.02	±0.09
Eragrostis rigidior	640	60	538	175	117	2.0	1.50
	±37	±6	±35	±21	±10	±0.3	±0.06
Tragus berteronianus	1215	18	284	274	76	20.7	0.35
	±130	±3	±17	±35	±2	±2.2	±0.03
Avoided species							
Datura stramonium	4160	79	2480	195	126	8.37	1.10
	±225	±1	±122	±5	±1	±0.31	±0.01
Dipcadi glaucum	4925	103	1070	433	123	7.52	0.49
	±641	±17	±34	±53	±17	±3.17	±0.19
Tribulus terrestris	3550	57	522	720	95	8.20	0.40
	±130	±13	±17	±80	±7	±1.40	±0.10

Loranthaceae parasitizing the Combretaceae *Combretum zeyheri* and *Terminalia sericea*, which are well known for their great capacity for accumulating these micronutrients (Tolsma *et al.* 1987).

A calculation of the amounts of nutrients stored in the parasite *Erianthemum ngamicum* and those in the leaf biomass of its host *Acacia fleckii* (Table 8) showed that the seven medium-sized individuals of *E. ngamicum* on this tree diverted between 3.8% (zinc) and 13% (iron and potassium) of the nutrient mass from the tree to the parasite.

Foliar nutrients after tree damage

Damaging the tree by cutting or fire caused a breakdown of the apical dormancy so that many small twigs and branches started regrowing from the stump. In the first year after cutting trunks of *Acacia luederitzii* and *A. tortilis*, the con-

TABLE 7. Mean nutrient concentrations (μmol g^{-1} dry leaf) in the parasitic Loranthaceae and their host plants in tree savannas at the Gaborone and Kumakwane sites. Samples were collected on 8 and 9 November 1986 (S.E. less than 10% of the mean in all cases; $n = 3$)

Plant species	N	P	K	Ca	Mg	Fe	Mn	Zn
Erianthemum ngamicum	2240	44.5	467	380	85	1.42	0.38	0.23
on *Acacia mellifera*	3660	73.3	361	447	192	1.09	0.30	0.58
at Gaborone								
Erianthemum ngamicum	2085	43.2	572	54	106	4.55	0.53	0.12
on *Acacia fleckii*	3020	20.9	154	177	173	2.76	1.25	0.17
at Kumakwane								
Erianthemum ngamicum	2330	46.1	487	396	111	1.10	0.39	0.24
on *Acacia mellifera*	2840	58.0	327	591	239	0.93	0.31	0.46
at Gaborone								
Loranthus lugardi	2660	31.6	314	171	120	6.61	2.95	0.24
on *Combretum zeyheri*	2142	11.6	193	139	83	3.76	2.06	0.09
at Kumakwane								
Loranthus lugardi	2300	56.6	960	94	124	6.53	2.36	0.37
on *Terminalia sericea*	1230	27.2	211	110	70	1.42	2.18	0.26
at Kumakwane								
Tapinanthus oleifolius	2355	74.4	469	215	50	3.18	0.75	0.33
on *Dichrostachys*	2670	39.4	262	472	149	11.6	2.66	0.24
cinerea at Kumakwane								
Tapinanthus oleifolius	1720	27.4	800	82	131	0.72	1.88	0.12
on *Rhus marlothii*	1600	24.4	151	360	108	1.05	3.20	2.82
at Kumakwane								

TABLE 8. Leaf biomass and nutrient content of the parasitic Loranthaceae *Erianthemum ngamicum* ($n = 6$) and its host *Acacia fleckii* ($n = 1$) in a tree savanna at the Gaborone site. Samples were collected on 8 November 1986

Plant species	Dry wt. (g)	N	P	K	Na	Ca	Mg	Fe	Mn	Zn
					(μmol plant $^{-1}$)					
Erianthemum ngamicum	274	614	12.2	128	1.83	104	23	0.39	0.105	0.06
Acacia fleckii	2700	9880	198	975	19.8	1206	518	2.93	0.822	1.56
Amount in parasite as % of the host leaves	10.1	6.2	6.2	13.1	9.2	8.6	4.4	13.3	12.8	3.8

centrations of some elements significantly changed in leaves (Table 9). In both *Acacia* species, nitrogen concentrations were higher in the new leaves, indicating a better nutrient supply to the low leaf biomass of the regrowing twigs. This tendency, although not statistically significant, was also present for phosphorus and potassium.

TABLE 9. Mean concentrations (±S.E.) of nutrients (μmol g^{-1} dry wt.) in leaves of *Acacia luederitzii* and *Acacia tortilis* from a fully developed tree and from the regrowth after felling the trunk at the Morwa Forest site (samples were taken on 17 November 1983; $n = 3$)

	N	P	K	Ca	Mg	Fe	Mn	Zn
Acacia luederitzii								
Mature tree	2260	56	342	381	135	1.64	0.37	1.19
	±80	±5	±11	±27	±2	±0.71	±0.11	±0.66
Regrowing twigs	2645	60	370	396	87	1.07	0.23	0.68
	±50	±7	±16	±25	±1	±0.03	±0.03	±0.30
Acacia tortilis								
Mature tree	2630	50	387	333	98	3.50	0.38	0.51
	±93	±0	±13	±10	±5	±0.42	±0.06	±0.03
Regrowing twigs	4060	118	487	447	100	1.96	0.47	0.38
	±214	±3	±19	±39	±2	±0.32	±0.03	±0.02

Internal retranslocation and allocation

Allocation to fruits and seeds

Nutrients which are in short supply in the soil are efficiently retranslocated from senescent leaves to the perennial organs, e.g. the parenchyma and phloem of the twig, branches and stems of trees, or rhizomes and roots of herbs and grasses. Those nutrients, which are available in larger amounts, may be accumulated in older leaves (Tolsma, Ernst & Verweij 1987; Tolsma *et al.* 1987).

With the exception of plants with large flowers, e.g. *Catophractes alexandri*, or large inflorescences, e.g. *Aloe marlothii*, the demand of flowers for nutrients is low. The developing fruit and seeds, however, can be a large sink for car-bohydrates and some nutrients. A comparison of the relative biomass increase from flowers to fruits and of the relative increase in nutrients shows that species with heavy fruits have a high demand for nutrients. In most cases, however, the relative biomass increase from flowers to fruits is different from that of nutrients (Table 10). The increase is three times higher for phosphorus than for biomass in *Cadaba termitaria* with seeds embedded in a powdery pulp, two times higher for zinc than for biomass in *C. termitaria* and for nitrogen than for biomass in *Combretum zeyheri* with large cotyledons in the winged fruit, and 1.5 times higher for potassium than for biomass in *C. zeyheri*, for iron than for biomass in *Acacia erioloba*, for nitrogen than for biomass in *Acacia tortilis* and for manganese than for biomass in *Terminalia sericea*. A consequence of this high demand may be the abscission of flowers and inflorescences at an early stage of fruit development. In all investigated *Acacia* spp., *Combretum zeyheri*, *Dichros-tachys cinerea* and *Terminalia sericea* the abscission of inflorescences varies from 90 to 98%. If all inflorescences developed to the fruiting stage, the demand for nutrients would be increased by a factor of up to 20.

Table 10. Increase in biomass and amount of nutrients from one flower to one fruit (*Boscia foetida* and *Cadaba termitaria*) or from one inflorescence to one infructescence (*Acacia erioloba, Combretum zeyheri, Terminalia sericea*) in an *Acacia erubescens* tree savanna at the Gaborone site ($n = 3$)

	Weight of Flower/inflorescence (mg)	Weight of Fruit/infructescence (mg)	Relative increase between flowering and fruiting (infructescence/inflorescence)						
			Weight	Nitrogen	Phosphorus	Potassium	Iron	Zinc	Manganese
Acacia erioloba	41±7	10400±7000	252	290	148	157	392	94	131
Boscia foetida	5±1	128±38	26	14	16	16	35	31	8
Cadaba termitaria	34±2	194±27	6	3	18	2	1	11	5
Combretum zeyheri	70±7	1610±207	23	55	23	36	25	19	2
Terminalia sericea	38±4	875±130	23	18	11	8	15	18	36

A calculation of the annual nutrient demands of flowers and fruits of a tree (Table 11) demonstrates that the allocation of certain nutrients to reproductive organs may be the decisive factor for flower abortion (cf. Thompson & Stewart 1981). The high phosphorus demand of fruits has been postulated as the reason for the high abscission rate of inflorescences of *Acacia tortilis* and *A. erubescens* (Tolsma *et al.* 1987). High potassium demand may be involved for *A. erubescens*, magnesium and zinc for *A. nilotica*, and copper (not in Table 11) for *Combretum zeyheri*. In the latter species 25% of the total copper which is accumulated in the above-ground biomass is allocated to the fruits.

Another aspect of nutrient shortage may be the production of fruits without seeds. For example, *Acacia erubescens* often flowers well before the rainy season and the number of flowers and fruits is as great as those produced during the rainy season. The contribution of the pre-rainy-season pods to the above-ground biomass of the tree is only 0.1%, compared with the 4.3% of the rainy-season pods, because the former pods contain no seeds. Therefore the loss of nutrients by shedding pre-rainy-season pods is less than 3% of the amounts stored in the tree, compared with very high losses by the rainy-season pods (up to 23% for potassium and 26.7% for phosphorus). The nutrient demand of the pre-rainy-season seeds has to be met from retranslocation from the stem, twigs and leaves because of the difficulties of nutrient supply from a dry soil.

Litterfall

An important aspect of nutrition is the annual shedding of leaves, fruits and dead twigs. This process is very variable between species, as can be demonstrated for the *Croton gratissimus* woodland intermingled with *Terminalia-Combretum zeyheri* tree savanna at the Kumakwane site (Table 11). Owing to the high nutrient concentrations in leaves and fruits, the annual loss of nutrients is higher than that of the remaining biomass, despite retranslocation. A comparison of *Terminalia sericea* and *Combretum zeyheri* shows that both species differ by a factor of two for the annual loss of their biomass, but vary strongly in the percentage loss of nutrients. *Terminalia sericea* keeps the loss between 4.0% (phosphorus) and 24.2% (zinc), whereas *Combretum zeyheri* has a high loss of nitrogen (65.4%) and a low loss of iron (8.3%) and calcium (5.3%). The loss may increase if leaves or fruits are browsed before the retranslocation process ends.

Effects of overgrazing on nutrients

In areas with overgrazing by cattle and goats, e.g. at Mochudi, the tree savanna is very open, with only a few trees of *Acacia tortilis, Boscia albitrunca, B. foetida* and *Terminalia sericea*. The field layer is either dominated by *Dipcadi glaucum*, or just after the spring rains by a more or less closed mat of grazing-resistant annuals, e.g. *Tragus berteronianus* (with all leaves pressed on the soil) and

TABLE 11. Above-ground biomass (kg dry wt.), plant nutrient content (mmol) and the percentage allocation to the deciduous parts of some savanna trees in a *Croton gratissimus* savanna woodland at the Kumakwane site.

	Biomass	N	P	K	Ca	Mg	Fe	Mn	Zn
Acacia erubescens									
Total	24.35	29500	319	2250	14600	3020	47.4	3.57	3.11
Percentage in deciduous parts									
Inflorescences	0.3	0.9	2.8	1.9	0.2	0.3	1.4	1.6	2.4
Pre-rainy-season infructescences	0.1	0.8	1.8	2.9	0.9	0.6	0.6	1.8	0.7
Rainy-season infructescences	4.3	11.3	26.7	23.0	2.0	3.8	2.8	10.1	12.4
Leaves	9.6	16.6	15.9	16.1	16.6	9.3	27.8	73.8	18.6
Acacia nilotica									
Total	28.31	26400	603	6460	9630	834	60.9	9.96	5.17
Percentage in deciduous parts									
Inflorescences	1.5	2.0	3.3	2.6	0.5	2.9	2.0	4.7	3.3
Infructescences	10.1	12.5	20.3	11.8	8.9	18.5	4.7	9.2	16.8
Leaves	19.1	33.3	32.1	16.3	35.8	42.4	56.0	65.7	15.7
Combretum zeyheri									
Total	70.75	27800	833	8570	58400	3760	620	10.40	10.20
Percentage in deciduous parts									
Inflorescences	0.1	0.03	0.04	0.02	0.003	0.02	0.4	0.1	0.03
Infructescences	1.1	1.1	3.1	4.9	0.3	1.8	2.1	3.6	11.9
Leaves	10.8	64.3	31.2	22.1	5.0	4.5	5.8	61.8	20.3
Terminalia sericea									
Total	128.7	55700	2250	7230	25300	5140	172	92.1	19.8
Percentage in deciduous parts									
Inflorescences	0.04	0.12	<0.01	<0.01	<0.01	<0.01	<0.01	<0.01	<0.01
Infructescences	0.77	1.9	0.9	2.0	0.8	1.1	2.2	3.3	1.5
Leaves	4.97	9.4	3.1	10.3	10.9	17.5	14.2	13.8	22.7

Tribulus terrestris (which causes photosensitization in animals) (Glastonbury *et al.* 1984). The palatable grasses are very rare. The above-ground biomass of the field layer ranges from 650 kg ha^{-1} in a grazed savanna with predominant palatable grasses to about 60–250 kg ha^{-1} (Table 12) in overgrazed savannas. An ungrazed savanna at Gaborone had a corresponding biomass of 4160 kg ha^{-1}.

It is remarkable that a heavily grazed savanna has about the same biomass, whether it has a very open *Dipcadi glaucum* layer (Fig. 2(b)) or a patchy grass layer of *Eragrostis rigidior* or *Tragus berteronianus*. A nearly closed layer with *Tribulus terrestris* had a low biomass of 63 kg ha^{-1}. The plant nutrients, especially phosphorus and potassium, decreased with biomass. The *Tribulus terrestris* area

TABLE 12. Above-ground biomass (mean ± S.E.) and its nutrient concentrations (kg ha^{-1}) in the field layer of savanna ecosystems (overgrazed and ungrazed). All samples were taken at the end of November 1986 at maximum development of the plants in (a) an overgrazed *Terminalia sericea-Combretum zeyheri* shrub savanna at the Mochudi site, and (b) in an ungrazed tree savanna with *Acacia erubescens* at the Gaborone site

Dominant plant species in the field layer	Biomass (kg ha^{-1})	Concentration of nutrients (kg ha^{-1})						
		N	P	K	Ca	Mg	Fe	Mn
(a) *Dipcadi glaucum*	219±35	12.3	0.63	8.2	3.6	0.67	0.061	0.003
Eragrostis rigidior	211±47	3.8	0.22	14.9	1.6	0.18	0.195	0.034
Tragus berteronianus	256±80	4.4	0.14	2.8	2.8	0.47	0.298	0.005
Tribulus terrestris	63±28	3.1	0.11	1.3	2.5	0.19	0.074	0.007
(b) *Eragrostis rigidior*	4160±475	108.0	6.22	81.1	37.5	14.2	0.533	0.613

had much less potassium. The area covered by large populations of *Dipcadi glaucum* had the highest above-ground content of nitrogen and phosphorus, but even these elements were a factor of nine (nitrogen) or ten (phosphorus) lower than in an ungrazed savanna.

Impact of wood harvesting

The greatest use of savanna trees by people in Botswana is for fuelwood and fencing (Tietema 1985; Tietema & Geche 1987). For both activities twigs and branches are used in preference to boles. The concentration of many nutrients, especially phosphorus and nitrogen, is higher in twigs than in boles (Table 13) so that an increasing demand for firewood may have a severe impact on the nutrient budget of the savanna. There is no difference in the concentration of minerals in the bark and wood of the preferred fuelwood species *Combretum apiculatum* and *C. imberbe* compared with the concentration in the less preferred tree species.

DISCUSSION

In south-eastern Botswana changes in soil types, even in the absence of alterations in relief and climate, are sharply correlated with vegetation type, as found in western Botswana (Cole & Brown 1976). In contrast, it has been shown that the nutrient concentration of the leaves from the various grass, herb and tree species does not reflect that of the soils because of species-specific uptake and translocation (Tolsma, Ernst & Verweij 1987; Tolsma *et al.* 1987). Species-specific accumulation of nutrients in senescent leaves of savanna trees (especially the accumulation of divalent and polyvalent cations such as calcium, iron and manganese) shows similar patterns to shrubs and trees in other ecosystems, e.g. miombo woodland (Ernst 1975) or cool-temperate forests in North America

TABLE 13. Mean concentrations ($\pm$ S.E.) of nutrients (μmol g^{-1} dry wt.) in the wood and bark of twigs (<2 cm diameter) and boles of some tree species harvested as fuelwood near the Morwa Forest site in Botswana ($n = 3$)

	P	K	Ca	Mg	Fe	Mn
Acacia tortilis						
Twig wood	21±2	103±7	330±16	18±2	0.82±0.01	0.16±0.06
Twig bark	16±1	128±31	1995±600	15±2	1.29±2	0.37±0.03
Bole wood	8.6±1.1	80±2	214±5	8±1	0.61±0.13	0.12±0.03
Bole bark	2.3±0.4	5±1	1270±34	13±1	0.73±0.02	0.46±0.01
Combretum apiculatum						
Bole wood	10±1	65±2	243±39	54±1	2.78±1.64	0.53±0.01
Bole bark	9±1	92±1	1130±518	74±3	1.83±0.11	1.63±0.31
Combretum erythrophyllum						
Twig wood	9±2	200±7	880±320	46±9	0.84±0.29	0.01±0.01
Twig bark	4±1	20±5	1670±9	63±3	5.19±0.23	0.32±0.03
Bole wood	11±2	111±3	790±212	55±3	1.01±0.06	0.02±0.01
Bole bark	5±1	35±5	1590±2	75±3	3.89±0.67	0.32±0.04
Combretum imberbe						
Bole wood	2±0	26±1	1460±76	80±5	0.58±0.01	0.02±0.01
Bole bark	4±1	20±4	1590±121	21±1	2.12±1.28	0.10±0.04
Terminalia sericea						
Bole wood	18±1	50±3	118±54	86±3	0.20±0.85	0.38±0.05
Bole bark	19±1	63±2	616±25	90±1	0.90±0.01	2.43±0.04

(Borman & Likens 1979) and Europe (Ellenberg, Mayer & Schauermann 1986). Species-specific accumulation of nutrients modifies the nutrient concentrations of the topsoil, as a comparison of soil outside and beneath the tree canopy of *A. erubescens* and *A. karroo* has shown. The effect of grasses (Tolsma *et al.* 1987) and trees on the distribution of soil nutrients is worthy of further study.

Knoop & Walker (1985) have suggested that the ratio of topsoil to subsoil nutrients may be important in determining the grass : woody-plant balance in savanna ecosystems. They did not mention that the tree canopy can also affect the distribution of grasses which differ in tolerance to shade, e.g. the well-known positive relationship between *Acacia* canopy and the occurrence of *Panicum maximum* (Field 1976, this study). Knoop & Walker (1985) stated that grasses should have access to both topsoil (10–30 cm) and subsoil (30–130 cm) water; therefore grass species and tree seedlings may explore the same soil layers (APRU 1978). Consequently, the equilibrium of woody and herbaceous vegetation will be governed by more factors than suggested by the hypothesis of the two-layered soil–water system (Walter 1971; Walker & Noy-Meir 1982). Deep-rooting trees, such as *Acacia erubescens*, come into leaf and flower before the summer rains because they are capable of tapping groundwater, sometimes at 2 to 3 m depth (A.

Gieske, personal communication). The differences of seed realization in pre-rainy-season and rainy-season pods suggest a difference in nutrient quality of topsoil water and subsoil water, which is now under investigation by us.

In the *Acacia* savanna of Botswana shifts of woody and herbaceous vegetation are caused by man, cattle, sheep and goats. The increase in the human population may have a strong impact on the savanna nutrients, because it is estimated (ERL 1985) that the average fuelwood consumption is 500 kg wood per person per year. Such an export of nutrients from the savanna to villages and towns may impoverish the savanna more seriously than the wood harvest in cool-temperate regions of Europe affected that area during the last century (Ernst & Joosse-van Damme 1983); this is because the nutrient concentrations in trunks, twigs and branches of savanna trees are higher than those in trees from cool-temperate environments (Morrison & Foster 1979). Another impact on the nutrients is the use of trees and shrubs for fencing. In rural areas the wood consumption for fenc-ing has been calculated to be about the same amount as that for firewood (Tietema & Geche 1987). This aspect of the nutrition of savannas urgently needs further research, because afforestation programmes may be severely affected by nutrient depletion.

The introduction of domestic cattle, sheep and goats in the savanna of Botswana and the tremendous increase in the cattle herd, from an estimated 100 000 in the first decade of this century (van Vegten 1981) to 7 000 000, has caused severe degradation of the natural vegetation over the last 50 years (Pole Evans 1948; Strang 1974; Guy 1981; van Vegten 1983). This process can be subdivided into three phases.

The first phase was initiated by the introduction of domestic ungulates, causing a significant reduction of indigenous large mammalian herbivores. The consequence was a lowering of the reproduction and survival of palatable species and a shift to less-productive unpalatable species because of selective grazing (Skarpe & Bergström 1986). In this phase the impact on the savanna nutrients was probably low.

The second phase was characterized by a dramatic increase in the domestic livestock, exceeding the carrying capacity of the vegetation, especially during the drought years (when the cattle population crashed) 1915, 1935, 1947, 1961, 1975 (van Vegten 1981) and 1982. During periods of overgrazing the reproduction of palatable species was further reduced. If overgrazing coincided with severe drought, then the vitality of the less palatable species also diminished; there was an increase in annual plant species and an increase in browsing (including tree seeds) (Skarpe 1986). In an experiment in which previously ungrazed savanna on an arenosol in Botswana was grazed at the rate of 1 livestock unit per 8 ha, the grass biomass decreased from 1400 kg ha^{-1} to 500 kg ha^{-1} within 3 years (APRU 1979). In some of our study sites overgrazing has occurred for various periods during the past 50 years, as documented by Pole Evans (1948) during his travel through south-eastern Botswana in 1931. In contrast with the undisturbed savanna, nutrients were exported from the cattle-grazed savanna to the abattoirs. One of the consequences of this export was that the supply of some nutrients, especially phosphorus and manganese, to cattle by the remnant vegetation became so low that an additional supply of bone meal fertilizer was necessary to sustain cattle productivity (APRU 1979).

Owing to the decline of perennial herbs, the competition with tree seedlings for light, nutrients and water was lessened, and was followed by an increase of the woody vegetation (bush encroachment), in the most severe case in the form of shrub and thickets (van Vegten 1981, 1983). This change in biomass distribution severely affected the nutrient budget of the savanna (Tolsma, Ernst & Verweij 1987). It increased susceptibility to fire (bush fires) and led to an increase of fire-resistant grasses.

The third phase involved a magnification of the nutrient depletion by the frequent (annual) burning and also by the provision of additional water supplies from a regular pattern of bore holes. The creation of artificial waterpoints has imposed a new environmental gradient on the savanna ecosystem with a directional nutrient transport to the waterpoints by the deposition of dung and urine there (Tolsma, Ernst & Verweij 1987). There is diminished vegetation cover away from the water supply involving the loss of most perennial herbs and grasses.

As the model of stability of semi-arid savanna systems by Walker *et al.* (1981) has indicated, a small increase in stocking rate or an exogenous event such as drought can easily lead to a collapse of the cattle grazing system by causing a dominance of grazing-resistant annual plant species which protect the soils only during a small part of the year due to the very short life cycle (Ernst & Tolsma 1988). Another aspect of overgrazing is the increasing problem of soil erosion by water and wind; water erosion gives rise to sheet wash and in certain areas it has progressed to gully erosion. Wind erosion occurs on dry days and can be seen as the so-called sand devils, moving through the savanna. There is no knowledge of the amount of surface soil and mineral nutrients transported by wind, but it must reduce the fertility of the savanna ecosystems. There is an urgent need for regulations to control processes which lead to nutrient loss.

ACKNOWLEDGEMENTS

The investigations were supported partly by the Netherlands Foundation for the Advancement of Tropical Research (WOTRO) which is subsidized by the Netherlands Organization for the Advancement of Pure Research (ZWO) and partly by the Netherland's University Foundation for International Cooperation (NUFFIC). We thank Dr J. Proctor for valuable comments and improvement of the English text, Miss D. Hoonhout and Miss T. Laan for typing the manuscript, Mr H. J. M. Nelissen and R. J. Verweij for analytical help and the National Institute for Research, University of Botswana, for hospitality and cooperation.

REFERENCES

APRU (1979) *Livestock and Range Research in Botswana.* Animal Production Unit, Ministry of Agriculture, Gaborone.

Baumeister, W. & Ernst, W. (1978). *Mineralstoffe und Pflanzenwachstum,* 3rd edn. G. Fischer, Stuttgart.

Bernhard-Reversat, F. (1986). Le recyclage des éléments minéraux par la strate herbacée dans un peuplement naturel à Acacia et dans un plantation d'Eucalyptus au Sénégal. *Acta Oecologia, Oecologia Generalis,* 7, 353–364.

Bernard-Reversat, F. (1987). Les cycles des éléments minéraux dans un peuplement à Acacia seyal et leur modification en plantation d'Eucalyptus au Sénégal. *Acta Oecologia, Oecologia Generalis,* 8, 3–16.

Bormann, F.H. & Likens, G.E. (1979). *Patterns and Process in a Forested Ecosystem.* Springer, New York.

Chen, P.S., Toribara, T.Y. & Warner, H. (1956). Microdetermination of phosphorus. *Analytical Chemistry,* 28, 1756–1758.

Coates Palgrave, K. (1984) *Trees of Southern Africa.* Struik Publishers, Cape Town.

Cole, M.M. (1963). Vegetation and geomorphology in Northern Rhodesia: an aspect of the distribution of the savanna of Central Africa. *Geographical Journal,* 129, 290–310.

Cole, M.M. (1971). Biogeographical/geobotanical and biogeochemical investigations connected with exploration for nickel–copper ores in the hot, wet summer/dry winter savanna woodland environment. *Journal of the South African Institute of Mining and Metallurgy,* 1971, 199–214.

Cole, M.M. & Brown, R.C (1976). The vegetation of the Ghanzi area of Western Botswana. *Journal of Biogeography,* 3, 169–196.

Cole, M.M. & Le Roex, H.D. (1978). A role of geobotany, biogeochemistry and geochemistry in mineral exploration in Southwest Africa and Botswana — a case history. *Transactions of the Geological Society of South Africa,* 81, 277–317.

Ellenberg, H., Mayer, R. & Schauermann, J. (1986). *Ökosystemforschung, Ergebnisse des Sollingprojekt 1966–1986.* E. Ulmer, Stuttgart.

ERL (1985). *A Study of Energy Utilization and Requirements in the Rural Sector of Botswana.* Ministry of the Mineral Resources and Water Affairs, Gaborone.

Ernst, W.H.O. (1972). Ecophysiological studies in heavy metal plants in South Central Africa, *Kirkia,* 8, 125–145.

Ernst, W.H.O. (1975). Variation in the mineral contents of leaves of trees in miombo woodlands in South Central Africa. *Journal of Ecology,* 63, 801–808.

Ernst, W.H.O. & Joosse-van Damme, E.N.G. (1983). *Umwelbelastung durch Mineralstoffe, Biologische Effekte.* VEB G. Fischer, Jena.

Ernst W.H.O. & Tolsma, D.J. (1988). Dormancy and germination of semi-arid annual plant species. *Tragus berteronianus* and *Tribulus terrestris. Flora (Jena),* 18, 243–251.

Field, D.I. (1976). *A Handbook of Common Grasses in Botswana.* Ministry of Agriculture, Gaborone, Botswana.

Gammon, D.M. & Roberts, B.R. (1978). Patterns of defoliation during continuous and rotational grazing of the Matapos sandveld in Rhodesia. *Rhodesian Journal of Agricultural Research,* 16, 117–131.

Glastonbury, J.R.W., Doughtry, F.R., Whitaker, S.J. & Sergeant, E. (1984). A syndrome of hepatogenous photosensitisation, resembling geeldikkop, in sheep grazing *Tribulus terrestris. Australian Veterinary Journal,* 61, 314–316.

Guy, P.R. (1981). Changes in the biomass and productivity of woodlands in the Sengwa Wildlife Research Area, Zimbabwe. *Journal of Applied Ecology,* 18, 507–519.

Högberg, I. (1982). Mycorrhizal associations in some woodland and forest trees and shrubs in Tanzania. *New Phytologist,* 92, 407–415.

Humphreys, L.R. (1981). *Environmental Adaptation of Tropical Pasture Plants.* MacMillan, London.

Huntley, B.J. (1982). Southern African savannas. *Ecology of Tropical Savannas* (Ed. by B.J. Huntley & B.H. Walker), pp. 101–119. Springer, Berlin.

Huntley, B.J. & Morris, J.W. (1982). Structure of the Nylsvley savanna. *Ecology of Tropical Savannas* (Ed. by B.J. Huntley & B.H. Walker), pp. 433–455. Springer, Berlin.

Kgathi, D.L. (1984). Firewood border between Botswana's rural Kwening and urban Gaborone: employment creation and deforestation. *Annual Journal of the Forestry Association of Botswana*, **1**, 41–54.

Kirsten, W.J. (1979). Automatic methods for the simultaneous determination of carbon, hydrogen, nitrogen, and sulfur, and for sulfur alone in organic and inorganic materials. *Analytical Chemistry*, **51**, 1173–1175.

Knoop, W.T. & Walker, B.H. (1985). Interactions of woody and herbaceous vegetation in a Southern African savanna. *Journal of Ecology*, **73**, 235–253.

Korn, H. (1987). Densities and biomasses of non-fossorial Southern African savanna rodents during the dry season. *Oecologia*, **72**, 410–413.

Merz, W. (1970). Ein neuer Apparat zur Stickstoffbestimmung. *Laboratorium*, **1970**, 617–625.

Morrison, J.K. & Foster, N.W. (1979). Biomass and element removal by complete-tree harvesting of medium rotation forest stand. *Impact of Intensive Harvesting on Forest Nutrient Cycling*, pp. 111–151. USDA Forest Service, Broomall.

Mott, J.J., Williams, J., Andrew, M.H. & Gillison, A.N. (1985). Australian savanna ecosystems. *Ecology and Management of the World's Savannas* (Ed. by J.C. Totthill & J.J. Mott), pp. 56–82. Australian Academy of Science, Canberra.

Pole Evans, J.B. (1948). *A Reconnaissance Trip Through the Eastern Portion of the Bechuanaland Protectorate*. Botanical Survey Memoir 21, 5–73 Pretoria.

Proctor, J. (1984). Tropical forest litterfall II: the data set. *Tropical Rain Forest: The Leeds Symposium* (Ed. by A.C. Chadwick & S.L. Sutton), pp. 83–113. Blackwell Scientific Publications, Oxford.

Scheffer, F. & Schachtschabel, P. (1982). *Lehrbuch der Bodenkunde*, 11th edn. Enke, Stuttgart.

Skarpe, C. (1980). Observations on two bushfires in the Western Kalahari, Botswana. *Acta Phytogeographica Suedica*, **68**, 131–140.

Skarpe, C. (1986). Plant community structure in relation to grazing and environmental changes along a north–south transect in the western Kalahari. *Vegetatio*, **68**, 3–18.

Skarpe, C. & Bergström, R. (1986). Nutrient content and digestibility of forage plants in relation to plant phenology and rainfall in the Kalahari, Botswana. *Journal of Arid Environments*, **11**, 147–164.

Smart, N.O.E., Hatton, J.C. & Spence, D.H.N. (1985). The effect of long-term exclusion of large herbivores on vegetation in Murchison Falls National Park, Uganda. *Biological Conservation*, **33**, 229–245.

Strang, R.M. (1974). Some man-made changes in successional trends on the Rhodesian Highveld. *Journal of Applied Ecology*, **11**, 249–263.

Tainton, N.M. & Mentis, M.T. (1984). Fire in grassland. *Ecological Effects of Fire in South African Ecosystems* (Ed. by P. de V. Booysen & N.M. Tainton), pp. 115–147. Springer, Berlin.

Thompson, K. & Stewart, A.J.A. (1981). The measurement and meaning of reproductive effort in plants. *American Naturalist*, **117**, 205–211.

Tietema, T. (1985). The growth performance in indigenous trees in Botswana. The case of *Acacia tortilis*. *Forestry Association of Botswana, Annual Journal 1985*, 22–23.

Tietema, T. & Geche, J. (1987). A quantitative determination of the amount of wood needed for the erection of bush fences around arable fields in Botswana. *Forestry Association of Botswana, Annual Journal 1986–1987*, 19–25.

Timberlake, J. (1980). *Vegetation Map of Southeast Botswana*. Ministry of Agriculture, Gaborone.

Tolsma, D.J., Ernst, W.H.O. & Verweij, R.A. (1987). Nutrients in soil and vegetation around two artificial waterpoints in eastern Botswana. *Journal of Applied Ecology*, **24**, 991–1000.

Tolsma, D.J., Ernst, W.H.O., Verweij, R.A. & Vooijs, R. (1987). Seasonal variation of nutrient concentrations in a semi-arid savanna ecosystem in Botswana. *Journal of Ecology*, **75**, 775–779.

Tomowa, M.P. & Gjulemeetowa, Th. (1978). Steroidsaponines and steroidsapogenines. VI Furostanolbisglycoside from *Tribulus terrestris* L. *Planta Medica*, **34**, 188–191.

Trollope, W.S.W. (1982). Ecological effects of fire in South African savannas. *Ecology of Tropical*

Savannas (Ed. by B.J. Huntley & B.H. Walker), pp. 292–306. Springer, Berlin.

Turrill, W.B. & Milne-Redhead, E. (1952–1974). *Flora of Tropical East Africa.* Crown Agents, London.

Vahrmeijer, J. (1981). *Poisonous Plants of Southern Africa that Cause Stock Losses.* Tafelberg Publishers, Cape Town.

van Vegten, J.A. (1981). *Man-made Vegetation Changes: An Example from Botswana's Savanna.* Working paper No. 41, National Institute for Research, University of Botswana, Gaborone.

van Vegten, J.A. (1983). Thornbush invasion in a savanna ecosystem in eastern Botswana. *Vegetatio,* **56**, 3–7.

Walker, B.H., Ludwig, D., Holling, C.S. & Peterman, R.M. (1981). Stability of semi-arid savanna grazing systems. *Journal of Ecology,* **69**, 473–498.

Walker, B.H. & Noy-Meir, I. (1982). Aspects of stability and resilience of savanna ecosystems. *Ecology of Tropical Savannas* (Ed. by B.J. Huntley & B.H. Walker), pp. 577–590. Springer, Berlin.

Waller, G.R. & Nowacki, E.K. (1978). *Alkaloid Biology and Metabolism in Plants.* Plenum Press, New York.

Walter, H. (1971). *Ecology of Tropical and Subtropical Vegetation.* Oliver and Boyd, Edinburgh.

Werger, M.J.A. & Coetzee, B.J. (1978). The Sudano–Zambezian region. *Biogeography and Ecology of Southern Africa* (Ed. by M.J.A. Werger), pp. 301–462. Junk Publishers, The Hague.

Wild, H. (1978). The vegetation of heavy metal and other toxic soils. *Biogeography and Ecology of Southern Africa* (Ed. by M.J.A. Werger), pp. 1301–1332. Junk Publishers, The Hague.

Wild, H. & Fernandez, A. (1968). *Vegetation Map of the Flora Zambesiaca Area.* Collins, Salisbury, Rhodesia.

Root symbioses of trees in savannas

P. HÖGBERG
Department of Forest Site Research,
Swedish University of Agricultural Sciences,
S-901 83 Umeå, Sweden

SUMMARY

1 Savanna soils have low concentrations of available nitrogen and phosphorus. In general, there is a decline in nitrogen relative to phosphorus along transects from moist to dry conditions.

2 Nitrogen-fixing trees are often dominant in dry savanna areas, e.g. the genera *Acacia* in Africa, *Prosopis* in America and *Acacia* and *Casuarina* in Australia. Analysis of leaf samples taken along a gradient of soil phosphorus : nitrogen ratios in moist savanna in Tanzania suggests that low availability of phosphorus limits the growth of nitrogen-fixing species. This condition is thought to be typical of moist savannas.

3 Non-nodulated ectomycorrhizal trees conspicuously dominate in many moist savannas, e.g. the genera *Brachystegia*, *Isoberlinia*, *Julbernardia*, *Marquesia*, *Monotes* and *Uapaca* in Africa, *Pinus* and *Quercus* in Central America and *Eucalyptus* and *Melaleuca* in Australia. Work on temperate mycorrhizas, as well as a limited set of leaf samples from Tanzania, suggests that ectomycorrhizal species may be good at taking up less available forms of both nitrogen and phosphorus.

4 It is suggested that nitrogen-fixing species dominate soils poor in nitrogen but relatively rich in phosphorus, non-nodulated ectomycorrhizal species dominate soils poor in both elements, and non-nodulated vesicular-arbuscular (VA) mycorrhizal species dominate soils poor in phosphorus but relatively rich in nitrogen.

5 These hypotheses could be tested by applications of nitrogen and phosphorus to mixed communities. The subsequent effects on nitrogen-fixing symbioses could be monitored by ^{15}N techniques, but suitable analogous methods for field-work on mycorrhizas are lacking.

INTRODUCTION

Root symbioses, such as nitrogen-fixing root nodules, ectomycorrhizas and vesicular-arbuscular (VA) mycorrhizas (Fig. 1), have often been shown to increase nutrient uptake by trees (e.g. Sprent 1979; Harley & Smith 1983). Under conditions of limiting nutrient supply, root symbioses may thus be of selective advantage to the trees. This in turn will have an influence on the species composition of tree communities, and thereby also on patterns of nutrient cycling.

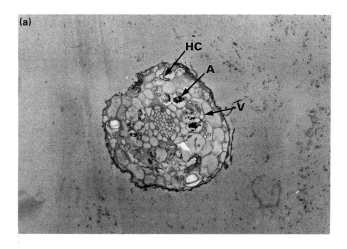

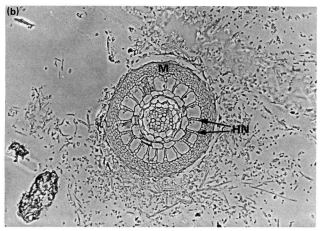

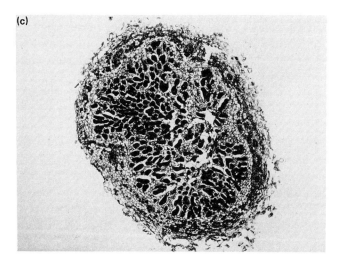

A review of tree species composition in tropical Africa has provided circumstantial evidence on the interactions between soil nutrient availability and root symbioses (Högberg 1986a). Nitrogen-fixing legume trees were found to be almost absent from rain forests on soils poor in phosphorus, but became increasingly important, concurrent with a decline in soil nitrogen relative to soil phosphorus, along transects from equatorial forests over savannas to deserts. In contrast, a dominance of non-nodulated ectomycorrhizal trees was found to be associated with low availability of phosphorus (e.g. Gartlan *et al.* 1986; Newbery *et al.* 1986); however, there was no clear latitudinal trend in the balance between non-nodulated ectomycorrhizal and non-nodulated VA-mycorrhizal trees.

An advantage to the host plant should occur when it costs less, e.g. in terms of carbon compounds, to obtain a limiting nutrient via a microbial symbiont than via an ordinary root. Recent advances in plant physiology have allowed accurate estimates of some of the processes involved, for example the respiratory cost of nitrogen fixation in root nodules of herbaceous legumes (e.g. Warembourg 1983; Fernandez & Warembourg 1986). However, there are no complete and comparable budgets for the costs and benefits of different symbioses in mature trees growing under varying conditions.

Nodulating tree species, which mostly form VA mycorrhizas, and non-nodulating ectomycorrhizal and VA-mycorrhizal tree species occur in savannas, either together or in more or less separate communities (Högberg 1986a). In this paper, the evidence that root symbioses are agents mediating the effects of soil nutrient availability on the distribution of tree species is re-examined.

AVAILABILITY OF NUTRIENTS IN SAVANNA SOILS

Strong seasonal variation in the soil water regime is thought to be the major determinant of the structure of savannas (Huntley & Walker 1982), which are defined here as tropical ecosystems dominated by grasses, which have the C_4 pathway for carbon fixation, and in which fire-tolerant trees occur as scattered individuals or form a more or less open woodland (Huntley 1982). Fire and variations in soil nutrient status are generally agreed to impose modifications on this basic vegetation structure (Huntley & Walker 1982).

The chemical properties of free-draining tropical soils change markedly with climate, although the soils are not only products of the present climate (Sanchez 1976; Young 1976; Buringh 1979; Jordan 1985). Together with a decrease in rainfall, there is a decline in soil carbon and nitrogen along transects from

---

FIG. 1. Root symbioses. (a) Transverse section through a vesicular-arbuscular mycorrhiza formed by *Cassia abbreviata*: A, arbuscule; HC, hyphal coil; V, vesicle. The mycorrhiza is 0.3 mm in diameter. Extraradical hyphae were removed during preparation. (b) Transverse section through an ectomycorrhiza formed by *Brachystegia spiciformis*: HN, Hartig net; M, mantle or sheath. External hyphae form a dense network. The mycorrhiza is 0.2 mm in diameter. (c) Section through a root nodule formed by *Acacia albida*. The dark enlarged cells in the central area contain rhizobial bacteroids. The large intercellulars are artefacts. The nodule is 2–3 mm in diameter.

tropical rain forests to deserts. At the same time the soils of the humid areas are highly weathered and leached, and have their cation exchange sites dominated by Al^{3+} and H^+ ions. In dry areas, saline and alkaline soils have their cation exchange sites dominated by exchangeable bases. Phosphorus is fixed into insoluble iron and aluminium phosphates in the acid Ferralsols (FAO/UNESCO 1974), which are common in the humid tropics, and precipitates as calcium phosphates under alkaline conditions. According to this generalization, phosphorus should be most available in savanna areas with slightly acid or nearly neutral soils (cf. Brady 1974). It is difficult to support this statement by data from field studies since methods of extraction of phosphorus vary. Comparative studies of available and organic forms of phosphorus in different tropical soils are therefore needed.

Evidence from studies of agricultural soils (Sanchez 1976; Young 1976) suggests that both nitrogen and phosphorus may limit plant growth throughout the tropics. Phosphorus deficiency is more common in the humid areas and nitrogen deficiency in the dry areas. Soils under forest and savanna woodland contain more carbon and nitrogen than agricultural soils, and this may exacerbate a possible phosphorus deficiency in humid areas. The low concentration of phosphorus in litterfall in many tropical lowland forests suggests that this is so (Vitousek 1984). The fact that nitrogen is usually limiting in dry areas is clear, as stated for Africa (FAO/UNESCO 1977) and Australia (Beadle 1981; Williams & Raupach 1983). However, exceptions do occur, e.g. areas with low soil phosphorus availability in the Sahel (Penning de Vries, Krul & van Keulen 1980). In Australia, deficiencies of sulphur, potassium, molybdenum, copper, zinc and manganese are usually associated with phosphorus deficiency (Williams & Raupach 1983).

Placed along a continuum from wet to dry conditions, savannas thus cover a range of soils, with acid soils low in exchangeable bases and available phosphorus at the moist end of the spectrum, and near-neutral soils richer in bases and phosphorus at the dry end. Soil carbon and nitrogen decrease along the same gradient, and are always lower than in adjacent forests due to losses in recurrent grass fires. In the short term, fires cause a release of nitrogen as well as bases and phosphorus. Cycles of drying and wetting of the soil increase mineralization, and hence contribute to the discontinuity in nutrient supply. The zonal soil changes are especially interesting because savanna ecologists now emphasize a distinction between moist/dystrophic and arid/eutrophic savannas with characteristically different floras (Huntley & Walker 1982).

NODULATED NITROGEN-FIXING VERSUS
NON-NODULATED TREES

Most nodulating tropical tree species are legumes associated with *Rhizobium* bacteria; the Casuarinaceae of South-East Asia, Australia and Polynesia are the only prominent exceptions forming root nodules with the actinomycete *Frankia*. Up to 1981, roughly 16% of legume species had been examined for nodulation; it was found that root nodules were formed by 28% of the Caesalpinioideae, 90% of the Mimosoideae and 98% of the Papilionoideae examined to that date (Allen & Allen 1981). The nodulating species in the Caesalpinioideae were mainly herbs of the genus *Cassia*. The fact that not all legume species form root nodules has not been made clear to many plant ecologists, and has thus probably obscured many interesting plant–soil relations.

Nodulating woody species are especially abundant in dry savannas and semi-arid communities, e.g. *Acacia* spp. in Africa, *Prosopis* in America and *Acacia* and *Casuarina* in Australia. The proportion of nodulated trees often increases along transects from moist to dry savanna. Of the 13 species mentioned as typical for the southern moist zone of the African Sudanian woodlands (White 1983), only two species (both *Acacia*) are potentially nodulated. In the dry zone eight of the 20 species listed are confirmed or potentially nodulated (five *Acacia* spp., *Albizia chevalieri*, *Dalbergia melanoxylon* and *Lonchocarpus laxiflorus*). Further to the dry north, *Acacia* spp. reach total dominance in many semi-arid communities. The pattern is similar in South-Central and South Africa, where *miombo* (*Brachystegia–Isoberlinia–Julbernardia*) woodland, dominated by ectomycor-hizal species of the Caesalpinioideae and with few nodulated trees, is the moist extreme, and wooded grassland and bushland with potentially nodulating *Acacia* spp. is the dry extreme. A parallel situation in Australia is the dominance by ecto-mycorrhizal *Eucalyptus* and *Melaleuca* spp. in moist woodlands and by poten-tially nodulating *Acacia* and *Casuarina* in dry communities.

The *cerrado*, a major moist savanna woodland ecosystem in south-central Brazil, is very rich in species. Eighteen out of 80 genera of trees listed as common in this ecosystem are leguminous (Eiten 1972). Species of some of these leguminous genera have been found to nodulate in north-east Brazil (Vasconcelos & Almeida, cited by Faria *et al.* (1984)) and in forests in south-east Brazil (Faria *et al.* 1984; Faria *et al.* 1987), but for several genera the reports are negative. More information is required about *cerrado* legume trees, especially because they occur on soils with properties thought to have an adverse effect on nitrogen fixation, i.e. extreme acidity, high levels of exchangeable aluminium and low levels of available phosphorus (Goedert 1983). The nitrogen concentration in these soils is known to be relatively high (Goedert 1983). The drier *caatinga* typical of north-east Brazil contains several nodulating leguminous genera, but more detailed information is also needed in this case.

The regional increases in the abundance of nodulating species in Africa and Australia apparently coincide with the decline in soil nitrogen relative to phosphorus towards drier areas. An interesting pattern on a smaller scale is the frequent occurrence of nodulating species on the relatively rich soils of valley bottoms in situations where non-nodulated species dominate the poor adjoining soils. Examples are *Acacia* spp. on East African *mbugas* (Högberg 1986a) and on the corresponding *black earth* clay soils in Australia (cf. Beadle 1981; Cole 1982; Williams & Raupach 1983), within matrices of principally non-nodulating Combretaceous or *miombo* woodlands in East Africa and *Eucalyptus* woodlands in Australia. Another example not involving obvious confounding influences of effects of topography and soil texture on the water regime is the abrupt transition from *Acacia* woodlands on fertile volcanic soils to woodlands dominated by non-nodulated species on poor soils derived from basement rocks in northern Tanzania (Bell 1982).

More direct evidence of the critical role played by phosphorus can be derived from cases when soils are enriched by the input of urine and faeces. When this happens, much of the nitrogen is lost, e.g. through volatilization (Parton & Risser 1979), leaching and denitrification, while phosphorus is strongly retained. A good example is the threefold increase in nitrogen compared with the eightyfold increase in available phosphorus found at an artificial waterpoint in Botswana by Tolsma, Ernst & Verweij (1987). During a survey of nitrogen-fixing trees in Tanzania (Högberg 1986b), a patch of *miombo* woodland remarkably rich in confirmed or potentially nodulating species was found at a major pass along a part of the main road between Dar-es-Salaam and Zambia that had been abandoned after road realignment. There was ample evidence that the site had been used as a resting place for many years. *Acacia polyacantha, Albizia versicolor, Dalbergia melanoxylon, Dichrostachys cinerea, Entada abyssinica, Pericopsis angolensis* and *Pterocarpus angolensis*, all nodulating species, were particularly abundant close to the roadside, but their numbers fell rapidly along transects into surrounding woodland. Both the soils and the leaves of non-nodulating tree species had high phosphorus concentrations close to the road (cf. site V in Fig. 2).

To my knowledge, the effect of fertilizers on the growth of savanna trees forming different types of root symbioses has not been reported. However, in fairly open Australian *karri* forest, application of nitrogen increased the biomass of *Eucalyptus diversicolor* and non-nodulating understorey species, but depressed the understorey legume *Bossiaea laidlawiana* (Grove 1988), which is a nodulating species (Allen & Allen 1981). Phosphorus improved the growth of this legume substantially, had no effect alone on the eucalypt, but doubled its growth when applied together with nitrogen. In Australian *jarrah (Eucalyptus marginata)* forest, the yield of legume understorey seedlings of *Acacia pulchella* and two *Kennedia* species increased after application of phosphorus, and so did their nitrogenase activity as measured by the acetylene reduction method (Hingston, Malajczuk & Grove 1982).

These observations all agree with the commonly held view that the growth of nitrogen-fixing species in the tropics is most often limited by phosphorus (Munns & Mosse 1980; Gianinazzi-Pearson & Diem 1982; Dommergues *et al.* 1984). Mycorrhizas are, therefore, very important for nitrogen-fixing trees as they enhance their uptake of phosphorus. Cole & Heil (1981) hypothesized that nitrogen fixation and a number of other biological processes would ultimately lead to a balance between the level of biologically active nitrogen and the supply of biologically active phosphorus. In many savannas, recurrent losses of nitrogen in grass fires result in low concentrations of soil nitrogen, thereby creating an imbalance between this element and other nutrients that favour nitrogen-fixing species.

It would be useful to define more precisely the P : N ratios that favour nitrogen-fixing species. The proportions of nutrients required for optimal growth by a wide range of species (*Alnus* (in this case not inoculated with nitrogen-fixing *Frankia*), *Avena, Betula, Cucumis, Hordeum, Lemna, Paulownia, Picea, Pinus, Populus, Salix, Secale, Triticum* and *Vaccinium*) have been shown to be similar under controlled conditions in the laboratory (Ingestad & Lund 1986). The relative (to a specific growth rate) nitrogen addition rate was used as driving variable, and the lack or excessive quantities of other elements in nutrient solutions and plant tissues were eliminated. Expressed as a percentage of the nitrogen requirement by weight, the phosphorus required was found to be around 13%. When the relative phosphorus addition rate was used as a treatment variable in an experiment with *Betula pendula* (Ericsson & Ingestad 1988), it was later demonstrated that optimum nutrition was obtained at the weight proportion 8–10 P : 100 N. The addition of phosphorus resulted in an uptake in excess of immediate requirements, but had only a small effect on growth, and hence increased tissue phosphorus concentration. This lower figure of 8–10 P relative to 100 N corresponds well with the inverse of the critical N : P ratios (9–16 N : 1 P ≈ 6–11 P : 100 N) found in field trials with a number of non-nitrogen-fixing tree species (Comerford & Fisher 1984). Proportionally less phosphorus in foliar samples indicates phosphorus deficient sites (cf. Penning de Vries *et al.* 1980), while higher phosphorus indicates nitrogen deficiency. Therefore a working hypothesis could be that nitrogen-fixing species are favoured when the P : N ratio in non-nitrogen-fixing species is above 11 P : 100 N, whereas a ratio of less than 6 P : 100 N favours non-nitrogen-fixing species. The long period of slow decline in the concentrations of both elements in mature leaves of deciduous trees is the most suitable time for sampling (see Högberg (1986b) for references).

In a survey of savanna woodland trees in Tanzania (Högberg 1986b), the foliar nutrient relations of a number of nodulating species were compared with those of non-nodulating ectomycorrhizal or VA-mycorrhizal species at five moist savanna woodland sites (hereafter sites I–V). In all, 48 species–site combinations were studied. Nodulation and nitrogenase (acetylene reduction) activity were confirmed in 12 species of the genera *Acacia, Dalbergia, Dichrostachys, Entada, Pericopsis, Pterocarpus* and *Xeroderris*, but not in *Albizia versicolor* and *Erythrophleum africanum*, which are known to form nodules elsewhere (Allen & Allen 1981). The negative result for the last two species was probably due to difficulties of tracing roots without disconnecting root nodules, and not to lack of nodules *per se*. The high foliar nitrogen concentration in all these species indicated that nitrogen fixation actually occurred throughout (on average 2.71% as compared with 1.63% in non-nitrogen-fixing species). Results of the ^{15}N natural abundance method also indicated that nitrogen-fixing species in general derived a large proportion of their nitrogen from the atmosphere (Högberg 1986b). This method is based on the often lower abundance of the heavy nitrogen isotope in the atmosphere compared with the soil. The ^{15}N abundance of non-nitrogen-fixing 'control' species, relying solely on soil nitrogen, is compared with that of nitrogen-fixing species, which also have access to atmospheric nitrogen (e.g. Shearer & Kohl 1986).

Nitrogen-fixing species maintained a very low P : N ratio (4–6 P : 100 N) despite large variations in soil P : N among the sites I–V (Fig. 2). Non-nitrogen-fixing species, however, showed an increase in leaf phosphorus concentration

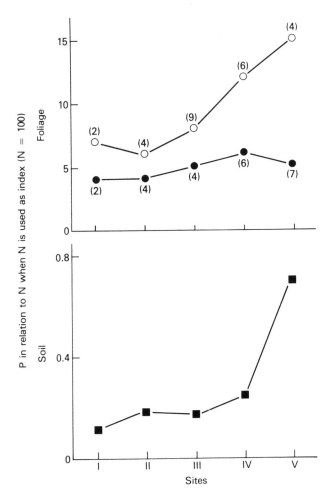

FIG. 2. Foliar and available soil phosphorus relative to nitrogen (when nitrogen is used as index, i.e. N = 100) at moist savanna woodland sites in Tanzania (data from Högberg (1986b)) : O, non-nitrogen-fixing species (mean); ●, nitrogen-fixing species (mean). The number of tree species of each group sampled at the site is given in parentheses ($n = 5$ individuals per species and site). The differences between the two groups of species are significant ($p < 0.05$, Mann–Whitney U-test) at sites III–V. Average P : N ratios for nitrogen-fixing species at sites II and V are 0.12 : 3.02% and 0.15 : 2.79%, respectively, as compared with 0.11 : 1.81% and 0.27 : 1.59% for non-nitrogen-fixing species. Data points in the lower part of the figure represent analyses of 45 soil samples per site (representing 0–50 cm soil depth). Average available P : total N ratios at sites I and V are 0.7 ppm : 0.06% and 3.5 ppm : 0.05%, respectively.

(from 6 P : 100 N to 15 P : 100 N) with increasing soil supply. At the site with the highest soil phosphorus concentration, a clear difference in leaf phosphorus concentration between the two groups of species provided evidence of growth dilution in nitrogen-fixing species. It was suggested (Högberg 1986b) that nitrogen-fixing species were limited throughout by low supply of phosphorus, and that non-nitrogen-fixing species were, on the basis of their low leaf nitrogen concentrations, limited by nitrogen at most sites. Considering the P : N ratio, perhaps the statement about non-nitrogen-fixing species should be revised; nitrogen is only clearly limiting at sites IV and V, whereas phosphorus is likely to be limiting at site II, and sites I and III fall in between.

A preliminary survey of four *miombo* woodland sites in north-eastern Zambia provided evidence of low availability of soil phosphorus (S. Holden, B. Wessén & P. Högberg, unpublished). Potentially nitrogen-fixing species had an average foliar P : N relation of 5.0 P : 100 N (nine species–site combinations) as compared with 6.8 P : 100 N in non-nitrogen-fixing species (19 species–site combinations). The concentration of nitrogen in leaves of potentially nitrogen-fixing species was on average 2.76% compared with 1.90% in non-nitrogen-fixing (mostly ectomycorrhizal) species.

It should be possible to determine the P : N relation critical for a balance between nitrogen-fixing and non-nitrogen-fixing species, and, in particular, whether or not soil nutrient availability is as important as suggested in this paper. This will require applications of nitrogen and phosphorus to mixed communities, and subsequent analyses of abundance, growth and tissue nutrient concentrations. In addition, the partial contribution of atmospheric nitrogen to nitrogen-fixing species will need to be determined. Provided that the soil studied is sufficiently rich in ^{15}N, the natural ^{15}N abundance method will be a good and inexpensive option (Shearer & Kohl 1986). The ^{15}N dilution method, in which the soil is enriched with ^{15}N to make a large difference in ^{15}N abundance between the soil and air, may be too costly to apply in this type of study, but will give the most accurate estimate of nitrogen fixation (Knowles 1980; Danso 1986). Such experiments would test the idea put forward here that nitrogen-fixing species are limited by low supply of phosphorus in many moist savanna areas, but are usually favoured by soil conditions in dry savannas.

ECTOMYCORRHIZAL VERSUS VA-MYCORRHIZAL TREES

Most tropical tree species form VA mycorrhizas (Malloch, Pirozynski & Raven 1980; Redhead 1980; Harley & Smith 1983; Janos 1983). Ectomycorrhizas seem to be a constant phenomenon only in Dipterocarpaceae, Fagaceae, *Pinus*, some genera of the tribes Amherstieae and Detarieae of the legume subfamily Caesalpinioideae (Alexander 1989) and in the subfamily Leptospermoideae of the Myrtaceae. In addition, ectomycorrhizas have been reported in a few species of families dominated by VA-mycorrhizal species; some of these observations need to be reconfirmed as pointed out by Janos (1983) and Alexander (1989). Ectomycorrhizas and VA mycorrhizas may occur simultaneously on a root system. When a species is denoted ectomycorrhizal in this paper it means that only this type of mycorrhiza is reported or is most regularly reported. Nodulating species are usually VA-mycorrhizal (e.g. Alexander 1989). Ectomycorrhizal tree species are sometimes conspicuously dominant in tropical moist savannas. Good examples are the extensive African *miombo* woodlands and Sudanian woodlands (White 1983) in which *Isoberlinia* spp. predominate, woodlands of *Eucalyptus* and *Melaleuca* in Australia, and savanna with *Pinus* and *Quercus* in Central America. It is frequently stated that communities dominated by ectomycorrhizal species are especially poor in species (e.g. Malloch, Pirozynski & Raven 1980). However, in a *miombo* stand in Zambia 28 species were found; 11 ectomycorrhizal species (four *Brachystegia* spp., *Isoberlinia angolensis*, *Julbernardia paniculata*, *Marquesia macroura*, *Monotes africanus*, *Periopsis angolensis* and two *Uapaca* spp.) contributed 73% of the basal area (Högberg & Piearce 1986). The remaining 17 species were either confirmed or presumed to be VA-mycorrhizal or non-mycorrhizal. Six nodulated species contributed 11% of the basal area of the stand. By contrast, the VA-mycorrhizal species *Colophospermum mopane* (Caesalpinioideae) forms vast monospecific woodlands on neutral to slightly alkaline clay soils that are seasonally flooded (Högberg & Piearce 1986). At a *miombo* site in eastern Tanzania (site II in Figs. 2 and 3), 25 species were found (Högberg 1982). Four ectomycorrhizal species (three *Brachystegia* spp. and *Julbernardia globiflora*) contributed *c.* 55% of the volume of the stand. Seven nodulated species contributed *c.* 25% of the volume. The total number of species compared well with the taxonomic diversity in nearby VA-mycorrhizal *Combretum* woodland (Högberg 1982). Hence, the generalization that ectomycorrhizal species regularly form relatively species-poor stands is not valid for African savannas.

Several factors can enforce the dominance of a type of mycorrhiza. Janos (1980) suggested that a prolonged dominance of one type of mycorrhiza would deplete the number of fungal propagules of other types. The same mechanism would also work directly on the plant components of the system. Furthermore, both ectomycorrhizal and VA-mycorrhizal plants join hyphal networks with species forming the same type of mycorrhiza (Read, Francis & Finlay 1985). By doing this, seedlings can receive carbon compounds from larger donors (Francis & Read 1984; Finlay, Söderström & Read 1986), e.g. possibly from mature trees. It has also been demonstrated that phosphorus is passed via hyphal links from senescent roots to a living neighbour VA-mycorrhizal plant, which need not be of the same species (Ritz & Newman 1985). The intracellular infection in senescent ectomycorrhizas (e.g. Nylund 1981) may be a similar mechanism minimizing losses from the network. There may be competition between plants linked to the same hyphal network, as well as between ectomycorrhizal and VA-mycorrhizal networks. Fitter (1977) found that two grass species, *Lolium perenne* and *Holcus lanatus*, each responded positively to VA-mycorrhizal infection when grown separately. However, when both species were grown together, *L. perenne* contributed less to the total mass of the two grasses, and this effect increased with increasing mycorrhizal infection. It is particularly interesting in this respect that savanna grasses form VA mycorrhizas (cf. Newman, Child & Patrick 1986), and that tree species may be connected with them.

A major effect on plants, often described as the major effect of infection by both ectomycorrhizal and VA-mycorrhizal fungi, is enhanced uptake of poorly mobile nutrients (e.g. Bowen 1980). The fungal hyphae act as bridges over the depletion zone, which develops nearest the root if the rate of uptake of a nutrient exceeds the supply through mass flow and diffusion (Nye & Tinker 1977). Much of the research on this aspect of mycorrhizas has focused on phosphorus, but evidently the uptake of ammonium will also be enhanced (Bowen & Smith 1981).

In studies of rain forests in Cameroun, a correlation was found between low availability of soil phosphorus (during the wet season) and the dominance of Caesalpinioideae (Gartlan et al. 1986; Newbery et al. 1986), many of which were later confirmed to be ectomycorrhizal (I.J. Alexander, personal communication; Alexander, this volume). Another hint at a correlation between ectomycorrhizas and soils low in phosphorus is the report that Allocasuarina, which more frequently forms ectomycorrhizas than does Casuarina, is also more often associated with lower concentrations of soil phosphorus (Reddell, Bowen & Robson 1986).

A dominance of ectomycorrhizal trees in moist savannas could also be associated with soils low in phosphorus. However, it is not clear why this should be so, since it has been proved experimentally that VA mycorrhizas also greatly enhance plant phosphorus uptake (Harley & Smith 1983). One major difference between these two types of mycorrhiza is the presence of a large fungal sheath (or mantle, see Fig. 1(b)) in ectomycorrhizas. This has been estimated to contribute c. 40% of the mass of the dual organ in temperate angiosperm ectomycorrhizas (Harley & Smith 1983) and c. 56% in their tropical counterparts (Alexander & Högberg 1986). The maximum amount of fungal tissue found in a study of VA mycorrhizas was 17% (Hepper 1977). Some authors have stressed that the large storage capacity of the sheath should be an advantage when the supply of nutrients is discontinuous, e.g. in seasonal climates (Alexander 1983; Harley & Smith 1983; Read 1983). However, this feature would seem to be of even greater importance in the dry savannas. In Africa, indigenous ectomycorrhizal trees are rare or absent in dry savannas and semi-arid environments, but in Australia ectomycorrhizal species are also found in dry habitats (McGee 1986).

The capacity of ectomycorrhizas to utilize nitrogen in proteins (Abuzinadah, Finlay & Read 1986) is another fundamental difference between ectomycorrhizas and VA mycorrhizas. This feature may have some bearing on the suggestion that ectomycorrhizal species themselves create conditions, i.e. accumulations of organic matter on top of the mineral soil, of which they are the most efficient exploiters (Alexander 1983). However, this situation is unlikely in savannas where recurrent grass fires will leave only the ash of above-ground litters. In miombo woodland, for example, the concentration of soil organic carbon is frequently less than 1% (of dry mass) in the topsoil, and total nitrogen is often less than 0.1% (e.g. Högberg 1986b). Ectomycorrhizal and VA-mycorrhizal tree root tips are prolific particularly at a soil depth of 10–20 cm, which is below the most extensive development of grass roots. Foliar analysis of non-nodulated *miombo* trees has indicated a higher nitrogen concentration in ectomycorrhizal than in VA-mycorrhizal species throughout four sites along a soil P : N gradient (2.01% of dry mass as compared with 1.50%) (Högberg 1986b). The foliar P : N ratios suggest that VA-mycorrhizal species are good at obtaining phosphorus but not nitrogen from soils where these elements are in short supply (Fig. 3). Ectomycorrhizal species seem to be efficient at obtaining both elements (Fig. 3). It is interesting that Reeves (1988), who studied semi-arid environments, concluded that an elevated P : N ratio is a major response to VA-mycorrhizal infection.

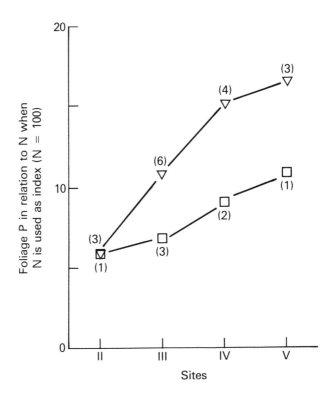

FIG. 3. Foliar phosphorus relative to nitrogen at four *miombo* woodland sites in Tanzania (data from Högberg (1986b)): ▽, non-nodulated VA-mycorrhizal species (mean); □, non-nodulated ectomycorrhizal species (mean). The number of species of each group sampled at the site is given in parentheses (*n* = 5 individuals per species and site). Average P : N ratios for ectomycorrhizal species at sites II and V are 0.13 : 2.13% and 0.21 : 1.76%, respectively, as compared with 0.10 : 1.70% and 0.28 : 1.53% for VA-mycorrhizal species. The four sites were also used in Fig. 2, and thus represent a gradient from low soil P : N (to the left) to high soil P : N (to the right).

Perhaps the ability to utilize intractable sources of nitrogen under conditions of low availability of phosphorus gives ectomycorrhizal species an advantage over VA-mycorrhizal species. The latter seem to be favoured by soils with low availability of phosphorus but with high rates of nitrogen mineralization, which is the type of habitat described as typical for temperate VA-mycorrhizal species by Read (1983).

It may be possible to test these hypotheses experimentally by applications of nitrogen and phosphorus. However, it will probably be difficult to analyse the role played by various organic sources of these nutrients. Another problem will be to distinguish between nutrients taken up via mycorrhizal hyphae and those taken up by non-infected fine roots. Many potential differences between ectomy-corrhizas and VA mycorrhizas, other than differences in nutrient uptake, may also be important. For example, nothing is known about possible differences in the carbon cost of turnover of ectomycorrhizal compared with VA-mycorrhizal fine roots, although the turnover of fine roots is a major sink for carbon in mature trees (Ågren *et al.* 1980).

ACKNOWLEDGEMENTS

This study was financially supported by the Swedish Agency for Research Cooperation with Developing Countries (SAREC). I would like to thank Drs I. J. Alexander, P. J. Grubb, D. P. Janos and J. Proctor and two anonymous reviewers for valuable criticism.

REFERENCES

Abuzinadah, R.A., Finlay, R.D. & Read, D.J. (1986). The role of proteins in the nitrogen nutrition of ectomycorrhizal plants. II. *New Phytologist*, **103**, 495–506.

Ågren, G.I., Axelsson, B., Flower-Ellis, J.G.K., Linder, S., Persson, H., Staaf, H. & Troeng, E. (1980). Annual carbon budget for a young Scots pine. *Ecological Bulletins (Stockholm)*, **32**, 25–64.

Alexander, I.J. (1983). The significance of ectomycorrhizas in the nitrogen cycle. *Nitrogen as an Ecological Factor* (Ed. by J.A. Lee, S. McNeill & I.H. Rorison), pp. 69–93. Blackwell Scientific Publications, Oxford.

Alexander, I.J. (1989). Systematics and ecology of ectomycorrhizal legumes. *Annals of the Missouri Botanical Garden*, in press.

Alexander, I.J. & Högberg, P. (1986). Ectomycorrhizas of tropical angiospermous trees. *New Phytologist*, **102**, 541–549.

Allen, O.N. & Allen, E.K. (1981). *The Leguminosae. A Source Book of Characteristics, Uses and Nodulation.* Macmillan, London.

Beadle, N.C.W. (1981). *The Vegetation of Australia.* Gustav Fischer, Stuttgart.

Bell, R.H.V. (1982). The effect of soil nutrient availability on community structure in African ecosystems. *Ecology of Tropical Savannas* (Ed. by B.J. Huntley & B.H. Walker), pp. 193–216. Springer, Berlin.

Bowen, G.D. (1980). Mycorrhizal roles in tropical plants and ecosystems. *Tropical Mycorrhiza Research* (Ed. by P. Mikola), pp. 165–190. Clarendon Press, Oxford.

Bowen, G.D. & Smith, S.E. (1981). The effects of mycorrhizas on nitrogen uptake by plants. *Ecological Bulletins (Stockholm)*, **33**, 237–247.

Brady, N.C. (1974). *The Nature and Properties of Soils,* 8th edn. Macmillan, New York.

Buringh, P. (1979). *Introduction to the Study of Soils in Tropical and Subtropical Regions.* Centre for Agricultural Publishing and Documentation, Wageningen.

Cole, C.V. & Heil, R.D. (1981). Phosphorus effects on terrestrial nitrogen cycling. *Ecological Bulletins (Stockholm),* **33**, 363–374.

Cole, M.M. (1982). The influence of soils, geomorphology and geology on the distribution of plant communities in savanna ecosystems. *Ecology of Tropical Savannas* (Ed. by B.J. Huntley & B.H. Walker), pp. 145–174. Springer, Berlin.

Comerford, N.B. & Fisher, R.F. (1984). Using foliar analysis to classify nitrogen-deficient sites. *Soil Science Society of America Journal,* **48**, 910–913.

Danso, S.K.A. (1986). Review: estimation of N_2-fixation by isotope dilution: an appraisal of techniques involving ^{15}N enrichment and their application — comments. *Soil Biology and Biochemistry,* **18**, 243–244.

Dommergues, Y.R., Diem, H.G., Gauthier, D.L., Dreyfus, B.L. & Cornet, F. (1984). Nitrogen-fixing trees in the tropics: potentialities and limitations. *Advances in Nitrogen Fixation Research* (Ed. by C. Veeger & W.E. Newton), pp. 7–13. Martinus Nijhoff/Dr W. Junk, The Hague and PUDOC, Wageningen.

Eiten, G. (1972). The cerrado vegetation of Brazil. *The Botanical Review,* **38**, 201–341.

Ericsson, T. & Ingestad, T. (1988). Phosphorus nutrition of birch seedlings. *Physiologia Plantarum,* **72**, 227–235.

FAO/UNESCO (1974). *Soil Map of the World, 1 : 5 000 000, Vol. I, Legend.* UNESCO, Paris.

FAO/UNESCO (1977). *Soil Map of the World, 1 : 5 000 000, Vol. VI, Africa.* UNESCO, Paris.

Faria, S.M. de, Franco, A.A., Jesus, R.M. de, Menandro, M.S. de, Baitello, J.B., Mucci, E.S.F., Döbereiner, J. & Sprent, J.I. (1984). New nodulating trees from South-East Brazil. *New Phytologist,* **98**, 317–328.

Faria, S.M. de, Lima, H.C. de, Franco, A.A., Mucci, E.S.F. & Sprent, J.I. (1987). Nodulation of legume trees from South-East Brazil. *Plant and Soil,* **99**, 347–356.

Fernandez, M.P. & Warembourg, F.R. (1986). Distribution and utilization of assimilated carbon in red clover during the first year of vegetation. *Plant and Soil,* **97**, 131–143.

Finlay, R.D., Söderström, B. & Read, D.J. (1986). Factors influencing the flux of carbon through ecto-mycorrhizal mycelium forming interplant connections. *Physiological and Genetical Aspects of Mycorrhizae* (Ed. by V. Gianinazzi-Pearson & S. Gianinazzi), pp. 301–306. INRA, Paris.

Fitter, A.H. (1977). Influence of mycorrhizal infection on competition for phosphorus and potassium by two grasses. *New Phytologist,* **79**, 119–125.

Francis, R. & Read, D.J. (1984). Direct transfer of carbon between plants connected by vesicular-arbuscular mycorrhizal mycelium. *Nature,* **307**, 53–56.

Gartlan, J.S., Newbery, D.McC., Thomas, D.W. & Waterman, P.G. (1986). The influence of topography and soil phosphorus on the vegetation of Korup Forest Reserve, Cameroun. *Vegetatio,* **65**, 131–148.

Gianinazzi-Pearson, V. & Diem, H.G. (1982). Endomycorrhizae in the tropics. *Microbiology of Tropical Soils and Plant Productivity* (Ed. by Y.R. Dommergues & H.G. Diem), pp. 209–251. Martinus Nijhoff/Dr W. Junk, The Hague.

Goedert, W.J. (1983). Management of the Cerrado soils of Brazil: a review. *Journal of Soil Science,* **34**, 405–428.

Grove, T.S. (1988). Growth responses of trees and understorey to applied nitrogen and phosphorus in karri (*Eucalyptus diversicolor*) forest. *Forest Ecology and Management,* **23**, 87–103.

Harley, J.L. & Smith, S.E. (1983). *Mycorrhizal Symbiosis.* Academic Press, London.

Hepper, C.M. (1977). A colorimetric method for estimating vesicular-arbuscular mycorrhizal infection in roots. *Soil Biology and Biochemistry,* **9**, 15–18.

Hingston, F.J., Malajczuk, N.A. & Grove, T.S. (1982). Acetylene reduction (N_2-fixation) by Jarrah forest legumes following fire and phosphate application. *Journal of Applied Ecology,* **19**, 631–646.

Högberg, P. (1982). Mycorrhizal associations in some woodland and forest trees and shrubs in Tanzania. *New Phytologist,* **92**, 407–415.

Högberg, P. (1986a). Soil nutrient availability, root symbioses and tree species composition in tropical Africa: a review. *Journal of Tropical Ecology*, **2**, 359–372.

Högberg, P. (1986b). Nitrogen fixation and nutrient relations in savanna woodland trees (Tanzania). *Journal of Applied Ecology*, **23**, 675–688.

Högberg, P. & Piearce, G.D. (1986). Mycorrhizas in Zambian trees in relation to host taxonomy, vegetation communities and successional patterns. *Journal of Ecology*, **74**, 775–785.

Huntley, B.J. (1982). Southern African savannas. *Ecology of Tropical Savannas* (Ed. by B.J. Huntley & B.H. Walker), pp. 101–119. Springer, Berlin.

Huntley, B.J. & Walker, B.H. (1982). Conclusions: characteristic features of tropical savannas. *Ecology of Tropical Savannas* (Ed. by B.J. Huntley & B.H. Walker), pp. 657–660. Springer, Berlin.

Ingestad, T. & Lund, A.-B. (1986). Theory and techniques for steady state mineral nutrition and growth of plants. *Scandinavian Journal of Forest Research*, **1**, 439–453.

Janos, D.P. (1980). Mycorrhizae influence tropical succession. *Biotropica*, **12** (Supplement), 56–64.

Janos, D.P. (1983). Tropical mycorrhizas, nutrient cycles and plant growth. *Tropical Rain Forest: Ecology and Management* (Ed. by S.L. Sutton, T.C. Whitmore & A.C. Chadwick), pp. 327–345. Blackwell Scientific Publications, Oxford.

Jordan, C.F. (1985). *Nutrient Cycling in Tropical Forest Ecosystems.* John Wiley, Chichester.

Knowles, R. (1980). Nitrogen fixation in natural plant communities and soils. *Methods for Evaluating Biological Nitrogen Fixation* (Ed. by F.J. Bergersen), pp. 557–582. John Wiley, Chichester.

Malloch, D.W., Pirozynski, K.A. & Raven, P.H. (1980). Ecological and evolutionary significance of mycorrhizal symbioses in vascular plants (a review). *Proceedings of the National Academy of Sciences (U.S.A.)*, **77**, 2113–2118.

McGee, P. (1986). Mycorrhizal associations of plant species in a semiarid community. *Australian Journal of Botany*, **34**, 585–593.

Munns, D.N. & Mosse, B. (1980). Mineral nutrition of legume crops. *Advances in Legume Science* (Ed. by R.J. Summerfield & A.H. Bunting), pp. 115–125. Royal Botanic Gardens, Kew.

Newbery, D.McC., Gartlan, J.S., McKey, D.B. & Waterman, P.G. (1986). The influence of drainage and soil phosphorus on the vegetation of Douala-Edea Forest Reserve, Cameroun. *Vegetatio*, **65**, 149–162.

Newman, E.I., Child, R.D. & Patrick, C.M. (1986). Mycorrhizal infection in grasses of Kenyan savanna. *Journal of Ecology*, **74**, 1179–1183.

Nye, P.H. & Tinker, P.B. (1977). *Solute Movement in the Soil-Root System.* Blackwell Scientific Publications, Oxford.

Nylund, J.-E. (1981). *The formation of ectomycorrhiza in conifers: structural and physiological studies with special reference to the microbiont* Piloderma croceum *Erikss. & Hjortst.* PhD Thesis, University of Uppsala, Uppsala.

Parton, W.J. & Risser, P.G. (1979). Simulated impact of management practices upon the tallgrass prairie. *Perspectives in Grassland Ecology* (Ed. by N.R. French), pp. 135–155. Springer, New York.

Penning de Vries, F.W.T., Krul, J.M. & van Keulen, H. (1980). Productivity of Sahelian grasslands in relation to the availability of nitrogen and phosphorus from the soil. *Nitrogen Cycling in West African Ecosystems* (Ed. by T. Rosswall), pp. 95–113. SCOPE/UNEP/Royal Swedish Academy of Sciences, Stockholm.

Read, D.J. (1983). The biology of mycorrhiza in the Ericales. *Canadian Journal of Botany*, **61**, 985–1004.

Read, D.J., Francis, R. & Finlay, R.D. (1985). Mycorrhizal mycelia and nutrient cycling in plant communities. *Ecological Interactions in Soil* (Ed. by A.H. Fitter), pp. 193–217. Blackwell Scientific Publications, Oxford.

Reddell, P., Bowen, G.D. & Robson, A.D. (1986). Nodulation of Casuarinaceae in relation to host species and soil properties. *Australian Journal of Botany*, **34**, 435–444.

Redhead, J.F. (1980). Mycorrhiza in natural tropical forests. *Tropical Mycorrhiza Research* (Ed. by P. Mikola), pp. 127–142. Clarendon Press, Oxford.

Reeves, F.B. (1988). Mineral nutrition, mycorrhizal fungi and succession in semiarid environments. *Trees and Mycorrhiza* (Ed. by F.S.P. Ng), pp. 33–50. Forest Research Institute, Malaysia, Kuala Lumpur.

Ritz, K. & Newman, E.I. (1985). Evidence for rapid cycling of phosphorus from dying roots to living plants. *Oikos*, **45**, 174–180.

Sanchez, P.A. (1976). *Properties and Management of Soils in the Tropics.* John Wiley, New York.

Shearer, G. & Kohl, D.H. (1986). N_2-fixation in field settings: estimations based on ^{15}N natural abundance. *Australian Journal of Plant Physiology*, **13**, 699–756.

Sprent, J.I. (1979). *The Biology of Nitrogen-Fixing Organisms.* McGraw-Hill, London.

Tolsma, D.J., Ernst, W.H.O. & Verweij, R.A. (1987). Nutrients in soil and vegetation around two artificial waterpoints in eastern Botswana. *Journal of Applied Ecology*, **24**, 991–1000.

Vitousek, P.M. (1984). Litterfall, nutrient cycling, and nutrient limitation in tropical forests. *Ecology*, **65**, 285–298.

Warembourg, F.R. (1983). Estimating the true cost of dinitrogen fixation by nodulated plants in undisturbed conditions. *Canadian Journal of Microbiology*, **29**, 930–937.

White, F. (1983). *The Vegetation of Africa.* UNESCO, Paris.

Williams, C.H. & Raupach, M. (1983). Plant nutrients in Australian soils. *Soils: an Australian Viewpoint* (compiled by CSIRO), pp. 777–793. CSIRO, Melbourne and Academic Press, London.

Young, A. (1976). *Tropical Soils and Soil Survey.* Cambridge University Press, Cambridge.

Mineral nutrient dynamics during savanna–forest transformation in Central America

M. KELLMAN

Department of Geography, York University,
North York, Ontario M3J 1P3, Canada

SUMMARY

1 The sources and mechanisms of accumulation of phosphorus, potassium, calcium and magnesium during tropical forest development in treeless savanna were examined in a Neotropical savanna.

2 The accumulation of these nutrients is being driven primarily by nutrient sequestering in biomass, and two groups of woody plants were identified as essential to this process: (i) woody savanna dicotyledons which can rapidly increase their populations during fire-free intervals; (ii) larger forest trees whose seedlings are capable of establishing themselves in the micro-habitats provided by savanna trees.

3 There are insufficient of these nutrients in the savanna ecosystem to sustain forest development, and weathering at depth does not appear to be a significant nutrient source during the process. Accumulation appears to be achieved by the capture of atmospheric accessions, whose small annual magnitude requires that the woody transitional plants be slow growers. The nutrient capital of a forest community could be established at this site in less than 500 years by this means.

4 Temporary nutrient immobilization by the kaolinitic and sesquioxide-rich soils of the savanna is very effective and appears to be essential in the accumulation process. It is suggested that forest re-establishment can probably be achieved on most tropical soils that possess similar mineralogies if suitable transitional species exist locally and if sufficient time is available.

INTRODUCTION

Many studies of nutrient cycling in tropical ecosystems have concentrated on how nutrients are retained and recirculated within an extant system. Indeed, the term 'cycle' emphasizes internal processes rather than external linkages. However, situations exist in which external links can be of critical significance to ecosystem functioning or transformation. One example is the widespread invasion of savanna communities by forest that has occurred in the Holocene, and presumably also in earlier interglacials of the Pleistocene (Van der Hammen 1974; Livingstone 1975; Kershaw 1978; Flenley 1979).

The savanna environment poses a suite of problems for a potential forest invader, not all of which are necessarily present at every place. In the Neotropics, insufficient mineral nutrients presents one fundamental problem, as most savannas in this region are associated with intensely weathered soils of low fertility (Hardy 1960; Lopes & Cox 1977; Sarmiento 1984). While it is conceivable that Holocene forest invasion has been confined to more fertile soils, leaving the less fertile soils covered with savanna, many Neotropical forests do exist on soils of low fertility, and the start of forest invasion has been observed on infertile savanna soils after fire suppression (Munro 1966; Kellman 1976; San José & Fariñas 1983). Both phenomena suggest that the large mineral nutrient capital of tropical forest can be re-established on low fertility sites, in contradiction with the irreversible nutrient decline which is commonly assumed to be the inevitable consequence of chemical weathering under tropical conditions (Charter 1941; Walker *et al.* 1981).

This apparent reversal of the nutrient 'rundown' phenomenon poses basic questions about the sources of nutrients that could be available for forest development, and about the retention and accumulation mechanisms that may operate during such a process. Answers to these questions have been sought in a Central American savanna where fire suppression for four decades has initiated forest invasion. Although the data come only from an early phase of forest invasion, they provide some clues about the mechanisms involved and the likely nutrient-accumulation process. The discussion in this paper is confined to the four macro-nutrients phosphorus, potassium, calcium and magnesium. Unfortunately there are insufficient data available for nitrogen and other nutrient elements.

STUDY AREA

The Mountain Pine Ridge savanna of Belize (17°N, 89°W) consists of a 500 km^2 area surrounded by broadleaf forest. It receives about 1600 mm of rainfall annually with a 4-month dry season. The area comprises a granite plateau of about 500 m altitude, together with adjacent metasedimentaries which form more complex topography to the south and east. The bedrock is intensely weathered to a depth of many metres and exposures occur only in steep terrain and as granite core stones at ridge crests. On the granite plateau, where most data were collected, the soils are ultisols, with coarse sandy loam topsoils of varying depth that overlie a well-developed clay-rich B horizon containing much kaolinite and sesquioxides. Cation exchange capacities are about 5 m-equiv. 100 g^{-1} in the topsoil, but rise to about 15 m-equiv. 100 g^{-1} in the clay-rich subsoil (Table 1). Base saturations are very low (1–2%), with calcium and magnesium being the main cations retained. Truog extractable phosphorus occurs in trace quantities only. Much larger quantities of nutrients are revealed in a total analysis of soils but, presumably, most of these are in minerals which are highly resistant to further weathering. Localized variability in soil fertility is associated mainly with the depth of sandy topsoils, and is greatest where this is shallow.

Early reports (Lundell 1940) describe the area as open savanna with only scattered pine and Romney (1959) classified the vegetation as orchard savanna with pine. Today, treeless grassland persists only on the most exposed ridge crests

TABLE 1. Chemical properties of the upper 60 cm of soil at a treeless site in the Mountain Pine Ridge savanna, Belize

Depth (cm)	pH (log units)	Organic C (%)	$P_{Truog's}$ ($\mu g\ g^{-1}$)	Extractable cations (m-equiv. 100 g^{-1})			CEC (m-equiv. 100 g^{-1})	Total elemental concentration ($\mu g\ g^{-1}$)			
				K	Ca	Mg		P	K	Ca	Mg
0–15	5.0	0.46	<0.66	0.004	0.043	0.058	4.77	32.3	429	<125	86.8
15–30	4.8	0.27	<0.66	0.001	0.025	0.045	9.29	50.8	696	<125	72.4
30–45	4.7	0.37	<0.66	0.002	0.100	0.111	17.6	53.1	373	<125	293
45–60	4.7	0.26	<0.66	0.002	0.125	0.190	13.3	57.5	578	<125	410

in the metasedimentary area. Here the dominant herbaceous stratum is comprised of a limited number of widespread grass and sedge species among which the most common are *Axonopus purpusii* (Mez) Chase, *Mesosetum filifolium* F. T. Hubb, *Paspalum plicatulum* Michx. and *Trachypogon plumosus* (Humb. & Bonpl. ex. Willd.) Nees. Scattered populations of woody dicotyledonous trees and shrubs also exist in the savanna, among which the most common species are *Byrsonima crassifolia* (L.) Kunth, *Quercus oleoides* Cham & Schlecht., *Q. schippii* Standl. and the melastomataceous shrubs *Clidemia sericea* D. Don and *Miconia albicans* (Swartz) Triana. Also present are diffuse populations of *Pinus caribaea* Morelet and, at higher altitudes, *P. oocarpa* Schiede. The two pines are post-fire opportunists and can form woodland when fires occur at intervals of more than 25 years (Hutchinson 1977). Using fire maps for the 1960–1971 period, Hutchinson (1977) calculated a mean natural fire recurrence interval of 18 years for the eastern part of the savanna which was not subject to fire control. However, because fire which spread from the western area was precluded during this period, this probably represents an overestimate of recurrence intervals prior to fire control. Charcoal collected from a soil pit in the eastern part of the savanna has been carbon dated at 11 210 BP (Kellman 1975), and a short sediment core taken from a small nearby pond shows savanna taxa throughout its length (M. Kellman, unpublished). A ^{14}C date of 2610 BP was obtained at 11 cm depth in this core which, if a constant sedimentation rate is assumed, suggests a basal age of about 15 000 years. These results strongly suggest that the savanna is old and probably represents a remnant of a more widespread Glacial-Age community that has resisted Holocene forest invasion.

The most potent proximal deterrent to forest invasion of the savanna appears to be fire. Today, much of the area in which fire has been suppressed is covered by open pine woodland within which occur patches of open grassland and thickets of dicotyledonous trees and shrubs, suggesting variable stages of progress towards closed woodland. However, the main woody species are all savanna taxa that have increased their populations since fire suppression. Pine becomes insensitive to ground fires at about 20 years of age (Hutchinson 1977); *Clidemia sericea* and *Miconia albicans* do so at about 7 and 13 years, respectively (Miyanishi & Kellman 1986). The development of dense stands of these two species appears to date from the beginning of fire suppression (Miyanishi 1984). Less is known about the population dynamics of larger woody dicotyledonous plants. However, mature stems of these species can normally survive fires and resprout epicormically, while younger shoots are killed but the genet resprouts basally. This suggests that individual genets may achieve considerable age even in regularly burned savannas.

Within this matrix of changing savanna vegetation occasional seedlings and saplings of forest tree species can be found. These comprise a limited subset of the regional forest flora: *Bursera simaruba* (L.) Sarg., *Calophyllum brasiliense* Camb., *Simaruba glauca* D.C., *Terminalia obovata* (R. & P.) Steud. and *Vochysia hondurensis* Sprague (Kellman 1985b). They are found primarily beneath thickets of woody savanna plants (Kellman & Miyanishi 1982).

NUTRIENT CAPITAL AND CYCLING IN OPEN SAVANNA

In this area a grass- and sedge-dominated community with scattered trees may be taken as the initial condition in a savanna-to-forest transformation. Results are available on the storage of nutrients in shoots of grasses and sedges 1 year after fire and for others that have not been burned for several decades (Table 2; Kellman *et al.* 1987). Storage of nutrients in below-ground tissues has been estimated from these data using shoot : root nutrient-content ratios of individual elements calculated for a Venezuelan savanna at Bariñas by Sarmiento (1984). Most storage of potassium, calcium and magnesium, but not of phosphorus, in live biomass takes place in the first year after a fire, with subsequent accumulation being mainly in dead material (Table 2). In the edaphically similar Llaños savannas of Venezuela (Sarmiento 1984), the above-ground biomass reaches asymptotic levels approximately 5 years after a fire, suggesting that the results for older stands in Table 2 represent the maximum nutrient storage achievable by this stratum in the Mountain Pine Ridge. Comparison of these storages with exchangeable pools in the soil (Table 3) shows that the graminoid layer contains only a small proportion of exchangeable calcium and magnesium, but many times the quantity of exchangeable potassium and phosphorus in the soil.

In the absence of fire, nutrient concentrations in the soil solution of treeless savanna remain low and decrease with depth to only trace values below 40 cm, where few fine roots are found (Kellman & Sanmugadas 1985). Presumably, this reflects the slight but steady mineralization and absorption of nutrients that is characteristic of moist savannas (Menault *et al.* 1985). Much larger nutrient fluxes follow periodic fire which mineralizes most nutrients in the above-ground tissues. A temporarily increased concentration of nutrients in topsoil solutions ensues, but does not appear in deeper layers despite the passage of percolating water (Kellman *et al.* 1985). In the topsoil, nutrient concentrations return to ambient levels within a week as a result of ion adsorption by the soil exchange complex, where, presumably, these ions are available for more gradual plant

TABLE 2. Nutrient storage in herbaceous plant tissues in the Mountain Pine Ridge savanna, Belize and annual inputs of nutrients in bulk precipitation (all data in kg ha^{-1}) (source: Kellman & Carty (1986); Kellman *et al.* (1987)) (* denotes estimates of nutrient storage in roots based on root : shoot nutrient ratios for Bariñas, Venezuela, from Sarmiento (1984))

	P	K	Ca	Mg
1-year-old tissues				
Above-ground live	0.17	5.65	0.58	0.99
Above-ground dead	0.26	1.00	0.81	1.66
Roots*	0.25	2.17	0.79	0.60
Total	0.67	8.69	2.18	2.39
Tissues ⩾ 5 years old				
Above-ground live	0.82	6.72	0.68	1.00
Above-ground dead	3.42	2.28	2.88	2.21
Roots*	0.83	3.02	1.77	1.07
Total	2.21	12.07	4.86	4.28
Annual bulk precipitation input	0.12	3.40	1.96	0.28

uptake. Any net loss of nutrients after burning is, thus, more likely to be due to removals in overland flow than in leaching.

The magnitude of such losses were estimated in prescription-burned savannas in Honduras by Hudson *et al.* (1983). Some accelerated loss of all elements was recorded, primarily in washed-off sediments rather than in solution. However, herb layer recovery was rapid and losses from burned plots approached the quantities of those from unburned controls within 2 years. Consequently, the total losses from burned plots were not large, representing only about 1 year's influx of nutrients in bulk precipitation (Kellman *et al.* 1982).

Thus treeless savanna represents a system that is highly conservative of its small nutrient capital. Even after multiple annual burns, no declines in concentrations of exchangeable nutrients have been detected in savanna soil, but rather increased concentrations of calcium and magnesium, suggesting transfer between compartments rather than losses (Kellman *et al.* 1985). Any small losses from the system in gradual leaching or erosion after fire are presumably offset by accessions from other sources. Of these, inputs from further weathering within the solum seem an unlikely source in these intensely weathered soils, although there is some evidence for gradual release of immobilized phosphorus (see below). In contrast, relatively large quantities of nutrients are being released by chemical weathering at depth in the watershed, as shown by the persistently high concentrations of these elements in river water (Kellman & Sanmugadas 1985). However, there is no evidence that shallow-rooted herbs have access to these. Much more accessible are the small quantities of nutrients delivered in bulk precipitation to this site (Table 2). Although these arrive at the soil surface in an extremely dilute form, soil solutions leaving the rooting zone are even more dilute, suggesting immobilization in passage, and a laboratory experiment has implicated soil adsorption, rather than plant uptake, as the proximal retention mechanism (Kellman & Sanmugadas 1985). Consequently, atmospheric accessions represent the most probable source of nutrients sustaining these ecosystems over long periods. It seems that as far as phosphorus, potassium, calcium and magnesium are concerned such a system may persist indefinitely, despite it being disconnected from the main geochemical cycle of the region.

Savanna dicotyledonous trees represent specialized microcosms within the matrix of dominant grasses and sedges of open savanna. They sustain a biomass far larger than that of the graminoids and contain foliar concentrations of nutrients that are similar to those of tropical forest trees (Ahmad & Jones 1969; Kellman 1976; Montes & Medina 1977; Sarmiento 1984). Unfortunately, we do not know the total quantities of nutrients stored in these trees in the Mountain Pine Ridge or elsewhere in Neotropical savannas. However, surface soils beneath them show appreciable nutrient enrichment and, in some instances, this approaches that of tropical forests (Kellman 1979). Because enrichment is confined to the topsoil and because the trees examined were all shallow rooted, it is concluded that the pattern is plant-induced and that transfer of nutrients from weathering at depth is not involved. The enrichment (discussed in detail by Kellman (1979)) appears to be the result of an enlarged plant–litter–soil cycle that is driven by the larger biomass and greater litter production of the trees whose persistent genets have gradually accumulated nutrients over a long time.

The quantity of nutrients stored in the biomass of tropical forests occupying low-fertility soils equivalent to those of the Mountain Pine Ridge savanna may be compared with those present in open savanna using data of Klinge (1973, 1976a, b) and Uhl & Jordan (1984) for tropical forests (Table 3). The quantities of exchangeable nutrients in the soils of treeless savanna and beneath trees are insufficient to meet the demand of a developing forest. While there are sufficient total reserves of nutrients in the soil to meet these demands, it is unlikely that significant quantities would be released by further chemical weathering except over geological time. Consequently, the establishment of forest must depend on an external source of nutrients.

TABLE 3. The nutrient storage in biomass of two tropical forests growing on infertile soils compared with the nutrient sources present in open savanna of the Mountain Pine Ridge, Belize (all data in kg ha^{-1}) (sources: *Klinge (1973, 1976a, b); [†]Uhl & Jordan (1984); [‡]Kellman & Sanmugadas (1985); [§]Kellman (1979))

	P	K	Ca	Mg
Estimated forest storage				
Brazil*	64	466	487	227
Venezuela[†]	51	300	261	71
Estimated nutrient sources				
Graminoid tissue	2.2	12.1	4.9	4.3
Soil exchangeable (0–60 cm), treeless areas[‡]	<0.04	5.9	150	62.5
Soil exchangeable (0–60 cm), beneath *Byrsonima crassifolia*[§]	12.5	16.7	297	87.5
Soil total (0–60 cm)[‡]	353	4960	<1000	2590

NUTRIENT ACCUMULATION BY PINE WOODLAND

An open woodland of *Pinus caribaea* with an understorey of melastomataceous shrubs represents the most widespread community that has developed after four decades of fire suppression in the Mountain Pine Ridge. A similar community in Nicaraguan savannas has been described by Munro (1966). The role of the predominant plants in such a community in accumulating nutrients and facilitating a transition to broadleaf forest is assessed here.

Nutrient storage has been estimated for a 30-year-old pine stand, with an understorey of *Miconia albicans*, that established during a long period without burning but which now experiences occasional ground fires. Nutrient storage estimates for pine (Table 4) are based on allometric regressions for above-ground organs developed by Stewart & Kellman (1982) and shoot : root ratios of nutrients for 10-year-old trees provided by Egunjobi & Bada (1979) and Kadeba & Aduayi (1986). Storage in above-ground *M. albicans* 5 years after a fire is based on a growth simulation of this species at average densities (Miyanishi 1984) and measured nutrient content of tissues (Kellman *et al.* 1987).

The total quantities of nutrients stored in these tree and shrub strata (Table 4) are far larger than those accumulated in the biomass of open savanna (Table 2). They are also large relative to the quantities of exchangeable nutrients present in savanna soils (Table 3). Sufficient quantities of exchangeable calcium and magnesium exist in savanna soils to develop such a stand although these would be severely depleted. However, the quantities of exchangeable potassium and phosphorus are insufficient to meet this demand. Some declines of exchangeable calcium and magnesium have been found beneath a 24-year-old pine (Kellman & Hudson 1982), but no decline of potassium was found (phosphorus was not examined). Because pine trees possess well-developed tap roots (in contrast with other savanna plants), the possibility exists that they may be drawing on nutrients

TABLE 4. Nutrient storage in the biomass of a 30-year-old stand of *Pinus caribaea* in the Mountain Pine Ridge, Belize, and estimated accessions of nutrients to this ecosystem from atmospheric sources (all data in kg ha^{-1}). (*Data from Kellman & Carty (1986). [†] Root storage estimates assume a similar root : shoot allocation of nutrients to those measured by Egunjobi & Bada (1979) and Kadeba & Aduayi (1986). [‡]Data from Kellman *et al.* (1987).)

	P	K	Ca	Mg
Storage				
30-year pine shoots*	12.1	94.6	103	32.3
30-year pine roots[†]	3.7	17.4	26.7	10.9
30-year pine total	15.8	112	128	43.2
5-year *Miconia albicans* understorey				
(shoots only)[‡]	0.7	13.0	8.2	4.2
Total storage	16.3	125	137	47.4
Accessions*				
30-year bulk precipitation	3.6	102	58.8	8.4
30-year pine canopy filtration	0.9	8.4	5.7	3.3
30-year total accession	4.5	110	64.5	11.7

released by weathering at depth. However, the experimental cutting of tap roots resulted in no significant decrease in the concentrations of nutrients in the foliage or in growth rates of trees over 5 years (Kellman & Hudson 1982; Kellman 1986). Consequently, the tap root appears to play, at most, a minor role in tree nutrition and cannot account for the large increase in nutrient storage that has taken place in these communities over four decades.

Because of the brief time period, it is improbable that weathering within the surface soil could have provided a significant input for this development, leaving atmospheric accession as the most probable source. Estimates of inputs from the atmosphere during a 30-year period are provided in Table 4, and include those in bulk precipitation and aerosols filtered by the pine canopy (Kellman & Carty 1986). The aerosol estimate (which assumes that a pine canopy existed throughout the period) is an overestimate, but the filtration component is small relative to that of bulk precipitation. These figures show that potassium influx is sufficient to meet the demands of stand development, while the influx of calcium and magnesium would be adequate if supplemented by extractable reserves in the soil. However, the input of phosphorus is insufficient to meet the demand, suggesting that some immobilized phosphorus in surface soils is used. High concentrations of phosphorus have been found to disappear from savanna soil solutions extremely rapidly (Kellman 1985a; Kellman & Sanmugadas 1985; Kellman *et al.* 1985), and presumably this element is precipitated in relatively insoluble compounds. However, the above nutrient budget suggests that these reserves of phosphorus are at least partially accessible to pines, probably by way of mycorrhizal associations.

Although such pine stands represent an appreciable accumulation of nutrients relative to that stored in the biomass of open savanna, they do not appear to represent an essential facilitating stage in the transformation of savanna to forest for two reasons. Firstly, in common with many other members of the genus (Miller *et al.* 1979), *P. caribaea* is highly conservative of its nutrients. The nutrient content of its litter is low relative to that of other woody plants (Kellman 1976) and surface soils beneath it show little nutrient enrichment (Kellman & Hudson 1982). Secondly, pine stands remain fire-prone and even infrequent, cool, ground fires will eliminate seedlings of forest trees. However, the establishment of pine woodlands in these Central American savannas indicates that an accumulation of nutrients can be achieved on infertile soils by taxa that are capable of slow growth to a large size.

THE ESTABLISHMENT OF FOREST TAXA

Any interpretation of further vegetation change towards a broadleaved forest is speculative as there are no sites which have been protected from fire for long periods. However, occasional areas, in the lee of natural fire breaks along the savanna–forest boundary, support large relict pine trees with a continuous understorey of woody savanna dicotyledons. These indicate a further developmental stage towards forest and, in the absence of pine, would be equivalent to the closed woodland of savanna species that pollen records suggest have periodically replaced some open savannas in South America (Wymstra & Van der Hammen 1966; Van der Hammen 1974).

We have no estimate of the total nutrient accumulation achieved by these communities, but it must be well below that required by fully developed tropical forest. However, in one important respect these communities represent a significant development towards forest, for a closed canopy of woody dicotyledons normally decreases the flammability of ground fuels dramatically. This appears to be due to both a micro-climatic effect and the physical and chemical properties of the litter produced by such communities (Kellman 1984). Such communities, presumably, are also developing the enlarged nutrient cycles and enriched surface soils that have been observed beneath their more isolated progenitors.

However, further nutrient accumulation towards that of forest requires species capable of achieving a far larger biomass. The existence of enriched surface soils beneath savanna woody dicotyledons suggests that these places could act as nutritional 'safe sites' for the establishment of such forest taxa. This hypothesis has been tested by planting tree seed and transplanting seedlings of three forest tree species beneath and beyond savanna trees (Kellman & Miyanishi 1982; Kellman 1985b). None of the three survived in treeless savanna. One, *Swietenia macrophylla* King, also failed beneath savanna trees after rapid early growth, and a subsequent growth-chamber experiment implicated potassium deficiency as the likely cause (Kellman & Miyanishi 1982). However, the other two species, *Calophyllum brasiliense* Camb. and *Xylopia frutescens* Aubl. showed high survivorship and slow but steady growth beneath trees over 3 and 5 years, respectively (Kellman 1985b). Thus savanna trees appear to be able to play a facilitative role in the invasion of savanna by forest, but only a specialized subset of the forest flora can participate in this process.

DISCUSSION

Although the Mountain Pine Ridge in Belize and other Central American savannas are unique in possessing pine trees as a prominent component, they possess many plant species and soil conditions that are common to Neotropical savannas in general (Sarmiento 1984). Consequently, conclusions derived from them can probably be extended, with some qualification, to the larger domain of New World savannas.

The major nutrient storage in tropical forest systems that occupy soils of low fertility is plant biomass (Richards 1952; Jordan & Kline 1972; Golley 1983). Where this storage already exists, nutrients can be retained and recirculated by a suite of effective recycling mechanisms such as root mats (Stark & Jordan 1978), epiphyllae (Jordan *et al.* 1980), canopy roots (Nadkarni 1982) and mycorrhizal associations (Herrera *et al.* 1978). However, the initial establishment of tropical forest on such soils clearly requires an external nutrient source. The results presented here identify two other essential components of the accumulation process: soils capable of temporarily immobilizing extraneous nutrient accessions, and plants capable of achieving a large biomass by slow incremental development.

The data do not contain any evidence that supports deep weathering as being a significant source of nutrients during forest establishment. Further weathering of surface soils also appears to be an unlikely source, except for some immobilized phosphorus. Other macro-nutrients are either too dilute or released too slowly to be adequate sources for the accumulation that has occurred in pine stands over three decades. In contrast, atmospheric accessions provide a small, but steady, influx and this may be augmented periodically by large inputs from volcanic activity (Kellman *et al.* 1982). These nutrients are delivered in a soluble form to root systems that are already deployed for nutrient recycling. Provided that the accessions are retained, the total time required to accumulate a forest's nutrient store is modest. If an annual rate of influx equal to that received by the 30-year-old pine savanna is assumed, the Venezuelan forest's nutrient store (Table 3) could be achieved in the following: 350 years for phosphorus, 82 years for potassium, 121 years for calcium, and 182 years for magnesium. Similarly, the accumulation of the Brazilian forest's store would be achieved in 427, 127, 227 and 582 years, respectively for phosphorus, potassium, calcium and magnesium. Allowing for some augmentation from soil reserves, it would seem probable that as far as these four nutrients are concerned a tropical forest could be established from this source in less than 500 years.

While inherent soil infertility appears not to be of critical significance to forest establishment in savannas, other soil properties contributing to a high adsorptive capacity are important. Natural flushes of nutrients are immobilized rapidly by savanna soils (Kellman & Sanmugadas 1985) and artificial loading of soils has shown retention to be primarily a function of cation exchange capacity (CEC), with deep sandy topsoils retaining less than clay-rich horizons with larger exchange capacities (Kellman 1985a). The effectiveness of cation adsorption in these soils can be attributed to two mechanisms. Firstly, in the presence of hydrated iron and aluminium oxides, strong adsorption of polyvalent anions takes place, leading to an increase in CEC and complexing of cations (Johnson & Cole 1980; Wiklander 1980; Vitousek 1983). Secondly, at low values of pH and CEC, the adsorption energy of hydrogen ions is low relative to that of other cations, and the leaching effect of percolating water is minimal (Wiklander 1974). Insofar as many highly weathered tropical soils possess these features, it is probable that they possess adsorptive capacities similar to those in the Mountain Pine Ridge.

While there is no experimental evidence from the Mountain Pine Ridge that soil adsorption is an essential prerequisite of effective nutrient retention, there is strong circumstantial evidence from there and elsewhere that root absorption alone could not have achieved this. Plants capable of withstanding low soil fertilities are often obligate slow growers and incapable of absorbing nutrient flushes rapidly (Chapin 1980). The rates of nutrient disappearance from soil solutions in the rooting zone in the Mountain Pine Ridge were not significantly different from those in the subsoil (Kellman & Sanmugadas 1985). This suggests an ineffective short-term nutrient-absorption capacity by the root systems, and conforms to one of Chapin's generalizations about such plants. Cavalcanti (1978) estimated that 3 months were required for the re-absorption of nutrients that were released during fire in Brazilian cerrado and retained temporarily in topsoils. Moreover, at the Cooloola dunes in Australia, nutrient 'rundown' and vegetation deterioration were associated with the development of deep bleached quartz sand A_2 horizons, stripped of their original sesquioxide coatings (Walker et al. 1981; Thompson 1983). This suggests an inability of root systems alone to effectively retain atmospheric accessions.

However, while a soil-adsorptive capacity is apparently an essential prerequisite to nutrient accumulation, it is not sufficient, as witnessed by the inability of grassland soils in the Mountain Pine Ridge to accumulate nutrients from atmospheric accessions. Presumably, long-term 'chronic' leaching in the absence of a large biomass compartment is sufficient to offset any suppression of 'acute' leaching of nutrient flushes. Consequently, species that are capable of both establishing in savanna and achieving a large biomass by slow development, appear to be an essential prerequisite to achieving nutrient accumulation.

A schematic model of the postulated nutrient demand and supply relationships of two potential tree colonizers is shown in Fig. 1. One is an obligate fast-growing forest species such as *Swietenia macrophylla* and the other an obligate or facultative slow-growing 'transitional' species such as *Calophyllum brasiliense*. Cumulative atmospheric input is shown as a sigmoid curve that approaches a constant slope, reflecting the addition of a canopy filtration component of accession as the tree canopy expands, initially in isolation, and later as part of a closed canopy. Cumulative demand curves for trees are shown as sigmoid curves approaching asymptotic values at the maximum nutrient quantity immobilizable by a tree of that species. Differences between tree demand and atmospheric supply must be met by finite reserves of nutrients available in the soil plus those released from pre-existing savanna plants that have been suppressed by the tree. The success of the transitional tree in these situations results from its ability to maintain a small differential between tree demand and atmospheric supply. Immobilization by the transitional tree of a quantity of nutrients comparable with that achievable by the forest tree requires either great longevity of the individual or multiple tree generations with effective re-absorption of nutrients from the necromass of predecessors.

There appear to be at least two groups of transitional species necessary for forest invasion: woody savanna dicotyledons and slow-growing forest trees. Broad-leaved woody savanna plants are capable of establishing in savanna, become fire-tolerant at an early stage, and are thus able to begin accumulation of nutrients. Of equal importance is the ability of these species to increase their populations

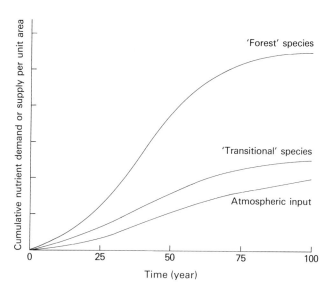

FIG. 1. Schematic model of the postulated nutrient demand and supply relationships of two potential tree colonizers of a savanna site: an obligate fast-growing 'forest' species (e.g. *Swietenia macrophylla*) and an obligate or facultative slow-growing 'transitional' species (e.g. *Calophyllum brasiliense*).

rapidly during fire-free intervals to form a closed woodland that is resistant to fire. While the time required for this is probably only a few decades, nutrient accumulation by them is a more prolonged process and sites of old genets must remain preferentially enriched 'safe sites' for the establishment of forest species during extended periods of time. In addition, these trees also probably act as favourable habitats for the animal dispersers of forest tree seed and as sources of mycorrhizal infection of establishing forest tree seedlings.

The establishment of forest tree seedlings is facilitated by broadleaved woody savanna plants, and the subsequent nutrient requirements of those capable of sufficiently slow growth can be met mainly from atmospheric accessions (Fig. 1). The main obstacle to these species achieving full size is fire, the probability of which is much reduced once a continuous canopy of savanna trees becomes established. The first-generation forest composed of these species would be floristically distinct. Transitional broadleaved forest in which species of *Calophyllum, Miconia, Terminalia, Vochysia* and *Xylopia* are prominent was described in Belize by Romney (1959), who interpreted it as a stage in the degeneration of forest to savanna. It seems equally likely that it is a stage in the transition from savanna to forest. The broadleaved seasonal *Calophyllum–Terminalia* forest occupying granite, quartzite, sandstone and shale described by Romney (1959) may provide the closest analogue of the forest that could ultimately develop in the Mountain Pine Ridge.

Therefore it is concluded that the establishment of tropical forest on most in-fertile tropical soils is feasible, provided that suitable transitional species are present and a sufficient fire-free time interval is available. Most tropical soils do not progress inexorably towards zero fertility as a result of weathering, except on such specialized substrates as deep quartzitic sands (e.g. Thompson 1983). Instead, the weathering of silicate minerals usually leads to relatively stable soil mineral substrates that are high in kaolinitic clays and sesquioxides (Loughnan 1969). Such soils are of inherently low fertility, but possess the adsorptive properties that enable the savanna communities occupying them to exist upon atmospheric accessions, and they can be transformed gradually to more eutrophic systems once prolonged fire suppression allows the development of large biomass forest communities.

This conclusion offers some hope for the re-establishment of tropical forest on soils of even marginal fertility, provided that the necessary taxa have not been eliminated. Tropical floras are not a homogeneous nutritional guild and most probably contain transitional species capable of re-establishing a forest's nutrient store. However, the long time necessary for the completion of this process, for the four nutrients emphasized in this paper, poses a serious practical constraint in view of the speed with which tropical forest is now being destroyed.

ACKNOWLEDGEMENTS

The results presented represent the joint efforts of several colleagues and former students: Gus Carty, Pamela Hiebert, Alan Hill, John Hudson, Ian Hutchinson, Christine Manville, Kiyoko Miyanishi, Kandiah Sanmugadas and Howard Stewart. In addition, I wish to thank many personnel in the Belize Forestry Department for helpful cooperation. Financial support was provided by the Natural Sciences and Engineering Research Council of Canada and the Guggenheim Foundation.

REFERENCES

Ahmad, N. & Jones, R.L. (1969). A plinthaquult of the Aripo savannas, North Trinidad. I. Properties of the soil and chemical composition of the natural vegetation. *Soil Science Society of America, Proceedings,* **35** 762–768.

Cavalcanti, L.H. (1978). *Efeito das cinzas resultantes da queimada sobre a productividade do estrato herbaceo subarbustivo do cerrado de Emas.* D.Sc. Thesis, Universidade de Sao Paulo, Brazil (cited in Coutinho 1982).

Chapin, F.S. (1980). The mineral nutrition of wild plants. *Annual Review of Ecology and Systematics,* **11**, 233–260.

Charter, C.F. (1941). *A Reconnaissance Survey of the Soils of British Honduras.* Government Printer, Port-of-Spain, Trinidad.

Coutinho, L.M. (1982). Ecological effects of fire in Brazilian cerrado. *Ecology of Tropical Savannas* (Ed. by B.J. Huntley & B.H. Walker), pp. 273–291. Springer, New York.

Egunjobi, J.K. & Bada, S.O. (1979). Biomass and nutrient distribution in stands of *Pinus caribaea* L. in the dry forest zone of Nigeria. *Biotropica,* **11**, 130–135.

Flenley, J.R. (1979). *The Equatorial Rain Forest: A Geological History.* Butterworths, London.

Golley, F.B. (1983). Nutrient cycling and nutrient conservation. *Tropical Rain Forest Ecosystems. Structure and Function* (Ed. by F.B. Golley), pp. 137–156. Elsevier, New York.

Hardy, F. (1960). *Edaphic savannas of tropical America (with particular reference to those caused by nutrient deficiency*). Instituto Interamericano de Ciencias Agricolas, Turrialba, Costa Rica (mimeographed).

Herrera, R., Merida,T., Stark, N. & Jordan, C.F. (1978). Direct phosphorus transfer from leaf litter to roots. *Naturwissenschaften*, **65**, 208–209.

Hudson, J., Kellman, M., Sanmugadas, K. & Alvarado, C. (1983). Prescribed burning of *Pinus oocarpa* in Honduras II. Effects on nutrient cycling. *Forest Ecology and Management*, **5**, 283–300.

Hutchinson, I. (1977). *Ecological modelling and the stand dynamics of* Pinus caribaea *in Mountain Pine Ridge, Belize*. PhD Thesis, Simon Fraser University, Vancouver.

Johnson, D.W. & Cole, D.W. (1980). Anion mobility in soils: relevance to nutrient transport from forest ecosystems. *Environment International*, **3**, 79–90.

Jordan, C.F., Golley, F.B., Hall, J. & Hall, J. (1980). Nutrient scavenging of rainfall by the canopy of an Amazonian rain forest. *Biotropica*, **12**, 61–66.

Jordan, C.F. & Kline, J.R. (1972). Mineral cycling: some basic concepts and their application in a tropical rain forest. *Annual Review of Ecology and Systematics*, **3**, 33–50.

Kadeba, O. & Aduayi, E.A. (1986). Dry matter production and nutrient distribution in a *Pinus caribaea* stand planted in a subhumid savanna site. *Oikos*, **46**, 237–242.

Kellman, M. (1975). Evidence for Late Glacial Age fire in a tropical montane savanna. *Journal of Biogeography*, **2**, 57–63.

Kellman, M. (1976). Broadleaved species interference with *Pinus caribaea* in a managed pine savanna. *Commonwealth Forestry Review*, **55**, 229–245.

Kellman, M. (1979). Soil enrichment by Neotropical savanna trees. *Journal of Ecology*, **67**, 565–577.

Kellman, M. (1984). Synergistic relationships between fire and low soil fertility in Neotropical savannas: a hypothesis. *Biotropica*, **16**, 158–160.

Kellman, M. (1985a). Nutrient retention by savanna ecosystems. III. Response to artificial loading. *Journal of Ecology*, **73**, 963–972.

Kellman, M. (1985b). Forest seedling establishment in Neotropical savannas: transplant experiments with *Xylopia frutescens* and *Calophyllum brasiliense*. *Journal of Biogeography*, **12**, 373–379.

Kellman, M. (1986). Long-term effects of cutting tap roots of *Pinus caribaea* growing on infertile savanna soils. *Plant and Soil*, **93**, 137–140.

Kellman, M. & Carty, A. (1986). Magnitude of nutrient influxes from atmospheric sources to a Central American *Pinus caribaea* woodland. *Journal of Applied Ecology*, **23**, 211–226.

Kellman, M. & Hudson, J. (1982). Nutrition of *Pinus caribaea* in its native savanna habitat. *Plant and Soil*, **64**, 381–391.

Kellman, M., Hudson, J. & Sanmugadas, K. (1982). Temporal variability in atmospheric nutrient influx to a tropical ecosystem. *Biotropica*, **14**, 1–9.

Kellman, M. & Miyanishi, K. (1982). Forest seedling establishment in Neotropical savannas: observations and experiments in the Mountain Pine Ridge savanna, Belize. *Journal of Biogeography*, **9**, 193–206.

Kellman, M., Miyanishi, K. & Hiebert, P. (1985). Nutrient retention by savanna ecosystems. II. Retention after fire. *Journal of Ecology*, **73**, 953–962.

Kellman, M., Miyanishi, K. & Hiebert, P. (1987). Nutrient sequestering by the understorey strata of natural *Pinus caribaea* stands subject to prescription burning. *Forest Ecology and Management*, **21**, 57–73.

Kellman, M. & Sanmugadas, K. (1985). Nutrient retention by savanna ecosystems. I. Retention in the absence of fire. *Journal of Ecology*, **73**, 935–951.

Kershaw, A.P. (1978). Record of last interglacial-glacial cycle from north-eastern Queensland. *Nature (London)*, **272**, 159–161.

Klinge, H. (1973). Root mass estimation in lowland tropical rain forests of central Amazonia, Brazil. I. Fine root mass of a pale yellow latosol and a giant humus podzol. *Tropical Ecology*, **14**, 29–38.

Klinge, H. (1976a). Bilanzierung von Hauptnahrstoffen im Okosystem tropischer regenwald (Manaus) — vorlaufige daten. *Biogeographica*, **7**, 59–76.

Klinge, H. (1976b). Root mass estimation in lowland tropical rain forests of central Amazonia, Brazil. IV. Nutrients in fine roots from latosols. *Tropical Ecology*, **17**, 79–88.

Livingstone, D.A. (1975). Late Quaternary climatic change in Africa. *Annual Review of Ecology and Systematics*, **6**, 249–280.

Lopes, A.S. & Cox, F.R. (1977). A survey of the fertility status of surface soils under 'cerrado' vegetation in Brazil. *Soil Science Society of America Journal*, **41**, 742–747.

Loughnan, F.C. (1969). *Chemical Weathering of Silicate Minerals*. Elsevier, New York.

Lundell, C.L. (1940). Botany of the Maya area. Miscellaneous Papers XVI. *The 1936 Michigan–Carnegie Botanical Expedition to British Honduras. Publications of the Carnegie Institute 522*, pp. 1–57. Carnegie Institute, Washington DC.

Menault, J.C., Barbault, R., Lavelle, P. & Lepage, M. (1985). African savannas: biological systems of humification and mineralization. *Ecology and Management of the World's Savannas* (Ed. by J.C. Tothill & J.J. Mott), pp. 14–33. Australian Academy of Science, Canberra.

Miller, H.G., Cooper, J.M., Miller, J.D. & Pauline, O.J.L. (1979). Nutrient cycles in pine and their adaptation to poor soils. *Canadian Journal of Forest Research*, **9**, 19–26.

Miyanishi, K. (1984). *The effects of prescribed burning on the population dynamics of* Miconia albicans *and* Clidemia sericea. PhD Thesis, York University, Toronto.

Miyanishi, K. & Kellman, M. (1986). The role of root nutrient reserves in regrowth of two savanna shrubs. *Canadian Journal of Botany*, **64**, 1244–1248.

Montes, R. & Medina, E. (1977). Leaf nutrient content and ecological behaviour of trees and grasses in the *Trachypogon* savannas of Venezuela. *Geo-Eco-Tropica*, **1**, 295–307.

Munro, N. (1966). The fire ecology of Caribbean pine in Nicaragua. *Proceedings of the Tall Timbers Fire Ecology Conference*, **5**, 67–83.

Nadkarni, N. (1982). Canopy roots: convergent evolution in rainforest nutrient cycles. *Science*, **214**, 1023–1024.

Richards, P.W. (1952). *The Tropical Rain Forest*. Cambridge University Press, Cambridge.

Romney, D.H. (Ed.) (1959). *Land in British Honduras. Report of the British Honduras Land Use Survey Team. Colonial Research Publications 24*. HMSO, London.

San José, J.J. & Fariñas, M.R. (1983). Changes in tree density and species composition in a protected *Trachypogon* savanna, Venezuela. *Ecology*, **64**, 447–453.

Sarmiento, G. (1984). *The Ecology of Neotropical Savannas* (translated by O. Solbrig). Harvard University Press, Cambridge, MA.

Stark, N.M. & Jordan, C.F. (1978). Nutrient retention by the root mat of an Amazonian rain forest. *Ecology*, **59**, 434–437.

Stewart, H. & Kellman, M. (1982). Nutrient accumulation by *Pinus caribaea* in its native savanna habitat. *Plant and Soil*, **69**, 105–118.

Thompson, C.H. (1983). Development and weathering of large parabolic dune systems along the subtropical coast of eastern Australia. *Zeitschrift für Geomorphologie*, **45**, 205–225.

Uhl, C. & Jordan, C.F. (1984). Succession and nutrient dynamics following forest cutting and burning in Amazonia. *Ecology*, **65**, 1476–1490.

Van der Hammen, T. (1974). The Pleistocene changes of vegetation and climate in tropical South America. *Journal of Biogeography*, **1**, 3–26.

Vitousek, P.M. (1983). Mechanisms of ion leaching in natural and managed ecosystems. *Disturbance and Ecosystems. Components of Response* (Ed. by H.A. Mooney & M. Godron), pp. 129–144. Springer, New York.

Walker, J., Thompson, C.H., Fergus, I.F. & Tunstall, B.R. (1981). Plant succession and soil development in coastal sand dunes of subtropical eastern Australia. *Forest Succession, Concepts and Applications* (Ed. by D.C. West, H.H. Shugart & D.B. Botkin), pp. 107–131. Springer, New York.

Wiklander, L. (1974). Leaching of plant nutrients in soils. I. General principles. *Acta Agriculturae Scandanavica*, **24**, 349–356.

Wiklander, L. (1980). Interactions between cations and anions influencing adsorption and leaching. *Effects of Acid Precipitation on Terrestrial Ecosystems* (Ed. by T.C. Hutchinson & M. Havas), pp. 239–254. Plenum Press, New York.

Wymstra, T.A. & Van der Hammen, T. (1966). Palynological data on the history of tropical savannas in northern South America. *Overdruk uit Leidse Geologische Mededelingen*, **38**, 71–90.

Mineral nutrients in tropical dry deciduous forest and savanna ecosystems in India

K. P. SINGH

Centre of Advanced Study in Botany,
Banaras Hindu University,
Varanasi 221005, India

SUMMARY

1 A comparison of biomass production and nutrient cycling was made between tropical dry deciduous forest (with the dominant trees *Anogeissus latifolia*, *Buchanania lanzan* and *Diospyros melanoxylon*) and savanna (with the dominant grasses *Bothriochloa pertusa* and *Heteropogon contortus* and with bushes of *Zizyphus jujuba*), both located in close proximity on the Vindhyan plateau in northern India.
2 Forest biomass (95 t ha^{-1}) was about 13 times greater than that of the savanna. The forest (including soils) contained 1.5 times more nitrogen (3623 compared with 2487 kg ha^{-1}) and phosphorus (182 compared with 133 kg ha^{-1}) and over 3.5 times more potassium (838 compared with 245 kg ha^{-1}) than the savanna. The larger part of the mass of all nutrients was held by the soil in both ecosystems.
3 The mean concentrations (biomass weighted) of nitrogen, phosphorus and potassium in the savanna vegetation as a whole were 77, 100 and 105% greater than the corresponding concentrations in the forest.
4 The annual nitrogen and phosphorus uptake and return through litterfall were similar in both ecosystems. The savanna, however, showed a greater uptake and return of potassium. The annual below-ground nutrient return in the savanna was about 1.5 times greater than in the forest.
5 Relative to their low share (<2%) in the nutrient content of the forest vegetation, the herbs accounted for 15–24% of the annual uptake of the major nutrients.
6 The forest was moderately nutrient-use efficient as judged from the litterfall mass/nutrient content quotient (gram dry matter per gram nutrient): nitrogen, 79; phosphorus, 1059; potassium, 167. The forest required smaller quantities than the savanna of all the major nutrients for the same amount of energy flow through the vegetation. Compared with the savanna, the forest had slower nutrient cycling but greater nutrient-use efficiency.

INTRODUCTION

Eighty-six per cent of the forested area of India is under tropical forest, of which 37% is of the moist deciduous type, 53% is dry deciduous, and the rest is wet ever-green or semi-evergreen (Kaul & Sharma 1971). The deciduous forest regions have been preferred as human settlement sites (northern India has a present day

153

mean population density of 200 people km^{-2}) because they contain valuable timber species such as teak (*Tectona grandis* L. Verbenaceae) and sal (*Shorea robusta* Gaertn. Dipterocarpaceae), and have long sustained permanent agriculture and forest plantations. Heavy anthropogenic pressures for centuries have caused large-scale conversion of tropical deciduous forests into savannas. *Landsat* data for 1972–1975 and 1980–1982 suggest that this process continues. During the 8-year period the closed forest area in India decreased by 10×10^6 ha, but the open forest area increased by 1.3×10^6 ha (NRSA 1983). The present day regional landscape appears as a mosaic of various stages of savanna interspersed with remnant forest patches varying in size (Misra 1983). The increase in the intensity of biotic disturbances leads to a change from one stage of savanna to another; at each stage some species are recruited while others are reduced or eliminated. Sustained disturbances result in semi-stable stages, while relaxation of disturbance initiates a recovery which is rarely complete. Usually each single potential savanna type is made up of many communities disturbed to varying degrees (Singh, Hanxi & Sajise 1985). Considerable information has been collected on various aspects of nutrient cycling in moist tropical forests (Vitousek & Sanford 1986), but such information is scarce for dry tropical forests (Murphy & Lugo 1986). The International Biological Programme studies on energy flow and nutrient cycling through the herbaceous component of the Indian savannas have been summarized by Singh *et al.* (1979). Singh & Pandey (1981) have quantified nitrogen cycling in a dry deciduous forest. However, data are available from insufficient sites to permit regional generalizations for deciduous forests or even savannas.

In the Chandraprabha sanctuary (25°52′N, 83°9′E) in the Vindhyan plateau region, about 80 km away from Varanasi, several stands of dry deciduous forest, shrub savanna and teak plantation under similar soil and climatic conditions have been investigated for biomass production and nutrient cycling (Singh & Misra 1979; Singh, Srivastava & Singh 1984). This paper provides a comparison of nutrient storages and transfers in these dry deciduous forest and savanna ecosystems.

TROPICAL DECIDUOUS FOREST ENVIRONMENT

The climatic limits of the dry tropical forests have been defined in various ways. For example, according to the classification of Holdridge (1967), the dry tropical and subtropical forests and woodlands occur in frost-free areas having mean annual temperatures of higher than 17 °C, mean annual rainfall of between 250 and 2000 mm, and a ratio of potential evapotranspiration (PET) to precipitation (P) of greater than unity. In the absence of accurate estimates of the PET : P ratio, Brown & Lugo (1982) suggested the use of the ratio of mean annual temperature (T) to mean annual precipitation (P). Of the 18 tropical dry forest sites, with markedly different annual rainfall, studied by Murphy & Lugo (1986), the T : P ratio varied between 4.1×10^{-2} °C mm^{-1} at the driest site (600 mm rainfall,

Udaipur, India) and $1.4 \times 10^{-2}\,°C\,mm^{-1}$ at the wettest site (1800 mm rainfall, La Pacifica, Costa Rica). However, in the Indian subcontinent, these climatic limits encompass the broad range from moist deciduous forest to the xerophilous thorn forest. Here the mean annual temperature ranges between 20 °C and 30 °C, with a mean January (the coldest month) temperature of greater than 15 °C. The range of mean temperatures widens in the forests of drier regions (Table 1). From the wet evergreen forest zone to the dry deciduous forest zone, the mean annual rainfall decreases from more than 2400 mm to as low as 750 mm, and the number of dry months increases from 3–5 to 5–8 (Champion & Seth 1968). Thus, water scarcity prevails to varying degrees in all tropical forests in India, and the various forest types are mainly regulated by the amount and seasonal distribution of annual rainfall.

TABLE 1. Climatic and vegetational features of selected tropical forests in India (from Champion & Seth (1968), Singh & Misra (1979), Singh & Singh (1984), Singh, Srivastava & Singh (1984) and Singh *et al.* (1984))

Forest type	Wet evergreen	Moist deciduous	Dry deciduous
Climate			
Mean annual temperature (°C)	23–27	20–29	20–29
Mean January temperature (°C)	15–21	12–26	16–25
Annual rainfall (mm)	>2400	1200–3000	750–1400
Number of dry months	3–5	4–8	5–8
Vegetation			
Evergreenness	Entirely or nearly so	Predominantly deciduous, subcanopy evergreen	Entirely deciduous or nearly so
Species richness	Extremely rich	Rich	Poor
Shannon–Wiener index	3.5–4.1		1.4–1.9
Canopy height (m)	30–40	20–30	8–20
Basal area ($m^2\,ha^{-1}$)	40–55	35–50	15–20
Biomass ($t\,ha^{-1}$)	400–600	300–350	50–200

The Chandraprabha region is characterized by a mean annual temperature of 26 °C and about 1050 mm annual rainfall. The climate is strongly seasonal; 93% of the rainfall is received during the rainy season (July–October) when the ambient temperature fluctuates around 30 °C (Fig. 1). Out of the average number of 55 rainy days every year, 48 occur during the rainy season. The lowering of the temperature in early November marks the beginning of the dry, winter season, and the low temperature extreme is attained in January, when the night-time temperature occasionally falls to 4 °C. Only 2% of the annual rainfall occurs in winter. During the succeeding dry hot summer less than 5% of the annual rainfall is received, and the temperature continuously rises until May, when the mean monthly values approach 45 °C.

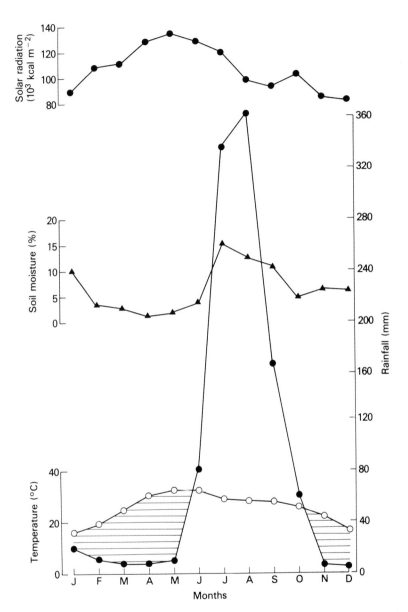

Fig. 1. Climatic diagram for Varanasi showing wet and dry (hatched area) periods; open circles represent mean monthly temperatures, full circles represent monthly rainfall; also shown is the variation in soil moisture content (full triangles) and the solar radiation through the year (full circles at the top).

Forest and savanna soils in the Chandraprabha sanctuary are shallow, of residual origin, reddish-brown colour and of sandy loam texture (Table 2). The pH of the soils varies from 6.6 to 7.2. Their water-holding capacity is moderate, but the organic matter (1.6–2.0%) and total nitrogen (0.5–0.9%) concentrations are low.

TABLE 2. Chemical and physical properties of the surface layer of soils in the forest and savanna ecosystems in the Chandraprabha sanctuary (Pandey 1980)

	Forest	Savanna
pH (log units)	6.6–7.2	6.6–7.2
Organic matter (%)	1.6–2.1	1.6–1.8
Total nitrogen (%)	0.06–0.09	0.05–0.07
Colour	Reddish brown	Reddish brown
	(5 YR 4/4)	(2.5 YR 5/4)
Texture	Sandy loam	Sandy loam
Mechanical composition		
Clay (%)	13.3–16.5	12.8–15.1
Silt (%)	26.7–30.2	27.9–30.1
Sand (%)	50.4–54.8	52.0–56.0
Bulk density (g cm^{-3})	1.23–1.37	1.34–1.42
Water-holding capacity (%)	43–49	40–46
Field capacity (%)	29–34	27–32

STUDY SITES

The Chandraprabha sanctuary vegetation consists of localized Northern Tropical Dry Deciduous forest (subgroup 5-B of Champion & Seth (1968)) interspersed amongst vast expanses of savanna. The savannas are derived from the original forests, and are now maintained by grazing and fire. The top storey trees in the forests form a continuous 15–20 m high canopy, underlain by a discontinuous lower storey of trees, a thin shrub layer and a seasonal herb layer including several grasses. The most common woody species in the forest are *Anogeissus latifolia* Wall. (Combretaceae), *Buchanania lanzan* Spreng. (Anacardiaceae), *Diospyros melanoxylon* Roxb. (Ebenaceae) (among 25 spp.) and *Holarrhena antidysentrica* Wall. (Apocynaceae) (among four shrubs). The savanna vegetation is formed by the dominant grasses *Bothriochloa pertusa* (L.) A. Camus and *Heteropogon contortus* (L.) Room & Schult, the sparsely distributed shrub *Zizyphus jujuba* Lamk. (Rhamnaceae), and more than 30 herbaceous species.

A remarkable feature of the vegetation is the striking contrast between the rainy season and summer season aspects. During the rainy season, both forest and savanna become lush green due to the presence of fully expanded leaves of trees and shrubs and a dense herbaceous layer (Table 3). All the woody species are deciduous and the early-summer aspect is pale and parched dry because of the leafless trees and shrubs and a dried-up herb layer. New tree foliage slowly begins to emerge later during the summer. The savanna herbage remains dried up throughout the summer and the new green shoots rapidly develop after the onset of the rains.

TABLE 3. Vegetation, biomass and net production in tropical dry deciduous forest and savanna ecosystems in the Chandraprabha sanctuary (*denotes a rainy season)

	Forest	Savanna
Density		
Trees (ha^{-1})	1055	0
Shrubs (ha^{-1})	343	104
Herbs (m^{-2})*	416	672
Leaf-area index (ha ha^{-1})*	3–7	4
Plant biomass (t ha^{-1})	95	67
Trees (%)	94	0
Shrubs (%)	4	34
Herbs (%)	2	66
Net production (t ha^{-1} year^{-1})	15	11
Trees (%)	86	0
Shrubs (%)	5	22
Herbs (%)	9	78
Energy capture efficiency in net production (%)	0.87	0.72

METHODS

The methods are described in detail by Singh & Misra (1979).

For the forest biomass and nutrient studies, six permanent plots (20 m × 25 m) were established in each of two stands. One stand was in natural forest, the other in degraded forest. In each plot the girths of all trees and shrubs (*c.* 250 individuals) were repeatedly measured for 3 years. Girth : component biomass regressions were developed for 12 woody species by harvesting more than 200 selected individuals outside the sample area. Separate (from the allometric estimations) estimates were made for litterfall (on 18 areas of 1 m^2, collected every 4 weeks for 12 months), litter accumulation on the soil (collected from six different 1-m^2 areas every 4 weeks for 12 months), fine root growth, and litter decomposition. The net production was calculated as the sum of the annual increment in the non-green parts and peak leaf biomass (by species), with appropriate corrections for fine root growth and various litterfall categories. The herbs in the forest stands were estimated every month by excavating four soil monoliths (25 cm × 25 cm × 30 cm), and separating the plants into their different components.

The savanna shrubs were studied in five permanent sample plots (20 m × 25 m) in each of two stands. One stand was protected and the other grazed. The shrubs were grouped into four girth classes. Seasonal variation in the biomass of each girth class was determined by felling three individuals of each girth class from outside the stand and dividing them into their components. The savanna herbs were studied from nine soil monoliths (25 cm × 25 cm × 30 cm) excavated monthly from the two stands. Savanna litter collections were made from each monolith excavated for biomass estimation.

Soil samples were collected monthly for 1 year at three randomly located points within each stand. At each point the samples were collected at three depths (0–10, 10–20 and 20–30 cm) and bulk density measurements were made. The soils were lightly ground to pass a 2 mm mesh before analysis.

The samples collected by the above methods were dried and powdered and the plants and litter were analysed for total concentrations of nitrogen, phosphorus and potassium, whilst the soils were analysed by the methods of Jackson (1958) for total nitrogen, extractable phosphorus and exchangeable potassium.

In the plant analyses, the species and their components were kept separately and were used to calculate biomass-weighted mean concentrations for the ecosystems as a whole. For the forest this involved a separate calculation of nutrient content for each of the 12 main woody species and the use of the mean concentrations for these 12 species as values for the concentrations in each of the rarer species.

RESULTS

The results (Tables 2–7 and Fig. 2) are presented as means for the two stands of forest and of savanna. Data for the stands separately are given in Singh & Misra (1979).

Biomass

The plant biomass in the Chandraprabha forest (95 t ha^{-1}) was over 13 times greater than the mean biomass of the savanna through the year (Table 3). The trees accounted for 94% of the total biomass in the forest. In the savanna the share of shrubs was one-third and that of herbs two-thirds of the total biomass. The forest had a slightly higher net production than the savanna. Relative to their contribution to the biomass, the herbs made a greater contribution to the net production in both ecosystems.

Nutrient concentrations

The seasonal variations in nitrogen, phosphorus and potassium concentrations in different components of savanna and forest vegetation are summarized in Fig. 2. In forest trees the nitrogen and phosphorus concentrations were always highest in the leaves, followed in decreasing order by twigs and fine roots (<10 mm diameter) and then by branches, trunk and major roots (>10 mm diameter); in the case of potassium, however, the twigs had slightly higher concentrations than the leaves. In the savanna shrubs the leaves always had the highest concentrations. In herbs the nutrient concentrations in the above-ground components always exceeded those of the below-ground components. These concentration differences were small in the savanna but were well marked in the forest.

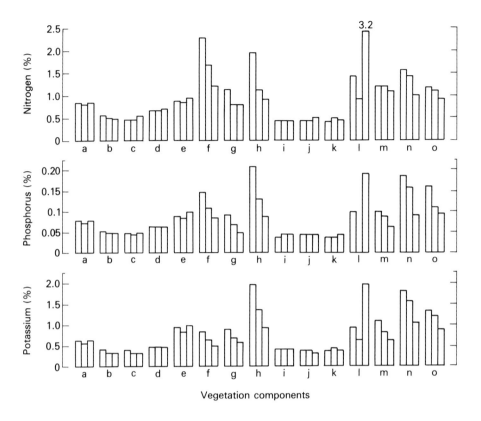

FIG. 2. Seasonal pattern of mean nutrient concentrations (%) in vegetation components in the forest and savanna ecosystems in the Chandraprabha sanctuary. In each cluster (a–o) the bar on the left stands for rainy season, the central bar for winter, and the bar on the right for summer. Values for forest trees are the means of 11 species, those of savanna herbs are the means of three dominant species and those of forest herbs are for composite plant material; shrub data in forest and savanna refer to the dominant species. Cluster code: forest trees: a, fine roots; b, major roots; c, trunks; d, branches; e, twigs; f, leaves; forest herbs: g, below-ground; h, above-ground; savanna shrubs: i, major roots; j, trunks; k, branches; l, leaves; savanna herbs: m, below-ground; n, green shoot; o, standing dead shoot.

In both ecosystems clear seasonal variations occurred in the nutrient concentrations in some plant components; in others the variations were indistinct. The forest tree leaves exhibited concentration peaks in mid-rainy season and thereafter a consistent decline occurred until abscission in early summer (Fig. 2). Around this time the nutrient concentrations in the twigs, after attaining a winter low, appeared to increase, probably due to retranslocation of nutrients from the senescing leaves. Fine roots also showed an increase in nutrient concentrations in the summer, which may partly be due to high root mortality in this season and the possible retranslocation of nutrients from the senescing fine roots. Singh & Srivastava (1986) have shown a marked decline in the fine root biomass in teak plantations through the summer and a rapid rise in the total non-structural carbohydrate concentration during the same period.

TABLE 4. Biomass-weighted mean nitrogen, phosphorus and potassium concentrations (%) in different life forms in the forest and savanna ecosystems in the Chandraprabha sanctuary

| | Forest | | | Savanna | | |
	N	P	K	N	P	K
Trees	0.71	0.05	0.46			
Shrubs	0.98	0.09	0.70	1.13	0.09	0.65
Herbs	0.97	0.08	0.81	1.38	0.14	1.23
Vegetation	0.73	0.06	0.48	1.29	0.12	1.11

Thus the shedding of both above-ground and below-ground plant parts in summer seems to be accompanied by nutrient withdrawals from these parts, adding to the conservation of nutrients in the forest biomass.

In other components (branches, trunks and major roots) of the forest trees the seasonal variations in nutrient concentrations were small and irregular (Fig. 2). The savanna shrubs showed pronounced seasonal variations; young leaves exhibited peak concentrations in summer, and non-photosynthetic components showed a maximum in winter. In both ecosystems, especially in the forest, the herbs showed strong seasonality; in all components concentration peaks were attained in the rainy season and lows in the summer.

On the basis of biomass-weighetd means (Table 4), the mean concentrations of nitrogen, phosphorus and potassium in the savanna vegetation, as a whole, were 77, 100 and 105% greater than the corresponding concentrations in the forest. Nevertheless, the mean nutrient concentrations in the Chandraprabha deciduous forest were similar to those in moist tropical forests on moderately fertile soils, and higher than those of the moist forests on infertile soils (cf. data in Vitousek & Sanford (1986)). The weighted mean concentrations in five tropical forests in Colombia (Golley & Clements 1978) are less for phosphorus (0.03–0.6%) but greater for potassium (0.5–1.2%) than the corresponding concentrations in the Chandraprabha forest.

Of the three life forms in the forest, biomass-weighted concentrations of all nutrients in the trees were distinctly lower than those in shrubs and herbs, because of the predominance of low-nutrient woody tissues. While nitrogen and phosphorus concentrations in forest shrubs and herbs were similar, the potassium concentration in herbs was distinctly higher. In the savanna, however, the herbs had greater concentrations than shrubs for all nutrients, the difference being most marked in the case of potassium. Comparing the two ecosystems, the shrubs showed similar phosphorus and potassium concentrations but a marginally greater nitrogen concentration in the savanna. On the other hand, the savanna herbs were richer in all nutrients than the forest herbs.

Nutrient contents

The forest and savanna differed not only in the total nutrient contents but also in the nutrient distribution in the vegetation components and the soil (Table 5). The forest contained about 1.5 times more nitrogen (3623 compared with 2487 kg ha^{-1}) and phosphorus (182 compared with 133 kg ha^{-1}), and over 3.5 times more potassium (838 compared with 245 kg ha^{-1}) than the savanna (Table 5). The phosphorus contents of the forest and savanna soils were similar, but the forest soil had about 25% more nitrogen and about 150% more potassium than the savanna soil. In the forest, 80% of the total nitrogen content was held in the soil, 1% in the litter and 19% in the vegetation. The distribution of phosphorus in the forest was 69% in the soil, 2% in the litter and 29% in the vegetation and that of potassium was 45% in the soil, 1% in the litter and 54% in the vegetation. In the savanna, however, the soil accounted for 97% of the total nitrogen, 93% of the phosphorus and 65% of the potassium. (These calculations are based on total nitrogen, available phosphorus and exchangeable potassium in the soil.) In the Vindhyan region soils the proportion of available phosphorus to total phosphorus is 1 : 5 (Singh 1974), and the proportion of exchangeable potassium to total potassium is 1 : 20 (Tiwari & Ram 1976). Thus the expected total amounts of phosphorus in the soils of forest and savanna are 630 and 670 kg ha^{-1}, respectively and the expected total amounts of potassium are 7540 and 3200 kg ha^{-1}, respectively. In both ecosystems the soil probably accounts for over 90% of the total phosphorus and potassium.

The greater nutrient richness of forest compared with savanna soil has also been observed in the American tropics. According to Tothill (1984), in the llama of Colombia several studies comparing forest soils with savanna soils, within the same climatic region, have shown that forest soil has 33% more nitrogen, 13–15% more phosphorus and 80% more potassium.

Some nutrient distributions were similar for the two ecosystems; for instance, both had about three-quarters of the vegetation nutrient content in the above-ground parts and one-quarter in the below-ground parts, and the distribution of the total nutrient content amongst trees, shrubs and herbs paralleled their respective biomass distributions.

Although the plant biomass was over 13 times greater in the forest, its nutrient contents were only about 6–8 times greater than those in the savanna, reflecting the relative nutrient richness of the savanna.

Nutrient uptake

In spite of the widely varying nutrient contents, the annual uptake of nutrients in the forest and savanna was similar except for the slightly higher potassium uptake in the savanna (Table 5). In both ecosystems the percentage share of herbs in the total nutrient uptake was distinctly greater than their percentage contribution to the total nutrient content in the stand. The herbs accounted for 15–24% of the total uptake of various nutrients in the forest (cf. 2.5% of the vegetation content), and 88–93% of the uptake in the savanna (cf. about 70% of the vegetation content). The bulk of the uptake in herbs occurred during the rainy season, because the majority of grass and herb species grow and reproduce then (Misra 1983).

TABLE 5. Nutrient content and cycling in tropical dry deciduous forest and savanna ecosystems in the Chandraprabha sanctuary (*available phosphorus; [†]exchangeable potassium; [‡]vegetation content/annual uptake; [§] mean litter content/litterfall content; **soil content/total nutrient release)

| Parameters | | Forest | | | Savanna | |
	N	P*	K[†]	N	P*	K[†]
Nutrient content (kg ha^{-1})						
Trees	625	48	410			
Shrubs	41	4	30	26	2	20
Herbs	14	1	11	61	6	54
Vegetation (1)	680	53	451	87	8	74
Vegetation above-ground (%)	77	77	78	71	75	72
Vegetation below-ground (%)	23	23	22	29	25	28
Litter (2)	37	3	11	14	1	11
Soil (0–30 cm depth) (3)	2906	126	377	2386	134	160
Stand (1 + 2 + 3)	3623	182	838	2487	133	245
Nutrient uptake in net production (kg ha^{-1} year^{-1})	172	13	97	157	15	133
Trees (%)	77	69	68	0	0	0
Shrubs (%)	8	8	8	11	7	12
Herbs (%)	15	23	24	89	93	88
Total litterfall (kg ha^{-1} year^{-1})	80	6	38	82	8	77
Litter decomposition release (kg ha^{-1} year^{-1})	74	6	36	81	8	76
Root decomposition release (kg ha^{-1} year^{-1})	30	2	22	43	3	31
Total release (kg ha^{-1} year^{-1})	104	8	58	124	11	107
Retention in vegetation (kg ha^{-1} year^{-1})	62	4	38	20	2	17
Turnover time (year)						
Vegetation[‡]	3.9	4	4.6	0.5	0.5	0.6
Litter[§]	0.5	0.5	0.6	0.2	0.2	0.1
Soil**	27.9	15.0	6.5	19.2	11.1	1.5

Profuse growth of fine roots occurred in the forest in the rainy season. Singh & Singh (1981) have estimated that fine root production averages 40 kg ha^{-1} day^{-1} in the rainy season. In the woody species about one-half of the annual total uptake of nutrients was incorporated in leaf production (active period July–January) and about one-fifth in the production of fine roots.

Litterfall nutrients

The major portion of the transfer of nutrients from the above-ground plant parts to the soil through litterfall occurred in the dry part of the year, the second half of winter to early summer. In the savanna much of the above-ground herbage dried up by November, and the resulting standing dead mass gradually turned into litter through the summer. In the forest the non-leaf litterfall and leaf litterfall peaks were obtained during September–October and February–March, respectively. Forest and savanna returned closely similar amounts of nitrogen and phosphorus annually through the total litterfall (Table 5), but the return of potassium was almost double in the savanna.

Nutrient release during decomposition

The quantity of litter which accumulated over the soil surface varied seasonally in both ecosystems; the maximum occurred during the summer, and thereafter the quantity of litter declined rapidly through the rainy season until the minimum in early winter. These estimates of the litter disappearance over the soil under natural conditions indicated that in both forest and savanna the amounts of the three nutrients released through decomposition were about 95% or more of the amounts returned through annual litterfall (Table 5). It is assumed that the bulk of these nutrients enter into the soil.

Rapid breakdown of leaf litter enclosed in nylon net bags was noticed under field conditions (Table 6). In the savanna litter, 92% or more of the initial mass and nutrient stocks were lost in 1 year. However, the forest leaf litter showed smaller losses of nutrients, and some immobilization of nitrogen and phosphorus seemed to occur. About one-half of the annual loss of nitrogen and phosphorus in the decomposing leaf litter occurred during the rainy season; however, a relatively larger fraction of potassium was lost during the same period.

Fine root biomass in the forest showed a distinct decline from a peak in the rainy season to a trough in the summer (Singh & Singh 1981). In the savanna also the below-ground biomass of the herbs continuously declined until the summer. Calculations of the disappearance of fine roots in the forest after the rainy season suggested considerable below-ground nutrient return, which amounted to about one-half of the annual return of nitrogen and phosphorus through the litterfall (Table 5). The annual below-ground nutrient return in the savanna was about 1.5 times greater than the corresponding return in the forest. When the annual nutrient uptake by the vegetation and the total return (from above-ground and

TABLE 6. Annual loss (% initial) in mass, nitrogen, phosphorus and potassium during decomposition of leaf litter in the Chandraprabha sanctuary (forest values are the means of the litter of three tree species; savanna values are the means of combined shrub and herb litter; values in parentheses are for the rainy season)

	Forest	Savanna
Mass loss	77 (53)	95 (66)
N stock loss	63 (35)	92 (57)
P stock loss	62 (33)	92 (51)
K stock loss	85 (70)	96 (71)

below-ground parts) were compared, the estimated annual nutrient retention in the vegetation was found to be 2–3 times greater in the forest relative to the savanna.

Since the leaf litter decomposes rapidly it is likely that the detritus produced below-ground is largely decomposed through the year. Thus it is suggested that the total amounts of nutrients (above-ground and below-ground) released in the savanna exceed the total release in the forest particularly in the case of potassium (Table 5).

The turnover time, calculated as the ratio of nutrient stock to nutrient input, in different components reflects the relative speed of nutrient cycling in the ecosystems. In terms of turnover time, the cycling of the three nutrients was faster in all components of the savanna; about 8 times faster in the vegetation, 2.5 times faster in the litter, and 1.5 times faster in the soil (Table 5).

Nutrient-use efficiency

Efficient nutrient use results in a large amount of organic matter produced per unit of nutrient uptake; such efficiency is characterized by high carbon : nutrient ratios (low nutrient concentration) in litterfall, wood and root detritus (Vitousek 1984). (In this paper the term nutrient-use efficiency is used as in Vitousek (1984); the concept is fully discussed by Grubb (*this volume*).) The retranslocation of nutrients from senescing plant parts improves the nutrient-use efficiency. In the Chandraprabha forest the quantities of nutrients contained in the leaf litterfall were less (by 10–30% in different species) than those in the mature leaves, suggesting considerable retranslocation. However, these differences in nutrient concentrations may not reflect the true extent of the nutrient retranslocation because of the variable amounts of organic matter lost during leaf senescence. Vitousek & Sanford (1986) have suggested that a comparison of the nutrient : calcuim ratio of mature leaf and leaf litter will yield a better estimate of retranslocation, since calcium is practically immobile during senescence. More recent information using nutrient : calcium ratios from teak plantations raised in the same region showed 57–74% retranslocation of the various nutrients during senescence (Table 7). In teak the tendency for the conservation of nitrogen and phosphorus was greater than for potassium. These values may be compared with 34% retranslocation for nitrogen, 68% for phosphorus, and no retranslocation for potassium in a dry tropical forest in Puerto Rico (Lugo & Murphy 1986).

An assessment of the nutrient-use efficiency through the litterfall mass and concentration data indicated relatively moderate efficiency in the Chandraprabha forest with values (gram dry matter per gram nutrient) of 79 for nitrogen, 1059 for phosphorus and 167 for potassium. According to Vitousek (1984), values of 130 for nitrogen and 3000 for phosphorus are found in tropical forest with efficient nutrient economy. By extending this analogy of major nutrient use to the savanna, the Chandraprabha forest was found to be more efficient than the savanna (Table 7).

TABLE 7. Efficiency of nutrient use in the tropical dry deciduous forest and savanna in the Chandraprabha sanctuary. (*Retranslocation calculated by dividing the nutrient : Ca ratio in the leaf litterfall by the nutrient : Ca ratio in the mature leaf (Vitousek & Sanford 1986). [†]Nutrient-use efficiency = litterfall mass/litterfall nutrient content. [‡]Nutrient uptake (mg) per 1000 kcal energy capture in net production.)

	Forest			Savanna		
	N	P	K	N	P	K
Retranslocation (%)*	74	68	57			
Litterfall nutrient use[†]	79	1059	167	43	450	46
Nutrient uptake per unit energy capture[‡]	3000	225	1720	3290	320	2740

An evaluation of the efficiency of the nutrient cycling was made by calculating the nutrient uptake per unit of energy stored in the net production (through biomass increments and calorific value estimations) (Table 7). In both ecosystems the requirements of the three nutrients for each unit of energy capture was in the order: nitrogen > phosphorus > potassium. It was evident that the forest needed smaller amounts of all three nutrients than the savanna to support the same amount of energy flow through the vegetation. In other words, more energy was required by the forest than the savanna to pump similar amounts of these nutrients into the biological system.

CONCLUSION

Relatively little attention has been paid to the role of nutrients in dry tropical forests. These forests are characterized, among other features, by a large storage of major nutrients in the soil in comparison with their storage in the vegetation (Singh & Pandey 1981; Arnason & Lambert 1982; Lugo & Murphy 1986). Nutrient limitations to primary production seem unlikely in the dry deciduous forest in the Vindhyan region. In these forests the quantities of nutrients cycled annually are quite high compared with the quantities stored in the vegetation, indicating a rapid turnover. Moreover, they have rapid litter breakdown, considerable annual increment in the vegetation, and substantial growth of herbaceous species. Unlike the forests of the wet tropics (e.g. Proctor *et al.* 1983), in the dry deciduous forests the nutrient-rich herbs play a greater role in within-stand nutrient cycling.

During the short rainy season, when the dried soil is suddenly wetted, the peak rates of several ecosystem processes are more or less synchronized in time as well as in space; for instance, nutrient release from the decomposing litter, soil mineralization, the growth of herbs including many annuals, and fine root growth of woody species all occur near the soil surface. Therefore, it is suggested that in the dry tropical forests, rapid development of the ground flora and fine roots, during the short rainy season, is a nutrient conservation mechanism to reduce losses in runoff.

The conversion of the dry deciduous forest into savanna in the Vindhyan region in northern India involves several structural and functional changes including nutrient relations. While the biomass and nutrient content in the dry deciduous forest are much higher than those in the savanna, the annual net production and nutrient uptake in these two ecosystems are similar. The transformation from the stable forest to the quasi-stable savanna results in the speeding up of nutrient cycling, with little permanent nutrient storage, and significant nutrient leakages from the system, reflected in lower soil contents. The derived savanna systems have a lower nutrient-use efficiency. With strong nutrient withdrawal mechanisms operating in the deciduous forest, there is slightly slower but more efficient nutrient cycling.

ACKNOWLEDGEMENTS

Most of the research reported in this paper was carried out on an MAB research project (1975–1979) supported by the Department of Science and Technology, Government of India, and on a project studying fine tree roots (1981–1984) supported by the University Grant Commission. I wish to thank the Head of the Botany Department, Banaras Hindu University for facilities, and Mr S. B. Karmacharya and Mr A. P. Singh for help in the preparation of this paper.

REFERENCES

Arnason, J.T. & Lambert, J.D.T. (1982). Nitrogen cycling in the seasonally dry forest zone of Belize, Central America. *Plant and Soil*, **67**, 333–342.
Brown, S. & Lugo, A.E. (1982). The storage and production of organic matter in tropical forests and their role in the global carbon cycle. *Biotropica*, **14**, 161–187.
Champion, H.G. & Seth, S.K. (1968). *Revised Survey of the Forest Types of India*. Government of India, New Delhi.
Golley, F.B. & Clements, R.G. (1978). Elemental concentration in tropical forests and soil of northwestern Colombia. *Biotropica*, **10**, 144–151.
Holdridge, L.R. (1967). *Life Zone Ecology*. Tropical Science Center, San Jose.
Jackson, M.L. (1958). *Soil Chemical Analysis*. Prentice-Hall, New Jersey.
Kaul, O.N. & Sharma, D.C. (1971). Forest types statistics. *Indian Forester*, **97**, 435–436.
Lugo, A.E. & Murphy, P.G. (1986). Nutrient dynamics of a Puerto Rican subtropical dry forest. *Journal of Tropical Ecology*, **2**, 55–72.
Misra, R. (1983). Indian savannas. *Tropical Savannas* (Ed. by F. Bourliere), pp. 151–166. Elsevier, Amsterdam.
Murphy, P.G. & Lugo, A.E. (1986). Ecology of tropical dry forest. *Annual Review of Ecology and Systematics*, **17**, 67–88.
NRSA (1983). *Nationwide Mapping of Forest and Non-Forest Areas using Landsat False Colour Composites for the Periods 1972–1975 and 1980–1982, Project Report*. National Remote Sensing Agency, Department of Space, Hyderabad.
Pandey, O.N. (1980). *Cycling of Nitrogen, Phosphorus and Potassium in the Soil Vegetation System of Tropical Dry Deciduous Forest of Chandraprabha Region, Varanasi*. Ph.D. Thesis, Banaras Hindu University.
Proctor, J., Anderson, J.M., Chai, P. & Vallack, H.W. (1983). Ecological studies in four contrasting lowland rain forests in Gunung Mulu National Park, Sarawak. I Forest environment, structure and floristics. *Journal of Ecology*, **71**, 237–260.

Singh, J.S., Hanxi, Y. & Sajise, P. (1985). Structural and functional aspects of Indian and Southeast Asian savanna ecosystems. *Ecology and Management of the World's Savannas* (Ed. by J.C. Tothill & J.C. Mott), pp. 34–51. Australian Academy of Science, Canberra.

Singh, J.S., Singh, K.P. & Yadav, P.S. (1979). Ecosystem synthesis. *Grassland Ecosystems of the World. Analysis of Grasslands and Their Uses* (Ed. by R.T. Coupland), pp. 231–239. I.B.P. Vol. 18, Cambridge University Press, London.

Singh, J.S. & Singh, S.P. (1984). *An Integrated Ecological Study of Eastern Kumaun Himalaya with Emphasis on Natural Resources. Final Technical Report (3 Volumes)*. Department of Science and Technology, Kumaun University, New Delhi.

Singh, J.S., Singh, S.P., Saxena, A.K. & Rawat, Y.S. (1984). India's Silent Valley and its threatened rain-forest ecosystem. *Environmental Conservation*, **11**, 223–233.

Singh, K.P. & Misra, R. (Eds.) (1979). *Structure and Functioning of Natural, Modified and Silvicultural Ecosystems in Eastern Uttar Pradesh. October 1975–October 1978*. MAB Research Project I, Banaras Hindu University.

Singh, K.P. & Pandey, O.N. (1981). Cycling of nitrogen in a tropical deciduous forest. *Nitrogen Cycling in South-East Asian Wet Monsoonal Ecosystems* (Ed. by R. Wetselaar, J.R. Simpson & T. Rosswall), pp. 123–130. Australian Academy of Science, Canberra.

Singh, K.P. & Singh, R.P. (1981). Seasonal variation in biomass and energy of small roots in tropical dry deciduous forest, India. *Oikos*, **37**, 88–92.

Singh, K.P., Srivastava, S.K. & Singh, R.K. (1984). *Analysis of Seasonal Dynamics and Nutrient Relations of Tree Roots in Tropical Deciduous Forests. Final Technical Report, U.G.C. Project*. Banaras Hindu University.

Singh, R.P. (1974). *A Study of Primary Productivity and Nutrient Cycling in Chakia Forest, Varanasi*. Ph.D. Thesis, Banaras Hindu University.

Tiwari, R.C. & Ram, P. (1976). Potassium status of some Vindhyan soils of Dudhi, Mirzapur, Uttar Pradesh. *Indian Journal of Agricultural Research*, **10**, 25–31.

Tothill, J.C. (1984). American savanna ecosystems. *International Savanna Symposium 1984* (Ed. by J.C. Tothill & J.C. Mott), pp. 52–55. Australian Academy of Science, Canberra.

Vitousek, P.M. (1984). Litterfall, nutrient cycling, and nutrient limitation in tropical forest. *Ecology*, **65**, 285–298.

Vitousek, P.M. & Sanford, Jr., R.L. (1986). Nutrient cycling in moist tropical forests. *Annual Review of Ecology and Systematics*, **17**, 137–167.

Mycorrhizas in tropical forests

I. ALEXANDER

Department of Plant and Soil Science, University of Aberdeen,
Aberdeen AB9 2UE

SUMMARY

1 The majority of tropical trees form VA mycorrhizas, but an important minority form ectomycorrhizas.

2 Poorly-soluble phosphorus and organic phosphorus are the most important pools in tropical forest soils. Recent evidence indicates that poorly-soluble iron phosphates are chemically and positionally more available to mycorrhizas than to uninfected roots. On the basis of measured fungal phosphatase activity, organic phosphorus utilization seems more likely to be a feature of ectomycorrhizas than VA mycorrhizas, but research on tropical isolates is required.

3 Utilization of organic nitrogen has been conclusively demonstrated for certain temperate ectomycorrhizas, but not for VA mycorrhizas. Comparable work on tropical isolates is required.

4 Ectomycorrhizas in tropical rain forest are associated with decomposing organic matter. Delayed breakdown of organic matter imposes a distinctive nutrient cycle on the forest and establishes conditions in which ectomycorrhizas are likely to be the most effective competitors for nutrients.

5 VA-mycorrhizal inoculum is unlikely to be absent except where soil surface layers have been destroyed. The availability and spread of inoculum is more likely to limit the regeneration of ectomycorrhizal trees.

6 Both ectomycorrhizal and VA-mycorrhizal plants can be interconnected by hyphal bridges. If transfer of assimilates through a common mycelial network takes place, this could promote diversity in populations of VA-mycorrhizal trees. Because so few tropical tree taxa form ectomycorrhizas, the benefits of incorporation into a mycelial network would reduce, rather than increase, diversity. The two most important ectomycorrhizal tropical taxa, Dipterocarpaceae and Leguminosae, subtribe Amherstieae, are normally dominant components of the forests in which they occur.

INTRODUCTION

In his paper to the Leeds Tropical Rain Forest Symposium in 1982, Janos (1983) reviewed the occurrence of mycorrhizas in the lowland humid tropics, their potential role in nutrient cycling, their effects on plant growth and their possible influence on species composition of lowland humid tropical plant communities. In this paper these areas are re-examined in the light of subsequent work on tropical tree mycorrhizas and with reference to the much greater volume of recent work on temperate species relevant to tropical forest conditions. The study is restricted to lowland humid forests of indigenous trees. Savanna woodlands are admirably covered in another contribution to this volume (Högberg *this volume*), and the practical applications of mycorrhizas in forest regeneration, agroforestry and the introduction of exotics have been extensively reviewed elsewhere (Janos 1988; Le Tacon, Garbaye & Carr 1988).

Mycorrhizas are ubiquitous on tropical trees. The great majority of species form vesicular-arbuscular (VA) mycorrhizas, but certain others, including taxa which may be dominant components of the forest over large areas, form ectomycorrhizas. Very few woody species are non-mycorrhizal. These generalizations are based on surveys of roots from the surface (often highly organic) layers of the soil. It may be significant that, where roots from deeper in the profile have been sampled, the percentage of mycorrhizal infection is much lower (St John & Machado 1978; Rose & Paranka 1987) and there is some indication that deep non-mycorrhizal roots are a consistent feature of certain species (St John 1980).

VA MYCORRHIZAS

In VA mycorrhizas the fungus penetrates the root cortex intercellularly and intracellularly and gives rise to characteristic hyphal coils, vesicles and arbuscules. These latter structures, so typical of the infection of temperate herbaceous species, are often absent in tropical tree roots (I. Alexander, unpublished; St John 1980), whereas coarse hyphal coils are much more evident. External to the root, the characteristic hyphae of VA fungi form a loose weft in the substrate. Estimates from pot trials with onion, soya bean, rye-grass or clover put the extent of this external mycelium at 0.5–1.4 m cm^{-1} of root length infected (Harley & Smith 1983). Comparable data are not available for tropical trees but, in my experience, infected roots vary from those with apparently few entry points and little extramatrical mycelium to those whose surface is obscured by hyphae and hyphal fans. VA infection is not thought to influence host-root morphogenesis, but this is an assumption which requires re-examination with regard to tropical tree roots, where swollen, carrot-shaped, or even spherical, infected ultimate root members are encountered.

The fungi of VA mycorrhizas belong to the zygomycete genera *Glomus*, *Sclerocystis*, *Gigaspora*, *Acaulospora*, *Scutellospora* and *Entrophospora*. As far as is known these fungi display little host specificity and most have a cosmopolitan distribution. In our own studies in West Africa and Malaysia (I. Alexander & N. Ahmad, unpublished), the large spores and auxiliary cells (Pons & Gianinazzi-Pearson 1985) of *Gigaspora* spp. were particularly common, and the presence of this genus was also commented on by Rose & Paranka (1987) working in Brazil.

Phosphorus

Phosphorus is normally present in soil solution at very low concentrations (<0.1 μg ml^{-1}). In tropical soils, particularly the oxisols and ultisols on which lowland humid forest largely occurs, this is partly due to the incorporation ('fixation') of soluble phosphate into less soluble iron or aluminium phosphate. The largest fraction of total soil phosphorus, up to 80% on highly weathered oxisols and ultisols under forest (Sanchez 1976), is organic phosphorus. In such conditions the uptake of phosphorus by plants is limited by the slow diffusion of phosphate ions in the soil and by the development of depletion zones around roots (Nye & Tinker 1977). The hyphae of VA-mycorrhizal fungi, by growing into undepleted soil, can absorb phosphate more rapidly, and thus increase the inflow of phosphorus to the host plant. This is the conventional model of enhanced phosphorus uptake by mycorrhizal plants (Tinker 1975), and one which concludes that VA-mycorrhizal plants exploit a larger volume of soil for 'labile' phosphorus than do nonmycorrhizal plants, but that VA-mycorrhizal fungi do not make available to plants chemical forms of phosphorus otherwise unavailable to them. The two most important phosphorus pools in tropical forest soils, poorly-soluble phosphorus and organic phosphorus, fall into this category, and this conclusion therefore deserves close examination.

As Bolan, Robson & Barrow (1987) have pointed out, the conclusion is based on two types of studies. In the first, ^{32}P is incubated with soil prior to the growth of mycorrhizal and non-mycorrhizal plants. Similar specific activity in the phosphorus absorbed by infected and uninfected plants is then taken to indicate that both obtain their phosphorus from the same pools or sources in the soil (Sanders & Tinker 1971; Hayman & Mosse 1972; Mosse, Hayman & Arnold 1973; Powell 1975; Pichot & Binh 1976; Owusu-Bennoah & Wild 1980). However, similar specific activities merely indicate that mycorrhizal and nonmycorrhizal plants absorb similarly labelled phosphorus and it is unsafe to assume that phosphorus in soil that is uniformly labelled with ^{32}P does not differ in availability to mycorrhizal and non-mycorrhizal plants (Bolan *et al.* 1984). These workers, by amending soil with FeOH, a procedure of direct relevance to tropical soils, and subsequently labelling with ^{32}P, were able to demonstrate experimentally that there was phosphorus accessible to ^{32}P and mycorrhizal plants but not to non-mycorrhizal plants.

Another approach has been to compare the relative growth and phosphorus uptake of mycorrhizal and non-mycorrhizal plants supplied with inorganic phosphorus sources of different solubility (e.g. Murdoch, Jacobs & Gerdemann 1967; Ross & Gilliam 1973), and a number of these studies have been carried out with tropical soils and plants (e.g. Mosse, Powell & Hayman 1976; Moawad 1979; Waidynatha, Yogaratnam & Ariyaratne 1979). In general, growth and phosphorus uptake from insoluble sources are enhanced by mycorrhizal infection, but only at high rates of application, suggesting that in fact the enhancement is merely a reflection of the more efficient use of chemically dissociated phosphorus entering the soil solution. This conclusion is supported by those studies where complete response curves have been obtained (Barrow, Malacjuk & Shaw 1977; Pairunan, Robson & Abbot 1980). However, there is evidence that mycorrhizal plants may have a higher affinity for phosphorus in solution (Cress, Throneberry & Lindsey 1979) or a lower threshold concentration for absorption (Mosse *et al.* 1973; Howeler, Asher & Edwards 1982). Such mechanisms would tend to increase the rate of depletion of soil solution pools and consequently increase desorption of phosphorus and increase availability.

In a recent experiment of considerable relevance to tropical soils, Bolan *et al.* (1987) compared the growth response to mycorrhizal infection of subterranean clover and rye-grass over a range of applications of potassium dihydrogen phosphate, colloidal iron phosphate and crystalline iron phosphate (strengite). As expected the greatest benefits occurred with strengite, the least soluble source of phosphate; however, as its solubility is so low, increasing applications are unlikely to have resulted in increasing soil solution concentration, but rather in a greater number of 'point' sources. These are then more readily located by the thorough exploration of the soil volume by mycorrhizal hyphae. Taken with the previous work by the same group (Bolan *et al.* 1984), this study leads to the conclusion that (in addition to the more efficient exploitation of labile soil phosphorus) there may indeed be iron phosphates in tropical soils which are chemically and positionally more available to VA mycorrhizas than to uninfected roots.

There remains the question of organic phosphorus utilization by VA mycorrhizas. The association between extramatrical mycelium and soil organic matter particles has been recognized for many years (Dowding 1959; Mosse 1959; Nicolson 1959; Koske, Sutton & Sheppard 1975; St John, Coleman & Reid 1983); however, such association does not itself demonstrate that the fungus utilizes organic materials, but merely that it proliferates in nutrient-rich microsites. There is also evidence to support the rapid transfer of phosphorus from dying roots to living plants via VA fungal hyphae (Heap & Newman 1980; Ritz & Newman 1985). Again it is not yet clear whether fungal hydrolysis of organic phosphorus in dying root tissue is involved. However, VA fungi do have the potential to synthesize a range of phosphatase enzymes (Gianinazzi, Gianinazzi-Pearson & Dexheimer 1979) and there is indirect evidence for enhanced phytate utilization by mycorrhizal plants (Allen *et al.* 1981; Gianinazzi-Pearson *et al.* 1981; Gianinazzi-Pearson & Gianinazzi 1986). This is an area more thoroughly researched in ectomycorrhizal systems (see below) and one which deserves more attention in view of the association between living VA-mycorrhizal tree roots, dying roots and decaying organic matter in tropical forest (Jordan & Escalante 1980).

Nitrogen

Compared with phosphorus, effects of VA-mycorrhizal infection on nitrogen uptake have received little attention, and care is required to distinguish direct effects from indirect effects associated with improved phosphorus nutrition of test plants. This is clearly the case where increased nodulation and N_2 fixation (e.g. Asimi, Gianinazzi-Pearson & Gianinazzi 1980) or nitrate reductase activity (Oliver *et al.* 1983) are concerned. However, there is some evidence that ammonium absorption may be directly enhanced by VA-mycorrhizal infection. As numerous workers have pointed out, this might be expected since the NH_4^+

ion is relatively immobile in soil, certainly much more so than nitrate. The VA-mycorrhizal fungus *Glomus mosseae* has been shown to translocate ^{15}N from $(^{15}NH_4)_2SO_4$ placed outside the rooting zone to infected plants. The same fungus increased the inflow of nitrogen to mycorrhizal plants over a range of soil phosphorus levels, apparently due, in part, to fungal glutamine synthetase activity (Smith *et al.* 1985). Enhanced ammonium uptake is clearly of particular relevance to those tropical forest situations where nitrification is reduced (Nye & Greenland 1960; Jordan, Todd & Escalante 1979), but even where this is not the case, competition for ammonium between mycorrhizal hyphae and nitrifiers will occur and reduce the potential for eventual nitrogen loss through deep leaching or denitrification.

Utilization of nitrogen from organic sources by VA mycorrhizas has not been conclusively demonstrated, but the close association with decaying organic matter is again often cited as circumstantial evidence. Although mycorrhizal plants derived significantly more ^{15}N from labelled ground plant tissue than uninfected plants in the experiments of Ames *et al.* (1983), there was no suggestion that uptake was not from mineral sources released by the active saprophytic microflora present in the growth medium. The utilization of organic nitrogen by ectomycorrhizal fungi has recently received renewed attention (see below) and it is clear that considerable differences exist between fungal isolates. Investigation of VA-mycorrhizal fungi from surface root mats as opposed to temperate isolates from mineral soils is therefore needed.

ECTOMYCORRHIZAS

The distinctive features of a typical angiospermous ectomycorrhiza are the fungal sheath, which surrounds the host root, and the labyrinthine fungal tissue, which penetrates between the root epidermal cells to form the Hartig net. From the sheath surface, hyphae or hyphal strands radiate out into the substrate. In tropical material the sheath can account for more than 50% of the weight of the mycorrhiza and strand development can be prolific (Fassi & Fontana 1962; Alexander & Högberg 1986). There is clear evidence from temperate studies that these strands function in the transport of water, dissolved nutrients and carbon (Read 1984; Read, Francis & Finlay 1985; Finlay, Söderström & Read 1986).

The occurrence of ectomycorrhizas in tropical rain forest is undoubtedly more widespread than at one time thought (Malloch, Pirozynski & Raven 1980; Janos 1983; Alexander & Högberg 1986), although not all existing citations are likely to withstand critical scrutiny. All Dipterocarpaceae form ectomycorrhizas (Singh 1966; Shamsuddin 1979; de Alwis & Abeynayake 1980; Alexander & Högberg 1986), as do most legumes in the tribe Amherstieae of the Caesalpinioideae, *Afzelia*, *Intsia* and *Eperua* in the tribe Detarieae, and *Aldina*, *Swartzia* and *Pericopsis* in the Papilionoideae (Alexander 1988). The existence of ectomycorrhizas in these important taxa demonstrates the potential importance of this type of symbiosis throughout the rain forests of South-East Asia, Africa and certain parts of South America. In addition, ectomycorrhizas have been reported from

Uapaca (Uapacaceae; Redhead 1974; Högberg & Piearce 1986), *Glycoxylon* (Sapotaceae; Singer & Araujo 1979), *Neae* (Nyctaginaceae; Janos 1980; Alexander & Högberg 1986), *Coccoloba* (Polygonaceae; Kreisel 1971) and all Fagaceae and Myrtaceae subfamily Leptospermoideae. Other minor or unsubstantiated reports are listed in Malloch *et al.* (1980), Harley and Smith (1983) and Janos (1983).

The fungi of tropical rain forest ectomycorrhizas, where these have been recorded (Fassi & Fontana 1962; Redhead 1968; Hong 1979; Singer & Araujo 1979, 1986; I. Alexander & R. Watling, unpublished; Singer, Araujo & Ivory 1983), come from the same basidiomycete genera which provide the fungal partners of temperate ectomycorrhizas. Host specificity, i.e. the restriction of a fungus to one, or a few related, host taxa, occurs in temperate ectomycorrhizas at the level of the host genus or above (Duddridge 1986) and incompatibility mechanisms are evident when non-hosts are challenged with host-specific fungi in the laboratory (Malacjuk, Molina & Trappe 1984; Duddridge 1986). Specificity is more readily, although less certainly, recognized in the field by the restriction of sporocarps to a genus, group of genera, or family of tree host (Molina & Trappe 1982). As well as these narrow host-range fungi, there are also many with a very broad host range. Few studies have addressed this question with regard to tropical forest. Thoen & Ba (1987) have reported that of the 40 putative ectomycorrhizal fungi fruiting with *Afzelia africana* and *Uapaca guineensis* in Senegal only three occur with both species. Surveys of mycorrhizal types on dipterocarp seedlings (Alexander 1987) indicate the presence of host-specific fungi, but also others with broader host ranges. The evidence so far, such as it is, therefore suggests that the situation is much the same in tropical and temperate forest.

A related concept, and one which has been confused by some commentators, is that of a host species requiring certain specific fungal associates in order to grow. There is no evidence for this from temperate ectomycorrhizal associations, although it is obvious that certain fungi are more effective than others in promoting growth of their host in a given set of environmental conditions. Smits (1983, 1985) has reported that seedlings and cuttings of *Shorea obtusa* and *Anisoptera marginata* only form ectomycorrhizas and develop normally in greenhouse trials with inoculum from parent trees of the same (rather than other) dipterocarp species. If this phenomenon is widespread, and much more detailed evidence is required than currently available, it will undoubtedly have far reaching consequences for the regeneration of the host trees concerned and for forest dynamics.

Phosphorus

In that they also possess variable amounts of extramatrical mycelium which crosses depletion zones around roots and economically exploits large volumes of substrate, similar considerations apply to the uptake of soluble and sparingly-soluble phosphorus by ectomycorrhizas as to VA mycorrhizas. However, two features of ectomycorrhizas set them apart. The first is the fungal sheath, which covers the greater part of the host root surface and through which all absorbed nutrients must pass. This sheath has been shown to have important storage functions, not only for phosphorus, but also for other absorbed nutrients and for carbon. Harley & Smith (1983) stress that the selective advantage of this aspect of the association will be greatest in habitats where the growth period is seasonal or intermittent. This reasoning obviously applies to temperate, boreal or mediter-ranean climates and also to legumes and dipterocarps in tropical savanna woodlands or monsoon forest, (Högberg *this volume*). It is less readily apparent in rain forest, although here also the growth of many species is intermittent (Longman & Jenik 1987). Where a distinct dry season occurs (as in the Guinea-Congolian and some of the South-East Asian forests where ectomycorrhizal legumes and dipterocarps are plentiful), periodicity may be pronounced. A number of factors related to rainfall and edaphic conditions may lead to a distinctly pulsed input of litter, and thus nutrient release in the forest floor, creating conditions where the sheath may indeed be of selective advantage.

The second feature is the capacity, mentioned above, of the extramatrical mycelium of ectomycorrhizas to become, in some species, organized into strands or rhizomorphs. These function in long-distance transport of solutes, including phosphorus, and establish a framework for the exploitation of a large volume of substrate. Although comparative data are not available, it seems likely that the strands of ectomycorrhizal fungi extend further from the host root, and are more permanent, than the extramatrical mycelium of VA mycorrhizas.

Despite the obvious differences in the mycobionts and in the morphology and development of the associations, there have been no controlled comparative studies of the relative efficiency of VA mycorrhizas and ectomycorrhizas in the exploitation of soil pools of labile, sparingly-soluble or organic phosphorus. However, similar experimental approaches have been applied to both types of association and from these it is possible to draw inferences. Thomas *et al.* (1982) compared the specific activity of phosphorus absorbed by mycorrhizal and non-mycorrhizal spruce grown in soils incubated with ^{32}P, but did not find lower spe-cific activity in the mycorrhizal plants. This is the type of result discussed above with reference to VA mycorrhizas and suffers from the same uncertainties.These workers also wisely caution against applying this result, obtained with *Thelephora terrestris* (Ehrh) Fr., to other ectomycorrhizal fungi. The possibility that ectomycorrhizas may improve access to insoluble forms of soil inorganic phosphorus has also been investigated directly (Stone 1950; Ritter & Lyr 1965; Bowen & Theodorou 1967), but complete response curves are not available. However, there is evidence for the secretion of chelating agents by certain ectomycorrhizal fungi (Cromack *et al.* 1979; Szaniszlo *et al.* 1981) capable of bringing phosphorus into solution. The extrusion of H^+ associated with NH_4^+-based nitrogen nutrition (see below) would also increase phosphorus dissociation.

More attention has been directed to the utilization of organic phosphorus by ectomycorrhizas and, in view of the association of ectomycorrhizas and decomposing organic matter in tropical rain forest, it is of particular relevance. Cytochemical, enzymatic and physiological studies have shown that ectomycorrhizas possess high phosphatase activity, that more than one phosphatase is present, that activity differs between different fungal isolates, and that activity is enhanced in the absence of inorganic phosphorus (e.g. Theodorou 1968; Bartlett & Lewis 1973; Williamson & Alexander 1975; Alexander & Hardy 1981; Bousquet, Mousain & Salsac 1986; Doumas *et al.* 1986). Clearly, ectomycorrhizal fungi have the potential to utilize organic phosphorus particularly if, as Harley & Smith (1983) suggest, the surface nature of the phosphatases brings them into contact with suitable substrates. This is an important point as organic phosphorus is no more soluble or mobile in soil than inorganic phosphorus. The photomicrograph of Herrera *et al.* (1978) showing ^{32}P transfer from litter fragments to what is now presumed to have been an ectomycorrhiza (Janos 1983) is often cited as evidence that organic phosphorus utilization is widespread in tropical forest. In fact, there is no way of ascertaining whether the ^{32}P came direct from the litter via mycorrhizal enzyme activity or was absorbed from a previously degraded soil pool. 'Direct' cycling of phosphorus is assumed by many to be a feature of tropical forest, and may well be a reality, at least in the case of ectomycorrhizas, but experimental evidence using tropical fungal isolates is not yet available.

Nitrogen

Much of our understanding of nitrogen utilization by ectomycorrhizas is based on pure culture studies of ectomycorrhizal fungi. To date, few potentially ectomycorrhizal fungi from tropical rain forest have been obtained in pure culture (de Alwis & Abeynayake 1980, 1988) and no physiological studies have been reported. Temperate isolates all show an ability to utilize ammonium; in addition, most utilize amino and simple organic nitrogen, but many have a reduced, or no, ability to use nitrate (Alexander 1983; Sangwanit & Bledsoe 1985). Of course in many temperate and boreal ectomycorrhizal forests nitrate pools in soil are low or negligible. The reasons for this are likely to include, separately or together, low rates of nitrogen mineralization associated with litter high in lignin and low in nitrogen and phosphorus, competition for ammonium between ectomycorrhizal fungi and nitrifiers, and possibly the inhibition of nitrification by phenolic residues in litter. These factors also probably interact in tropical ectomycorrhizal forests, at least where ectomycorrhizas are associated with surface organic matter (Singer & Araujo 1979, 1986; Newbery *et al.* 1988). Chandler's (1985) data from Malaysian dipterocarp forest show that while potential nitrification rates, as exhibited in laboratory incubations, were high and unaffected by simple phenolics, field levels of available nitrate were extremely low. This could indicate effective depletion of ammonium pools by ectomycorrhizal fungi.

The possibility that more complex organic nitrogen compounds could be a significant source of nitrogen for ectomycorrhizas, one of the early theories of their function (Frank 1894), has recently received renewed attention (Read 1987). Read and his group (Abuzinadah & Read 1986a,b; Abuzinadah, Finlay & Read 1986) have demonstrated that certain ectomycorrhizal fungi can use protein as a sole source of nitrogen and that nitrogen from protein is readily transferred to the host plant. Earlier attempts to demonstrate proteolytic activity in ectomycorrhizal fungi (e.g. Lundeberg 1970) probably failed because of the presence of proteolysis inhibitors and because the protease(s) apparently has a very low pH optimum. Utilization of more recalcitrant organic nitrogen, e.g. protein–phenol complexes, has not been demonstrated, although the enzyme systems now known to be present in some ectomycorrhizal fungi make this a distinct possibility (see below). On current evidence, the likely source of protein in the field is in fresh leaf and root litter or from the turnover of the soil microbial pool, and this is in accord with the spatial development of ectomycorrhizas in some tropical situations. It is important to note, however, that Read and his colleagues stress the existence of distinct categories of ectomycorrhizal fungi, ranging from those which utilize protein readily to those, often isolated from mineral soils, which display little or no proteolytic ability. Here again comparable work on tropical isolates is required. A comparison of the enzyme systems of the ectomycorrhizal associates of legumes in Guinea–Congolian forest (where the mycorrhizas are associated with surface organic matter) with those of congeneric legumes in East and South-Central African miombo (where they are not) would be particularly enlightening.

FUNCTION IN THE FIELD

Mycorrhizal effects on plant nutrient uptake are readily demonstrated in pure culture or pot experiments, but caution is required in applying the results to the much more complex soil environment of natural vegetation. On the one hand a number of factors, singly or together, may reduce the effectiveness of the fungus (Fitter 1985), while on the other the activities of the mycorrhizal fungus itself may influence the direction of soil processes, and thus nutrient availability.

Limits to effectiveness

Fitter (1985) cites three possible causes of mycorrhizal ineffectiveness, which merit consideration with respect to ectomycorrhizas as well as to the VA mycorrhizas to which they were originally applied. The first is the occurrence of ineffective fungal strains ('cheaters' — Boucher, James & Keeler 1982); however, we know so little of the composition of populations of mycorrhizal fungi on field root systems in temperate conditions, let alone in tropical forest, to do more than acknowledge this as a possibility. The second is the length of the period over which the external hyphae of the mycorrhiza may be expected to contribute significantly to nutrient uptake after the period of high inflow associated with young roots and before root senescence starts. Fitter argues that for grasses this period is short enough to restrict the benefits of infection. For woody perennials this is less likely to be the case, indeed increased longevity is thought to be a feature of ectomycorrhizas (Harley & Smith 1983). Here again the absence of information on the phenology and mortality of individual fine roots and mycorrhizas of rain forest trees makes it difficult to reach any conclusions. Finally, Fitter points out that mycorrhizal hyphae are probably a major food source for the soil fauna. Both nematodes (Sutherland & Fortin 1968) and collembola (Warnock, Fitter & Usher 1982; Finlay 1985) have been shown to feed on mycorrhizal fungi and in the latter case grazing of external mycelia reduced yield and phosphorus uptake of VA-mycorrhizal clover and onion. Grazing by nematodes, collembola, mites or termites can be expected in tropical forest soils and may prevent the external mycelia of mycorrhizas realizing their full potential in nutrient acquisition. These are speculative points, and contradict the conventional view that mycorrhizas are essential to adequate nutrient uptake by native plants on all but the most fertile soils. However, they require to be answered, not least because two recent experiments specifically designed to test the hypothesis that induced reductions in mycorrhizal colonization of grasses lead to reduced leaf phosphorus levels, conspicuously failed to demonstrate this effect (Fitter 1986; Wallace 1987).

Interactions with other soil processes

From the discussion in previous sections it is clear that competition between mycorrhizal fungi and nitrifiers or saprotrophs for, say, ammonium or organic nitrogen, can contribute to the 'tightening' of nutrient cycles which is a feature of tropical forest on oligotrophic sites (Jordan 1985). However, the possibility of a more specific interaction between ectomycorrhizal and saprotrophic fungi raises issues of particular ecological interest. Gadgil and Gadgil (1971, 1975) presented data which indicated that the exclusion of living roots and mycorrhizas from the forest floor of a *Pinus radiata* plantation led to more rapid organic matter decomposition. They attributed this to suppression of obligate saprotroph activity by ectomycorrhizal fungi, through antibiosis and/or physical exclusion and/or competition for water and nutrients. Subsequent attempts to confirm the 'Gadgil hypothesis' (Berg & Lindberg 1980; Harmer & Alexander 1985) have failed to demonstrate such a dramatic effect, and Cuenca, Aranguren & Herrera (1983) found no effect of colonization by VA-mycorrhizal roots on decomposition rates of coffee and shade tree leaf litter in litter bags. However, support comes from Singer and Araujo (1979, 1986) and Singer (1984) who contrast the accumulation of raw humus and the preponderance of ectomycorrhizal over litter decomposing basidiomycete carpophores in Amazonian *campinarana* and *igapo* forest containing ectomycorrhizal *Swartzia*, *Aldina* and *Glycoxylon*, with the absence of humus layers, the increased frequency of litter decomposer carpophores and the absence of ectomycorrhizal trees in *terra firme* or *varzea* forest. Our own studies (Newbery *et al.* 1988) indicate that those areas of Korup National Park, Cameroon where the basal area of ectomycorrhizal trees is greatest are also characterized by the greater surface accumulations of organic matter. Earlier reports of other African ectomycorrhizal forest (Germain & Evrard 1956; Peyronel & Fassi 1957; Gerard 1960) also describe surface humus.

The association between ectomycorrhizas and this type of soil development in tropical rain forest therefore seems to be strong. However, investigations to date do not allow a judgement to be made on the extent to which ectomycorrhizas are responsible for the accumulation, as opposed to merely reinforcing a suite of characters associated with trees of oligotrophic sites, which more directly lead to reduced decomposition, i.e. sclerophyll, high levels of secondary compounds, and withdrawal of nutrients prior to leaf abscission. This is an area in need of investigation, made even more complex by the demonstration that some ectomycorrhizal fungi, contrary to previous opinions, are themselves capable of using lignin as a carbon source (Trojanowski, Haider & Hutterman 1984; Haselwandter, Bonn & Read 1987). Whatever the mechanisms, humus accumulation imposes a distinctive nutrient cycle on the forest, establishes conditions in which ectomycorrhizas are likely to be effective competitors for nutrients, and gives rise to soil surface conditions which may reduce the regeneration of non-ectomycorrhizal trees. This idea is pursued in the next section.

COMMUNITY COMPOSITION AND STAND DYNAMICS

In his reviews of tropical mycorrhizas, Janos (1980, 1983, 1985) proposed a model for the effects of mycorrhizas on succession and community composition in tropical forest based on the competitive interactions between species of differing dependence on mycorrhizal infection, host–fungus specificity, soil fertility and inoculum availability. Obligately mycotrophic species replace 'facultatively' mycotrophic species as fertility declines, provided that suitable inoculum is available. VA-mycorrhizal species are abundant at relatively high fertility, but ectomycorrhizal species become more competitive at very low fertility. Lack of host specificity encourages diversity in VA-mycorrhizal forest, while highly efficient host-specific fungi promote dominance by single or related hosts in ectomycorrhizal forest. At low fertility, where inoculum availability has been reduced, non-mycorrhizal species can succeed.

Janos' views are stimulating and have helped to bring mycorrhizas to the attention of tropical forest biologists. However, the field suffers from a lack of the experimentation required to test the hypotheses generated by the model. Current views on two of the components of the model, host–fungus specificity and soil fertility, have already been discussed; the problems of inoculum availability and mycorrhizal dependence are now examined.

There are few viable VA-mycorrhizal spores in the soils of lowland tropical rain forest (Janos 1983) and infection is assumed to pass from living root to living root. Therefore it follows that forest clearance or disturbance may give rise to a situation where lack of spore inoculum influences the course of subsequent succession (Janos 1980). This is unlikely to be widespread, as it is now known that hyphae can survive in dead root fragments for at least 6–9 months (Tommerup & Abbot 1981; Norani Ahmad, personal communication) and then regrow to form VA mycorrhizas with living roots, i.e. dead root fragments may be more important propagules than spores. However, where natural or man-made disturbance leads to the loss of the surface, intensely rooted, layers of the soil, this important source of infection will be reduced and regrowth may be affected. A further factor which merits investigation where propagules are few is the extent to which soil physical or chemical factors, or low seed input, reduce overall root density and slow down the spread of infection in the population.

Even less is known about inoculum availability of ectomycorrhizal fungi. Here again infection is presumed to spread largely from living root to living root. Epigeous sporocarps are produced, but nothing is known of the spread, viability or persistence of spores. The well-documented (Mikola 1970) need to provide inoculum for exotic pines introduced to the lowland tropics is circumstantial evidence that native inoculum does not spread or persist outside areas colonized by ectomycorrhizal trees. Although this reasoning is confounded by questions of host specificity and incompatibility, there must be a strong possibility that the successful establishment of indigenous ectomycorrhizal trees is limited to areas where inoculum already exists. Those species which also form VA mycorrhizas (e.g. *Afzelia*, *Intsia*, *Eperua*) may have a less absolute requirement. In our own work in the forest of Korup National Park, Cameroon (Newbery *et al.* 1988), we have found that some, but not all, of the ectomycorrhizal trees have a very distinctive distribution. They occur as canopy dominants in groves set in a diverse matrix of VA-mycorrhizal trees. Inoculum limitation is one possible cause of such a distribution.

Mycorrhizal dependence is a concept fraught with difficulty. Some use 'dependence' to indicate the increase in growth obtained by mycorrhizal infection at a given level of soil fertility normally measured as soluble inorganic phosphorus supply (e.g. Gerdemann 1975; Smith 1985). This is more usefully regarded as 'responsiveness' (Janos 1988) and is a feature not only of the host but also of the nature of the fungal symbiont(s) and level of infection. It is also better measured not at one, but over a full range of fertility (soluble phosphorus), as the ratio of the regression coefficients of the response curves for the mycorrhizal and non-mycorrhizal plants (Pairunan *et al.* 1980; Bolan *et al.* 1987). 'Dependence', which is an intrinsic property of the host plant, is better restricted to describe the threshold level of soluble phosphorus below which non-mycorrhizal plants do not grow, or alternatively the level above which there is no response to infection (Yost & Fox 1979; Janos 1988). Those species for which this latter level is never reached in the most fertile of their natural soils are the obligately mycotrophic species of Janos (1980, 1983).

It would undoubtedly be useful to obtain more data on the relative response of mycorrhizal and non-mycorrhizal individuals of a range of tropical tree species to increasing phosphorus supply; however, the difficulties of generalizing from this approach are great. Phosphorus interacts with other soil factors, notably H_2O supply, and although important, is not the only component of soil fertility. Over what period of time and at what stage of the life cycle of a long-lived perennial tree are such mycorrhizal/non-mycorrhizal comparisons most relevant? In addressing the problems of the interaction between environment and benefit in mycorrhizas, Fitter (1986) has called for field studies to examine the influence of infection on survivorship, fecundity and overall fitness of a plant population. In tropical forest, such studies seem a long way off and for some time to come we will have to continue to infer dependence of a given species from the morphology of its root system (Baylis 1975; Janos 1987), rather than from objective evidence.

In one area, however, there is growing evidence for a possible direct mycorrhizal role in determining community composition. A number of studies have demonstrated that both ectomycorrhizal and VA-mycorrhizal plants of the same and different species can be interconnected by hyphal bridges and that both carbon and phosphorus can be transferred between plants via hyphal connections (Heap & Newman 1980; Chiarello, Hickman & Mooney 1982; Whittingham & Read 1982; Brownlee et al. 1983; Francis & Read 1984; Read et al. 1985). Interplant transfer of carbon via connections formed by non-host-specific fungi has been suggested (Janos 1987) to be one factor contributing to high tree species diversity in VA-mycorrhizal rain forest. In addition, species infected with the same few VA-mycorrhizal fungi will differ little in their ability to compete for limited mineral nutrients. Janos (1983, 1985) reported that VA-mycorrhizal infection increased the survival of four tropical tree species in mixed plots of nine competing species. More recently, Grime et al. (1987) demonstrated that VA-mycorrhizal infection increased diversity in turf microcosms by raising the biomass of the subordinate species relative to that of the canopy dominant. Exposure of the canopy dominant to $^{14}CO_2$ revealed that export of assimilate to understorey species sharing a common mycorrhizal network may have contributed to the observed effect. Export of assimilate has also been shown to be possible under field conditions, over greater distances, from mature ectomycorrhizal *Pinus contorta* to surrounding shaded pine seedlings (Read et al. 1985). In proposing transfer of assimilate (and water and mineral nutrients) as a mechanism influencing community composition, no concept of 'aid' to individuals of the same or a different species is required, but merely the recognition that mycelial networks allow the concept of 'sources' and 'sinks' to apply outside the confines of an individual host plant. Carbon transfer via a shared fungus is the basis of 'epiparasitism' by, for example, achlorophyllous *Monotropaceae* (Harley & Smith 1983). The same principle, if not the physiological and structural detail, can be applied to subordinate individuals in forest communities whose capacity for carbon fixation is reduced by shading. It seems possible therefore that transfer of assimilate through a common mycelial network, together with enhanced nutrient capture, might lead to increased diversity in populations of VA-mycorrhizal species. However, in the case of ectomycorrhizal species identical transfer processes would have a diametrically opposite effect. Because so few tropical tree taxa are susceptible to infection by ectomycorrhizal fungi, the benefits of incorporation into a mycelial network would, in this case, tend to reduce rather than increase diversity. Here then is another mechanism, in addition to the exclusion of competitors brought about by the combination of slowly decomposing litter and ability to utilize organic nitrogen and phosphorus, which suggests a role for ectomycorrhizas in determining forest composition.

Is tropical forest where ectomycorrhizas occur of low diversity? Certainly there are striking examples of ectomycorrhizal trees attaining almost monospecific dominance, e.g. *Gilbertiodendron dewevrei* (Gerard 1960), *Brachystegia laurentii* (Germain & Evrard 1956), *Eperua falcata* (Davis & Richards 1934), *Tetraberlinia tubmaniana* (Voorhoeve 1964), *Shorea albida* (Anderson 1958) and *Stemonoporus* spp. (Greller *et al.* 1987). It must be said, however, that this trait is by no means restricted to ectomycorrhizal trees. There are also situations where an assemblage of ectomycorrhizal trees dominate the vegetation; the miombo trees discussed elsewhere in this volume (Högberg *this volume*) are a good example. However, ectomycorrhizal trees also occur in forest, notably in South-East Asia, which by any standards is diverse and species-rich. In these forests, as the data in Table 1 illustrate, the minority ectomycorrhizal species contribute a disproportionately large percentage of stems and basal area.

We therefore have hypotheses to explain how ectomycorrhizas might operate to influence community composition, and we have floristic information on the communities themselves. Long-term demographic studies on the regeneration and establishment of ectomycorrhizal trees and more experimental work are now required to test the hypotheses.

TABLE 1. Relative contribution of ectomycorrhizal tree species to floristic composition, stem numbers and basal area (BA) in a number of species-rich tropical rain forests. (*Data from Nicolson (1965): stems >30 cm gbh; ectomycorrhizal species are Dipterocarpaceae and Fagaceae; an unknown proportion of Myrtaceae (6% BA) and Leguminosae (1% BA) may also be ectomycorrhizal. [†]Data from Poore (1968): canopy trees (>91 cm gbh) only; ectomycorrhizal species are Dipterocarpaceae, Fagaceae and *Intsia palembanica*. [‡]Data from Ho, Newbery & Poore (1987): canopy trees (>91 cm gbh) only; soils richer in nutrients, especially phosphorus, than Batu Anam ultisols and forest probably recovering from a catastrophe 38 years previously. [§]Data from Newbery *et al.* (1988): stems >30 cm gbh; ectomycorrhizal species are Leguminosae and *Uapaca staudtii*; ectomycorrhizal legumes may form up to 60% BA in groves within forest)

Site	Sample area (ha)	Number of species	Contribution of ectomycorrhizal species		
			% species	% stems	% basal area (BA)
Sepilok, Sabah*	1.82	198	14	30	74
Jengka, Malaysia[†] (Batu Anam ultisols)	23.04	375	12	29	44
Jengka, Malaysia[‡] (Segamat oxisols)	11.70	261	10	13	22
Korup, Cameroon[§]	9.92	185	10	8	29

REFERENCES

Abuzinadah, R.A., Finaly, R.D. & Read, D.J. (1986). The role of proteins in the nitrogen nutrition of ectomycorrhizal plants. II. Utilization of protein by mycorrhizal plants of *Pinus contorta. New Phytologist,* **103**, 495–506.

Abuzinadah, R.A. & Read, D.J. (1986a). The role of proteins in the nitrogen nutrition of ectomycorrhizal plants.1. Utilization of peptides and proteins by ectomycorrhizal fungi. *New Phytologist,* **103**, 481–493.

Abuzinadah, R.A. & Read, D.J. (1986b). The role of proteins in the nitrogen nutrition of ectomycorrhizal plants. III. Protein utilization by *Betula, Picea* and *Pinus* in mycorrhizal association with *Hebeloma crustiliniforme. New Phytologist,* **103**, 507–514.

Alexander, I.J. (1983). The role of ectomycorrhizas in the nitrogen cycle. *Nitrogen as an Ecological Factor* (Ed. by J.A. Lee, S. McNeill & I.H. Rorison), pp. 69–93. Blackwell Scientific Publications, Oxford.

Alexander, I.J. (1987). Ectomycorrhizas in indigenous lowland tropical forest and woodland. *Mycorrhizae in the Next Decade* (Ed. by D.M. Sylvia, L.L. Hung & J.H. Graham), pp. 115–117. University of Florida, Gainesville.

Alexander, I.J. (1989). Systematics and ecology of ectomycorrhizal legumes. *Annals of the Missouri Botanical Garden,* in press.

Alexander, I.J. & Hardy, K. (1981). Surface phosphatase activity of Sitka spruce mycorrhizas from a serpentine site. *Soil Biology and Biochemistry,* **13**, 301–305.

Alexander, I.J. & Högberg, P. (1986). Ectomycorrhizas of tropical angiospermous trees. *New Phytologist,* **102**, 541–549.

Allen, M.F., Smith, W.K., Moore, T.S. & Christensen, M. (1981). Comparative water relations and photosynthesis of mycorrhizal and non-mycorrhizal *Bonteloua gracilis. New Phytologist,* **88**, 683–693.

Ames, R.N., Reid, C.P.P., Porter, L.K. & Cambardella, C. (1983). Hyphal uptake and transport of nitrogen from two ^{15}N-labelled sources by *Glomus mosseae,* a vesicular-arbuscular mycorrhizal fungus. *New Phytologist,* **95**, 381–388.

Anderson, J.A.R. (1958). Observations on the ecology of the peat-swamp forests of Sarawak and Brunei. *Proceedings of the Symposium on Humid Tropics Vegetation.* UNESCO, Tjiawi.

Asimi, S., Gianinazzi-Pearson, V. & Gianinazzi, S. (1980). Influence of increasing soil phosphorus levels on the interactions between vesicular-arbuscular mycorrhizae and *Rhizobium* in soybeans. *Canadian Journal of Botany,* **58**, 2200–2205.

Barrow, N.J., Malacjuk, N. & Shaw, T.C. (1977). A direct test of the ability of vesicular-arbuscular mycorrhiza to help plants take up fixed soil phosphate. *New Phytologist,* **78**, 269–276.

Bartlett, E.M. & Lewis, D.H. (1973). Surface phosphatase activity of mycorrhizal roots of beech. *Soil Biology and Biochemistry,* **5**, 249–257.

Baylis, G.T.S. (1975). The magnolioid mycorrhiza and mycotrophy in root systems derived from it. *Endomycorrhizas* (Ed. by F.E. Sanders, B. Mosse & P.B. Tinker), pp. 373–389. Academic Press, London.

Berg, B. & Lindberg, T. (1980). Is litter decomposition retarded in the presence of mycorrhiza in forest soil? *Swedish Coniferous Forest Project Internal Report 95,* p. 10.

Bolan, N.S., Robson, A.D. & Barrow, N.J. (1987). Effects of vesicular-arbuscular mycorrhiza on the availability of iron phosphates to plants. *Plant and Soil,* **99**, 401–410.

Bolan, N.S., Robson, A.D., Barrow, N.J. & Aylmore, L.A.G. (1984). Specific activity of phosphorus in mycorrhizal and non-mycorrhizal plants in relation to the availability of phosphorus to plants. *Soil Biology and Biochemistry,* **16**, 299–304.

Boucher, D.H., James, S. & Keeler, K.H. (1982). The ecology of mutualism. *Annual Review of Ecology and Systematics,* **13**, 315–347.

Bousquet, N., Mousain, D. & Salsac, L. (1986). Use of phytate by ectomycorrhizal fungi. *Physiological and Genetical Aspects of Mycorrhizae* (Ed. by V. Gianinazzi-Pearson & S. Gianinazzi), pp. 363–368. INRA, Dijon.

Bowen, G.D. & Theodorou, C. (1967). Studies on phosphate uptake by mycorrhizas. *14th IUFRO Congress,* **5**, 116–138.

Brownlee, C., Duddridge, J.A., Malibari, A. & Read, D.J. (1983). The structure and function of mycelial systems of ectomycorrhizal roots with special reference to their role in forming inter-plant connections and providing pathways for assimilate and water transport. *Plant and Soil*, **71**, 433–443.

Chandler, G. (1985). Mineralization and nitrification in three Malaysian forest soils. *Soil Biology and Biochemistry*, **17**, 347–353.

Chiarello, N., Hickman, J.C. & Mooney, H.A. (1982). Endomycorrhizal role for interspecific transfer of phosphorus in a community of annual plants. *Science*, **217**, 941–943.

Cress, W.A., Throneberry, G.O. & Lindsey, D.L. (1979). Kinetics of phosphorus absorption by mycorrhizal and non-mycorrhizal tomato roots. *Plant Physiology*, **64**, 484–487.

Cromack, K., Sollins, P., Graustein, W.C., Speidel, K., Todd, W.A., Spycher, G., Ching, Y.-Li. & Todd, R.L. (1979). Calcium oxalate accumulation and soil weathering in mats of the hypogeous fungus *Hysterangium crassum*. *Soil Biology and Biochemistry*, **11**, 463–468.

Cuenca, G., Aranguren, J. & Herrera, R. (1983). Root growth and litter decomposition in a coffee plantation under shade trees. *Plant and Soil*, **71**, 477–486.

Davis, T.A.W. & Richards, P.W. (1934). The vegetation of Moraballi Creek, British Guiana: an ecological study of a limited area of tropical rain forest. Part 11. *Journal of Ecology*, **22**, 106–155.

de Alwis, D.P. & Abeynayake, K. (1980). A survey of mycorrhiza in some forest trees of Sri Lanka. *Tropical Mycorrhiza Research* (Ed. by P. Mikola), pp. 146–153. Clarendon Press, Oxford.

de Alwis, D.P. & Abeynayake, K. (1988). Aseptic synthesis of mycorrhizae of *Dipterocarpus zeylanicus*. *Trees and Mycorrhiza. Proceedings of the Asian Seminar* (Ed. by F.S.P. Ng), pp. 215–226. Forest Research Institute, Malaysia.

Doumas, P., Berjand, C., Calleja, M., Coupe, M., Espiau, C. & d'Anzac, J. (1986). Extracellular phosphatases and phosphorus nutrition in mycorrhizal fungi and host plants. *Physiologie Vegetale*, **24**, 173–184.

Dowding, E.S. (1959). Ecology of *Endogone*. *Transactions of the British Mycological Society*, **42**, 449–457.

Duddridge, J.A. (1986). Specificity and recognition in mycorrhizal associations. *Physiological and Genetical Aspects of Mycorrhizae* (Ed. by V. Gianinazzi-Pearson & S. Gianinazzi), pp. 45–58. INRA, Paris.

Fassi, B. & Fontana, A. (1962). Micorrize ectotrofiche di *Brachystegia laurentii* e di alcune altre di Caesalpiniaceae minori del Congo. *Allionia*, **8**, 121–131.

Finlay, R.D. (1985). Interactions between soil micro-arthropods and endomycorrhizal associations of higher plants. *Ecological Interactions in Soil: Plants, Microbes and Animals* (Ed. by A.H. Fitter, D. Atkinson, D.J. Read & M.B. Usher), pp. 319–331. Blackwell Scientific Publications, Oxford.

Finlay, R.D., Söderström, B. & Read, D.J. (1986). Factors influencing the flux of carbon through ecto-mycorrhizal mycelium forming inter-plant connections. *Physiological and Genetical Aspects of Mycorrhizae* (Ed. by V. Gianinazzi-Pearson and S. Gianinazzi), pp. 301–307. INRA, Paris.

Fitter, A.H. (1985). Functioning of vesicular-arbuscular mycorrhizas under field conditions. *New Phytologist*, **99**, 257–265.

Fitter, A.H. (1986). Effect of benomyl on leaf phosphorus concentration in alpine grasslands: a test of mycorrhizal benefit. *New Phytologist*, **103**, 767–776.

Francis, R. & Read, D.J. (1984). Direct transfer of carbon between plants connected by vesicular-arbuscular mycorrhizal mycelium. *Nature*, **307**, 53–56.

Frank, A.B. (1894). Die Bedeutung de Mykorrhizapilze fur die gemeine Kiefer. *Forstwissenschaftliches Centralblatt*, **16**, 1852–1890.

Gadgil, R.L. & Gadgil, P.D. (1971). Mycorrhiza and litter decomposition. *Nature*, **233**, 133.

Gadgil, R.L. & Gadgil, P.D. (1975). Suppression of litter decomposition by mycorrhizal roots of *Pinus radiata*. *New Zealand Journal of Forest Science*, **5**, 33–41.

Gerard, P. (1960). Etude écologique de la fôret dense à *Gilbertiodendron dewevrei* dans la région de l'Uele. *Publications de l'Institut National pour l'Etude Agronomique du Congo, Série Scientifique*, **87**, 1–159.

Gerdemann, J.W. (1975). Vesicular-arbuscular mycorrhizae. *Development and Function of Roots* (Ed.

by J.G. Torrey & D.T. Clarkson), pp. 575–591. Academic Press, London.

Germain, R. & Evrard, C. (1956). Etude ecologique et phytosociologique de la foret a *Brachystegia laurentii*. *Publications de l'Institut National pour l'Etude Agronomique du Congo Belge*, **67**, 1–105.

Gianinazzi, S., Gianinazzi-Pearson, V. & Dexheimer, J. (1979). Enzymatic studies on the metabolism of vesicular-arbuscular mycorrhiza. III. Ultra-structural localisation of acid and alkaline phosphatase in onion roots infected with *Glomus mosseae* (Nicol & Gerd). *New Phytologist*, **82**, 127–132.

Gianinazzi-Pearson, V., Fardeau, J.C., Asimi, S. & Gianinazzi, S. (1981). Source of additional phosphorus absorbed from soil by vesicular-arbuscular mycorrhizal soybeans. *Physiologia Vegetale*, **19**, 33–43.

Gianinazzi-Pearson, V. & Gianinazzi, S. (1986). The physiology of improved phosphate nutrition in mycorrhizal plants. *Physiological and Genetical Aspects of Mycorrhizae* (Ed. by V. Gianinazzi-Pearson & S. Gianinazzi), pp. 101–116. INRA, Dijon.

Greller, A.M., Gunatilleke, I.A.U.N., Jayasuriya, A.H.M., Gunatilleke, C.V.S., Balasubramanian, S. & Dassanayake, M.D. (1987). *Stemonoporus* (Dipterocarpaceae)-dominated montane forests in the Adam's Peak Wilderness, Sri Lanka. *Journal of Tropical Ecology*, **3**, 243–254.

Grime, J.P., Mackey, J.M.L., Hillier, S.H. and Read, D.J. (1987). Mechanisms of floristic diversity: evidence from microcosms. *Nature*, **328**, 420–421.

Harley, J.L. & Smith, S.E. (1983). *Mycorrhizal Symbiosis*. Academic Press, London.

Harmer, R. & Alexander, I.J. (1985). Effects of root exclusion on nitrogen transformations and decomposition processes in spruce humus. *Ecological Interactions in Soil: Plants, Microbes and Animals* (Ed. by A.H. Fitter, D. Atkinson, D.J. Read & M.B. Usher), pp. 267–277. Blackwell Scientific Publications, Oxford.

Haselwandter, K., Bonn, G. & Read, D.J. (1987). Degradation and utilization of lignin by mycorrhizal fungi. *Mycorrhizae in the Next Decade* (Ed. by D.M. Sylvia, L.L. Hung & J.H. Graham), p. 331. University of Florida, Gainesville.

Hayman, D.S. & Mosse, B. (1972). Plant growth responses to vesicular-arbuscular mycorrhiza. III. Increased uptake of labile P from soil. *New Phytologist*, **71**, 41–47.

Heap, A.J. & Newman, G.I. (1980). Links between roots by hyphae of vesicular-arbuscular mycorrhizas. *New Phytologist*, **85**, 169–171.

Herrera, R., Merida, T., Stark, N. & Jordan, C.F. (1978). Direct phosphorus transfer from leaf litter to roots. *Naturwissenschaften*, **65**, 208–209.

Ho, C.C., Newbery, D.McC. & Poore, M.E.D. (1987). Forest composition and inferred dynamics in Jenka Forest Reserve, Malaysia. *Journal of Tropical Ecology*, **3**, 25–56.

Högberg, P. & Piearce, G.P. (1986). Mycorrhizas in Zambian trees in relation to host taxonomy, vegetation communities and successional patterns. *Journal of Ecology*, **74**, 775–785.

Hong, L.T. (1979). A note on Dipterocarp mycorrhizal fungi. *Malayan Forester*, **42** (3), 280–284.

Howeler, R.H., Asher, C.J. & Edwards, D.G. (1982). Establishment of an effective endomycorrhizal association on cassava in flowing solution culture and its effects on phosphorus nutrition. *New Phytologist*, **90**, 229–238.

Janos, D.P. (1980). Mycorrhizae influence tropical succession. *Biotropica*, **12** (supplement), 56–64.

Janos, D.P. (1983). Tropical mycorrhizas, nutrient cycles and plant growth. *Tropical Rain Forest: Ecology and Management* (Ed. by S.L. Sutton, T.C. Whitmore & A.C. Chadwick), pp. 327–345. Blackwell Scientific Publications, Oxford.

Janos, D.P. (1985). Mycorrhizal fungi: agents or symptoms of tropical community composition? *Proceedings of the 6th North American Conference on Mycorrhizae* (Ed. by R. Molina), pp. 98–103. Oregon State University, Corvallis.

Janos, D.P. (1987). VA mycorrhizas in humid tropical ecosystems. *Ecophysiology of VA Mycorrhizal Plants* (Ed. by E.R. Safir), pp. 000–000. CRC Press, Boca Raton.

Janos, D.P. (1988). Mycorrhiza applications in tropical forest; are temperate-zone approaches appropriate? *Trees and Mycorrhiza. Proceedings of the Asian Seminar* (Ed. by F.S.P. Ng), pp. 133–188. Forest Research Institute, Kuala Lumpur.

Jordan, C.F. (1985). *Nutrient Cycling in Tropical Forest Ecosystems.* Wiley, Chichester.
Jordan, C.F. & Escalante, G. (1980). Root productivity in an Amazonian rain forest. *Ecology,* **61,** 14–18.
Jordan, C.F., Todd, R.L. & Escalante, G. (1979). Nitrogen conservation in a tropical rain forest. *Oecologia (Berlin),* **39,** 123–128.
Koske, R.E., Sutton, J.C. & Sheppard, B.R. (1975). Ecology of *Endogone* in Lake Huron sand dunes. *Canadian Journal of Botany,* **53,** 87–93.
Kreisel, H. (1971). Ektotrophe Mykorrhiza bei *Coccoloba uvifera* in Kuba. *Biologische Rundschau,* **9,** 97–98.
Le Tacon, F., Garbaye, J. & Carr, G. (1988). The use of mycorrhizas in tropical forests. *Trees and Mycorrhiza. Proceedings of the Asian Seminar* (Ed. by F.S.P. Ng), pp. 15–26. Forest Research Institute, Malaysia.
Longman, K.A. & Jenik, J. (1987). *Tropical Forest and its Environment,* 2nd edn. Longman, Singapore.
Lundeberg, G. (1970). Utilization of various nitrogen sources, in particular bound soil nitrogen, by mycorrhizal fungi. *Studia Forestalia Suecica,* **79,** 1–95.
Malacjuk, N., Molina, R. & Trappe, J.M. (1984). Ectomycorrhiza formation in *Eucalyptus* II. The ultrastructure of compatible and incompatible mycorrhizal fungi and associated roots. *New Phytologist,* **96,** 43–53.
Malloch, D.W., Pirozynski, K.A. & Raven, P.H. (1980). Ecological and evolutionary significance of mycorrhizal symbiosis in vascular plants (a review). *Proceedings of the National Academy of Sciences of the U.S.A.,* **77,** 2113–2118.
Mikola, P. (1970). Mycorrhizal inoculation in afforestation. *International Review of Forestry Research,* **3,** 123–196.
Moawad, M. (1979). Nutzung der vesikular-arbuskularen mykorrhiza im tropischen Pflanzenbau. *Angewandte Botanik,* **53,** 99–109.
Molina, R. & Trappe, J.M. (1982). Patterns of ectomycorrhizal host specificity and potential among Pacific North West conifers and fungi. *Forest Science,* **28,** 423–458.
Mosse, B. (1959). Observations on the extramatrical mycelium of a vesicular arbuscular endophyte. *Transactions of the British Mycological Society,* **42,** 439–448.
Mosse, B., Hayman, D.S. & Arnold, D.J. (1973). Plant growth responses to vesicular-arbuscular mycorrhiza. V. Phosphate uptake by three plant species from P-deficient soils labelled with ^{32}P. *New Phytologist,* **72,** 809–815.
Mosse, B., Powell, C.L. & Hayman, D.S. (1976). Plant growth responses to vesicular-arbuscular mycorrhiza. IX. Interactions between VA mycorrhiza, rock phosphate and symbiotic nitrogen fixation. *New Phytologist,* **76,** 331–342.
Murdoch, C.L., Jacobs, J.A. & Gerdemann, J.W. (1967). Utilization of phosphorus sources of different availability by mycorrhizal and non-mycorrhizal maize. *Plant and Soil,* **27,** 329–334.
Newbery, D. McC., Alexander, I.J., Thomas, D.W. & Gartlan, J.S. (1988). Ectomycorrhizal rain forest legumes and soil phosphorus in Korup National Park, Cameroon. *New Phytologist,* **109,** 433–450.
Nicolson, D.I. (1965). A study of virgin rain forest near Sandakan, North Borneo. *Proceedings of the Symposium on Ecological Research into Humid Tropics Vegetation, Kuching.* UNESCO, Paris.
Nicolson, T.H. (1959). Mycorrhiza in the Graminae 1. Vesicular-arbuscular endophytes with special reference to the external phase. *Transactions of the British Mycological Society,* **42,** 421–438.
Nye, P.H. & Greenland, D.J. (1960). *The Soil Under Shifting Cultivation.* Commonwealth Agricultural Bureau, Farnham.
Nye, P.H. & Tinker, P.B. (1977). *Solute Movement in the Soil–Root System.* Blackwell Scientific Publications, Oxford.
Oliver, A.J., Smith, S.E., Nicholas, D.J.D., Wallace, W. & Smith, F.A. (1983). Nitrate reductase activity in *Trifolium subterraneum*: effects of mycorrhizal infection and phosphorus nutrition. *New Phytologist,* **94,** 63–79.
Owusu-Bennoah, E. & Wild, A. (1980). Effects of vesicular-arbuscular mycorrhiza on the size of the labile pool of soil phosphate. *Plant and Soil,* **54,** 233–242.

Pairunan, A.K., Robson, A.D. & Abbot, L.K. (1980). The effectiveness of vesicular-arbuscular mycorrhizas in increasing growth and phosphorus uptake of subterranean clover from phosphorus sources of different solubilities. *New Phytologist*, **84**, 327–338.

Peyronel, B. & Fassi, B. (1957). Micorrize ectotrofiche in una Caesalpiniaceae del Congo Belge. *Atti Academia delle Scienze di Torino*, **91**, 569–576.

Pichot, J. & Binh, T. (1976). Action of endomycorrhizae on growth and phosphorus nutrition of *Agrostis* in pots and on isotopically exchangeable phosphorus in soil. *Agronomie Tropical*, **31**, 375–378.

Pons, F. & Gianinazzi-Pearson, V. (1985). Observation on extramatrical vesicles of *Gigaspora margarita* in vitro. *Transactions of the British Mycological Society*, **84**, 168–170.

Poore, M.E.D. (1968). Studies in Malaysian rain forest. 1. The forest on triassic sediments in Jengka Forest Reserve. *Journal of Ecology*, **56**, 143–196.

Powell, C.L.L. (1975). Plant growth responses to vesicular-arbuscular mycorrhiza. VII. Uptake of P by onion and clover infected with different *Endogone* spore types in ^{32}P labelled soils. *New Phytologist*, **75**, 563–566.

Read, D.J. (1984). The structure and function of the vegetative mycelium of mycorrhizal roots. *The Ecology and Physiology of the Fungal Mycelium* (Ed. by D.H. Jennings & A.D.M. Rayner), pp. 215–240. Cambridge University Press, Cambridge.

Read, D.J. (1987). In support of Frank's organic nitrogen theory. *Angewandte Botanik*, **61**, 25–37.

Read, D.J., Francis, R. & Finlay, R.D. (1985). Mycorrhizal mycelia and nutrient cycling in plant communities. *Ecological Interactions in Soil* (Ed. by A.H. Fitter, D. Atkinson, D.J. Read & M.B. Usher), pp. 193–217. Blackwell Scientific Publications, Oxford.

Redhead, J.F. (1968). Mycorrhizal associations in some Nigerian forest trees. *Transactions of the British Mycological Society*, **51**, 377–387.

Redhead, J.F. (1974). *Aspects of the biology of mycorrhizal associations occurring on tree species in Nigeria*. Ph.D. Thesis, University of Ibadan.

Ritter, G. & Lyr, H. (1965). The significance of mycorrhizal fungi for the utilization of different sources of phosphate by *Pinus sylvestris*. *Plant Microbe Relationships* (Ed. by J. Macrura & V. Vancura), pp. 277–282. Czechoslovak Academy of Sciences, Prague.

Ritz, K. & Newman, E.I. (1985). Evidence for rapid cycling of phosphorus from dying roots to living plants. *Oikos*, **45**, 174–180.

Rose, S.L. & Paranka, J.E. (1987). Root and VAM distribution in tropical agricultural and forest soils. *Mycorrhizae in the Next Decade* (Ed. by D.M. Sylvia, L.L. Hung & J.H. Graham), p. 165. University of Florida, Gainesville.

Ross, J.P. & Gilliam, J.W. (1973). Effect of *Endogone* mycorrhiza on phosphorus uptake by soybeans from inorganic sources. *Soil Science Society of America Proceedings*, **37**, 237–239.

St John, T.V. (1980). A survey of mycorrhizal infection in an Amazonian rain forest. *Acta Amazonica*, **10**, 527–533.

St John, T.V., Coleman, D. & Reid, C.P.P. (1983). Association of vesicular-arbuscular mycorrhizal hyphae with soil organic particles. *Ecology*, **64**, 957–959.

St John, T.V. & Machado, A.D. (1978). Efeitos da profundidade e do sistema de manejo de um solo de terra firme em infestacoes por micorrizas. *Acta Amazonica*, **8**, 139–141.

Sanchez, P.A. (1976). *Properties and Management of Soils in the Tropics*. Wiley, New York.

Sanders, F.E. & Tinker, P.B. (1971). Mechanisms of absorption of phosphate from soil by *Endogone* mycorrhizas. *Nature (London)*, **33**, 278–279.

Sangwanit, V. & Bledsoe, C. (1985). Organic nitrogen uptake by axenically-grown mycorrhizal coniferous roots. *Proceedings of the 6th North American Conference on Mycorrhizae* (Ed. by R. Molina), p. 346. University of Oregon, Corvallis.

Shamsuddin, M.N. (1979). Mycorrhizas of tropical forest trees. *Abstracts of 5th International Symposium of Tropical Ecology* (Ed. by J. Furtado), p. 173. University of Malaya, Kuala Lumpur.

Singer, R. (1984). Adaptation of higher fungi to varzea conditions. *Amazonia*, **8**, 311–319.

Singer, R. & Araujo, I. (1979). Litter decomposition and ectomycorrhiza in Amazonian forest. 1. A comparison of litter decomposing and ectomycorrhizal basidiomycetes in latosol-terra-firme forest and white podzol campinarana. *Acta Amazonica*, **9**, 25–41.

Singer, R. & Araujo, I. (1986). Litter decomposition and ectomycorrhizal Basidiomycetes in an igapo forest. *Plant Systematics and Evolution,* **153,** 107–117.

Singer, R., Araujo, I. & Ivory, M.H. (1983). The ectotrophically mycorrhizal fungi of the neotropical lowlands, especially central Amazonia. *Nova Hedwigia,* **77,** 1–399.

Singh, K.G. (1966). Ectotrophic mycorrhiza in equatorial rain forests. *Malayan Forester,* **29,** 13–18.

Smith, S.E. (1985). The concept of effectiveness in symbiotic relationships. *Proceedings of 6th North American Conference on Mycorrhizae* (Ed. by R. Molina), pp. 146–149. University of Oregon, Corvallis.

Smith, S.E., St John, B.J., Smith, F.A. & Nicholas, D.J.D. (1985). Activity of glutamine synthetase and glutamate dehydrogenase in *Trifolium subterraneum* L. and *Allium cepa* L.: effects of mycorrhizal infection and phosphate nutrition. *New Phytologist,* **99,** 211–227.

Smits, W.Th.M. (1983). Dipterocarps and mycorrhiza. An ecological adaptation and a factor in forest regeneration. *Flora Malesiana Bulletin,* **36,** 3926–3937.

Smits, W.Th.M. (1985). Specificity of Dipterocarp mycorrhiza. *Proceedings of 6th North American Conference on Mycorrhizae* (Ed. by R. Molina), p. 364. Oregon State University, Corvallis.

Stone, E.L. (1950). Some effects of mycorrhizae on the nutrition of Monterey pine seedlings. *Soil Science Society of America Proceedings,* **14,** 340–345.

Sutherland, J.R. & Fortin, J.A. (1968). Effect of the nematode *Aphelenchus avenae* on some ectotrophic mycorrhizal fungi and on a red pine mycorrhizal relationship. *Phytopathology,* **58,** 519–523.

Szaniszlo, P.J., Powell, P.E., Reid, C.P.P. & Cline, G.R. (1981). Production of hydroxymate siderophore iron chelators by ectomycorrhizal fungi. *Mycologia,* **73,** 1158–1178.

Theodorou, C. (1968). Inositol phosphates in needles of *Pinus radiata* D. Don. and the phytase activity of mycorrhizal fungi. *Proceedings of the Ninth International Congress on Soil Science, Adelaide,* Vol. 3, pp. 483–493.

Thoen, D. & Ba, A.M. (1987). Observation on the fungi and the ectomycorrhizae of *Afzelia africana* and Uapaca guineensis in southern Senegal. *Mycorrhizae in the Next Decade* (Ed. by D.M. Sylvia, L.L. Hung & J.H. Graham), p. 132. University of Florida, Gainesville.

Thomas, G.W., Clarke, C.A., Mosse, B. & Jackson, R.M. (1982). Source of phosphate taken up from two soils by mycorrhizal (*Thelephora terrestris*) and non-mycorrhizal *Picea sitchensis* seedlings. *Soil Biology and Biochemistry,* **14,** 73–75.

Tinker, P.B. (1975). Soil chemistry of phosphorus and mycorrhizal effects on plant growth. *Endomycorrhizas* (Ed. by F.E. Sanders, B. Mosse & P.B. Tinker), pp. 353–371. Academic Press, London.

Tommerup, I.C. & Abbot, L.K. (1981). Prolonged survival and viability of VA mycorrhizal hyphae after root death. *Soil Biology and Biochemistry,* **13,** 431–433.

Trojanowski, J., Haider, K. & Hutterman, A. (1984). Decomposition of ^{14}C labelled lignin, holocellulose and lignocellulose by mycorrhizal fungi. *Archives of Microbiology,* **139,** 202–206.

Voorhoeve, I.A.G. (1964). Some notes on the tropical rain forest of the Yoma-Gola national forest near Bomi Hills, Liberia. *Commonwealth Forestry Review,* **43,** 17–24.

Waidyanatha, U.P. de S., Yogaratnam, N. & Ariyaratne, W.A. (1979). Effects of mycorrhizal infection on growth and nitrogen fixation of *Pueraria* and *Stylosanthes* and uptake of phosphorus from two rock phosphates. *New Phytologist,* **82,** 147–152.

Wallace, L.L. (1987). Mycorrhizas in grasslands: interactions of ungulates, fungi and drought. *New Phytologist,* **105,** 619–632.

Warnock, A.J., Fitter, A.H. & Usher, M.B. (1982). The influence of a springtail *Folsomia candida* (Insecta Collembola) on the mycorrhizal association of leek, *Allium porrum,* and the vesicular-arbuscular endophyte, *Glomus fasiculatus. New Phytologist,* **90,** 283–292.

Whittingham, J. & Read, D.J. (1982). Vesicular-arbuscular mycorrhizas in natural vegetation systems III. Nutrient transfer between plants with mycorrhizal interconnections. *New Phytologist,* **90,** 277–284.

Williamson, B. & Alexander, I.J. (1975). Acid phosphatases localized in the sheath of beech mycorrhiza. *Soil Biology and Biochemistry,* **7,** 195–198.

Yost, R.S. & Fox, R.L. (1979). Contribution of mycorrhizae to P nutrition of crops growing on an oxisol. *Agronomy Journal,* **71,** 903–908.

Chemical relationships between vegetation, soil and water in contrasting inundation areas of Amazonia

K. FURCH AND H. KLINGE

*Working Group Tropical Ecology, Max-Planck-Institute of Limnology,
D-2320 Plön/Holstein, Federal Republic of Germany*

SUMMARY

1 *Várzea* and *igapó* forest ecosystems of Central Amazonia, which are exposed to long-term seasonal flooding, were studied chemically and were compared with non-flooded *terra firme* forest.

2 The concentrations of nitrogen, phosphorus, potassium, sodium, calcium and magnesium were estimated in: the leaves, bark and wood of the trees, the soil (0–40 cm depth) and the water of rivers associated with the forest types.

3 The total element concentrations in the compartments of the *várzea* ecosystem were much higher than those of the corresponding compartments of the *igapó* and *terra firme* ecosystems. The *igapó* and *terra firme* ecosystems differed little in this respect.

4 The highest element concentrations within all of the three ecosystems were found in the tree leaves, bark and wood and the lowest concentrations were found in the water of associated rivers.

5 Leaves always had the highest total element concentrations of the tree fractions, bark had slightly less and wood had the lowest.

6 Differences in nitrogen concentrations between the *várzea* ecosystem and both the *igapó* and the *terra firme* ecosystems were relatively low when compared with differences in concentrations of other elements. Differences in calcium concentrations were very marked.

7 The concentrations of calcium (as a proportion of the elements analysed) in the compartments of the *várzea* ecosystem were greater than those in the corresponding compartments in the other ecosystems. The *igapó* and *terra firme* had, by contrast, a high concentration of nitrogen. Proportions of the other elements were fairly similar in all the ecosystems.

8 It was concluded that there are two distinct types of ecosystem chemical structure: type A represented by the *várzea* and type B represented by the *igapó* and *terra firme*.

9 The amount of leaf tissue produced by *igapó* trees per unit of nutrients was nearly twice that of the *várzea*. *Igapó* trees are able to grow efficiently under conditions of low nutrient supply.

INTRODUCTION

There are large chemical differences between the waters of Amazonian rivers such as the Rio Negro and the Rio Solimoes both of which have forested floodplains (Sioli 1950; Gibbs 1967; Furch, Junk & Klinge 1982; Stallard & Edmond 1983; Furch 1984, 1987). These differences find their explanation in the geological structure of their catchments (Putzer 1984). The Rio Negro has small quantities of both suspended inorganic sediments and solutes, and flows from the western Guiana Shield which is made up of old crystalline and other silicate rocks. The Rio Solimoes is rich in both suspended inorganic sediments and solutes, and rises in the eastern Andes and then flows through the deep young unconsolidated sandy–clayey sediments of the Andean foreland.

The hydrochemical differences between the rivers suggest that the trees and soils of their associated floodplains may be chemically different. In 1981 we started a programme of sampling and chemical analysis of tree leaves, bark and wood and soil from the floodplains (Klinge *et al.* 1983; Klinge, Furch & Harms 1984). In this paper, we present our understanding of the chemical relationships of the Amazonian floodplain ecosystems and compare our results with data for the better known non-flooded *terra firme* forests (Jordan 1985; Vitousek & Sanford 1986; Chauvel, Lucas & Boulet 1987).

The forests discussed in this paper occur on the three principal landscape types of Brazilian Amazonia: *terra firme*, *várzea* and *igapó*. *Terra firme* refers to the area which, because of its high topographic position, cannot be flooded. *Várzea* and *igapó* are regional names of active floodplains. A *várzea* is flooded by a muddy river rich in solutes (white water), an *igapó* by a darkly stained river poor in solutes (black water). One of the forest types studied is called a *campina*, a regional name for a nutrient-poor *terra firme* forest type on white sand.

STUDY SITES

The study sites were near Manaus, Brazil where there are extensive areas of *terra firme* forest, *várzea* forest on the floodplains of the Rio Solimoes and less extensive areas of *igapó* forest on the floodplains of the Rio Negro (Fig. 1). The two rivers experience an annual fluctuation in their water level of about 10 m (Fig. 2) and the trees and soils of the *igapó* and *várzea* forests are flooded for long periods (Junk, Bayley & Sparks 1989). The sites where trees and soils were sampled (Fig. 1) are flooded for 28 weeks per year on average (Fig. 2).

The mean annual temperature at Manaus is about 27 °C, and the mean annual rainfall is above 2000 mm. There is a short less rainy to dry season lasting from July to September.

All stands of floodplain forest are classified as seasonal inundation forests (Prance 1979). The deciduous *várzea* forests studied are located at Ilha de Marchantaria (V_{1a} and V_{1b}), Iranduba (V_2) and Marrecao (V_3) and all grow on

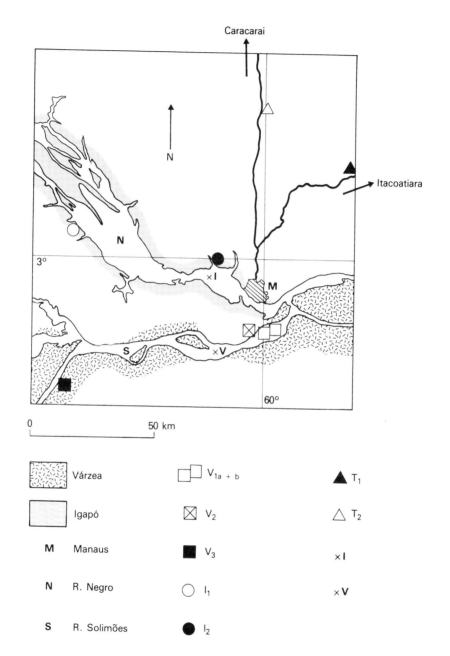

FIG. 1. Location of sampling sites in the study area: *várzea* sites, V_{1a+b}, V_2 and V_3; *igapó* sites, I_1 and I_2; *terra firme* sites, T_1 and T_2; river stations, xI and xV.

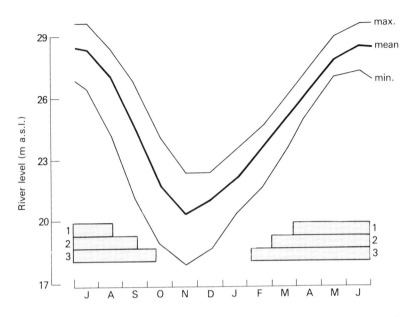

FIG. 2. Annual fluctuation of Rio Negro level at Manaus for the period 1969–1978 (Capitania dos Portos, Manaus), and length of inundation period of both the *igapó* and *várzea* forest sites (1 = minimum, 2 = mean, 3 = maximum).

loamy sediments deposited by the Rio Solimoes. The evergreen *igapó* forests studied are located at Praia Grande (I_1) on bleached quartz sands and at Taruma Mirim (I_2) on kaolinitic clay. The soils under both *igapó* forests are of fluviatile origin. The seasonal evergreen *terra firme* forest (T_1) has been described by Brünig & Klinge (1976) and grows on a yellow latosol (Falesi *et al.* 1969) of heavy texture. The evergreen *campina* forest (T_2) is on deep podzolized sand. The canopy heights of all the forests except T_2 are about 25–30 m. T_2 has trees up to 10 m high.

A summary of some features of the study sites is given in Table 1.

MATERIALS AND METHODS

Tree sampling

Adult healthy leaves were picked from a single tree, within the reach of a standing man (i.e. up to 2 m from the ground). A piece of bark plus attached woody tissue was cut from the bole or a branch of the tree from which leaves had been picked. At each locality, trees were sampled within an area of 200–500 m^2, except for V_2 where the area measured about 1000 m^2. Sampling was carried out in the *igapó* and *várzea* on a dry day of the low water period, and during the low rainfall season at *terra firme* sites. Samples were oven dried at 100 °C, shortly after collection. Petioles were severed from leaf blades, and woody tissue from bark.

TABLE 1. Some details of the study sites near Manaus, Brazil (the locations are shown in Fig. 1). ([1]Soil sampled only; [2]H. Klinge (unpublished); [3]J. Revilla (unpublished); [4]Revilla (1981); [5]Worbes (1983); [6]Klinge & Rodrigues (1971); [7]Anderson, Prance & Albuquerque (1975))

Study area	Year of sampling	Vegetation notes	No. of woody species (≥ 5 cm dbh)
Várzea			
Ilha de Marchantaria (V_{1a})	1981	Secondary forest (50–60 years old)[2]	56/ha
Ilha de Marchantaria (V_{1b})	1982	As above	18/192 m^2
Iranduba (V_2)	1981	Primary forest	Not known
Marrecao (V_3)	1985	Primary forest[3]	97 to 127/ha
Igapó			
Praia Grande (I_1)	1981	Primary forest[4]	Not known
Taruma Mirim (I_2)	1981[1]	Secondary forest[5]	43/2100 m^2
Terra firme			
North-east of Manaus (T_1)	1970	Primary forest[6]	Not known
North of Manaus (T_2)	1984	Primary *campina* forest[7]	39/225 m^2

Leaf and bark samples were not cleaned. After grinding the samples in a mill or sawing pieces of boles or branches to obtain the sawdust, the powder was oven dried at 105 °C for dry weight estimation, and sealed in plastic bags.

Soil sampling

A soil pit was dug to a depth of 40 cm under *terra firme* forest (T_1) and under *igapó* forest (I_1, I_2). Under *várzea* forest (V_1) four pits of the same depth were dug along a transect at intervals of about 500 m. All samples were taken in the low water period of 1982. Roots were hand picked from air-dried soil so that the soil analyses refer to root-free matter.

   The soil at Praia Grande (I_1) was not sampled at the site of the foliar element sampling, but about 100 m inland from the river bank and at a 5 m lower elevation. It is worth noting that a mineralogical study has indicated that this soil has developed from sediments once deposited by the Rio Solimoes (G. Irion, personal communication 1983) and it is not representative geochemically of Rio Negro *igapó* sites.

Water sampling

In the middle of both the Rio Solimoes and Rio Negro, surface water samples were collected at monthly intervals over a period of at least 2 years (1974–1976) (Furch 1984). Ten forest streams flowing from the *terra firme* and crossing the Manaus–Caracarai road up to 150 km north of Manaus (Fig. 1) were sampled once in October 1974 and once in March 1975 (Furch 1984).

Chemical analysis

For metal and phosphorus analysis of tree samples, 2 g of dry ground plant material were ashed in a quartz crucible for 2 h at 450 °C using a muffle furnace. The ash was digested with hot hydrochloric acid (10% w/v) and filtered through a membrane filter of 0.45 μm pore diameter. Soil samples were sieved through a 2-mm mesh and ground in an agate mill. One hundred milligrams of dry soil powder (105 °C) were ashed in a quartz crucible for 2 h at 550 °C using a muffle furnace. After cooling the ash was heated with 6 ml *aqua regia* (one part concentrated nitric acid : three parts concentrated hydrochloric acid) on a sand bath at 110 °C until nearly dry. Residues were dissolved in water and filtered through a 0.45 μm membrane filter. Filtrates were diluted with water up to a volume of 50 ml. Water samples were filtered through 0.45 μm membrane filters immediately after collection and acidification with 2 ml of concentrated hydrochloric acid. Metals were determined using a Perkin–Elmer atomic absorption spectrophotometer. Phosphorus was determined spectrophotometrically (vanadium molybdate method; Anonymous (1971)). Nitrogen analyses were made on separate samples of dry ground plant and soil material and the element was determined by the Kjeldahl method (Anonymous 1971). Data for nitrogen and phosphorus in freshwaters were taken from Ungemach (1967) and Schmidt (1972a,b).

RESULTS

Mineral nutrients in tree leaves, bark and wood

Várzea

The mean concentrations of six chemical elements in the leaves, bark and wood of trees sampled within the *várzea* of the lower Rio Solimoes are listed in Table 2. The order of element concentrations in the leaves of samples V_{1a}, V_{1b} and V_2 is $N > Ca > K > Mg > P > Na$. In sample V_3, potassium and calcium are reversed. The order of element concentrations in the bark samples (from V_{1a} and V_2 only) is $Ca > N > K > Mg > P > Na$. The order of element concentrations in the wood samples shows no consistent patterns, and concentrations, particularly of phosphorus and sodium, vary greatly between locations.

The variability of element concentrations between species is least for foliar nitrogen (from V_{1a}) and greatest for foliar sodium (from V_3). The variability of nitrogen concentration is relatively low as is the variability of the sum of the concentrations of the six elements. The element concentrations of bark samples are usually more variable than those of leaf samples, but no more variable than those of wood samples.

The highest concentrations of nitrogen, potassium, phosphorus and magnesium are observed in the leaves and are lowest in the wood, where the sum of the six element concentrations is of the order of 20.0 mg g^{-1}. Wood has the highest calcium concentration, leaves the lowest and bark intermediate. Sodium may occur in the bark and/or wood in much higher concentrations than in the leaves. Differences between the proportions of nitrogen, potassium, calcium and magnesium in the leaves are often more pronounced than the respective differences in concentrations.

The proportion (of the sum of the leaf elements analysed) of nitrogen is greater than that of calcium in the leaves. This is also the case for bark and wood when the sum of the element concentrations is below 18.0 mg g^{-1}. When the summed concentration exceeds this value, as in the wood sample V_{1b}, the proportion of calcium exceeds that of nitrogen.

Igapó and terra firme

The mean concentrations of chemical elements in the leaves, bark and wood of trees from one locality each in *igapó* (I_1) and *terra firme* (T_1) forest are given in Table 3. Comparable data for Amazonian *terra firme* trees exist for only two pod-

TABLE 2. Mean concentrations (mg g^{-1}) (with ranges) of mineral nutrients in the leaves, bark and wood of several tree species from *várzea* sites (Table 1) of the lower Rio Solimões (n is the number of tree species analysed)

	Site	N	P	K	Na	Ca	Mg	n
Leaves	V$_{1a}$	25.6 14.6–35.5	1.77 0.96–2.4	12.8 3.47–31.3	0.201 0.04–1.38	18.4 2.36–38.7	3.96 1.04–8.43	29
	V$_{1b}$	27.6 16.3–41.6	1.8 1.19–2.51	17 5.33–39.9	0.05 0.02–1.00	23.9 6.43–44.0	4.84 1.26–7.42	17
	V$_2$	24.9 16.8–41.3	0.871 0.30–1.79	8.6 2.55–25.5	0.084 0.020–0.219	16.3 6.27–30.7	4.03 1.92–7.34	13
	V$_3$	22.4 12.8–36.6	1.33 0.28–2.77	14.7 6.30–67.3	0.078 0.020–0.28	11.5 3.81–32.1	4.5 2.43–9.08	29
Bark	V$_{1a}$	13.0 5.7–28.6	0.862 0.04–2.30	8.6 1.42–18.2	0.134 0.01–0.49	25.6 2.50–46.9	3.05 0.67–9.51	29
	V$_2$	16.5 9.2–29.5	0.668 0.28–1.08	5.6 1.81–8.70	0.416 0.04–1.34	30.3 6.11–58.6	4.02 0.89–4.12	13
Wood	V$_{1a}$	4.75 2.2–9.1	0.815 0.22–2.49	6.59 1.83–16.7	0.113 0.01–0.6	3.25 0.57–12.4	1.45 0.44–2.65	29
	V$_{1b}$	5.52 2.3–9.2	0.278 0.01–0.79	8.65 1.80–15.1	0.466 0.16–1.03	7.13 0.60–17.6	1.36 0.20–4.3	18
	V$_2$	5.7 3.0–8.1	0.53 0.13–1.48	3.71 1.09–8.02	0.658 0.04–1.51	5.58 0.69–34.2	1.93 0.36–5.89	13

TABLE 3. Mean concentrations (mg g^{-1}) (with ranges for I_1 and T_2, and S.D. for T_1) of mineral nutrients in the leaves and wood of several tree species from *igapó* (I_1) and *terra firme* (T_1 and T_2) sites, and in bark from the *igapó* site (I_1) (T_1, Klinge (1976), Golley *et al.* (1980), T_2, Klinge (1985)) (*n* is the number of tree species analysed)

	Site	N	P	K	Na	Ca	Mg	n
Leaves	I_1	17.3 10.2–25.5	0.667 0.16–1.42	6.55 2.99–13.1	0.236 0.02–1.54	2.06 0.598–7.82	1.29 0.316–2.86	23
	T_1	18.0 –	0.538 0.148	4.99 2.30	1.15 0.827	4.26 3.48	2.9 1.40	183
	T_2	11.1 6.1–24.3	0.479 0.11–0.90	6.58 1.83–15.5	4.31 0.42–18.6	3.7 0.57–6.74	2.64 1.63–4.23	14
Bark	I_1	9.4 2.5–18.9	0.162 0.01–0.61	3.55 0.46–7.52	0.108 0.01–0.66	4.11 0.81–9.56	0.605 0.21–2.57	22
Wood	I_1	3.14 1.2–4.8	0.178 0.05–0.57	1.77 0.61–4.33	0.089 0.01–0.30	0.819 0.18–3.79	0.305 0.10–1.26	22
	T_1	4.8	0.126	1.35	0.327	1.78	0.992	224

zolized sand sites: one in southern Venezuela (Herrera 1979) and the other a *campina* forest in the Manaus area (Anderson, Prance & Albuquerque 1975; Klinge 1985). Foliar data of the latter (T_2) are included in Table 3. There are no other data for *igapó* trees.

The order of the mean concentrations of the elements in the leaves, bark and wood of the *igapó* (sample I_1) is N > K > Ca > Mg > P > Na. Leaf concentrations of *igapó* trees are higher than concentrations in the bark, except for calcium. The concentrations of all elements except phosphorus are higher in the bark than in wood. Between-species variability is lowest for nitrogen and greatest for phosphorus.

In the *terra firme* (T_1) leaf samples, the element order is N > K > Ca > Mg > Na > P; in wood from the same site the order is similar except that calcium and potassium are reversed. In the *terra firme* (T_2) leaf samples, the element order is N > K > Na > Ca > Mg > P. Between-species variability in the T_1 samples is lowest for phosphorus and greatest for calcium (no data are available for variability in nitrogen concentrations). In the T_2 leaf samples, between-species variability is lowest for magnesium and greatest for sodium.

The foliar samples from the two *terra firme* sites (Table 3) thus differ primarily in nitrogen (higher in T_1) and sodium (higher in T_2). Comparing *igapó* and *terra firme* samples (Table 3), the foliar concentrations of sodium, calcium and magnesium are substantially lower in the *igapó*, while those of nitrogen, phosphorus and potassium are similar. The wood of *igapó* trees is lower in nitrogen, sodium, calcium and magnesium, but higher in phosphorus and potassium, than the wood of *terra firme* trees. Between-species variability tends to be lower in *terra firme* samples.

Várzea trees, in general, have much higher concentrations of elements in leaves, bark and wood than *igapó* and *terra firme* trees (Tables 2 and 3). Even the lowest foliar concentrations (except for sodium) of *várzea* trees are higher. The relatively high concentrations of calcium in the *várzea* samples should be noted.

Chemical elements in soil

Despite a relatively small number of replicates, the soils from *várzea* and *igapó* (Table 4) show several clear differences. The data support the view that *igapó* soils have low agricultural potential. Many *várzea* soils, in contrast with the majority of Amazonian *terra firme* soils, have a good nutrient status and agricultural potential (Falesi *et al.* 1969; Cochrane & Sanchez 1982; Nascimento & Homma 1984; Sombroek 1984; Meggers 1985).

Várzea soils are lower in total nitrogen but generally richer in calcium and magnesium and, to a lesser extent, phosphorus than soils from both *igapó* and *terra firme* sites (Worbes 1986) (Table 4). *Igapó* soils are generally (particularly in the case of samples from I_1) richer in potassium, sodium, calcium and magnesium than *terra firme* soils. *Igapó* and *terra firme* soils of lower nutrient

TABLE 4. Concentration (mg g^{-1} oven dry weight) of total nitrogen, phosphorus, potassium, sodium, calcium and magnesium in soils at different depths from *várzea* (V$_1$), *igapó* (I$_1$, I$_2$) and *terra firme* (T$_1$) (where $n \geqslant 4$ standard deviations are given with the mean values)

Site	n	N	P	K	Na	Ca	Mg	Sum
0–1 cm depth								
V$_1$	4	5.63	0.46	5.60	0.88	4.39	5.42	22.4
		±0.39	±0.17	±0.73	±0.33	±0.22	±0.81	±1.57
I$_1$	1	4.20	0.10	1.31	0.19	0.18	0.56	6.54
I$_2$	1	2.90	0.08	0.56	0.05	0.13	0.26	3.98
T$_1$	1	4.60	0.33	0.23	0.08	0.15	0.11	5.49
10–20 cm depth								
V$_1$	4	1.30	0.26	5.45	0.63	2.47	5.57	15.7
		±0.08	±0.11	±1.55	±0.19	±0.38	±0.67	±2.59
I$_1$	1	3.60	0.36	1.77	0.41	0.05	1.61	7.81
I$_2$	1	1.40	0.21	0.53	0.06	0.30	0.32	2.81
T$_1$	1	0.80	0.16	0.12	0.03	0.01	0.03	1.15
10–40 cm depth								
V$_1$	6	0.95	1.02	5.01	0.72	3.22	5.96	16.9
		±0.43	±0.74	±1.25	±0.16	±0.44	±0.31	
I$_1$	4	4.05	0.26	2.68	0.42	0.09	1.70	9.20
		±3.20	±0.09	±1.26	±0.11	±0.03	±0.61	
I$_2$	6	1.60	0.27	0.59	0.08	0.05	0.36	2.95
		±1.01	±0.11	±0.05	±0.02	±0.04	±0.07	
T$_1$	4	1.00	0.16	0.12	0.03	0.02	0.03	1.36
		±0.05	±0.03	±0.01	±0.01	±0.01	±0.01	

status are remarkably low in calcium and relatively high in total nitrogen — a reversal of the situation for *várzea*.

Chemical elements in river water

The mean concentrations of the six elements in the Rio Negro and Rio Solimoes are reported in Table 5. Monthly values can be found in Schmidt (1972b), Furch (1982), Furch & Junk (1985) and Furch & Otto (1987). The Rio Solimoes has higher concentrations of all elements, particularly of phosphorus, calcium and magnesium. The concentrations of elements in the water of the *terra firme* streams are lower than those of the Rio Negro (Table 5). However, these differences are less than those between the Rio Solimoes and the Rio Negro. These rivers also differ regarding the relative proportions of individual elements. Calcium is easily the most prominent element in the Rio Solimoes water, which in this respect resembles the world average freshwater (Livingstone 1963). The most prominent cations in the water of both Rio Negro and *terra firme* streams are potassium and sodium. A clear relationship exists between the total element content (sum of the six elements analysed) and the proportional contributions of calcium and nitrogen: the lower the total elements, the lower the calcium and the higher the nitrogen.

TABLE 5. Mean concentrations of elements in the waters of the Rio Solimoes (V), Rio Negro (I) and *terra firme* streams (T) in $\mu g \ l^{-1}$ (mean $\pm$ standard deviation; n in parentheses) ([1]Furch (1984); [2]Schmidt (1972a); [3]Schmidt (1972b); [4]Ungemach (1967))

	V	I	T
N_{total}	603 (12)[3]	357[4]	253 (8)[2]
	±168		±178
P_{total}	74 (12)[3]	7[4]	4 (8)[2]
	±29		±2
K	900 (20)[1]	327 (24)[1]	150 (20)[1]
	±200	±107	±108
Na	2300 (29)[1]	380 (24)[1]	216 (20)[1]
	±800	±124	±58
Ca	7200 (29)[1]	212 (24)[1]	38 (20)[1]
	±1600	±66	±34
Mg	1100 (29)[1]	114 (24)[1]	37 (20)[1]
	±200	±35	±15
Sum	12177	1397	698

DISCUSSION

A comparison of the chemical data for the trees and soil of the three ecosystems under study reveals important characteristics: the high concentrations of elements in the tree leaves, bark and wood from the *várzea* floodplain correspond with high concentrations of elements in the *várzea* soil. The opposite is true for the *igapó* floodplains and the *terra firme* site which have low concentrations of elements in trees and soil. A low proportion of nitrogen and a high proportion of calcium are characteristic of *várzea*, whilst high nitrogen and low calcium are a feature of *igapó* and *terra firme* (Furch & Klinge 1978). It is useful to distinguish two distinct types of ecosystem chemical structure (Golley & Richardson 1977). Type A is represented by the *várzea* and type B by the *igapó* and *terra firme*.

Supporting information is provided by the results of chemical analyses of annual leaf fall in *várzea*, *igapó* and *terra firme* forests (Table 6). The comparatively high mineral element content of the annual leaf fall of the *várzea* forest (site V_1) reflects high concentrations of phosphorus, potassium, magnesium and particularly calcium. The element content of the lower annual leaf fall of *igapó* forest (I_2) is low and has a high proportion of nitrogen. Annual leaf fall of the *terra firme* forest (T_1) is as low as in the *igapó* forest, and resembles the latter in its chemical composition. The high calcium content of the leaf fall of the *várzea* forest in comparison with that of *igapó* and *terra firme* forests is a distinctive feature.

The parallels between the analyses of trees, soils and water in this study of floodplain ecosystems are striking. As in the trees and soil from *várzea* sites, calcium is prominent in the Rio Solimoes water and is accompanied by high concentrations of other mineral nutrients. The water of the Rio Negro is low in mineral nutrients as are the trees and soils from *igapó* sites, and lacks such a

TABLE 6. Leaf litterfall mass (t ha⁻¹ year⁻¹) and its element concentration (g m⁻² year⁻¹) from *várzea*, *igapó* and *terra firme* forest ([1]Adis, Furch & Irmler (1979); [2]Klinge & Rodrigues (1968))

	Várzea (V_1)	*Igapó* (I_2)[1]	*Terra firme* (T_1)[2]
Leaf litterfall	10.6	5.3	5.6
N	15.5	7.8	8.6
P	1.0	0.1	0.2
K	7.2	1.5	1.3
Na	0.2	0.04	0.5
Ca	31.4	2.8	1.8
Mg	6.1	0.7	1.3
Sum	61.4	12.9	13.7

prominence in calcium. The chemistry of the *terra firme* trees, soils and river water resembles that of the *igapó* ecosystem.

In order to place the type A and type B ecosystems in a pantropical perspective, it is useful to compare our data with those compiled by Vitousek & Sanford (1986) for lowland rain forests on non-flooded soils elsewhere. They have demonstrated that productive forests are rich in phosphorus, potassium and, particularly, calcium, cycle large quantities of nutrients and grow on comparatively fertile sites. On less fertile sites less productive forests contain and cycle smaller amounts of nutrients. In this group the *terra firme* forest of the Manaus area (T_1) is included. The chemical data from forests growing on fertile non-flooded sites agree with those reported here for the *várzea* forest which represents the type A ecosystem. This suggests that the latter is a floodplain counterpart of the former. In addition, the *igapó* forest may be considered as a floodplain counterpart of *terra firme* forests growing on less fertile sites.

To illustrate the nutritional contrasts between *várzea* and *igapó* ecosystems, we computed the combined amount of nutrients separately for the water of associated rivers, the soil and the trees of each ecosystem (Fig. 3). For river water the mean concentrations of Table 5 were used, and for soil averages of the 0–1 cm depth and 10–20 cm depth analyses (Table 4) were used. For the trees, arithmetic means of the concentrations of the fractions in Tables 2 and 3 were calculated. To obtain a measure of the trees' efficiency in utilizing nutrients, we calculated the amount of leaf fall (Table 6) of *várzea* and *igapó* forests per unit of K + Mg + Ca + P of leaf compartments (Tables 2 and 3). The amounts were then expressed as a ratio *várzea* : *igapó* and were drawn to scale when constructing Fig. 3.

The river water and soil from the *várzea* and *igapó* sites are very different. However, *igapó* trees are able to extract nutrients from the sources of lower concentration in amounts which result in relatively small differences in nutrient concentrations in the biomass of *várzea* and *igapó* forests. Regarding the leaf amount produced per unit of nutrients, the *igapó* seems substantially more efficient (Fig. 3). Therefore it is concluded that vegetation of the *igapó* forest, which is floristically distinct from that of the *várzea* forest (Prance 1979; Worbes 1983; Singer 1984), is well adapted to the chemical poverty of its environment.

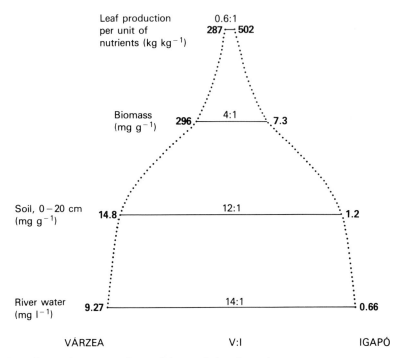

FIG. 3. Sum of potassium, magnesium, calcium and phosphorus in ecosystem compartments and leaf production per unit of these nutrients of *várzea* (left) and *igapó* (right) ecosystems. The respective ratios *várzea* : *igapó* drawn to horizontal scale are shown in the centre.

ACKNOWLEDGEMENTS

Field work was carried out in cooperation with the Instituto Nacional de Pesquisas da Amazônia (INPA), Manaus. We thank unknown referees for valuable comments, L. Côelho and J. Revilla (INPA) for species identification, J. Dieterich, E. Harms and T. Leitz for carrying out chemical analysis at Plön, E. Harms for the drawings and G. Lemke for typing the manuscript.

REFERENCES

Adis, J., Furch, K. & Irmler, U. (1979). Litter production of an Amazonian black-water inundation forest. *Tropical Ecology*, 20, 236–245.

Anderson, A.B., Prance, G.T. & de Albuquerque, B.W.P. (1975). Estudos sobre a vegetacao das campinas ámazonicas — III. A vegetacao lenhosa da campina da Reserva Biologica INPA-SUFRAMA (Manaus-Caracarai, 62 km). *Acta Amazonica*, 5, 225–246.

Anonymous (1971). Referenzmethoden für die Bestimmung der Mineralstoffe in den Pflanzen. I. Stickstoff, Phosphor, Kalium, Natrium, Kalzium, Magnesium. *Monatliche Mitteilungen des Internationalen Kali-Instituts, Bern (Schweiz)*, 1–18.

Brünig, E. & Klinge, H. (1976). Comparison of the phytomass structure of equatorial "rainforest" in Central Amazonas, Brazil and Sarawak, Borneo. *Garden's Bulletin (Singapore)*, 29, 81–101.

Chauvel, A., Lucas, Y. & Boulet, R. (1987). On the genesis of the soil mantle of the region of Manaus, Central Amazonia, Brazil. *Experientia*, 43, 234–241.

Cochrane, T.T. & Sanchez, P.A. (1982). Land resources, soil and their management in the Amazon region: A state of knowledge report. *Amazonia. Agriculture and Land Use Research* (Ed. by S.B. Hecht), pp. 137-209. Centro-Internacional de Agricultura Tropical Series 03 E-03, Cali, Colombia.

Falesi, I.C., de Souza Cruz, E., Pereira, F.B. & de Carvalho Lopes, E. (1969). *Os solos da area Manaus–Itacoatiara*. Impressora Polar, Rio de Janeiro.

Furch, B. & Otto, K.-R. (1987). Characterization of light regime changes (PAR) by irradiance reflectance in two Amazonian water bodies with different physico-chemical properties. *Archiv für Hydrobiologie*, **100**, 579-587.

Furch, K. (1982). Jahreszeitliche chemische Veränderungen in einem Várzea-See des mittleren Amazonas (Lago Calado, Brasilien). *Archiv für Hydrobiologie*, **95**, 47-67.

Furch, K. (1984). Water chemistry of the Amazon basin: the distribution of chemical elements among freshwaters. *The Amazon* (Ed. by H. Sioli), pp. 167-179. Junk, Dordrecht.

Furch, K. (1987). Amazon Rivers: their chemistry and transport of dissolved solids through their basins. 1. Major dissolved solids. *Mitteilungen aus dem Geologisch-Paläontologischen Institut der Universität Hamburg, SCOPE/UNEP Sonderband*, **64**, 311-323.

Furch, K. & Junk, W.J. (1985). Dissolved carbon in a floodplain lake of the Amazon and in the river channel. *Mitteilungen aus dem Geologisch-Paläontologischen Institut der Universität Hamburg, SCOPE/UNEP Sonderband*, **58**, 285-298.

Furch, K., Junk, W.J. & Klinge, H. (1982). Unusual chemistry of natural waters from the Amazon region. *Acta Cientifica Venezolana*, **33**, 269-273.

Furch, K. & Klinge, H. (1978). Towards a regional characterisation of the biogeochemistry of alkali and alkali-earth metals in northern South America. *Acta Cientifica Venezolana*, **29**, 434-444.

Gibbs, R.J. (1967). The geochemistry of the Amazon river system. I. The factors that control the salinity and the composition and concentration of suspended solids. *Geological Society of America Bulletin*, **78**, 1203-1232.

Golley, F.B. & Richardson, Th. (1977). Chemical relationships in tropical forests. *Geo-Eco-Trop*, **1**, 35-44.

Golley, F.B., Yantko, J., Richardson, Th. & Klinge, H. (1980). Biogeochemistry of tropical forests. 1. *Tropical Ecology*, **21**, 59-70.

Herrera, R. (1979). *Nutrient distribution and cycling in an Amazon Caatinga forest on spodosols in southern Venezuela*. PhD Thesis, University of Reading, UK.

Jordan, C.F. (1985). *Nutrient Cycling in Tropical Forest Ecosystems*. Wiley, Chichester.

Junk, W.J., Bayley, P.B. & Sparks, R.E. (1989). The "flood pulse"-concept in the floodplain systems. *Canadian Journal of Fisheries and Aquatic Sciences* (in press).

Klinge, H. (1976). Bilanzierung von Hauptnährstoffen im Ökosystem tropischer Regenwald (Manaus) — vorläufige Daten. *Biogeographica*, **7**, 59-76.

Klinge, H. (1985). Foliar nutrient levels of native tree species from Central Amazonia. 2. Campina. *Amazoniana*, **9**, 281-295.

Klinge, H., Furch, K. & Harms, E. (1984). Selected bioelements in bark and wood of native tree species from Central-Amazonian inundation forests. *Amazoniana*, **9**, 105-117.

Klinge, H., Furch, K., Harms, E. & Revilla, J. (1983). Foliar nutrient levels of native tree species from Central Amazonia. I. Inundation forests. *Amazoniana*, **8**, 19-45.

Klinge, H. & Rodrigues, W.A. (1968). Litter production in an area of Amazonian *terra firme* forest. I., II. *Amazoniana*, **1**, 287-310.

Klinge, H. & Rodrigues, W.A. (1971). Matéria organica e nutrientes na mata de *terra firme* perto de Manaus. *Acta Amazonica*, **1**, 69-72.

Livingstone, D.A. (1963). Chemical composition of rivers and lakes. *U.S. Geological Survey Professional Paper*, **440-G**, 1-64.

Meggers, B.J. (1985). Aboriginal adaptation to Amazonia. *Amazonia* (Ed. by G.T. Prance & T.E. Lovejoy), pp. 307-327. Pergamon Press, Oxford.

Nascimento, C. & Homma, A. (1984). Amazonia: meio ambiente e tecnologia agricola. *EMBRAPA-CPATU Documentos*, **27**, 1-182.

Prance, G.T. (1979). Notes on the vegetation of Amazonia III. *Brittonia*, **31**, 26-38.

Putzer, H. (1984). The geological evolution of the Amazon basin and its mineral resources. *The Amazon* (Ed. by H. Sioli), pp.15-46. Junk, Dordrecht.

Revilla, J. (1981). *Aspectos floristicos e fitossociologicos da floresta inundavel (igapó) Praia Grande, Rio Negro, Amazonas, Brasil.* Thesis, INPA and University of Amazonas, Manaus.

Schmidt, G.W. (1972a). Chemical properties of some waters in the tropical rain-forest region of Central Amazonia. *Amazoniana*, **3**, 199–207.

Schmidt, G.W. (1972b). Amounts of solids and dissolved substances in the middle reaches of the Amazon over the course of one year (August 1969–July 1970). *Amazoniana*, **3**, 208–223.

Singer, R. (1984). The role of fungi in Amazonian forests and in reforestation. *The Amazon* (Ed. by H. Sioli), pp. 603–614. Junk, Dordrecht.

Sioli, H. (1950). Das Wasser im Amazonasgebiet. *Forschungen und Fortschritte*, **26**, 274–280.

Sombroek, W.G. (1984). Soils of the Amazon region. *The Amazon* (Ed. by H. Sioli), pp. 521–535. Junk, Dordrecht.

Stallard, R.F. & Edmond, J.M. (1983). Geochemistry of the Amazon. 2. The influence of geology and weathering environment on the dissolved load. *Journal of Geophysical Research*, **88**, 9671–9688.

Ungemach, H. (1967). Sôbre o balanco metabolico de iônios inorganicos da area do sistema do Rio Negro. *Atas do Simposio Sôbre a Biota Amazonica*, **3**, 221–226.

Vitousek, P.M. & Sanford, R.L. (1986). Nutrient cycling in moist tropical forest. *Annual Review of Ecology and Systematics*, **17**, 137–167.

Worbes, M. (1983). Vegetationskundliche Untersuchungen zweier Überschwemmungswälder in Zentralamazonien — vorläufige Ergebnisse. *Amazoniana*, **8**, 47–65.

Worbes, M. (1986). Lebensbedingungen und Holzwachstum in zentralamazonischen Überschwemmungswäldern. *Scripta Geobotanica*. **17**, 1–112.

Are process rates higher in tropical forest ecosystems?

C. F. JORDAN

Institute of Ecology, University of Georgia, Athens, GA 30602, USA

SUMMARY

1 Tropical–temperate differences in the rates of ecosystem processes, if they occur, result from greater amounts of solar energy and higher average annual temperatures at lower latitudes.

2 Global and regional gradients of moisture and nutrient elements also exist, but these gradients do not often parallel the light gradient and so any attempt to correlate ecosystem processes with latitude is confounded with response to these other physical factors.

3 Since regional patterns of moisture and nutrients are generally known, it is possible to construct a model which shows process response to all three physical variables. Such a model suggests that ecosystem processes should be higher along a gradient of increasing yearly totals of light, when the other two variables are held constant.

4 An attempt to validate a global model of ecosystem processes as a function of light, moisture and nutrients is partially successful. A lack of a better fit may partly be due to biotic variables which vary in an unpredictable fashion and are not included in the model.

5 The title of this symposium, which implies that nutrient cycling is distinct in tropical ecosystems, seems justified.

6 An understanding that there are differences in ecosystem process rates, especially organic matter decomposition, between high and low latitude ecosystems, has important implications for agriculture and development in the tropics.

INTRODUCTION

Tropical rain forests have often been thought to have high rates of ecosystem processes such as productivity, decomposition and nutrient cycling. This impression may have its origin in the writings of nineteenth century tropical explorers such as A. R. Wallace (1878) who wrote, "The primeval forests of the equatorial zone are grand and overwhelming by their vastness, and by the display of a force of development and vigour of growth rarely or never witnessed in temperate climates" (Jordan 1981). The idea that ecological processes are more rapid in the tropics was given further impetus by Jenny, Gessel & Bingham (1949) who compared decomposition rates at different latitudes, and found rates to be higher at their tropical site.

In recent years, there have been a number of papers which have questioned the generalization that process rates are unusually high in the tropics. Proctor (1983a) stated, "A dogma of nutrient cycling processes in tropical rain forests is that of rapid decomposition and mineral-nutrient release from organic matter", but he concluded that generalizations about rapid decomposition rates in lowland forests must be made with caution. Anderson & Swift (1983) questioned the belief that plant litter decomposes rapidly in the humid tropics, and hence that tropical rain forest soils have a relatively low organic matter content. The results of decomposition studies in Sarawak led Anderson, Proctor & Vallack (1983) to state that, "The idea that the processes of decomposition and nutrient cycling are always rapid in tropical rain forests has become a dogma which is not supported by the results of these studies in the Mulu forests where litter decay rates, soil organic matter, standing crops and the chemical element capital in the soils are similar to some temperate deciduous forests".

Not only have generalizations about high rates of decomposition in the tropics been questioned. Statements proclaiming that net primary productivity in the tropics is unusually high are also open to doubt. Whitmore (1984, p. 122) concludes his chapter on growth rates and forest yields in tropical forests by saying, "The luxuriousness and appearance of unbridled growth given by the vegetation of the perhumid tropics does not therefore arise from an intrinsically higher growth rate than exists amongst temperate species".

Generalizations and global patterns

Generalizations in ecology are always subject to exception. Few, if any, ecological models are useful in predicting the exact outcome of any type of perturbation to natural systems. As a result, there are often objections to generalizations, especially when a generalization appears to gloss over specific data collected by the scientist raising the objection.

Yet without generalizations, ecology would be little more than a collection of facts. Data would be useless beyond the site from which they were collected, and even then they might be useless, since the time factor continually changes.

Generalizations are needed as organizing principles to guide further work. The title of the symposium from which the papers in this book are drawn, 'Mineral Nutrients in Tropical Forest and Savanna Ecosystems', suggests that mineral cycles in tropical ecosystems are somehow different from cycles in other types of ecosystem. Yet, except for this paper, the issue of whether nutrient cycles are in fact different in the tropics, and if so, how and why they are different, has not been addressed.

In this paper, the generalization that process rates are higher in the tropics is examined, and it is considered whether our understanding of this generalization can be improved in any way. To do this, a model is used based on our knowledge of physiological response to differences in physical factors of the environment. Quantitative limits are then imposed on the model based on data available in the literature. Finally, the model is tested by validation with an independent data set.

GLOBAL PATTERNS OF PROCESS RATES

Factors governing process rates

There are a number of physical factors which govern process rates in ecosystems. Only three of them have readily identifiable global and regional patterns. One is light energy. There are a number of parameters which are commonly measured, and which are an index of, or are roughly correlated with, light energy over large areas and long time-spans. They include: total solar radiation, net solar radiation, photosynthetically active radiation, average temperature, maximum and minimum temperature and degree-days. Totals are usually given per month or year. Tropical–temperate differences in ecosystem process rates, if they occur, result from greater amounts of solar energy at above-freezing temperatures (Jordan 1971). Incoming solar radiation strongly influences temperatures, with certain exceptions such as tropical mountains. Temperature is the physical factor most closely correlated with the latitudinal definition of the tropics (Jordan 1985), and when we talk about tropical ecosystems, we usually mean ecosystems that are warm throughout the year except on high mountains.

The second factor that governs ecosystem process rates is moisture. In the simplest form, it is given by rainfall per year, per month or per growing season. Humidity can be combined with temperature to give an index of evaporation potential, and the ratio between evaporation and rainfall is sometimes correlated with global or regional patterns of ecosystem processes.

The third factor is soil fertility. It is generally indexed by determining the amount of readily soluble major nutrients such as potassium and phosphorus and trace elements such as copper and zinc, and total stocks of nitrogen and sulphur. Although soils rich in one nutrient are often rich in others, all elements are not always correlated, and this can create a problem in ordinating a nutrient gradient.

Because global and regional patterns of light energy, moisture and nutrients are generally well known, gradients of ecosystem process rates are frequently examined as a function of these factors. There are a number of other physical factors which influence process rates, but which have ill-defined or non-existent global or regional patterns. Among them are oxygen and carbon dioxide concentration in the air and soil, and soil texture. Biological factors such as herbivory and disease also affect ecosystem processes. While these factors may sometimes show global and regional patterns, trends are not as easily identifiable as those of temperature and moisture.

Relation between factors and processes

Processes such as plant photosynthesis and leaf decomposition generally increase up to a point, with an increase in light energy, moisture and nutrients. For example, if, because of increasing light intensity, temperature gradually increases in a growth chamber containing plants, while moisture and nutrient supply are held steady, net photosynthesis will increase until a critical level is reached.

Critically high levels for each factor differ for each species. If factors are present in higher-than-critical levels, a decline in process rates may occur.

Similar responses to physical factors can be found in nature, although they are more difficult to detect. Jordan (1985, p. 68) plotted net primary productivity of natural forests in the United States as a function of the ratio between potential evapotranspiration and precipitation. This ratio is a useful index of the water that is available to plants. Productivity was lowest in the desert, and increased along a gradient through grassland and savannas. It reached a maximum in moist forest, and then declined in a forest where frequent occurrence of fog resulted in a relatively low evapotranspiration : precipitation ratio.

Correlation between factors and processes

Early studies of ecological change along environmental gradients usually considered only a single gradient at a time. For example, Whittaker (1975) reviewed structural changes along gradients of temperature and of moisture. However, single factor regressions are not satisfactory on global scales, because the major controls of process rates, light energy, water and nutrients, rarely if ever vary simultaneously along a single geographical gradient. Correlation coefficients of process rates with global patterns of single factors are usually low.

Recent comparisons have tried to deal with the independent variation of several factors governing process rates. For example, Jordan (1983) tried to eliminate the effect of moisture on a latitudinal gradient of leaf litter production by restricting comparisons to broadleaved, mature forests on mesic sites. Meentemeyer, Box & Thompson (1982) approached the problem by incorporating both energy and moisture into a single index, actual evapotranspiration. Proctor *et al.* (1983b) restricted their comparisons to four adjacent lowland tropical forests in Sarawak, which had similar temperature and rainfall regimes. However, there have been few models which incorporate nutrients, as well as light and moisture in an analysis. Jordan (1985 p. 52) included a nutrient gradient in a comparison of productivity and decomposition rates in tropical forest ecosystems, and to hold light energy and moisture constant, he used data only from lowland forests with a hot humid climate; however, data were available for seven sites only.

The lack of a model which incorporates the three major physical variables may be an important reason for the lack of a good fit in the attempts to determine how process rates vary on global and regional scales. While methodological differences emphasized by Proctor (1983b) cause part of the scatter apparent in comparisons of productivity and decomposition, it is suggested here that a suitable model can explain the anomalously low production and decomposition rates in Sarawak reported by Anderson *et al.* (1983) and Proctor *et al.* (1983b).

A THREE-DIMENSIONAL MODEL

Figure 1 is a three-dimensional model of global gradients of energy, moisture and

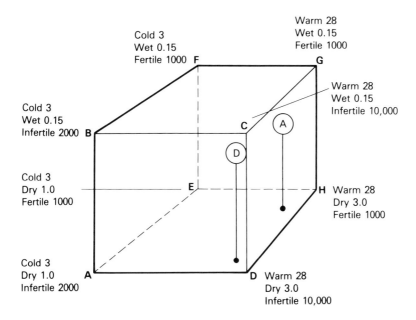

FIG. 1. Three-dimensional representation of global gradients of temperature, moisture and nutrients in forested regions of the world. Circles with D and A inside represent Dipterocarp forest and alluvial forest sites in Gunung Mulu National Park, Sarawak (Proctor *et al.* 1983a), and their position within global gradients.

nutrients in forested regions of the world. Point A is a cold, dry, infertile forest ecosystem. The gradient from A to B represents increasing moisture. The gradient from A to D represents increasing light energy (and temperature). The gradient from A to E represents increasing soil fertility. Point G is a wet, warm, fertile ecosystem, a tropical rain forest. The entire slice represented by D–C–G–H and extending about one-third of the way from D to A would represent tropical forests.

The gradients in Fig. 1 are quantified by the numbers beside the letters designating each corner. The first number is the mean annual biotemperature (Holdridge 1967), which is the average of all temperatures (°C) excluding those below 0 °C and above 30 °C. The second number is the ratio of annual potential evapotranspiration to precipitation. Values of less than unity indicate that precipitation is greater than evapotranspiration. Values of biotemperature and potential evapotranspiration ratio in Fig. 1 are taken from appropriate forest types appearing in the classification of world life zones or plant formations (Holdridge 1967). While there are weaknesses in this classification scheme, they are due mainly to local variations that cannot be incorporated into Holdridge's world model. Although a better quantitative model is desirable, none is really available on a global scale.

Quantifying the soil fertility gradient is more difficult, because there are insufficient comparable data for critical nutrients on a global scale. Vitousek (1984) argued that nutrient concentrations in leaf litter of natural forests may be a good index of the availability of limiting nutrients in the soil. He pointed out that in tropical forests, available phosphorus is usually the limiting nutrient, except on white sand podzols and on mountains, where nitrate or ammonium nitrogen is usually the limiting nutrient. Vitousek (1984) plotted the inverse of concentrations, i.e. dry mass of leaf litter divided by mass of nutrient; this convention is followed in Fig. 1, where the third number beside each letter is the reciprocal of phosphorus concentration in leaf litter. Nitrogen and other nutrients are not considered in this analysis, but should be in any multivariate analysis which includes more than the three independent variables considered here.

Process patterns

Two of the most commonly reported indices of ecosystem processes are annual production of leaf litter and decomposition constant k, or turnover coefficient k_1 (Anderson *et al.* 1983), which is the same as k when the forest is in a steady state (Olson 1963). The k term is useful for comparing data from studies of leaf decomposition in litter bags. It is defined as

$$\ln(X/X_o) = -kt$$

where X is the amount of litter in a bag after time interval t, and X_o is the original weight of litter in the bag (Olson 1963).

Figure 2 is a model of leaf litterfall and Fig. 3 is a model of decomposition constant in forested areas of the world. The axes correspond to the cube in Fig. 1. Values for leaf litterfall and decomposition constant were taken from the tables of Proctor *et al.* (1983b), Anderson *et al.* (1983), Jordan (1983) and Jordan (1985), who compared data from different sites. Data points were chosen which corresponded as closely as possible to the extremes represented by the corners of Fig. 1. Values in these tables suggest that forest leaf litterfall values range from 1 t ha^{-1} year^{-1} in the coldest, driest, most infertile forests, to 12 t ha^{-1} year^{-1} or greater in fertile, warm, moist forests. Turnover coefficients range from less than 0.4 to almost 4.0. Olson (1963) cited a value of 4.0 for hot, moist forests.

Differences in methodology and other problems may make comparisons between sites difficult (Anderson & Swift 1983; Proctor 1983b). In the case of litterfall comparisons, problems include definition of litterfall fractions, number of replicates, length of study period, variability of forest structure, differences in methodology and loss of mass before collection (Proctor 1983b). Difficulties in comparisons of decomposition studies also include methodology, as well as problems of litter quality (Anderson & Swift 1983). Despite these difficulties, there still appears to be some value in the summary comparison tables of Anderson *et al.* (1983) and Proctor *et al.* (1983b). This paper assumes that while their warnings are relevant, the problems are not as great as they expect and that at least a qualitative trend can be sought in their tables; however, 'real' values may be quantitatively different.

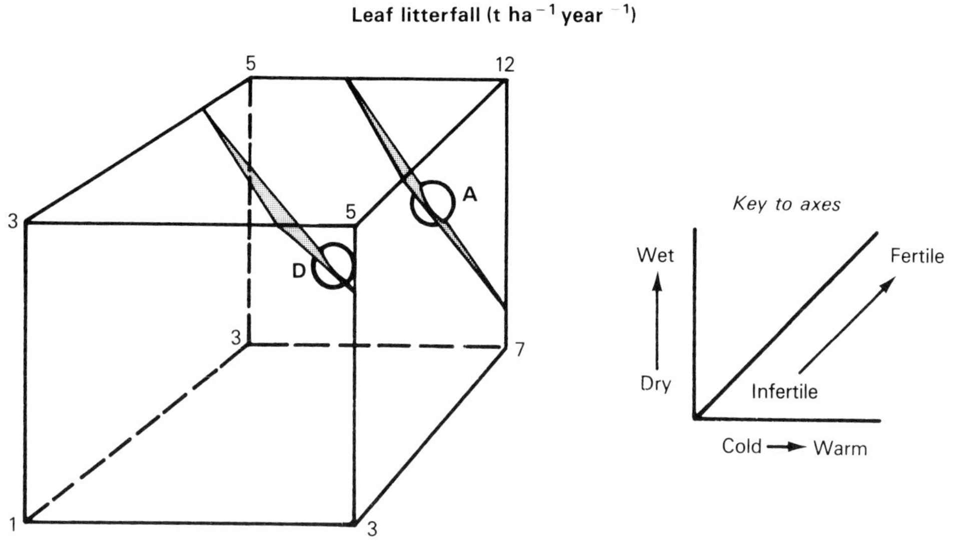

Leaf litterfall (t ha^{-1} year^{-1})

FIG. 2. Three-dimensional representation of global patterns of leaf litterfall as a function of temperature, moisture and nutrients. Axes correspond to those in Fig. 1. Circles with D and A as in Fig. 1.

Decomposition constant k or turnover coefficient k_1

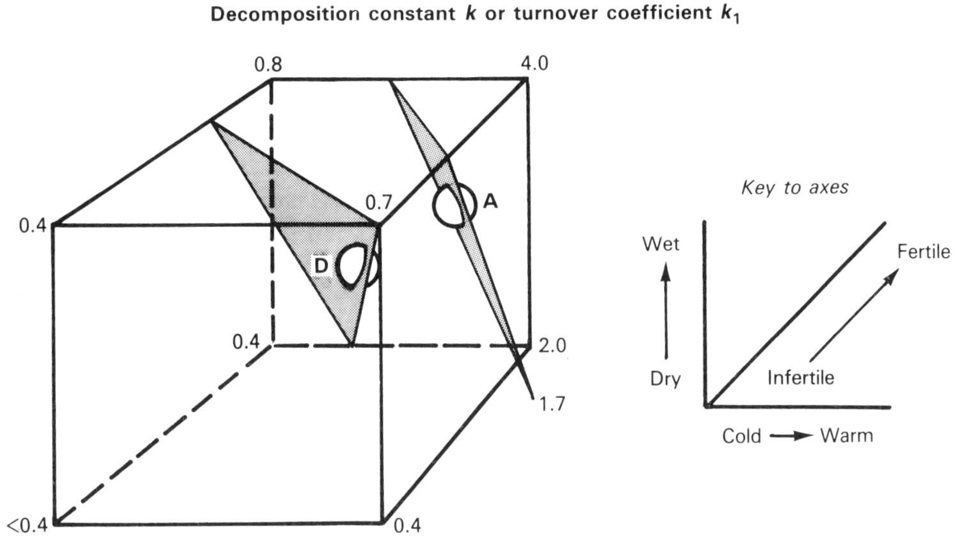

FIG. 3. Three-dimensional representation of global patterns of decomposition constant k or turnover coefficient k_1 as a function of temperature, moisture and nutrients. Axes correspond to those in Fig. 1. Circles with D and A as in Fig. 1.

The models show that leaf litterfall and decomposition increase along a latitudinal gradient (increase in average annual temperature) from high to low latitude, when the moisture and nutrient variables are held constant. In the model, the values of points along all lines parallel to the axis A–D increase from left to right. If these models are valid, it means that we can say that litterfall and decomposition are higher in the tropics, if it is understood that comparisons are limited to sites with similar moisture and nutrient conditions.

Validation data

The models in Figs. 2 and 3 were evaluated using the data of Proctor *et al.* (1983b) and Anderson *et al.* (1983) from Sarawak. These workers believe that their data contradict the idea that process rates are high in the tropics.

There were four study sites in Gunung Mulu National Park, Sarawak (Proctor *et al.* 1983a). In the heath forest site, nitrogen rather than phosphorus was probably the limiting factor (Jordan 1985). In the limestone site, soil phosphorus was unusually high due to the nature of the parent rock. Therefore, these two sites were not included in the validation. Only the Dipterocarp forest and the alluvial forest sites are evaluated here.

The models were validated first by plotting the Dipterocarp forest and alluvial forest sites of Sarawak in Fig. 1. Average temperature at the sites is about 25 °C, so we move along the A–D axis until we reach this value. Then we move along the diagonal fertility gradient. The reciprocal of the phosphorus concentration in the leaf litter from the Dipterocarp site is 9524; we move parallel to the D–H axis until we reach this value, and we put a point. The reciprocal from the alluvial site is 3745, so we continue on until we reach this value, and put another point. Then, beginning at each of these two points, we parallel the vertical axis along the moisture gradient. Evapotranspiration at Mulu in Sarawak is about 1500 mm per year, and rainfall is about 5090 mm, which gives an ET : P ratio of 0.29. We assume that the ratio is the same for both sites, so we go up the vertical axis to a value of 0.29 from both points, and plot with circles the Dipterocarp forest site labelled D and the alluvial forest site labelled A.

The next step in the validation is to determine how well the models in Figs. 2 and 3 predict the observed litterfall and decomposition data at sites A and D. To do this, the circles representing the Dipterocarp forest and alluvial forest sites were plotted within the cubes of Figs. 2 and 3 in exactly the same positions as they were in Fig. 1. The circles can then be used to predict what the litterfall and decomposition values should be, according to the models of Figs. 2 and 3.

To understand the procedure, it is important to note that all three axes in Fig. 2 have the same units, t ha^{-1} year^{-1} of litterfall. A plane can be drawn between points of equal value on each axis, for example 4.0 on the temperature axis, 4.0 on the moisture axis and 4.0 on the fertility axis. Any point which occurs on that plane will have a value of 4.0. There are an infinite number of such planes within the cube, but any point within the cube can occur on only one plane of equal value. Thus, any point within the cube predicts only one value of litterfall in Fig. 2, and only one decomposition constant in Fig. 3.

In Figs. 2 and 3, a plane can be drawn through whichever three axes are most convenient. The only restriction is that each plane must be defined by three points, and one of the points must be on a temperature axis, one on a moisture axis and one on a fertility axis. The statement that any point within the cube can occur on one and only one plane is true as long as only three of the 12 sides of the cube are considered in any one analysis.

Since any point within the cubes of Figs. 2 and 3 can be used to predict a single value, the point in the middle of the Dipterocarp forest circle (D) and the middle of the alluvial forest circle (A) can predict litterfall and turnover coefficients at each of these sites. The Dipterocarp site in Fig. 2 falls on the surface which has a value of 4.5. We can say that the model predicts that leaf litterfall at the Dipterocarp site should be 4.5 t ha^{-1} year^{-1}. The observed value for 1 year at the Dipterocarp site was actually 5.4 t ha^{-1} year^{-1} (Proctor et al. 1983b). The point for the alluvial site in Fig. 2 predicts a value of 7.5 t ha^{-1} year^{-1} and the observed value was 6.6.

By employing a similar procedure, we can use Fig. 3 to predict decomposition values for the two sites, and compare predicted with observed values. The surface predicted by the alluvial site has a value of 1.7, which corresponds exactly with the observed value of 1.7 (Anderson et al. 1983). (Note that one axis had to be extended in order to obtain a plane that had equal values and that passed through point A.) However, the Dipterocarp forest site has a predicted turnover coefficient of only 0.7, compared with an observed value of 1.7.

A lack of fit between model predictions and observations may be expected, given the problems of data comparison (Anderson & Swift 1983; Proctor 1983b). However, if the models cannot accurately predict values for a particular site, what use are they?

Utility of the models

The models explain how the Sarawak values can be lower than values in some temperate forests without contradicting the generalization, or 'dogma' as it is called by Anderson et al. (1983) quoted here in the introduction, that process rates are higher in tropical than in high latitude ecosystems. A temperate–tropical gradient, or a gradient from high to low latitude, extends along the A–D axis in Fig. 1. At any point on this single gradient, ecosystem processes can have a wide range of values, depending on where the ecosystem is on the moisture and soil fertility axes. Thus it is possible to locate a high latitude site that has a higher rate of leaf litterfall than a tropical site. However, if we restrict ourselves to a single value on the moisture axis, and a single value on the fertility axis, and move along the energy (temperature, latitude) gradient from A to D, or parallel to this axis, litterfall and decomposition do increase. Thus the generalization that process rates are higher in the tropics than at higher latitudes is true, if it is understood that latitudinal comparisons must be made only between sites which have a comparable soil fertility and water balance.

The models are not useful in understanding differences over small scales, where local effects overshadow the major global gradients. For example, there may be a large variation in leaf litter production along a soil catena of only several hundred metres. The models do not deal with variability at this level.

Practical implications of the model

Is the question, 'are process rates higher in tropical ecosystems than in temperate ecosystems' solely of academic interest, or has it any practical importance? It may have much significance in the debate about the type of agriculture most appropriate for developing tropical countries.

While some groups of farmers have known for perhaps centuries about the importance of organic matter in maintaining soil fertility, only recently has the subject become common in the scientific literature (Mongi & Huxley 1979; Vaughan & Malcolm 1985; Soil Science Society of America 1987). If organic matter decomposes more rapidly in the tropics than at higher latitudes, then the argument for agroforestry systems, in which there is a continual input of organic matter to the soil, becomes stronger for the tropics. The argument for large-scale clearing for monoculture of annuals becomes weaker.

CONCLUSION

A major reason why some recent studies have encountered relatively low process rates in certain humid tropical ecosystems is because of the low soil fertility at those sites. A three-dimensional model which incorporates nutrients, as well as light energy and moisture, is helpful in explaining the variation observed along global gradients of ecosystem processes. The generalization that process rates are higher in the tropics seems justified, as long as the sites examined on the tropical–temperate gradient have comparable moisture regimes and soil fertility.

ACKNOWLEDGEMENT

I thank Drs Tim Whitmore and Becky Brown for their comments on the manuscript.

REFERENCES

Anderson, J.M., Proctor, J. & Vallack, H.W. (1983). Ecological studies in four contrasting lowland rain forests in Gunung Mulu National Park, Sarawak III. Decomposition processes and nutrient losses from leaf litter. *Journal of Ecology*, **71**, 503–727.

Anderson, J.M. & Swift, M.J. (1983). Decomposition in tropical forests. *Tropical Rain Forest: Ecology and Management* (Ed. by S.L. Sutton, T.C. Whitmore & A.C. Chadwick), pp. 287–309. Blackwell Scientific Publications, Oxford.

Holdridge, L.R. (1967). *Life Zone Ecology.* Tropical Science Center, San José.

Jenny, H., Gessel, S.P. & Bingham, F.T. (1949). Comparative study of decomposition rates of organic matter in temperate and tropical regions. *Soil Science*, **68**, 419–432.

Jordan, C. F. (1971). A world pattern in plant energetics. *American Scientist*, **59**, 425–433.

Jordan, C.F. (Ed.) (1981). *Tropical Ecology. Benchmark Papers in Ecology No. 10.* Hutchinson Ross, Stroudsburg.

Jordan, C.F. (1983). Productivity of tropical rain forest ecosystems and the implications for their use as future wood and energy sources. *Tropical Rain Forest Ecosystems. Ecosystems of the World 14A* (Ed. by F.B. Golley), pp. 117–136. Elsevier, Amsterdam.

Jordan, C.F. (1985). *Nutrient Cycling in Tropical Forest Ecosystems.* Wiley, Chichester.

Meentemeyer, V., Box, E.O. & Thompson, R. (1982). World patterns and amounts of terrestrial plant litter production. *BioScience*, **32**, 125–128.

Mongi, H.O. & Huxley, P.A. (1979) *Soils Research in Agroforestry.* International Council for Research in Agroforestry, Nairobi.

Olson, J.S. (1963). Energy storage and the balance of producers and decomposers in ecological systems. *Ecology*, **44**, 322–331.

Proctor, J. (1983a). Mineral nutrients in tropical forests. *Progress in Physical Geography*, 7, 422–431.

Proctor, J. (1983b). Tropical forest litterfall. I. Problems of data comparison. *Tropical Rain Forest: Ecology and Management* (Ed. by S.L. Sutton, T.C. Whitmore & A.C. Chadwick), pp. 267–273. Blackwell Scientific Publications, Oxford.

Proctor, J., Anderson, J.M., Chai, P. & Vallack, H.W. (1983a). Ecological studies in four contrasting lowland rain forests in Gunung Mulu National Park, Sarawak I. Forest environment, structure, and floristics. *Journal of Ecology*, **71**, 237–260.

Proctor, J., Anderson, J.M., Fogden, S.C.L. & Vallack, H.W. (1983b). Ecological studies in four contrasting lowland rain forests in Gunung Mulu National Park, Sarawak II. Litterfall, litter standing crop and preliminary observations on herbivory. *Journal of Ecology*, **71**, 261–283.

Soil Science Society of America (1987). *Soil Fertility and Organic Matter as Critical Components of Production Systems. Special Publication No. 19.* American Society of Agronomy, Madison.

Vaughan, D. & Malcolm, R.E. (Eds.) (1985). *Soil Organic Matter and Biological Activity.* Nijhoff/Junk, Dordrecht.

Vitousek, P.M. (1984). Litterfall, nutrient cycling, and nutrient limitation in tropical forests. *Ecology*, **65**, 285–298.

Wallace, A.R. (1878). *Tropical Nature and Other Essays.* Macmillan, London. Reprinted AMS Press, New York (1975).

Whitmore, T.C. (1984). *Tropical Rain Forests of the Far East*, 2nd edn. Clarendon Press, Oxford.

Whittaker, R.H. (1975). *Communities and Ecosystems.* Macmillan, New York.

Patterns of nutrient accumulation and release in Amazonian forests of the upper Rio Negro basin

E. MEDINA* AND E. CUEVAS**

*Centro de Ecología, IVIC, Aptdo. 21827, Caracas 1020–A, Venezuela, and
**Institute of Tropical Forestry, Southern Forest Experiment Station, USDA-Forest Service,
Call Box 25 000, Río Piedras 00928–2500, Puerto Rico

SUMMARY

1 The results of the San Carlos project on Amazonian rain forest ecosystems are critically reviewed with emphasis on the functional properties of mature forests.

2 Forest types are characterized by dominant species, soil and topographical position in the sequence: mixed forest on oxisols, *yévaro* and *guaco* forests on ultisols and Amazon *caatinga* forest complex (including tall and low *caatinga*) on spodosols.

3 The first three types are generally non-flooded (*terra firme* forests), while the *caatinga* forests have a variety of flooding regimes depending on their topographical position.

4 *Terra firme* forests are relatively depleted in phosphorus, potassium, calcium and magnesium, but have relatively high nitrogen contents in both soil and vegetation.

5 Tall *caatinga* and the tall *bana* unit of low *caatinga* accumulate and circulate relatively large amounts of phosphorus, and have N : P ratios comparable with those of forests at nutrient-rich sites.

6 Root growth and decomposition appear to be limited by phosphorus, calcium and magnesium in mixed forest, by nitrogen in tall *caatinga*, and by nitrogen and phosphorus in low *caatinga*.

7 Endomycorrhizal roots are of general occurrence in all forest types and infection of adult trees and seedlings is often heavy.

8 The efficiency of the nutrient trapping process appears to be correlated with the density of fine roots in the upper soil layers, or the root mat above the soil.

INTRODUCTION

Early ecological analyses of tropical rain forests emphasized the critical role of nutrients for maintaining forest productivity. The general picture indicated high rates of organic matter production (Murphy 1975), accompanied by high rates of debris decomposition (Olson 1963; Rodin & Bazilevich 1967). Both characteristics imply a large nutrient uptake and efficient nutrient conserving mechanisms if protection against leaching, resulting from high rainfall, is to be attained. Furthermore, soils of tropical rain forests are generally strongly leached, have a low base saturation, low pH, and therefore, high aluminium mobility. Richards (1952) popularized the view (implicit in the work of Walter (1936)) that nutrient

217

capital in tropical forests, in contrast with temperate forests, is mainly in the living biomass. A direct implication of this concept is that the elimination of the forest biomass for any purpose will result in the loss of the ecosystem nutrient capital, and a drastic reduction in natural soil fertility.

Tropical soils have been described as oligotrophic, a term borrowed from limnology, to highlight their low nutrient content. However, plant nutrient availability in soils of tropical rain forests is not uniformly low. Nutrient cycling studies in several tropical forests have indicated that nitrogen is the main element being recycled through litterfall and in larger quantities than in any other terrestrial ecosystem (Rodin & Bazilevich 1967). On the other hand, most tropical lowland rain forests appear to be limited by phosphorus (Vitousek 1984; Vitousek & Sinford 1986), while their plant species seem to be tolerant of high soil concentrations of mobile aluminium (Sprick 1979; Sobrado & Medina 1980).

Among the most attractive nutrient conserving mechanisms proposed as responsible for tight nutrient cycles in tropical forests is that based on mycorrhizal symbiosis explicitly advanced by Went & Stark (1968). Frequent occurrence of mycorrhizal associations in Brazilian tropical forests suggested the hypothesis that protection against nutrient leaching, which will surely occur when nutrients are released during organic matter decomposition, may be increased if a 'direct' nutrient transfer occurs between decomposing litter and absorbing roots, in a process mediated mainly by mycorrhiza. This hypothesis captured the attention of many tropical ecologists, and stimulated a variety of projects intending to establish the role of mycorrhiza in nutrient cycling and tree growth in tropical forests (Janos 1975). Other properties of forest systems on poor soils, such as sclerophylly, slow decomposition rates, low nutrient demands and high nutrient-use efficiency for organic matter production, have been supposed to operate concurrently with direct nutrient transfer (Herrera *et al.* 1978a). Together, these functional properties are thought to be responsible for the small amounts of nutrients leached from Amazonian forest ecosystems (Brinkmann 1983).

Detailed studies on forest structure have demonstrated that soil can be a very heterogeneous factor under tropical climates, and is frequently responsible for the differentiation of forest types (Richards 1952). This concept has been expanded to a regional scale for the Amazon region of South America, and has led to the differentiation of geochemical regions based on the physicochemical properties of drainage waters (Sioli 1968; Fittkau 1971; Fittkau *et al.* 1975). Black water rivers, such as the Rio Negro, drain areas of sandy podzolized soils low in most essential nutrients for plant growth. They are characterized by a high content of humic acids, which remain dissolved because of the predominant low concentrations of polyvalent cations, mainly Ca^{2+} and Mg^{2+}. In contrast, white water rivers have high sediment content and are relatively rich in cations because they drain geologically younger Andean areas. Clear water rivers, which are common in the central Amazonian region, also drain from nutrient-poor soils.

Forests located in the Rio Negro basin in the northern part of the Amazon appear to be at the lower extreme of soil nutrient availability among tropical forests, a factor which emphasizes their vulnerability to human intervention. Extensive development projects undertaken rapidly in the early 1970s within the Amazon basin by several countries raised questions on the probable magnitude of environmental impacts, and exposed serious deficiencies in the ecological knowledge available to support forest management. To address these deficiencies, a research project organized by the Center of Ecology at the Venezuelan Institute for Scientific Research (IVIC), with the participation of the Institute of Ecology of the University of Georgia (U.S.A.) and the Max-Planck Institute of Limnology (Germany), was designed to study nutrient cycling and conservation in Amazonian forests. The goals of the project were to analyse nutrient balances at the level of the ecosystem, and the mechanisms operating at the level of the compartment (canopy, root, soil) or of the species, which result in nutrient conservation by reducing nutrient leaching from living and decomposing biomass. The site selected for study was located near the southernmost region of Venezuela, at the border with Brazil and Colombia, in an area centred on the town of San Carlos de Río Negro (01°54′N, 67°54′W).

A large number of papers from this project have been published since 1974, and emphasis has shifted from the study of natural forests to mechanisms of regeneration and the assessment of the ecological impact on forest lands by human intervention for agricultural purposes. In this paper we address the functional properties related to nutrient cycling of 'mature' forests. The frequent finding of charcoal at different soil depths in several forest sites near San Carlos has led to the recognition that forests hitherto considered undisturbed may have been burned as recently as 300 years ago (Sanford *et al.* 1985).

Our specific objective is to discuss the contribution of the San Carlos project to the following questions.

1 Which nutrients determine the oligotrophic character of forest soils in the lowland tropics?

2 Are there characteristic patterns of biomass and nutrient allocation in forests growing on nutrient-poor sites?

3 Are there unique mechanisms of nutrient conservation in forests growing on soils of extremely low nutrient availability?

CLIMATE, DIVERSITY OF FORESTS AND SOILS ALONG TOPOGRAPHICAL GRADIENTS IN SAN CARLOS

Climate

San Carlos de Rio Negro has an average annual rainfall of 3565 mm, with monthly rainfall generally higher than pan A evaporation, and with an average annual temperature of 26 °C. Data for the years 1974 to 1985 show that rainfall peaks towards the middle of the year when the average is more than 400 mm month^{-1}. Minimum rainfall (not less than 150 mm month^{-1}) is registered during December and January (Fig. 1). Evaporation rates are more homoge-

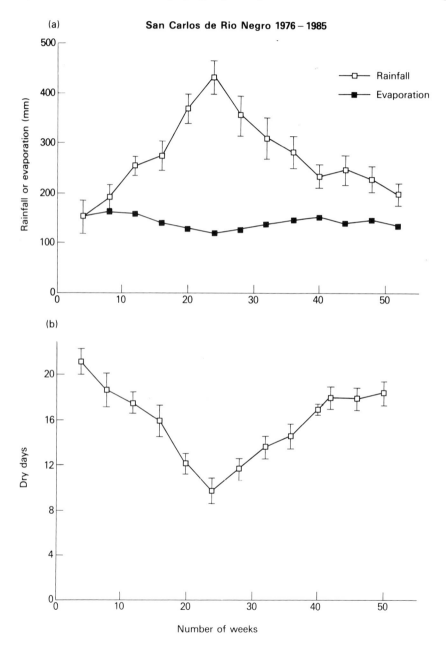

FIG. 1. Seasonal trends in climatic data from the meteorological station of San Carlos de Rio Negro. (a) Mean values (±S.E. of the mean) for rainfall and pan A evaporation on a 4-weekly (monthly) basis. (b) Mean number of dry days (rainfall ≤ pan A evaporation). Data provided by Ministerio del Ambiente y de los Recursos Naturales Renovables, Venezuela.

neous, although a clear reduction is observed during the months of higher rainfall, most likely due to increased cloud cover. Variability of rainfall is much higher than variability of evaporation. Mean annual relative humidity reaches 85%, and daily insolation averages 5.2 h, for an annual radiation of 1465 J cm^{-2} day^{-1}. Average pan A evaporation is 5.4 mm day^{-1}, and evaporation involves about 90% of available radiant energy (Heuveldop 1980).

In spite of the high monthly rainfall values a clear seasonality in the phenological behaviour of the dominant tree species in most forest types has been observed (Cuevas & Medina 1986). Annual variations in temperature and duration of photoperiod are slight at this latitude. Therefore the vegetation appears to be responding to annual variation in the number of dry days (rainfall $\leq$ pan A evaporation; Medina, Sobrado & Herrera (1978)) (Fig. 1). There is a significant negative correlation between number of dry days per month and rainfall during the same period (adjusted $r^2 = 0.96$, $F = 268$). A greater number of dry days in a given period is also correlated with the probability of obtaining a sequence of uninterrupted dry days.

Soils and vegetation

Three well differentiated soil types were found in the study area, all of them associated with distinct geomorphological positions and vegetation types (Herrera 1977; Dubroeucq & Sánchez 1981; Breimer 1985; W. Franco & N. Dezzeo unpublished; Schnütgen & Bremer 1985) (Table 1).

1 Concretional oxisols (ferralsols) located on the tops of rolling hills and associated with mixed forest characterized by species of Apocynaceae (*Aspidosperma* spp.), Burseracease (*Protium* spp.), Caryocaraceae (*Caryocar* spp.), Chrysobalanaceae (*Licania* spp.), legumes (*Swartzia* spp.), Moraceae (*Eschweilera* spp.), Palmae (*Jessenia bataua* (Martius) Burret, *Iryanthera* sp.), and Vochysiaceae (*Vochysia* spp.) (H. Clark & R. Liessner unpublished; Saldarriaga 1985).

2 Yellow ultisols (acrisols, Paleudults or Tropudults) located on the hillsides and characterized by a grey sandy topsoil over a yellow clay horizon caused by clay illuviation (Breimer 1985). On these soils grow the tallest forests in the area dominated by the legumes *Eperua purpurea* Bentham (*yévaro*) and frequently *Micrandra spruceana* (Baill.) R. Schultes (*cunuri*). Another leguminous tree species associated with *yévaro* forest and frequently found as a dominant along small creeks within the forest is *Monopterix uaucu* Spruce ex Bentham (*guaco*) (Buschbacher 1984). *Guaco* trees seem to be associated with grey ultisols (Paleaquult) on the lower parts of the hillsides (Breimer 1985; N. Dezzeo, personal communication). In this paper associations of *Monopterix uaucu* are considered as a separate entity, the *guaco* forest.

3 Ground water podzols (Tropaquods, spodosols) found between the rolling hills, and made up of sand probably originated *in situ* from weathering of local granite (Schnütgen & Bremer 1985). They are characterized by an A1 organic horizon about 30 cm thick, followed by a bleached sandy horizon about 1 m thick

TABLE 1. Basic characterization of forest types near San Carlos de Rio Negro, Venezuela

Forest type	Characteristic species	Elevation	Soil + roots	Geomorphological level
Mixed forest	*Aspidosperma* spp. *Caryocar* spp. *Licania* spp. *Protium* spp. *Vochysia* spp.	*c.* 122 m	Concretional oxisol Thick root mat above mineral soil	Rolling hills Laterite cap
Yévaro	*Eperua purpurea* *Micrandra spruceana*	*c.* 121 m	Yellow ultisols Thick root mat above mineral soil	Clayey hillsides
Guaco	*Monopterix cf. uacu*	*c.* 120 m	Grey ultisols	
Tall Amazon *caatinga*	*Eperua leucantha* *Glycoxylon inophyllum* *Hevea* spp. *Manilkara* sp. *Micrandra sprucei*	*c.* 117 m	Tropaquods Thick organic horizon Bh present Root mat embed- ded in organic A0 and A1	Sandy valley fills
Low Amazon *caatinga*		*c.* 118 m		
Tall *bana*	*Aspidosperma album* *Calycophyllum obovatum* *Glycoxylon inophyllum* *Micrandra sprucei*			
Low *bana*	*Catostemma* sp. *Clusia* spp. *Mouriri uncitheca* *Remijia involucrata* *Rodognaphalopsis* spp.			

and a Bh illuviation horizon of low permeability (Herrera 1979). On these soils grow the Amazon *caatinga* forest complex (Klinge, Medina & Herrera 1978), characterized by highly sclerophyllous species (Klinge & Medina 1979). This vegetation shows particular patterns of change in tree density and species dominance along subtle changes in relief and drainage. The lowest positions in the *caatinga* complex are dominated by *Eperua leucantha* Bentham (yaguácana), a legume which develops knee roots and seems to tolerate prolonged periods of shallow flooding. Also characteristic of this area are species of *Hevea* and *Manilkara*. Intermediate positions are dominated by *Micrandra sprucei* (M.-Arg.) R. Schultes (*cunuri banero*) and *Glycoxylon inophyllum* Ducke (*yuquito*). This mosaic has been described as tall Amazon *caatinga* (Klinge & Herrera 1983). Higher positions, less prone to shallow flooding, are occupied by a lower vegetation locally known as '*bana*'. This was described as low Amazon *caatinga* by Bongers, Engelen & Klinge (1985), who differentiated three units according to tree height and density: tall *bana*, low *bana* and open *bana*. Typical low Amazon *caatinga* has a low tree and shrub layer characterized by a palm (*Mauritia carana*

Wallace), *Aspidosperma album* (Vahl) R. Benoit ex Pichon, *Clusia* spp. and several species of Bombacaceae (*Rodognaphalopsis* spp., *Catostemma* spp.), Rubiaceae (*Calycophyllum obovatum* (Ducke) Ducke, *Remigia involucrata* K. Schumann, *Retiniphyllum* spp.) and Melastomataceae (*Mouriri uncitheca* Morley & Wurdack).

Mixed forest on oxisols and *yévaro* forest on ultisols are never flooded (hence the local name of *tierra firme* forests), and constitute the areas most frequently used for slash and burn agriculture. *Guaco* forest also belongs to the same category, although it may experience soil saturation when located in the lower part of the hillsides, in contact with the tall Amazon *caatinga* forest.

All *terra firme* forests have a well developed root mat of variable thickness on top of the mineral soil. This root mat, made up of apogeotropically growing fine roots (Sanford 1987), is readily separated from the mineral soil allowing easy measurement of fine root properties such as biomass, mycorrhizal infection, leaching and root respiration (Stark & Jordan 1978; Jordan & Escalante 1980; Medina *et al.* 1980). In tall and low *caatinga*, fine roots are also heavily concentrated near the soil surface (Klinge & Herrera 1978, 1983; Bongers *et al.* 1985; Sanford 1985), but are embedded in an organic matrix corresponding to the A_0 horizon. Another striking difference between *terra firme* and Amazon *caatinga* vegetation is that the former drain clear waters, while the latter drain black waters (Paolini 1980). The origin of the humic acids which colour drainage waters from the *caatinga* sandy soils, and the factors that determine their removal in oxisols are still a matter of research.

Although no precise phytosociological studies are available to substantiate all the above descriptions, we have based them on field experience, and on the association of characteristic dominant tree species with easily recognizable soil types. Structural studies have been conducted on mixed forests (Uhl & Murphy 1981; Saldarriaga 1985) and Amazon *caatinga* complex (Brünig *et al.* 1978; Alder *et al.* 1979; Bongers *et al.* 1985).

Soil water

Periods of two or more consecutive dry days are ecologically significant in a humid area such as San Carlos because of the low water retention capacity of the widespread sandy soils. In the Amazon *caatinga*, dry spells of 5–10 days result in fluctuations of the water table from 0.4–1.0 m (Herrera 1977; Bongers *et al.* 1985). Detailed tensiometer studies conducted along the soil–vegetation sequence described above (W. Franco & N. Dezzeo unpublished) revealed that the degree of soil saturation is related to the topographical position of the soils measured (Fig. 2). Average soil water tension was higher in the mixed forest on concretional oxisols, and decreased following the sequence *yévaro* forest → *guaco* forest → Amazon *caatinga*. Soils in tall and low Amazon *caatinga* were saturated more than 60% of the time, mainly at 45 and 75 cm depths. We consider the mixed, *yévaro* and *guaco* forests as non-flooded, while *caatinga* complex forests

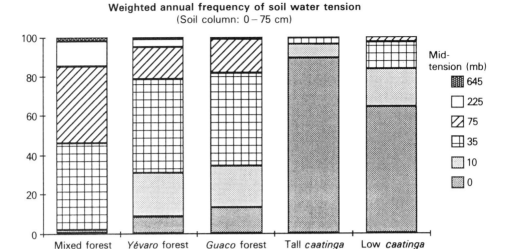

FIG. 2. Percentage frequency of soil water tension measured daily along a topographical gradient from mixed forest on oxisol, through *yévaro* and *guaco* forests, to tall *caatinga* and low *caatinga*. Values are weighted frequencies of soil tension measured daily at 20, 45 and 75 cm depths between 23 November, 1981 and 22 September, 1982 (data from Franco & Dezzeo 1982).

show variable degrees of flooding after heavy rains. It seems clear that the forest sequence observed in the study area results from an interaction between soil physicochemical properties and the predominant soil water regime. It is likely that those areas located at the lower positions in the topographical gradient will be less affected by sequences of dry days and will also be receiving nutrient-enriched leachates from surrounding forest systems.

BIOMASS INVENTORIES

Mixed and *yévaro* forests are frequently found growing side by side. As a result some biomass inventories conducted on *tierra firme* forests include a mixture of both (e.g. some plots measured by Jordan & Uhl (1978), Veillon (1983) and Saldarriaga (1985)). Also, biomass inventories in tall *caatinga* have included a range of vegetation units, which probably explains the large variability of biomass estimations reported for this forest (Klinge & Herrera 1983). A posteriori stratification of biomass values according to forest types gives a more logical picture of biomass accumulation. Evaluation of differences in biomass inventories between forest types at San Carlos should take into account the fact that the methods of determining above-ground biomass are not the same in all cases. In mixed and *guaco* forests estimations were based on regressions developed from felled trees in a range of size classes (Jordan & Uhl 1978; Buschbacher 1984; Saldarriaga 1985), while in *caatinga* forests estimations were based on clear felling and weighing of plots of 100 m^2 or less (Klinge & Herrera 1983; Bongers *et al.* 1985).

Along the forest sequence described, total biomass shows a peak at the interface between non-flooded forests (mixed forest and *yévaro* forest) and the less flood-prone areas of the *caatinga* complex (Table 2). Root : shoot ratios increase markedly within the *caatinga* complex, reaching values well above unity in the low *caatinga*. Total biomass values for *yévaro, guaco* and tall *caatinga* are within the range of variation reported for other non-flooded tropical rain forests. Values compiled by Cannell (1982) average 440 t ha^{-1}, while Brown & Lugo (1982) predict a total biomass of 370 t ha^{-1} for the temperature : precipitation ratio of this region (0.73×10^{-2} °C mm^{-1}). Mixed forest on oxisol and low Amazon *caatinga* fall below the range of biomass of other tropical forests. Lower biomass accumulation in these two forests is probably related to the frequent alternation of flooded and dry periods in low Amazon *caatinga*, while nutrients seem to be the most important factor in the mixed forest.

TABLE 2. Biomass and leaf area indices (LAI) for rain forests of the upper Rio Negro basin, Venezuela (values in t ha^{-1}). (1) Uhl & Jordan (1984); (2) Saldarriaga (1985); (3) Sanford (1985); (4) Veillon (1983) from calculations of S. Brown, A. Lugo & J. Chapman (personal communication); (5) Buschbacher (1984); (6) Klinge & Herrera (1983), eliminating outlier plots as suggested by authors; (7) Bongers, Engelen & Klinge (1985), in open *bana* non-woody plants contribute substantially to LAI (*values estimated from root : shoot ratio of similar forests)

Forest type	Leaf biomass	LAI	Above-ground	Below-ground	Total biomass	Root : shoot
Mixed forest on oxisol						
(1)	8.6		261	48.5	310	0.2
(2)	9.8	7.5	234	57	292	0.2
(3)	—	—	—	61	—	—
Yévaro forest on ultisols						
(4)	—	—	273	70*	343	—
Guaco forest on ultisols						
(5)	—	—	423	42	465	0.1
Tall Amazon *caatinga* on tropaquods						
(4)	—	—	266	134*	400	—
(6)	6.9	4.5	237	119	356	0.5
(3)	—	—	—	61	—	—
Low Amazon *caatinga* on tropaquod						
(7) Tall *bana*	9.7	4.8	182	128	310	0.7
Low *bana*	4.3	3.3	40	69	109	1.7
Open *bana*	1.1	1.4	6	42	48	7.0
(3) Tall *bana*	—	—	—	55	—	—

The strong accumulation of fine roots near the soil surface or above the soil as a root mat is a striking characteristic of the San Carlos forests. As an example, Sanford (1985) showed that, in the upper 10 cm of soil (including the root mat), the amount of fine roots was 17.6 t ha^{-1} in mixed forest (30% of total root biomass), 23.3 t ha^{-1} in tall *caatinga* (38% of total root biomass) and 15.9 t ha^{-1} in low *caatinga* (30% of total root biomass).

NUTRIENT INVENTORIES

Detailed soil nutrient inventories are not available for the whole range of forest types in San Carlos. Soil data are highly variable because a variety of extraction procedures have been used and there is no uniform reference to soil depth. Results available indicate that in both mixed and *guaco* forests similar amounts of nitrogen accumulate in the living vegetation as in the upper soil layers (Tables 3 and 4), while amounts of phosphorus are about 5–10 times higher in the upper soil layers than in the living vegetation. In the tall *caatinga* there appears to be slightly more nitrogen, and considerably more phosphorus, accumulated in the vegetation than in the top 40 cm of soil (Table 5). In all forests, accumulation of potassium, calcium and magnesium in the living biomass is higher than the amount of exchangeable cations measured in the soil. If total cations are considered, these proportions may be different, but no data are available. The fre-

TABLE 3. Nutrient inventory in living vegetation and soil in a mixed forest on oxisol (values in kg ha^{-1}). (1) Uhl & Jordan (1984); biomass data supersede earlier values given in Jordan & Uhl (1978); soil nutrient values were calculated from an independent sample to that cited in Jordan (1982); cations extracted with double acid solution. (2) Stark & Spratt (1977); cations extracted with ammonium acetate. (3) Jordan *et al.* (1982). (4) Herrera (1986). (5) Calculated from fig. 2.1 in Jordan (1987). (6) Sanford (1985)

Compartment	N	P	K	Ca	Mg
Vegetation (1)					
Leaves	160	5.1	37.7	11.5	6.1
Stems	785	26.0	207.2	194.1	49.3
Roots	540	17.1	43.1	45.4	11.6
Total living	1485	48.2	288.0	251.0	67.0
Fine litter	109	2.1	8.3	3.4	1.9
Dead wood	128	1.1	3.4	6.6	2.5

Depth (cm)		Total		Exchangeable cations		
Soil (1)	10	1474	210.6	19.8	6.0	4.5
(2)	48	—	—	67.7	41.9	24
(3) root depth		3507	—	—	—	—
(4) root depth		—	—	—	56.4	—
(5)	?	1739	250	25	14	—
(6)	20	2722	—	47	8	7

TABLE 4. Nutrient inventory in *guaco* forest (Buschbacher 1984) (cations extracted with double acid solution; values in kg ha^{-1})

Compartment	N	P	K	Ca	Mg
Live above-ground	1476	48.8	384	331	88.2
Below-ground (0–30 cm)	341	6.5	40	27	23
Total	1817	55	424	358	111
Plant litter (total)	69.5	1.06	5.8	17.1	6.3
Humus	629	12.4	28.6	28.6	16.5
	Total			Exchangeable cations	
Soil (0–30 cm)	2490	434	18.6	3.1	6.6

TABLE 5. Nutrient inventory of tall Amazon *caatinga* (values in kg ha^{-1}) (original data in Herrera (1979), Herrera & Jordan (1981) and Herrera (1986) have been modified to accommodate changes in average biomass data of tall Amazon *caatinga* in Klinge & Herrera (1983))

Compartment		N	P	K	Ca	Mg
Leaves		70	3.9	39	16.5	16.5
Stems		341	36	362	286	46
Roots		734	61	288	215	125
Total living		1145	101	689	518	188
Fine litter		52	3	6	33	16
Dead wood		80	2	4	34	6
Soil depth	Bulk density	Total			Exchangeable cations	
0–21 cm	0.235	716	21	64	118	14
21–40 cm	0.902	70	15	5	15	0.2
Total		786	36	69	133	14

quently flooded tall *caatinga* vegetation has a lower nitrogen content, but contains about twice as much phosphorus, potassium, calcium and magnesium as non-flooded forests. The same pattern is maintained in low *caatinga* except in the poorest stands with very low biomass (Table 6). Along the forest sequence, the biomass : nitrogen ratio remains nearly constant, but there is a clear accumulation of phosphorus in tall *caatinga*, and of potassium, calcium and magnesium both in tall *caatinga* and low *caatinga* (tall *bana* unit) (Fig. 3).

The peculiar distribution of nutrient inventories is probably a consequence of the relative topographical positions of the forest series. Mixed forest on oxisol is restricted to higher topographical positions and appears to be depleted in cations. *Guaco* forest, which occupies lower positions in the rolling hills, frequently in contact with the tall *caatinga*, is also depleted in cations. Phosphorus storages are similar in mixed forest, *guaco* forest and low *caatinga* (tall *bana* and low *bana*) in

TABLE 6. Total nutrient inventory of low Amazon *caatinga* vegetation (Bongers *et al.* (1985) and E. Cuevas & H. Klinge unpublished) (values in kg ha^{-1})

Subunit	N	P	K	Ca	Mg
Tall *bana*	1256	60	1061	763	390
Low *bana*	569	60	360	582	134
Open *bana*	322	11	123	114	45

spite of large differences in total biomass (Fig. 3). These relationships result from differences in nutrient concentrations in each forest compartment. The relative richness of nitrogen in the mixed and *guaco* forests is clearly demonstrated when nitrogen : nutrient ratios of total biomass are calculated: N : P (32), N : K (5) and N : Ca (6) ratios are about twice as high in these forests as in forests of the *caatinga* complex. Leaves, fine roots and litter have higher nitrogen concentrations in the mixed forest on oxisol, phosphorus is more concentrated in leaves and litter of tall *caatinga*, while potassium, calcium and magnesium are more concentrated in tall and low *caatinga* in leaves, fine roots and litter (Tables 7, 8 and 9). In the leaves and fine roots, which are more active metabolically, the N : P ratio in mixed forest is also higher (21–21) than in tall (16–11) and low (15–17) *caatinga*. The N : P ratios of fine litterfall increase, with respect to mature leaves, about twofold in mixed forest (51) and low *caatinga* (28), but remain unchanged in tall *caatinga* (14). This indicates that phosphorus is preferentially retranslocated in the former two ecosystems and confirms the previous suggestion that tall *caatinga* (and the almost identical tall *bana*) are systems relatively enriched in phosphorus. These considerations are relevant to observed differences in sclerophylly in these forests. In general, mixed and *guaco* forests are less sclerophyllous (as measured by specific leaf area and leaf hardness, Cuevas & Medina 1988) than the majority of species in the *caatinga* complex. Low *caatinga* (low *bana* subunit) has some of the most sclerophyllous species reported for the tropical forests (Sobrado & Medina 1980).

NUTRIENT UPTAKE AND RELEASE

Nutrient requirements for biomass production

Above-ground annual biomass production has been measured in mixed forest (C. F. Jordan & P. G. Murphy unpublished) and tall *caatinga* (Herrera 1979). Only mass and nutrient fluxes in leaf litterfall have been measured in the other forest types (Table 10). Leaf litter production is higher in mixed and *guaco* forests and decreases along the sequence of the *caatinga* complex units. Nitrogen return in litterfall follows the same trend as biomass. However, return of phosphorus, calcium and magnesium is higher in tall *caatinga*, and the amount of potassium returned in litter is similar in *guaco* forest, tall and low *caatinga* in spite of the large differences in litter biomass.

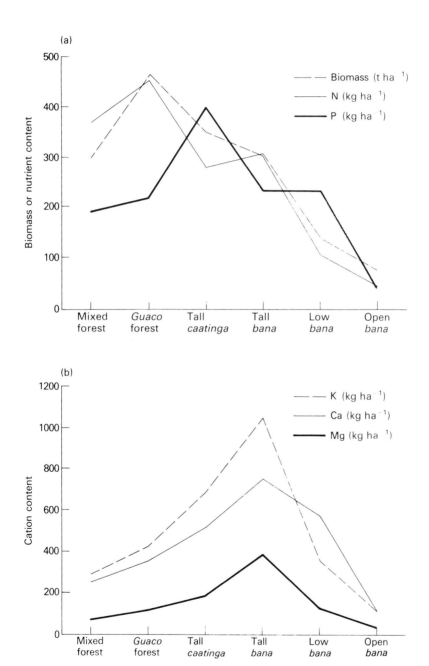

FIG. 3. Variations in total biomass and nutrient amounts in living biomass along the sequence from mixed forest on oxisol, through *guaco* forest, tall Amazon *caatinga* and low Amazon *caatinga* (tall *bana* unit), low *bana* unit and open *bana* unit.

TABLE 7. Mean (±S.D.) specific leaf area (SLA) (cm^2 g^{-1}) and nutrient concentration (mg g^{-1}) of leaves from different forest types near San Carlos de Rio Negro (Medina 1984)

Forest type	No. species	SLA	Nutrient concentration				
			N	P	K	Ca	Mg
Mixed forest	7	74 (12)	12.7 (2.7)	0.60 (0.30)	4.6 (1.2)	1.9 (0.7)	1.0 (0.2)
Tall *caatinga*	6	76 (33)	11.6 (4.6)	0.73 (0.19)	6.2 (1.1)	4.4 (1.6)	1.5 (0.5)
Low *caatinga* (low *bana*)	14	47 (12)	7.4 (2.4)	0.50 (0.17)	6.4 (3.0)	5.8 (3.4)	1.4 (0.3)

TABLE 8. Nutrient concentration in fine roots grown in vermiculite-filled cylinders inserted in the upper 10 cm of soil in several forests near San Carlos de Rio Negro. Numbers followed by the same letter in a column are not statistically different at $p = 0.05$ (from E. Cuevas & E. Medina (unpublished))

Forest type	N	P	K	Ca	Mg
Mixed forest on oxisol	23.8a	1.13a	6.7a	2.1a	2.6a
Tall *caatinga*	10.4b	0.95a	8.3ab	3.0a	3.9b
Low *caatinga*	8.4b	0.51b	12.2b	3.5a	3.7b

TABLE 9. Mean (±S.E.) nutrient concentration (mg g^{-1}) in freshly fallen leaf litter in several forest types near San Carlos de Rio Negro. Values are averages of ten collection periods (every 3 weeks) with 15 baskets per collection (Cuevas (1983) and new data for *guaco* forest)

Forest type	n	N	P	K	Ca	Mg
Mixed forest on oxisol	54	16.3 (1.7)	0.32 (0.08)	2.4 (0.5)	1.7 (0.4)	0.7 (0.1)
Guaco forest	10	12.2 (0.9)	0.26 (0.03)	1.3 (0.1)	1.8 (0.3)	0.9 (0.1)
Tall *caatinga*	54	7.0 (0.6)	0.50 (0.14)	2.1 (0.7)	7.7 (1.8)	3.1 (0.3)
Low *caatinga*	54	5.8 (1.3)	0.21 (0.06)	4.7 (1.6)	7.4 (2.1)	2.5 (0.3)

Wood biomass increment, and probably nutrient uptake in the process, is similar in both mixed and *guaco* forests (Table 10) and corresponds to the calculated values for *yévaro* forest (5.5 t ha^{-1} year^{-1}; Veillon (1983) and S. Brown *et al.* (personal communication)). Tall *caatinga* produces about 1 t year^{-1} less wood than mixed and *guaco* forests (Table 10 and Veillon (1983)).

Table 10. Nutrient input in rainfall, potential nutrient mass flow and above-ground nutrient fluxes in several forests near San Carlos de Rio Negro, Venezuela. (1) Biomass data from Jordan & Murphy (unpublished), Jordan & Uhl (1980) and Cuevas & Medina (1986); nutrient data from Uhl & Jordan (1984) and Cuevas & Medina (1986). (2) Mass data from Buschbacher (1984); nutrient concentration as in Table 8 and Uhl & Jordan (1984). (3) Herrera (1979). (4) Cuevas & Medina (1986). (5) Galloway *et al.* (1982). (6) Buschbacher (1984)

Forest type	Compartment	Production (t ha^{-1} year^{-1})	N	P	K	Ca	Mg
					(kg ha^{-1} year^{-1})		
Mixed forest	Wood increment	6.0	19	0.6	5	5	1
on oxisol	Leaf fall	6.5	105	2.1	16	11	5
(1)	Stem + branch fall	3.4	21	0.2	0.5	1.1	0.4
Guaco forest	Wood increment	5.0	16	0.5	4	4	1
(2)	Leaf fall	7.0	85	1.8	9	12	7
Tall *caatinga*	Wood increment	4.4	6	0.6	6	5	1
(3)	Leaf fall	5.2	37	2.6	11	40	16
	Stem + branch fall	1.9	2	0.3	1.6	1.6	0.3
Low *caatinga* (4)	Leaf fall	2.1	12	0.4	10	15	5
Nutrient input in rainfall							
(5)			2.4	0.65	1.1	0.2	0.2
(6)			2.3	0.45	6.9	5.2	0.7

The ratio of biomass increment plus total mass of litterfall and the amount of nutrient taken up plus that returned to the soil, or the ratio of mass and nutrients circulated in litterfall, constitute indices of within-stand nutrient-use efficiency (Vitousek 1984). Biomass : N ratios increase both for total above-ground production and fine litterfall from mixed forest to *caatinga* forests (Fig. 4). Indices for total above-ground production are higher than those corresponding to litterfall because wood increments have lower nutrient concentrations than fine litterfall. Biomass : P ratios show a completely different trend. Mixed and *guaco* forests have higher ratios than tall *caatinga*, indicating again that the latter has the larger phosphorus supply of the types analysed. Low *caatinga* (low *bana* unit) appears to be very low in phosphorus supply with a biomass : P ratio similar to those measured in mixed forest for total above-ground production.

Water balance and nutrient input in rainfall

Erroneous values for nutrient input in rainfall in the San Carlos area have been repeatedly reported (e.g. Jordan 1982; Herrera 1986). More probable values are those of Galloway *et al.* (1982) and Buschbacher (1984) given in Table 10. These values are strikingly similar to those for nitrogen, calcium and magnesium reported by Brinkmann (1983) for the Manaus area. Average nutrient input in rainfall in San Carlos contributes less than 10% of the nitrogen, calcium and mag-

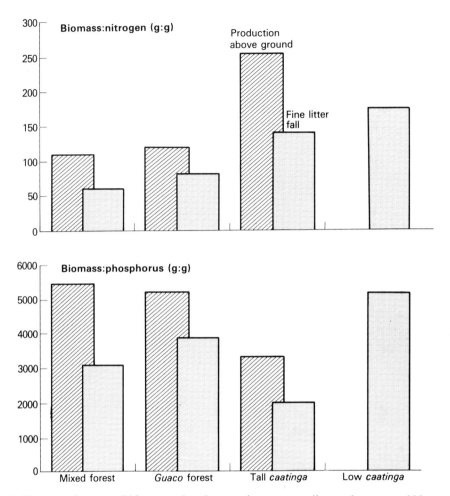

Fig. 4. Biomass : nitrogen and biomass : phosphorus ratios corresponding to above-ground biomass production and fine litterfall, along the sequence from mixed forest to low Amazon *caatinga*.

nesium requirements for above-ground production. However, rainfall supplies nearly 20% of the phosphorus and potassium requirements. These calculations do not include canopy leaching, but it may be of minor significance. Earlier reports, which require confirmation, have shown that nutrient scavenging occurs as rainfall passes through the canopy of mixed and *caatinga* forests (Jordan *et al.* 1980). Biological fixation can be an additional input of nitrogen and has been estimated as 16 kg ha^{-1} year^{-1} for the mixed forest (Jordan *et al.* 1982), i.e. an additional 11% of its nitrogen requirements for above-ground organic matter production.

Transpiration measurements with the tritium method (Jordan & Kline 1977) and rain interception in both mixed forest and tall *caatinga* (Heuveldop 1977) allow the calculation of a simple water balance sheet for closed forests in the San

Carlos area (Jordan & Heuveldop 1981). Potential evapotranspiration can be predicted accurately by pan A evaporation and these workers have shown that 48% of rainfall is lost as evapotranspiration.

Decomposition of organic matter and rate of nutrient release

Organic matter decomposition and nutrient release constitute the focal point of experiments designed to test direct nutrient cycling as a main nutrient conserving mechanism in these forests (Herrera *et al.* 1978b). Rates of organic matter decomposition on the forest floor have been shown to be relatively slow in San Carlos forests. In fact, most 95% turnover times measured are longer than 1 year (Table 11). In general, leaves of the mixed forest decompose faster than leaves from tall and low *caatinga*, in spite of the fact that the N : P ratios of their fine litterfall and fine forest floor litter are near 50, while *caatinga* forests have ratios which may be more favourable for decomposition (cf. Vogt, Grier & Vogt 1986). Slow decomposition is associated with the predominant scleromorphic character of the leaves of these forests (Sobrado & Medina 1980; Cuevas 1983; Medina 1984) and the low nitrogen : lignin ratio (Cuevas & Medina 1988). Waterlogging in tall *caatinga*, and alternation of dry and waterlogged periods in low *caatinga*, also contribute to lower rates of decomposition.

TABLE 11. Disappearance constants (exponential model) for leaf litter based on six collection dates, three replicates per collection and a total exposure time of 482 days (three representative tree species in each forest were measured) (from Cuevas (1983))

Forest type	k (year^{-1})	95% turnover $(3/k)$ (years)
Mixed forest on oxisol	3.68–0.34	0.8–8.8
Tall Amazon *caatinga*	0.93–0.62	3.2–4.8
Low Amazon *caatinga* (low *bana* unit)	0.38–0.21	7.9–14.3

Simultaneous measurements of biomass and nutrient disappearance from leaf litter in a mixed forest, a tall and a low *caatinga* (low *bana* unit) reveals an interesting pattern of nutrient dynamics in decomposing litter (Fig. 5). In all three forests nitrogen tends to accumulate in decomposing litter (indicated by biomass : N ratios < 1), but more so in the nitrogen-poor litter of the *caatinga* forests. In the three forest types phosphorus tends to disappear at the same or slightly faster rate than biomass, while potassium always disappears faster than biomass. Whereas calcium and magnesium in most terrestrial systems disappear at a similar or lower rate than biomass (Swift, Heal & Anderson 1979), after 70 days exposure in the mixed forest these two elements behave like potassium. This pattern of disappearance of calcium and magnesium in the mixed forest has been

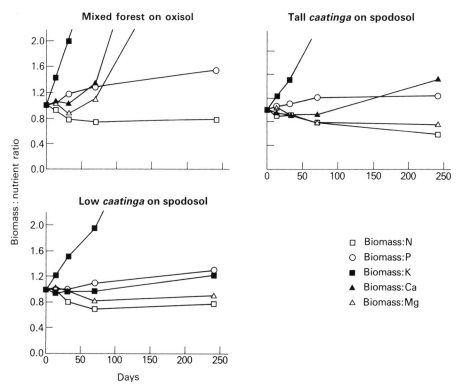

FIG. 5. Temporal variation of biomass : nutrient ratios in decomposing leaf litter in mixed forest, tall *caatinga* and low *caatinga*.

associated with root attachment to litter (Cuevas & Medina 1983). In tall and low *caatinga* calcium disappears at a lower rate than biomass, while magnesium is lost at slightly faster rates than biomass only after 240 days.

Root mat and the direct nutrient cycling hypothesis

The extraordinary development and growth pattern of the root mat in non-flooded forests (mixed, *yévaro* and *guaco* forests), and the large accumulation of fine roots near the soil surface in *caatinga*, suggest that active nutrient transfer processes take place in the upper soil layers and even above the soil.

Stark & Spratt (1977) observed that the majority of fine roots in the root mat of mixed forest were mycorrhizal. St John & Uhl (1983) examined ten mixed forest species, four *caatinga* species and ten species from secondary succession and found all collections to be predominantly endomycorrhizal. Tree seedlings were also infected in similar proportions as the adults. This study confirmed that the infection could spread through the layer of freshly fallen leaves on top of the root mat, and that endomycorrhizal hyphae attach to leaf litter. Interestingly, *caatinga* trees and seedlings showed heavy infection in spite of the waterlogged character of their soils.

Spraying of radioisotope solutions (^{32}P and ^{45}Ca) on top of the root mat of mixed forest, or exposure of leaf litter labelled with the same isotopes followed by natural leaching, showed that a negligible percentage was leached through the root mat and it stopped after 1–2 months (Stark & Jordan 1978). Similar results were obtained with ^{45}Ca in the heavily rooted, upper humus layer of the *caatinga*. These experiments also showed spreading of radioactivity through the root mat out of the labelled plot, suggesting that ions within the root mat are incorporated and transported quite rapidly. Nutrients released from decomposing litter are presumably captured with similar efficiency. The experiments, however, did not specify any particular uptake mechanisms. The solutions applied had high specific activity but were quite dilute, and therefore retention of cations and anions within the root mat may be a simple consequence of the ion exchange capacity of the root mat. B. Haines (unpublished) measured values of 20 and 11 m-equiv. 100 g^{-1} dry weight for the cation exchange capacity of roots of a mixed and a *caatinga* forest respectively. Anion exchange capacities were about 2 m-equiv. 100 g^{-1} dry weight in roots of both forests.

Apogeotropically growing roots in the mixed forest allowed an experiment to be carried out in the field where roots were grown for several weeks on dead leaves labelled with ^{32}P of high specific activity (Herrera *et al.* 1978b). Once roots were attached, a detailed electron microscope autoradiographic analysis showed the presence of radioactivity in dead leaf, fine root and a fungal hypha, presumed to be endomycorrhizal, connecting the two tissues. This experiment again shows very clearly the capacity of the root and fungus system in the root mat to capture ions being released from decomposing litter and has served as an argument for the direct nutrient transfer hypothesis.

The capacity of a root mat to capture free ions has been clearly demonstrated in the above experiments, the underlying mechanisms probably being similar to those operating in other forest ecosystems, even on sites richer in nutrients. However, in the San Carlos forests this process of nutrient capture may be especially effective as a result of the very high root density in the upper soil layers, as in *caatinga*, or above the soil, as in mixed and *guaco* forests, and the occurrence of heavy mycorrhizal infection throughout the forest sequence.

Litter decomposition experiments in which root attachment to litter was prevented by lifting decomposition bags from the forest floor on a weekly basis, showed that, at least in the mixed forest, the lack of root attachment (and/or as-sociated fungal hyphae) decreased the rate of organic matter disappearance. When roots were allowed to attach to the litter, decomposition was faster, which is most probably due to mechanical actions of root penetration. Root attachment was also associated with calcium and magnesium disappearance rates similar to that of potassium, the most leachable mineral nutrient in most forests (see Fig. 5). The same process is probably operating in *caatinga* forests, but its demonstration would require longer exposure periods, because in these forests the root mat is embedded in a matrix of humus.

Fine root growth in the root mat and upper 10 cm of soil is more responsive to phosphorus and calcium additions in the mixed forest, to nitrogen additions in the tall *caatinga* and to nitrogen and phosphorus additions in the low *caatinga* (Cuevas & Medina 1983). Furthermore, fine root growth into decomposition bags located on top of the root mat in a mixed forest showed highly significant correlations with the calcium and magnesium content of the decomposing leaves (Cuevas & Medina 1988). These experiments point to the different limiting nutritional factors operating in the forest sequence studied in San Carlos, and coincide with the results obtained in the analysis of patterns of nutrient allocation in the different forests.

CONCLUSION

The sequence of tropical rain forests at San Carlos shows a clear interaction between soil types and topography in determining gradients of soil nutrient availability and flooding regimes. It is obvious that the oligotrophic character of tropical rain forest soils is not uniform. Patterns of nutrient allocation depend on soil chemical properties (nutrient supply) and flooding regime (affecting nutrient uptake ability). Finally, there is no particular or exclusive nutrient conserving mechanism operating in the forest sequence. However, the set of structural and functional characteristics discussed above provide a clear picture of how specific environmental variables that determine lower rates of nutrient supply are reflected in changes in biomass and nutrient allocation in the forest. Properties of the forest ecosystems analysed here (e.g. root mat development, degree of mycorrhizal infection, sclerophylly and growth rates) may be traced to mechanisms that improve nutrient retention, increase nutrient capture from decomposing biomass, or increase nutrient-use efficiency in production of organic matter. Coming back to the questions asked in the introduction the following conclusions may be drawn.

1 Distribution of nitrogen and phosphorus between living tree biomass and soil clearly differentiates *terra firme* and *caatinga* complex forests. In mixed forest, around 30% of total nitrogen and 19% of total phosphorus are found in living biomass; corresponding figures in *guaco* forests are 42 and 11%. In tall *caatinga*, living biomass contains 59% of total nitrogen and 74% of total phosphorus in the ecosystem.

2 Phosphorus constitutes a limiting nutrient in all non-flooded (*terra firme*) forests and in the less flood-prone areas of the *caatinga* complex forests.

3 Tall *caatinga* and the tall *bana* unit of low *caatinga* accumulate and circulate relatively large amounts of phosphorus, and they have N : P ratios comparable with those of forests in nutrient-rich sites.

4 Nitrogen is accumulated and circulated in large amounts in *terra firme* forests, but appears to limit decomposition rates and root growth in the *caatinga* complex.

5 *Terra firme* forests have relatively low concentrations of potassium, calcium and magnesium compared to *caatinga* complex forests. The relatively high concentrations of potassium, calcium and magnesium in *caatinga* may be a consequence of cation leaching from adjacent forests located in higher topographical positions.

6 Direct nutrient cycling, which is a mechanism able to trap nutrients from decomposing material as soon as they are released, appears to be operative in the root mat of both mixed and *caatinga* forests.

7 Mycorrhizal symbiosis surely plays an important role in nutrient cycling as judged from the frequency and intensity of infection. The efficiency of the nutrient trapping process may possibly be correlated with the density of fine root development in the upper soil layers, or even above the soils, as is the case in non-flooded forest on oxisol and ultisols.

Ecological studies at San Carlos have established a firm basis for the understanding of forest differentiation in humid tropical environments on the basis of nutrient supply and nutrient-use efficiency. In our opinion, the study of the ecophysiological processes underlying the adaptation of woody species which are able to grow in acidic soils steadily washed through with a very dilute nutrient solution, is the logical pathway to follow. These studies are likely to provide a solid insight into the potential for forest management and forest recovery after disturbance, whether natural or induced by humans.

ACKNOWLEDGEMENTS

This paper is dedicated to Professor Heinrich Walter, a pioneer of tropical ecology, who celebrated his ninetieth birthday in October 1988. Professor Walter was the doctoral supervisor of E.M.

The San Carlos project was made possible because of the team effort of many people from several countries whose work is included in the references. Recognition is also due to the work of several dedicated personnel in the laboratories of the Centro de Ecología at IVIC, the Institute of Ecoiogy of the University of Georgia and the Max-Planck Institute for Limnology in Germany. We also thank Drs Ariel Lugo, project leader of the Institute of Tropical Forestry in Puerto Rico, and Sandra Brown, University of Illinois, for many discussions on the ecological properties of wetland forest ecosystems and for help with the manuscript. Dr R. Buschbacher allowed us to use some of his data on the *guaco* forest included in Tables 4 and 10. Our thanks also to three unknown reviewers who helped to improve the final version of this paper. The project was financed by the National Research Council of Venezuela (CONICIT), the National Science Foundation of the USA and the Deutsche Forschungsgemeinschaft. International support was provided by the UNESCO–UNEP MAB programme.

REFERENCES

Alder, D., Brünig, E.F., Heuveldop, J. & Smith, J. (1979). Struktur und Funktionen im Regenwald des internationalen Amazon Ökosystemprojektes: vorläufige Mitteilung über Klassifikation der Bestände, Variation der Bestandesstruktur und Niederschlagsmerkmale. *Amazoniana*, **6**, 423–444.

Bongers, F., Engelen, D. & Klinge, H. (1985). Phytomass structure of natural plant communities on spodosols in southern Venezuela: the Bana woodland. *Vegetatio*, **63**, 13–34.

Breimer, R.F. (1985). Some observations on soils in relation to forest types in San Carlos de Rio Negro, Venezuela. *Guidelines for Soil Survey in Ecological Research. MAB Technical Notes 17* (Ed. by R.F. Breimer, A.J. Van Kekem & H. Van Reuler), pp. 108–110. UNESCO, Paris.

Brinkmann, W.L.F. (1983). Nutrient balance of a central Amazonian rainforest: comparison of natural and man-managed ecosystems. *Hydrology of Humid Tropical Regions with Particular Reference to the Hydrological Effects of Agriculture and Forestry Practice, IAHS Publication No. 140,* pp. 153–163.

Brown, S. & Lugo, A.E. (1982). The storage of organic matter in tropical forests and their role in the global carbon cycle. *Biotropica*, **14**, 161–187.

Brünig, E.F., Heuveldop, J., Smith, J. & Alder, D. (1978). Structure and function of a rainforest in the International Amazon Ecosystem Project: floristic stratification and variation of some features of stand structure and precipitation. *Glimpses of Ecology* (Ed. by J.S. Singh & B. Gopal), pp. 124–144. International Scientific Publications, Jaipur, India.

Buschbacher, R.J. (1984). *Changes in productivity and nutrient cycling following conversion of Amazon rainforest to pasture.* PhD Thesis, University of Georgia, Athens, USA.

Cannell, M.G.R. (1982). *World Forest Biomass and Primary Production Data.* Academic Press, London.

Cuevas, E. (1983). *Crecimiento de raíces finas y su relación con los procesos de descomposición de materia orgánica y liberación de nutrientes en bosques del alto Río Negro en el Territorio Federal Amazonas.* PhD Thesis, IVIC, Caracas.

Cuevas, E. & Medina, E. (1983). Root production and organic matter decomposition in a tierra firme forest of the upper Rio Negro basin. *International Symposium on Root Ecology and its Applications* (Ed. by L. Kutschera), pp. 653–666. Gumpenstein, Austria.

Cuevas, E. & Medina, E. (1986). Nutrient dynamics within Amazonian forest ecosystems 1. Nutrient flux in fine litter fall and efficiency of nutrient utilization. *Oecologia*, **68**, 466–472.

Cuevas, E. & Medina, E. (1988). Nutrient dynamics within Amazonian forests. II. Fine root growth, nutrient availability and leaf litter decomposition. *Oecologia*, **76**, 222–235.

Dubroeucq, D. & Sánchez, V. (1981). Características ambientales y edáficas del área de muestra San Carlos de Río Negro-Solano. MARNR. *Dirección General de Información e Investigación. Dirección de Suelos, Vegetación y Fauna.* Caracas.

Fittkau, E.-J. (1971). Ökologische Gliederung des Amazonas-Gebietes auf geochemischer Grundlage. *Münsterische Forschungen zur Geologie und Paläontologie,* **20/21,** 35–50.

Fittkau, E.-J., Junk, W., Klinge, H. & Sioli, H. (1975). Substrate and vegetation in the Amazon. *Berichte der Internationalen Vereinigung für Vegetationskunde* (Ed. by R. Tüxen), pp. 73–90. J. Cramer, Vaduz, Liechtenstein.

Franco, W. & Dezzeo, N. (1982). Consideraciones sobre el régimen hídrico de los principales tipos de suelo de los alrededores de San Carlos de Río Negro. Paper presented at the Symposium *Structure and Function of Amazonian Forest Ecosystem of the Upper Río Negro.* IVIC, Caracas, November 1982.

Galloway, J.N., Likens, G.E., Keene, W.C. & Miller, J.M. (1982). The composition of precipitation in remote areas of the world. *Journal of Geophysical Research,* **87**, 8771–8786.

Herrera, R. (1977). Soil and terrain conditions in the International Amazon Project at San Carlos de Río Negro, Venezuela. Correlation with vegetation types. *Transactions of the International MAB-IUFRO Workshop on Tropical Rainforest Ecosystems Research* (Ed. by E.F. Brünig), pp. 182–188. Hamburg, West Germany.

Herrar, R (1979). *Nutrient distribution and cycling in an Amazon caatinga forest on spodosols in southern Venezuela.* PhD. Thesis. University of Reading, England.

Herrera, R. (1986). Nutrient cycling in Amazonian forests. *Key Environments: Amazonia* (Ed. by G.T. Prance & T.E. Lovejoy), pp. 95–105. Pergamon Press, Oxford.

Herrera, R. & Jordan, C.F. (1981). Nitrogen cycle in a tropical Amazonian rain forest : the Caatinga of low mineral nutrient status. *Ecological Bulletin (Stockholm)*, **33**, 493–505.

Herrera, R. Jordan, C.F., Klinge, H. & Medina, E. (1978a). Amazon ecosystems. Their structure and functioning with particular emphasis on nutrients. *Interciencia*, **3**, 223–232.

Herrera, R., Mérida, T., Stark, N. & Jordan, C.F. (1978b). Direct phosphorus transfer from dead litter to roots. *Naturwissenschaften*, **65**, 208–209.

Heuveldop, J. (1977). Erste Ergebnisse bestandesmeteorologischer Untersuchungen im Regenwald von San Carlos de Río Negro. *Mitteilungen der Bundesforschungsanstalt für Forst- und Holzwirtschaft (Hamburg-Reinbeck)*, **115**, 101–106.

Heuveldop, J. (1980). Das Bioklima von San Carlos de Río Negro, Venezuela, *Amazoniana*, **7**, 7–17.

Janos, D. (1975). *Vesicular-arbuscular mycorrhizal fungi and plant growth in a Costa Rican lowland rainforest*. PhD Thesis, University of Michigan, USA.

Jordan, C.F. (1982). The nutrient balance of an Amazonian rain forest. *Ecology*, **61**, 14–18.

Jordan, C.F. (1987). Shifting cultivation. *Amazonian Rainforests: Ecosystem Disturbance and Recovery* (Ed. by C.F. Jordan), pp. 9–23. Springer, New York.

Jordan, C.F., Caskey, W., Escalante, G., Herrera, R., Montagnini, F., Todd, R. & Uhl, C. (1982). The nitrogen cycle in a "Tierra Firme" rainforest in the Amazon territory of Venezuela. *Plant and Soil*, **67**, 325–332.

Jordan, C.F. & Escalante, G. (1980). Root productivity in an Amazonian rain forest. *Ecology*, **63**, 647–654.

Jordan, C.F., Golley, F., Hall, J. & Hall, J. (1980). Nutrient scavenging of rainfall by the canopy of an Amazonian rain forest. *Biotropica*, **12**, 61–66.

Jordan, C.F. & Heuveldop, J. (1981). The water budget of an Amazonian rain forest. *Acta Amazonica*, **11**, 87–92.

Jordan, C.F. & Kline, J.R. (1977). Transpiration of trees in a tropical rain forest. *Journal of Applied Ecology*, **14**, 853–860.

Jordan, C. F. & Uhl, C. (1978). Biomass of a 'tierra firme' forest of the Amazon basin. *Oecologia Plantarum*, **13**, 387–400.

Klinge, H. & Herrera, R. (1978). Biomass studies in Amazon caatinga forest in southern Venezuela. 1. *Tropical Ecology*, **19**, 93–110.

Klinge, H. & Herrera, R. (1983). Phytomass structure of natural plant communities on spodosols in southern Venezuela: the Tall Amazon Caatinga forest. *Vegetatio*, **53**, 65–84.

Klinge, H. & Medina, E. (1979). Río Negro Caatingas and Campinas, Amazonas States of Venezuela and Brazil. *Heathlands and Related Shrublands of the World. Descriptive Studies. Ecosystems of the World, Vol 9a* (Ed. by R.L. Specht), pp. 483–488. Elsevier, Amsterdam.

Klinge, H. Medina, E. & Herrera, R. (1978). Studies on the ecology of Amazon Caatinga forest in southern Venezuela. *Acta Científica Venezolana*, **28**, 270–276.

Medina, E. (1984). Nutrient balance and physiological processes at the leaf level. *Physiological Ecology of Plants of the Wet Tropics* (Ed. by E. Medina, H. A. Mooney & C. Vázquez-Yánes), pp. 139–154. Junk Publ, The Hague.

Medina, E., Klinge, H., Jordan, C.F. & Herrera, R. (1980). Soil respiration in Amazonian forests of the Río Negro basin. *Flora*, **170**, 240–250.

Medina, E., Sobrado, M. & Herrera, R. (1978). Significance of leaf orientation for leaf temperature in an Amazonian sclerophyll vegetation. *Radiation and Environmental Biophysics*, **15** 131–140.

Murphy, P.G. (1975). Net primary productivity in tropical terrestrial ecosystems. *Primary Productivity of the Biosphere* (Ed. by H. Lieth & R.G. Whittaker), pp. 217–231. Springer, New York.

Olson, J. (1963). Energy storage and balance of producers and decomposers in ecological systems. *Ecology*, **44**, 322–351.

Paolini, J. (1980). Caracterización de las substancias húmicas extraídas de suelos típicos del bosque húmedo tropical de San Carlos de Río Negro, T. F. Amazonas. *Acta Científica Venezolana*, **31**, 415–420.

Richards, P.W. (1952). *The Tropical Rain Forest*. Cambridge University Press, London.

Rodin, L.E. & Bazilevich, N.I. (1967). *Production and Mineral Cycling in Terrestrial Vegetation* (English translation). Oliver and Boyd, Edinburgh.

St. John, T.V. & Uhl, C. (1983). Mycorrhizae in the rain forest at San Carlos de Río Negro, Venezuela. *Acta Científica Venezolana*, **39**, 233–237.

Saldarriaga, J.G. (1985). *Forest succession in the upper Río Negro of Colombia and Venezuela*. PhD Thesis, University of Tennessee, Knoxville, USA.

Sanford, Jr., R.L. (1985). *Root ecology of mature and successional Amazon forests*, PhD Thesis, University of California, Berkeley.

Sanford, R.L. (1987). Apogeotropic roots in an Amazonian rain forest. *Science*, **235**, 1062–1064.

Sanford, R.L., Saldarriaga, J., Clark, K.E., Uhl, C. & Herrera, R. (1985). Amazon rain forest fires. *Science*, **227**, 54–55.

Schnütgen, A. & Bremer, H. (1985). Die Enstehung von Decksanden im oberen Río Negro-Gebiet. *Zeitschrift für Geomorphologie, N.F. Suppl.*, **56**, 55–67.

Sioli, H. (1968). Hydrochemistry and geology in the Brazil Amazon region. *Amazoniana*, **1**, 267–277.

Sobrado, M. & Medina, E. (1980). General morphology, anatomical structure and nutrient content of sclerophyllous leaves of the "Bana" vegetation of Amazonas. *Oecologia*, **45**, 341–345.

Sprick, E. (1979). *Composición foliar y contenido de fenoles foliares de especies leñosas de tres bosques contrastantes de la región amazónica*, Licenciatura Thesis, Escuela de Biologia, Universidad Central de Venezuela, Caracas.

Stark, N. & Jordan, C.F. (1978). Nutrient retention by the root mat of an Amazonian rainforest *Ecology*, **59**, 434–437.

Stark, N. & Spratt, M. (1977). Root biomass and nutrient storage in rain forest oxisols near San Carlos de Rio Negro. *Tropical Ecology*, **18**, 1–9.

Swift, M.J., Heal, O.W. & Anderson, J.M. (1979). *Decomposition in Terrestrial Ecosystems.* University of California Press, Berkeley.

Uhl, C. & Jordan, C.F. (1984). Succession and nutrient dynamics following forest cutting and burning in Amazonia. *Ecology*, **65**, 1476–1490.

Uhl, C. & Murphy, P.G. (1981). Composition, structure and regeneration of a Tierra Firme forest in the Amazon basin of Venezuela. *Tropical Ecology*, **22**, 220–237.

Veillon, J.P. (1983). *El crecimiento de algunos bosques naturales de Venezuela en relación con los parámetros del medio ambiente.* Instituto de Silvicultura, Facultad de Ciencias Forestales, Universidad de los Andes, Mérida, Venezuela.

Vitousek, P.M. (1984). Litterfall, nutrient cycling, and nutrient limitation in tropical forests. *Ecology*, **65**, 285–298.

Vitousek, P.M. & Sanford, Jr., R.L. (1986). Nutrient cycling in moist tropical forest. *Annual Review of Ecology and Systematics*, **17**, 137–167.

Vogt, K.A., Grier, C.C. & Vogt, D.J. (1986). Production, turnover, and nutrient dynamics of above- and belowground detritus of world forests. *Advances in Ecological Research*, **15**, 303–377.

Walter, H. (1936). Nährstoffgehalt des Bodens und natürliche Waldbestände. *Silva*, **24**, 201–213.

Went, F. & Stark, N. (1968). Mycorrhiza. *BioScience*, **18**, 1035–1039.

Soil nutrients and plant secondary compounds

P. G. WATERMAN AND S. MOLE*

*Phytochemistry Research Laboratories, Department of Pharmacy (Pharm. Chem.),
University of Strathclyde, Glasgow G1 1XW*

SUMMARY

1 The impact of soil nutrients on the production of secondary metabolites is reviewed.

2 The case for relating secondary metabolite production within a plant to the balance between carbon fixation and nutrient uptake (the resource allocation hypothesis) is examined.

3 The resource allocation model is employed to explain patterns in secondary metabolite investment in tree species in rain forest and savanna habitats.

INTRODUCTION

The products of plant metabolism are traditionally divided into primary and secondary components. Primary metabolites are ubiquitous, have an obvious physiological function and are structurally conservative; secondary metabolites are limited in distribution, have no obvious role in basic physiological processes and exhibit a high degree of structural diversity. Today, it is widely held that many secondary metabolites are of adaptive significance through their capacity to interact with environmental factors. These interactions may involve defence against herbivores, pathogens or competing plants, or the attraction of pollinators or seed dispersal agents (e.g. Rosenthal & Janzen 1979; Harborne 1982).

Despite high structural diversity among secondary metabolites their primary sources are limited. Most can be traced back to one, or a combination of, the following precursors: acetyl co-enzyme-A, mevalonic acid, shikimic acid and amino acids derived from phosphoenol pyruvate and the tricarboxylic acid cycle (Fig. 1). The biosynthesis of these compounds is supported by a wide array of enzymes, some highly specific in their function and others able to use a range of related substrates (Haslam 1986). The reaction sequences through which secondary metabolites are synthesized generally require an energy input so that, while some substrate is often regained through turnover of the product, the costs of formation are appreciable.

Each of the pathways shown in Fig. 1 is also involved in primary metabolism, so there could be competition for limited resources between primary and secondary processes (Coley 1986). Our remit is to examine the extent to which soil nutrients may influence the type and quantity of secondary metabolites produced by a plant. There is a shortage of data, particularly experimental, for tropical rain forest and savanna ecosystems. In this paper we examine the effects

---

*Present address: Department of Biochemistry, Purdue University, West Lafayette, IN 47907, USA.

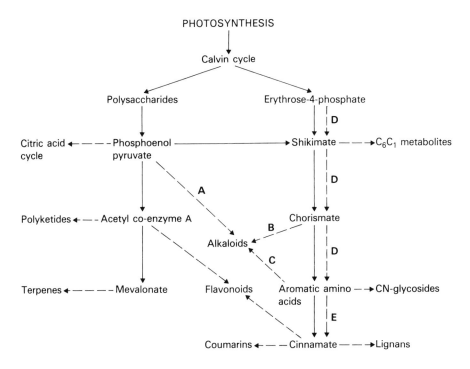

FIG. 1. Synopsis of some of the early pathways of primary metabolism (full lines) and major pathways of secondary metabolism (broken lines). A, source of ornithine and lysine; B, source of tryptophan; C, source of phenylalanine and tyrosine; D, possible distinct chloroplast (primary) and cytosolic (secondary, overflow) pathways (after Jensen (1986)); E, controlled by the key enzyme phenylalanine ammonia lysase (PAL).

of nutrient limitation on secondary metabolism in general, follow this by an analysis of the impact this and other factors influencing metabolic activity may have in natural environments, and assess these observations in the light of recent attempts to relate secondary metabolite production to carbon/nutrient balance (the resource allocation hypothesis).

IMPACT OF NUTRIENTS ON SECONDARY METABOLISM

Studies under controlled conditions

The influence of nutrients on the production of secondary metabolites in plants of pharmaceutical or agricultural interest has recently been reviewed (Gershenzon 1984). However, these data mainly concern relatively short-lived, fast growing species adapted to nutrient-rich and disturbed habitats. These are considered likely to be more responsive to increased nutrient supply than species adapted to low nutrient conditions (Chapin, Vitousek & van Cleve 1986; Sibly & Grime 1986).

In cyanogenic plants the response to increased nitrogen availability is enhanced synthesis of cyanogenic glycosides. Lowering available phosphorus has the same result, but potassium deficiency has no effect. Synthesis of gluco-sinolates and isothiocyanates is diminished by deficiencies of nitrogen or sulphur, both elements contained in these compounds. Wolfson (1982) reported that a deficiency of sulphur but not nitrogen led to reduction of isothiocyanate formation in *Brassica nigra* (L.) Koch. with a consequent increase in rate of development of larvae of two insect herbivores using the plant as a food source.

Most studies on alkaloids report that increasing nitrogen availability leads to increased alkaloid formation. Additional potassium appears to cause a reduction in alkaloid synthesis, while for phosphorus there is no obvious trend. The observation that increased availability of nitrogen enhances alkaloid production must be interpreted with care. In some cases while there is an increase in the quantity of alkaloid, there is a greater increase in total biomass, and the proportion of alkaloid decreases in relative terms. High sodium concentrations are reported to cause an increase in alkaloid formation in the leaves of *Datura innoxia* Mill. (Brachet & Cosson 1986) and enhanced amino acid production is often observed in plants growing under saline conditions (Greenway & Munns 1980). Gershenzon (1984) has observed that nitrogen fertilizer is more effective in increasing alkaloid levels where the alkaloids have a relatively low C : N ratio (4 : 1–16 : 1). At higher C : N ratios the effect is less reliable, perhaps because insufficient carbon can be supplied.

For phenolic products from the shikimate pathway, Gershenzon (1984) has reported that deficiencies in nitrogen, phosphorus, potassium and sulphur all lead to increased production. Synthesis of phenolics is also enhanced by boron deficiency (Rhodes 1985). In an investigation of light and nutrient stress on the synthesis of phenolics in *Salix dasyclados* Wimm., Larsson *et al.* (1986) found that under conditions in which neither light nor nutrients were limited, leaf phenolic concentrations were at their highest. With reduction in nutrient supply, high phenol concentrations were maintained, but where nutrients were freely available but carbon fixation was limited by reduced incident light (from 300 to 65 μE m^{-2} s^{-1}), phenolic concentrations diminished by about 75%.

Terpene metabolism shows no consistent relationship with nitrogen, phos-phorus or potassium nutrition (Gershenzon 1984). However, in a study of volatile terpenes in the leaf of *Heterotheca subaxillaris* (Lam). Britton & Rusby, it was found (Mihaliak and Lincoln 1985) that monoterpene and sesquiterpene concentrations were highest in young leaves of individuals subjected to low nitrate availability. Feeding trials using the soy-bean looper suggested that the greater quantity of terpenes found in the leaves of nitrate-limited plants may make them less acceptable to generalist insect herbivores (Mihaliak, Couvet & Lincoln 1987).

Dicosmo & Towers (1984) reviewed the influence of a range of environmental factors on secondary metabolism in plant cell cultures. They concluded that while nutrient availability did influence the production of many secondary metabolites the effects were unpredictable. A number of studies suggest that the level of incident light affects synthesis of secondary metabolites in cell cultures. It would be wrong to read too much into results from such experiments in which compartmentation of biochemical processes can differ from that occurring in the whole plant.

Field observations

Janzen (1974) proposed that levels of investment in secondary metabolites should be correlated with soil nutrient status. Central to Janzen's thesis were the so-called blackwater river habitats of South America and South-East Asia. These are characterized by white sand soils supporting a depauperate flora that appear to produce relatively large amounts of some secondary metabolites, notably polyphenolics and lignin (also derived through the shikimate pathway). When the water-soluble polyphenols are leached from the litter, they generate high concentrations of humic acids which will contribute to a lowering of soil pH. Acidic soil conditions certainly alter the availability of nutrients, micronutrients and toxic elements (Tivy 1971; Högberg 1986) and can lead to increased production of polyphenols in some plants (Davies, Coulson & Lewis 1964).

Janzen suggested two reasons for the emphasis on secondary metabolite synthesis in plants adapted to such soils. Firstly, in such habitats the loss of photosynthetic capacity through herbivory will be expensive in terms of replacement costs, making a heavy investment in defence chemistry cost effective. Secondly, species successful in forming low diversity stands on nutritionally poor soils are thought to come from families with a particular propensity for secondary metabolite production (i.e. there is a phylogenetic contribution). The importance of nutrient limitation in shaping plant communities and in influencing the emphasis placed in production of defensive secondary metabolites is now a well established tenet of plant physiological ecology (Chapin *et al.* 1986; Chapin *et al.* 1987).

Several central themes of Janzen's hypothesis, notably reduced rate of litter decomposition, extreme nutrient paucity of soils and occurrence of stands of low species diversity, have not been substantiated in comparative studies involving a heath forest in Sarawak (Anderson, Proctor & Vallack 1983; Proctor *et al.* 1983a, b). To test the hypothesis at the secondary metabolic level requires analysis of biochemical profiles for entire plant communities and this has not yet proved possible. However, a series of studies made on the feeding ecology of herbivorous primates in Old World rain forests has produced some relevant data. A comparison of the Cameroonian coastal forest of the Douala-Edea Forest Reserve and the mid-altitude gallery forest of Kibale in Uganda (Gartlan *et al.* 1980) has revealed appreciable differences in concentrations of phenolic compounds, protein and fibre occurring in the foliage of common species (Table 1). Alkaloids are more common among species from Kibale (11 out of 25 species tested positive for alkaloids), while at Douala-Edea (where 11 out of 70 tested

TABLE 1. The mean concentrations of fibre (measured as acid detergent fibre, ADF), condensed tannin (CT), protein (calculated as 6.25 × Kjeldahl nitrogen) and protein/ADF weighted quotient for three contrasting rain forest sites in Central Africa. Values are expressed on an oven-dry basis; $n = 25$ species for Korup, 38 species (which represent 56.3% of the tree biomass) at Douala-Edea and 23 species (representing 87.4% of the tree biomass) at Kibale. For methods of analysis see Oates, Waterman & Choo (1980). (* Values in parentheses are the means for the same species collected from Douala-Edea. † Values are weighted means (calculated by Waterman et al. (1988)) with ranges in parentheses. ‡ This quotient is considered to represent an estimate of nutritional value to herbivores (Waterman et al. 1988). § Insufficient biomass involved for meaningful computation)

	Korup	Douala-Edea	Kibale
ADF (%)	41.5 (40.4)*	55.2†(20.8–77.2)	34.6†(10.3–67.8)
CT (% quabracho tannin equivalents)	7.6 (5.9)*	4.2†(0–17.0)	1.3†(0–39.6)
Protein (%)	11.2 (12.4)*	11.0†(6.4–22.3)	16.5†(10.6-35.6)
Protein/ADF‡	— §	0.2†	0.510†

TABLE 2. Soil chemical and physical properties (from Gartlan et al. (1986) and Newbery et al. (1986)) from the three forest sites in Central Africa for which foliar analyses are given in Table 1. Values are means with ranges in parentheses and are expressed on a dry weight basis where appropriate. $n = 135$ for Korup, 97 (76 for NO_3^- and NH_4^+) for Douala-Edea and 10 for Kibale

	Korup	Douala-Edea	Kibale
pH (H_2O) (log units)	4.4(4.0–5.6)	3.9(2.7–4.8)	5.6(4.6–6.3)
C (organic) (%)	3.3(1.3–5.5)	5.2(1.5–12.5)	7.6(1–13)
NH_4^+ (water-soluble) ($\mu g\,g^{-1}$)	—	4.9(1–11.5)	17.6(2–38)
NO_3^- (water-soluble) ($\mu g\,g^{-1}$)	4.7(0.35)	14.4(4–40)	55.2(16–99)
P (extractable) ($\mu g\,g^{-1}$)	7.2(2–29)	27.6(7–90)	13.7(1–30)
K (extractable) ($\mu g\,g^{-1}$)	78.4(38–375)	63.1(27–188)	76.0(35–168)
Clay (%)	8.7(4–20)	6.9(0–21)	12.8(1–49)
Sand (%)	77.3(60–91)	88.3(71–100)	59.5(25–95)
Silt (%)	14.0(0–24)	4.8(0–28)	27.7(4–49)

species were positive for alkaloids) detailed investigations of families such as Guttiferae, Ebenaceae and Euphorbiaceae (Waterman 1986) have shown that the flora are a rich source of non-nitrogenous secondary metabolites. Analysis of soil structure and chemistry for the two sites (Gartlan et al. 1980; Newbery et al. 1986) suggest that Kibale soils have a higher pH, more silt and clay and higher concentrations of both nitrate and ammonium ions (Table 2).

The Korup National Park in Cameroon has considerable species overlap with Douala-Edea, but soils are less acidic and richer in silt, although not in mineral nutrients (Table 2) (Gartlan et al. 1986). Comparison of concentrations of phenolic compounds in leaves of species found at both sites does not show significant trends. Within Korup, areas of forest occur where soils are phosphorus deficient. These have their own characteristic flora (Gartlan *et al.* 1986), which are often characterized by high concentrations of foliar phenolics (Table 3).

Other factors

Feeny (1976) predicted a correlation between plant habit and secondary metabolite production. A number of studies (Coley 1983; Waterman & McKey 1988) have shown that rapidly growing species (secondary succession colonizers, forest-edge species, light-gap specialists, lianas) often produce less phenolic compounds than climax species. Long-lived leaves of evergreen tree species in a Costa Rican forest are likely to exhibit a polyphenol-centred secondary metabolism, whereas deciduous species tend to produce alkaloids or other toxins (Janzen & Waterman 1984). Prudhomme (1983) investigated carbon allocation in leaves of evergreen *Ledum groenlandicum* Michx. and deciduous *Betula glandulosa* Oeder and found that the former tended to allocate carbon to phenolics and terpenes and the latter to alkaloids and organic acids.

Exposure to high light intensity enhances production of phenolics in some plants. The leaves of *Barteria fistulosa* Mast. growing in light gaps in the Douala-Edea Forest Reserve are consistently richer in polyphenolics than are leaves of shaded individuals (Waterman, Ross & McKey 1984). In a more detailed study, Mole, Ross & Waterman (1988) have found that concentrations of leaf phenolics in the rain forest understorey tree *Diospyros thomasii* Hutch. & Dalz. correlate with incident light, both within and between trees (Fig. 2). High light intensity can enhance production of other secondary metabolites including simple phenolics and terpenes (e.g. Newbery & de Foresta 1985; Waring *et al.* 1985; Larsson *et al.* 1986; Spring, Priester & Hager 1986).

TABLE 3. Concentrations of total phenolics (based on tannic acid) and condensed tannins (based on quabracho tannin equivalents) in mature leaves of species occurring on soils of low and high phosphorus concentrations in the Korup National Park, Cameroon (Gartlan *et al.* 1986)

Species	% Condensed tannins	% Total phenolics
Phosphorus-poor soils		
Caloncoba glauca (P. Beauv.) Guill.	56.3	17.9
Diospyros iturensis (Gurke) Let. & White	8.5	15.3
Garcinia staudtii Engl.	12.9	8.0
Newtonia duparquetiana (Baill.) Keay	22.4	22.8
Tetraberlinia biofoliata (Harms)		
Hauman	27.7	26.8
Tetraberlinia moreliana Aubr.	35.4	22.5
Phosphorus-rich soils		
Grewia coriacea Mast.	4.9	3.0
Hypnodaphnis zenkeri (Engl.) Stapf.	0.7	1.7
Santiria trimera (Oliv.) Aubr.	1.0	22.4
Tabernaemontana brachyantha Stapf.	0.4	3.3
Vitex grandifolia Gurke	0.8	1.2

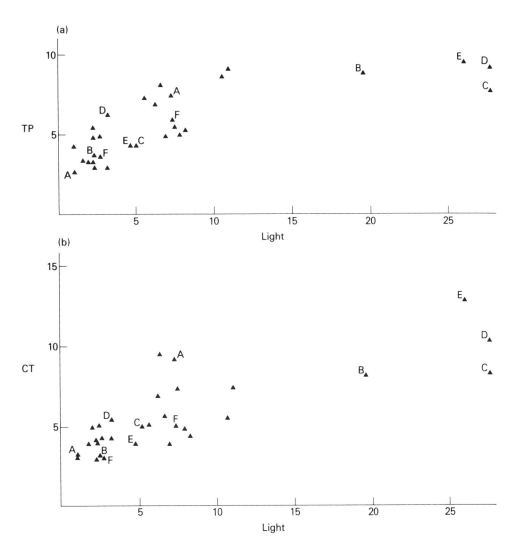

FIG. 2. Plot of incident light intensity (expressed as a percentage of light intensity in a large clearing) against the concentrations of (a) total phenolics (TP) and (b) condensed tannins (CT) in mature leaves of *Diospyros thomasii* Hutch. & Dalz. For six trees (designated A–F) two sets of leaves were taken from relatively shaded and sunny positions and these are distinguished in the plots by means of the appropriate letter (data from Mole, Ross & Waterman (1988)).

UNDERSTANDING PATTERNS IN THE
PRODUCTION OF SECONDARY
METABOLITES

It is self-evident that secondary metabolic processes will require input of nutrients from the soil and carbon and energy from photosynthesis. Species are thought to be adapted to specific nutrient conditions (Chapin 1980, 1983; Clarkson & Hanson 1980; Chapin *et al.* 1986). For example, acidic soil conditions will favour accumulation of nitrogen as ammonium rather than nitrate, and there is evidence that acidophilic plants are better able to use nitrogen in the ammonium form than are species that prefer more alkaline conditions (Beevers & Hageman 1983). Those species adapted to nutrient-poor conditions tend to have a slow growth rate and are characterized by an inability to respond rapidly to sudden nutrient flushes (Grime 1977; Chapin 1980; Gray & Schlesinger 1983; Chapin *et al.* 1986; Sibly & Grime 1986).

The resource allocation hypothesis (Coley, Bryant & Chapin 1985; Bazzaz *et al.* 1987) suggests that the types of secondary metabolite synthesized (within phylogenetic constraints) and the extent to which they are produced (at both species and community levels) are functions of the spare metabolic capacity brought about by the inevitable imbalance that occurs between influx of nutrients from the soil and carbon and energy from photosynthesis. If this is correct then the direction taken by secondary metabolism by and within a species (i.e. at both genotypic and phenotypic levels) can be predicted from imbalance between carbon and nutrient input in relation to requirements for growth and repro-duction (Bryant, Chapin & Klein 1983; Bloom, Chapin & Mooney 1985; Coley *et al.* 1985). In environments where carbon is probably limiting (nutrient-rich, shaded environments), species are more likely to have evolved pathways to allocate 'spare' nitrogen to nitrogen-containing secondary metabolites. The almost total absence of phosphorus-based secondary metabolites suggests that phosphorus is always in short supply (Coley *et al.* 1985). Where nutrients are limiting, then entirely carbon-based products, usually arising primarily from the shikimate pathway, will commonly be selected.

Support for the carbon/nutrient balance as one factor modulating secondary metabolism and consequent susceptibility to herbivory within a species has come from experimental studies on birch and willow in boreal ecosystems. As previously noted, *Salix dasyclados* grown under conditions where neither energy nor nutrients are limited responds by producing high levels of phenolic shikimate-based metabolites. When nitrogen is limiting, the usual situation for this species, these metabolic processes are maintained; however, where carbon is deficient, synthesis of phenolic secondary metabolites falls off markedly and the plant becomes more susceptible to herbivore damage (Larsson *et al.* 1986). Either increasing nutrient availability (fertilization with nitrogen and phosphorus) or reducing carbon/energy influx (through shading) causes a reduction in con-centration of phenolics and increasing susceptibility of paper birch (*Betula resinifera* Britton) and feltleaf willow (*Salix alaxensis* Coville) to herbivory (Bryant 1987; Bryant *et al.* 1987). Bryant (1987) uses resource allocation to explain succession in Alaskan woodlands; he suggests that the eventual re-placement of feltleaf willow by green alder (*Alnus crispa* Pursh.) is due to shading by the latter, which reduces the capacity of the former to produce phenolic chemical defences, leading to its preferential selection as a food plant.

The mechanism whereby a carbon/nutrient imbalance influences secondary metabolite output at the molecular level has been explored by Haslam (1986). He points out that the precursors of secondary metabolism (Fig. 1) originate from primary metabolism just prior to input into the tricarboxylic acid (TCA) cycle; he suggests that their channelling into the major pathways (notably shikimate) of secondary metabolism may be a mechanism for 'shunting' excess metabolites when carbon influx (through glycolysis) exceeds the requirements of the TCA cycle. A number of studies showing the occurrence of 'overflow' metabolism in microbial cell cultures under conditions of excess carbohydrate supply support this hypothesis (Dicosmo & Towers 1984; Haslam 1986). Trewavas (1986) notes the potential deleterious effects of such an imbalance at the physiological level and discusses the potential regulatory role of growth substances such as cytokinins, sensitivity to which may be influenced by a nitrogen deficiency.

An interesting recent development is the report (Jensen 1986) that the shikimate pathway may exist as two independent enzyme systems occupying separate intracellular niches (in chloroplast and cytosol). A similar dichotomy has been recorded for glycolytic enzymes (Gottlieb 1982). While the chloroplast system is under tight feedback control from end-products of the pathway, the cytosolic system seems to be unregulated. Jensen suggests that the cytosolic system is the channel for input of shikimate into secondary metabolism. The cytosolic system could be regarded as a sink for excess erythrose-4-phosphate and glycolytic products, converting them to aromatic amino acids for secondary metabolism. The occurrence of separate shikimate pathways would have consid-erable importance in the understanding of the impact of environmental factors on secondary metabolism. However, while it appears that increasing nitrogen deficiency most often causes increased activity through the shikimate pathway, it can also affect the mevalonate/acetate route. Thus changes cannot be explained by 'shikimate overflow' alone, but require that the concept of shunt metabolism be extended to other pathways. At this point a note of caution must be introduced. Present evidence (Luckner 1980) suggests that synthesis of secondary metabolites is often strictly compartmentalized and controlled. Such obser-vations do not negate the concept of 'overflow' pathways, but demand the ability to move spare intermediates between compartments, a process that would have the advantage of opening up further routes for the dissipation of carbon flux.

There is much to be learnt about the mechanisms through which precursors are allocated to the pathways of secondary metabolism. For example, what are the conditions that lead to accumulation of nitrogen-containing compounds?

Haslam (1986) suggests that they could represent a mechanism whereby nitrogen is stored and later reclaimed. If this is so then do the tyrosine- and tryptophan-derived alkaloids employ amino acid from the primary or from the overflow shikimate pathway?

IMPLICATIONS OF RESOURCE ALLOCATION FOR SECONDARY METABOLITE DISTRIBUTION IN RAIN FOREST AND SAVANNA TREE SPECIES

The degree of nutrient availability found in rain forest ecosystems is very variable (Högberg 1986). Evidence from one study in African forests (supported by studies in boreal ecosystems) suggests that in a nutrient-deficient site there is greater emphasis on shikimate-based phenolic chemical defences (Table 1). However, the correlation is not strong and is best interpreted in terms of phylogenetically-based secondary metabolic pathways that occur in taxa adapted to these conditions, rather than to species plasticity in secondary metabolic output in response to nutrient imbalance. There seem to be no specific predictions that can be sustained. For example, in the apparently nutrient-deficient conditions of Douala-Edea, the common tree *Enantia chlorantha* Oliv. has more than 2% alkaloids in the stem bark. Does this species have special sources of nitrogen through nitrogen fixation, or very specific niche requirements in terms of soil nutrients? In deciduous, colonizer and light gap species there seems to be a reduced emphasis on shikimate-based phenolic metabolites (Coley 1983; Janzen & Waterman 1984; Waterman & McKey 1988). An emphasis on sustained or intermittent rapid growth will clearly demand a different allocation of resources, even among deciduous species that appear to be part of the climax forest, e.g. *Rauvolfia vomitoria* Afzel. and *Cleistopholis staudtii* Engl. & Diels at Douala-Edea (Gartlan *et al.* 1980), both of which produce only small quantities of phenolic compounds.

In dry savanna ecosystems the tree flora is likely to be subject to short-term nutrient flushes associated with wet seasons. In such systems rainfall could lead to transient periods of unlimited (or even carbon-limited) growth, to be followed by a prolonged period of nutrient limitation until the next rains. Three possible resource allocation strategies for leaf production and associated synthesis of secondary metabolites in this situation would be: (i) the producion of long-lived leaves which are rapidly provided with high concentrations of shikimate-based chemicals through use of carbohydrate reserves built up during the phase of carbon excess; (ii) the production of relatively long-lived leaves which are most vulnerable when young, when the plant is in a nutrient-rich phase, but become invested with shikimate-based phenolic defences in the subsequent carbon excess phase; (iii) production of short-lived leaves which are not heavily defended, and with the maintenance of metabolic processes during the dry seasons through chlorophyllous stems which are often rich in secondary metabolites.

CONCLUSION

In this paper we have outlined some factors that appear to influence formation of secondary metabolites in plants. The significance of soil nutrients is well established in laboratory studies, but not in the far more complex field situation. What does seem clear is that their impact cannot be divorced from carbon influx and the need to balance the two. The importance of this balance is illustrated by the studies of Larsson *et al.* (1986) and Bryant (1987) which show that success of a shikimate-based chemical defence can be changed by altering incident light, without variation in nutrient availability.

Relating the balance between carbon and nutrients and hence resource allocation to secondary metabolite production is an attractive hypothesis now backed by some experimental data. As a rule of thumb, we interpret the roles of the two contributing factors as follows.

1 Nutrient availability (sometimes modified by symbiotic adaptations to aid nutrient capture) in relation to growth and reproduction will dictate which species can utilize a habitat. The secondary metabolism exhibited by a species (taking into account phylogenetic constraints) will be primarily based on those resources that are in excess supply to it. Thus nutrient-deficient environments will commonly lead to an emphasis on metabolites from what are viewed as the carbon 'overflow' pathways, whereas nutrient-rich environments will be characterized by a greater proportion of nitrogen-containing metabolites or enhanced growth rates. We suspect that the carbon 'overflow' pathways will lead to an anti-herbivore defence profile in a plant community that is more resistant to high rates of herbivore exploitation. Attention has been drawn to the possibility of a direct relationship between soil nutrient availability and carrying capacities for mammalian herbivores in both rain forest (Waterman & McKey 1988; Waterman *et al.* 1988) and savanna ecosystems (Bell 1982), but clearly more detailed studies on the interrelationship between soil and plant chemistry are needed if this is to become more than just speculation.

2 The emphasis that is placed on the production of secondary metabolites by an individual within an ecosystem can be influenced to a considerable extent by environmental factors that alter the balance between carbon and nutrients. The most obvious is light flux, which will have an effect on carbon availability and is likely to be important in rain forest ecosystems and in successional systems in general. Other stress conditions that influence secondary metabolism, notably salinity (Brachet & Cosson 1986) and drought (Pizzi & Cameron 1986; Osmond *et al.* 1987), are more likely to be important in arid environments.

ACKNOWLEDGEMENTS

Dr D. McKey and Mr R. Carlton are thanked for their valuable comments on drafts of this paper.

REFERENCES

Anderson, J.M., Proctor, J. & Vallack, H.W. (1983). Ecological studies on four contrasting lowland rain forests in Gunung Mulu National Park, Sarawak. III. Decomposition. *Journal of Ecology*, **71**, 503–527.

Bazzaz, F.A., Chiariello, N.R., Coley, P.D. & Pitelka, L.E. (1987). Allocating resources to reproduction and defense. *BioScience,* **37**, 58–67.

Beevers, L. & Hageman, R.H. (1983). Uptake and reduction of nitrate. *Inorganic Plant Nutrition* (Ed. by A. Lauchli & R.L. Bieleski), pp. 351–375. Springer, Berlin.

Bell, R.H.V. (1982). The effect of soil nutrient availability on community structure in African ecosystems. *Ecology of Tropical Savannas* (Ed. by B.J. Huntley & B.H. Walker), pp. 183–216. Springer, Berlin.

Bloom, A.J., Chapin, F.S. & Mooney, H.A. (1985). Resource limitation in plants — an economic analogy. *Annual Review of Ecology and Systematics*, **16**, 363–392.

Brachet, J. & Cosson, L. (1986). Changes in the total alkaloid content of *Datura innoxia* Mill. subjected to salt stress. *Journal of Experimental Botany*, **37**, 650–656.

Bryant, J.P. (1987). Feltleaf willow–snowshoe hare interactions: plant carbon/nutrient balance and floodplain succession. *Ecology*, **68**, 1319–1327.

Bryant, J.P., Chapin, F.S. & Klein, D.R. (1983). Carbon/nutrient balance in boreal plants in relation to vertebrate herbivory. *Oikos*, **40**, 357–368.

Bryant, J.P., Chapin, F.S., Reichardt, P.B. & Clausen, T.P. (1987). Response of winter chemical defense in Alaska paper birch and green alder to manipulation of plant carbon/nutrient balance. *Oecologia (Berlin)*, **72**, 510–514.

Chapin, F.S. (1980). The mineral nutrition of wild plants. *Annual Review of Ecology and Systematics*, **11**, 233–260.

Chapin, F.S. (1983). Adaptations of selected trees and grasses to low availability of phosphorus. *Plant and Soil*, **72**, 283–287.

Chapin, F.S., Bloom, A.J., Field, C.B. & Waring, R.H. (1987). Plant responses to multiple environmental factors. *BioScience*, **37**, 49–57.

Chapin, F.S., Vitousek, P.M. & van Cleve, K. (1986). The nature of nutrient limitation in plant communities. *American Naturalist*, **127**, 48–58.

Clarkson, D.T. & Hanson, J.B. (1980). The mineral nutrition of higher plants. *Annual Review of Plant Physiology*, **31**, 239–298.

Coley, P.D. (1983). Herbivory and defensive characteristics of tree species in a lowland tropical forest. *Ecological Monographs*, **53**, 209–233.

Coley, P.D. (1986). Costs and benefits of defense by tannins in a neotropical tree. *Oecologia*, **70**, 238–242.

Coley, P.D., Bryant, J.P. & Chapin, F.S. (1985). Resource availability and plant antiherbivore defense. *Science*, **230**, 895–899.

Davies, R.I., Coulson, C.B. & Lewis, D.A. (1964). Polyphenols in plant, humus and soil, IV. Factors leading to an increase in biosynthesis of polyphenol in leaves and their relationship to mull and mor formation. *Journal of Soil Science*, **15**, 310–318.

Dicosmo, F. & Towers, G.H.N. (1984). Stress and secondary metabolism in cultured plant cells. *Recent Advances in Phytochemistry*, **18**, 97–175.

Feeny, P. (1976). Plant apparency and chemical defense. *Recent Advances in Phytochemistry*, **10**, 1–40.

Gartlan, J.S., McKey, D.B., Waterman, P.G., Mbi, C.N. & Struhsaker, T.T. (1980). A comparative study of the phytochemistry of two African rain forests. *Biochemical Systematics and Ecology*, **8**, 401–422.

Gartlan, J.S., Newbery, D.McC., Thomas, D.W. & Waterman, P.G. (1986). The influence of topography and soil phosphorus on the vegetation of Korup Forest Reserve, Cameroon, *Vegetatio*, **65**, 131–148.

Gershenzon, J. (1984). Changes in the levels of plant secondary metabolites under water and nutrient stress. *Recent Advances in Phytochemistry*, **18**, 273–320.

Gottlieb, L.D. (1982). Conservation and duplication of isozymes in plants. *Science*, **216**, 373–380.

Gray, J.T. & Schlesinger, W.H. (1983). Nutrient use by evergreen and deciduous shrubs in southern California. II. Experimental investigations of the relationship between growth, nitrogen uptake and nitrogen availability. *Journal of Ecology*, **71**, 43–56.

Greenway, H. & Munns, R. (1980). Mechanisms of salt tolerance in non-halophytes. *Annual Review of Plant Physiology*, **31**, 149–190.

Grime, J.P. (1977). Evidence for the existence of three primary strategies in plants and its relevance to ecological and evolutionary theory. *American Naturalist*, **111**, 1169–1174.

Harborne, J.B. (1982). *Introduction to Ecological Biochemistry*, 2nd edn. Academic Press, London.

Haslam, E. (1986). Secondary metabolism — fact and fiction. *Natural Products Reports*, pp. 217–249. Royal Chemical Society, London.

Högberg, P. (1986). Soil nutrient availability, root symbiosis and tree species composition in tropical Africa: a review. *Journal of Tropical Ecology*, **2**, 359–372.

Janzen, D.H. (1974). Tropical blackwater rivers, animals and mast fruiting by the Dipterocarpaceae. *Biotropica*, **6**, 69–103.

Janzen, D.H. & Waterman, P.G. (1984). A seasonal census of phenolics, fibre and alkaloids in foliage of forest trees in Costa Rica: some factors influencing their distribution and relation to host selection by Sphingidae and Saturniidae. *Biological Journal of the Linnean Society*, **21**, 439–454.

Jensen, R.A. (1986). The shikimate/arogenate pathway: link between carbohydrate metabolism and secondary metabolism. *Physiologia Planta*, **66**, 164–168.

Larsson, S., Wiren, A., Lundgren, L. & Ericsson, T. (1986). Effects of light and nutrient stress on leaf phenolic chemistry in *Salix dasyclados* and susceptibility to *Galerucella lineola* (Coleoptera). *Oikos*, **47**, 205–210.

Luckner, M. (1980). Expression and control of secondary metabolism. *Encyclopedia of Plant Physiology* (Ed. by E.A. Bell & B.V. Charlwood), Vol. 8, pp. 24–63. Springer, Berlin.

Mihaliak, C.A., Couvet, D. & Lincoln, D.E. (1987). Inhibition of feeding by a generalist insect due to increased volatile leaf terpenes under nitrate-limiting conditions. *Journal of Chemical Ecology*, **13**, 2059–2067.

Mihaliak, C.A. & Lincoln, D.E. (1985). Growth patterns and carbon allocation to volatile leaf terpenes under nitrogen-limiting conditions in *Heterotheca subaxillaris* (Asteraceae). *Oecologia (Berlin)*, **66**, 423–426.

Mole, S., Ross, J.A.M. & Waterman, P.G. (1988). Light-induced variation in phenolic levels in foliage of rain-forest plants. I. Chemical changes. *Journal of Chemical Ecology*, **14**, 1–21.

Newbery, D.McC. & de Foresta, H. (1985). Herbivory and defense in pioneer, gap and understorey trees in tropical rain forest in French Guiana. *Biotropica*, **17**, 238–245.

Newbery, D.McC., Gartlan, J.S., McKey, D.B. & Waterman, P.G. (1986). The influence of drainage and soil phosphorus on the vegetation of Douala-Edea Forest Reserve. *Vegetatio*, **65**, 149–162.

Oates, J.F., Waterman, P.G. & Choo, G.M. (1980). Food selection by the South Indian leaf monkey *Presbytis johnii*, in relation to leaf chemistry. *Oecologia (Berlin)*, **45**, 45–56.

Osmond, C.B., Austin, M.P., Berry, J.A., Billings, W.D., Boyer, J.S., Dacey, J.W.H., Nobel, P.S., Smith, S.D. & Winner, W.E. (1987). Stress physiology and the distribution of plants. *BioScience*, **37**, 38–48.

Pizzi, A. & Cameron, F.A. (1986). Flavonoid tannins — structural wood components for drought-resistance mechanisms of plants. *Wood Science and Technology*, **20**, 119–124.

Proctor, J., Anderson, J.M., Chai, P. & Vallack, H.W. (1983a). Ecological studies on four contrasting lowland rain forests in Gunung Mulu National Park, Sarawak. I. Forest environment, structure and floristics. *Journal of Ecology*, **71**, 237–260.

Proctor, J., Anderson, J.M., Fogden, S.C.L. & Vallack, H.W. (1983b). Ecological studies on four contrasting lowland rain forests in Gunung Mulu National Park, Sarawak. II. Litterfall, litter standing crop and preliminary observations on herbivory. *Journal of Ecology*, **71**, 261–283.

Prudhomme, T.L. (1983). Carbon allocation to antiherbivore compounds in a deciduous and an evergreen subarctic shrub species. *Oikos*, **40**, 344–356.

Rhodes, M.J.C. (1985). The physiological significance of plant phenolic compounds. *The Biochemistry of Plant Phenolics* (Ed. by C.F. van Sumere & P.J. Lea), pp. 99–118. Clarendon Press, Oxford.

Rosenthal, G.A. & Janzen, D.H. (Eds.) (1979). *Herbivores: Their Interaction with Secondary Plant*

Metabolites. Academic Press, New York.

Sibly, R.M. & Grime, J.P. (1986). Strategies of resource capture by plants — evidence for adversity selection. *Journal of Theoretical Biology*, **118**, 247–250.

Spring, O., Priester, T. & Hager, A. (1986). Light-induced accumulation of sesquiterpene lactones in sunflower seedlings. *Journal of Plant Physiology*, **123**, 79–86.

Tivy, J. (1971). *Biogeography. A Study of Plants in the Ecosphere.* Oliver & Boyd, Edinburgh.

Trewavas, A. (1986). Resource allocation under poor growth conditions. A major role for growth substances in developmental plasticity. *Symposia of the Society of Experimental Biology*, **40**, 31–76.

Waring, R.H., McDonald, A.J.S., Larsson, S., Ericsson, T., Wiren, A., Arwidsson, E., Ericsson, A. & Lohammer, T. (1985). Differences in chemical composition of plants grown at constant relative growth rates with stable mineral nutrition. *Oecologia (Berlin)*, **66**, 157–160.

Waterman, P.G. (1986). A phytochemist in the African rain-forest. *Phytochemistry*, **25**, 3–17.

Waterman, P.G. & McKey, D.B. (1988). Secondary compounds in rain-forest plants: patterns of distribution and ecological implications. *Ecosystems of the World, Tropical Rain Forest* (Ed. by H. Leith & O.R. Werger), Vol. 14b, pp. 513–536. Elsevier, The Hague.

Waterman, P.G., Ross, J.A.M., Bennett, E.L. & Davies, A.G. (1988). A comparison of the floristics and leaf chemistry of two Malaysian rain-forests and the influence of leaf chemistry on populations of colobine monkeys in the Old World. *Biological Journal of the Linnean Society*, **34**, 1–32.

Waterman, P.G., Ross, J.A.M. & McKey, D.B. (1984). Factors affecting levels of some phenolic compounds, digestibility and nitrogen content of the mature leaves of *Barteria fistulosa* (Passifloraceae). *Journal of Chemical Ecology*, **10**, 387–401.

Wolfson, J.L. (1982). Developmental responses of *Pieris rapae and Spodoptera eridania* to environmentally induced variation in *Brassica nigra. Environmental Entomology*, **11**, 207–213.

Chemical elements in litter in forests on Volcán Barva, Costa Rica

A. HEANEY AND J. PROCTOR

School of Natural Sciences, University of Stirling, Stirling FK9 4LA

SUMMARY

1 The total non-woody and woody ($\leqslant 2$ cm diameter) annual litterfall and litter layer were compared in plots of 1 ha at each of four altitudes, 100, 1000, 2000 and 2600 m, on Volcán Barva, Costa Rica.

2 The total litterfall (t ha^{-1} $year^{-1}$) was 9.0 for the plot at 100 m, 6.6 for the plot at 1000 m, 5.8 for the plot at 2000 m and 5.3 for the plot at 2600 m.

3 The mass of the total litter layer (t ha^{-1}) was 3.55 for the plot at 100 m, 4.20 for the plot at 1000 m, 5.17 for the plot at 2000 m and 6.33 for the plot at 2600 m. The element concentrations in the litterfall and litter layer differed between each forest type. The most consistent trend was that of decreasing nitrogen concentration with altitude.

4 There were large differences between the four plots in the annual addition of elements in litterfall and in the element contents of the litter layer and soil. Nitrogen and calcium were the least mobile of the elements in all the plots.

5 After comparisons with other studies made on single wet tropical mountains, it was concluded that nitrogen is the element most likely to be in increasingly short supply with altitude. It may limit the rate of forest processes and influence floristic composition, but it is less likely to have an influence on forest biomass.

INTRODUCTION

The causes of forest changes with altitude on wet tropical mountains are still poorly known. Grubb (1971, 1977) argued that increasing shortages of nutrient elements might limit tree growth at increasing altitude and this view has received support (for nitrogen) following research on a montane forest in New Guinea (Edwards 1982). Tanner (1985) cautiously concluded following his research on nutrient capital and nutrient requirements for growth in Jamaican montane forests: "I suggest that there is some evidence that all montane forests studied to date may be limited by the supply of N and P, and perhaps K and Ca, compared to the most nutrient-rich lowland forests."

Few studies have been made of forests and soils at a range of altitudes on single wet tropical mountains. Such studies are desirable, since, even if the mountains are not of uniform lithology, the interpretation of the results is simpler than that involving comparisons of montane forests with geographically remote lowland forests. The present paper is one in a series on forests and soils at a range of altitudes on Volcán Barva, Costa Rica (Atkin & Proctor 1988; Marrs *et al.* 1988; Grieve, Proctor & Cousins 1990; Heaney & Proctor 1990).

There were no consistent altitudinal trends in several soil parameters investigated for Volcán Barva by Grieve *et al.* (1990) except for increases in soil organic matter and total nitrogen. However, Marrs *et al.* (1988) found that both nitrogen mineralization and nitrification decreased (in 0–12 cm deep soil samples) with altitude under field conditions. The evidence from the soil analyses of Marrs *et al.* (1988) therefore support the view that nitrogen is the element most likely to be in increasingly short supply with increasing altitude.

In this paper we report a study of the litterfall and litter layer in four forest plots on Volcán Barva. Vitousek (1984) has argued that the dry mass/nutrient quotients in litterfall are a good index of the nutrient economy in a stand as a whole and the main aim of this paper is to use analyses of litterfall to further test the hypothesis that nitrogen may be in short supply on Volcán Barva. (The analytical data are reported here as concentrations, i.e. the reciprocal of the dry mass/nutrient quotients.) Litterfall analyses are likely to give the best easily obtained guides to nutrient shortages in forests. This is because, unlike foliar analyses, they include the influence of nutrient and energy reabsorption during leaf senescence, and because of the way litterfall is sampled, it integrates material from the forest trees as a whole. The litterfall data for Volcán Barva are thus used to test the hypothesis that soil nitrogen may be in short supply and are then discussed in relation to information from other forests on wet tropical mountains.

STUDY SITES

The study was carried out along a transect from the La Selva Biological Station (10° 24′N, 84° 00′W) up the northern slope of Volcán Barva. Four plots (at 100, 1000, 2000 and 2600 m) of the six described by Heaney & Proctor (1990) were investigated for litter. A summary of some features of the topography and vegetation of the four plots is given in Table 1. The plots were all on flat or sloping broad areas and not on ridges or in gullies.

At La Selva the mean annual rainfall (1959–1985) was 4015 mm and the mean annual temperature was 24 °C. The rainfall is relatively aseasonal, but rainfall is generally higher in June to October and the study period shared this pattern (Fig. 1). Rainfall data are not available along the transect, but data collected from selected stations nearby (Table 2) suggest that it may be greatest in the mid-region of the mountain. The temperature lapse rate is not known. Ground frosts were observed in a clearing at 2600 m on several days in April 1985, but not during continuous daily observations between 5 March and 5 April 1985 at 1800 m.

The soils have been described by Grieve *et al.* (1990) and by Marrs *et al.* (1988). The parent materials are basaltic and andesitic lavas of Plio-Pleistocene age with a trend towards tuff or agglomerate-like materials with increasing elevation. A summary of surface-soil chemical features is given in Table 3.

TABLE 1. Some characteristics of the four 1 ha plots sampled for litterfall and litter layer on Volcán Barva, Costa Rica

Plot altitude (m)	Prevailing slope (deg)	Prevailing aspect	Basal area of woody species (≥10 cm dbh) (m²)	Height of main canopy (m)	Height of tallest tree (m)	No. of individuals of woody species (≥10 cm dbh)	No. of species of woody plants (≥10 cm dbh)	The five leading woody families ranked by % basal area (≥10 cm dbh)
100	7	E	22.7	35–40	45	494	111	Mimosaceae Palmae Burseraceae Vochysiaceae Euphorbiaceae
1000	7	NE	31.2	30–35	45	546	109	Mimosaceae Fabaceae Chrysobalanaceae Euphorbiaceae Vochysiaceae
2000	10	NW	28.6	20–25	35	448	69	Euphorbiaceae Cyatheaceae Melastomataceae Hamamelidaceae Staphyleaceae
2600	15	N	51.2	20–23	32	617	35	Araliaceae Aquifoliaceae Cunoniaceae Caprifoliaceae Brunelliaceae

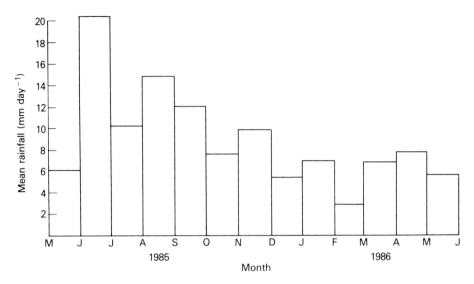

Fig. 1. Mean rainfall (mm day^{-1}) at La Selva Field Station, Costa Rica, from 1 May 1985 to 1 June 1986.

MATERIALS AND METHODS

Small litterfall

Small litterfall was collected for 12 months in sacks made of an interwoven plastic material which retained all particles greater than about 0.1 mm. Four metal rings were fixed to the mouths of the sacks so that adjustable cords could be attached to trees to form a trap about 0.5 m deep with a 0.5 m × 0.5 m horizontal opening, supported about 0.7 m above the ground. The traps were placed in a restricted random design at each site and the numbers of traps are given in Table 4. There was a variation in trap numbers because of thefts and subsequent replacements (Table 4). The traps were emptied at 2-weekly to 4-weekly intervals when their contents were placed in a cloth bag in which they were dried within 5 days of collection at 105 °C. The contents of each bag were then sorted into two fractions which were weighed separately: non-woody material (leaves, reproduc-

TABLE 2. Mean annual rainfall for four sites at a range of altitudes near the forest study plots (from Heaney & Proctor (1990)

Site	Altitude (m)	Rainfall (mm)	Duration of observations (years)	Distance (km) and direction from nearest study plot
La Selva	42	4015	26	3 N (100 m)
Cariblanco	970	5096	5	10 W (1000 m)
Vara Blanca	1804	3426	21	5 W (2000 m)
Sacramento	2260	3268	11	8 S (2600 m)

TABLE 3. Characteristics of 12-cm* or 15-cm deep soil samples collected from four plots on Volcán Barva, Costa Rica. Values are expressed on an oven-dry (105 °C) basis where appropriate. $n = 10$* or 25. Data are from Grieve, Proctor & Cousins (1990) and R. H. Marrs (unpublished)*

Altitude (m)	pH$_{H_2O}$	Loss-on-ignition (%)	Total N* (%)	Nitrification rates* (μg g^{-1} 14 days^{-1})	Nitrogen mineralization rates* (μg g^{-1} 14 days^{-1})	Total P* (%)	Extractable P* (μg g^{-1})	Exchangeable cations (m-equiv. 100 g^{-1})				Total exchangeable bases
								K	Na	Ca	Mg	
100	3.7	18.7	0.4	27	38	0.09	2.2	0.17	0.11	1.09	0.29	1.66
1000	4.1	36.4	1.4	10	11	0.15	1.3	0.26	0.21	0.21	0.33	1.01
2000	3.8	49.0	2.0	8	1	0.14	4.7	0.14	0.12	0.42	0.27	0.95
2600	3.7	37.2	1.9	3	−2	0.11	55.1	0.29	0.11	2.25	1.19	3.84

TABLE 4. The mass of non–woody and woody litterfall collected from 50 cm × 50 cm traps in plots at four altitudes on Volcán Barva, Costa Rica

Plot altitude (m)	Number of litter traps	Dates of collection	Litterfall mass (t ha^{-1} year^{-1})		
			Non–woody	Woody	Total
100	19–25	10 May 1985–10 May 1986	7.6	1.4	9.0
1000	12–20	23 May 1985–23 May 1986	5.5	1.1	6.6
2000	20–23	21 May 1985–21 May 1986	4.8	1.0	5.8
2600	22–23	4 May 1985–4 May 1986	4.6	0.7	5.3

tive parts and miscellaneous fragments) and small wood (branches ≤2 cm diameter, bark fractions ≤2 cm along their longest dimension and woody fruits). It was too laborious to sort a separate leaf fraction because of the very large numbers of leaflets of leguminous trees in the collections from the lower plots and hence it was impossible to categorize the litterfall according to the recommendations of Proctor (1983).

The litter layer and decomposition quotient k_L

At one randomly selected position in each of several (20 m × 20 m) subplots (the number of subplots is given in Table 5) on each plot all small litter was removed from within a 50 cm × 50 cm quadrat. The litter was dried at 105 °C and sorted into the two fractions described above for small litterfall. Unlike the litterfall collections, a miscellaneous fraction of small particles was not included because these could not be distinguished from portions of the soil organic matter. Three small-litter collections were made on each site; the collection dates are given in Table 5. The decomposition quotient $k_L = I/X$, where I is the annual litter input to the forest floor and X is the mean mass of the litter layer, was calculated for non-woody and total small litter. The value of k_L for these fractions is an approximation of the proportion of the litter layer decomposed in 1 year.

Chemical analyses

The oven-dried small litterfall samples were ground and the samples from all traps on each plot were combined to give monthly samples. For the litter layer, analyses were made separately on each of three bulked sets of samples for each of the four plots taken over a year.

Subsamples of 0.5 g of the ground litterfall or litter layer samples were redried at 105 °C, wet-ashed in concentrated nitric acid and analysed by atomic absorption spectrophotometry using an air/acetylene flame by the methods of Allen *et al.* (1974). Total nitrogen and phosphorus were determined colori-

TABLE 5. The mass of the non–woody and woody litter layer (t ha^{-1} ± 95% CL) collected from 50 cm × 50 cm samples at three sampling dates in plots at four altitudes on Volcán Barva, Costa Rica

Plot altitude (m)	Date of collection	n	Non-woody litter (t ha^{-1})	Woody litter (t ha^{-1})
100	27 & 28 July 1985	10	2.15 ± 0.59	0.93 ± 0.39
	4 December 1985	10	1.86 ± 0.41	1.33 ± 0.73
	30 May 1986	10	2.89 ± 0.70	1.49 ± 0.89
	$\bar{x}$		2.30	1.25
1000	1 September 1985	10	2.27 ± 0.47	2.04 ± 1.35
	29 January 1986	10	2.29 ± 0.42	2.29 ± 0.70
	13 May 1987	8	2.58 ± 0.44	1.13 ± 0.29
	$\bar{x}$		2.38	1.82
2000	22 August 1985	11	3.59 ± 1.69	1.92 ± 1.72
	28 January 1986	10	3.15 ± 0.59	2.45 ± 1.23
	29 June 1986	8	3.03 ± 0.84	1.37 ± 0.42
	$\bar{x}$		3.26	1.91
2600	25 August 1985	10	3.22 ± 1.16	3.93 ± 1.55
	27 January 1986	10	3.54 ± 0.99	2.30 ± 0.76
	24 June 1987	5	4.35 ± 1.53	1.66 ± 0.42
	$\bar{x}$		3.70	2.63

metrically, simultaneously by an auto-analyser technique (O'Neill & Webb 1970), after digestion of 0.5 g subsamples in a mixture of sulphuric acid and hydrogen peroxide with a selenium catalyst. Nitrogen was determined as ammonium after the formation of an indophenol blue complex and phosphorus after formation of a molybdenum blue complex. Analyses were made in duplicate and there was good agreement (< 10% difference) between replicates.

RESULTS

Litterfall

The total small litterfall on the four plots decreases with altitude from 9.0 t ha^{-1} year^{-1} at 100 m to 5.3 t ha^{-1} year^{-1} at 2600 m (Table 4). Because the number of traps varied, it is not possible to give confidence limits to the annual values in Table 4. However, for each monthly collection, trap numbers were constant and confidence limits are included in Fig. 2 for the monthly means.

Litter layer

There is an altitudinal trend of increase in the mass of the litter layer (Table 5) for both non-woody and woody litter.

Element concentrations in small litterfall and litter layer

Element concentrations in the litterfall and litter layer show many differences between sites (Tables 6 and 7), but the most consistent for woody and non-woody

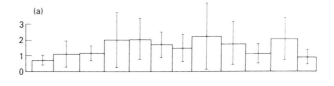

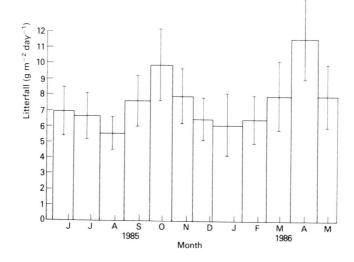

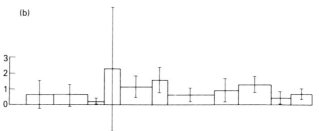

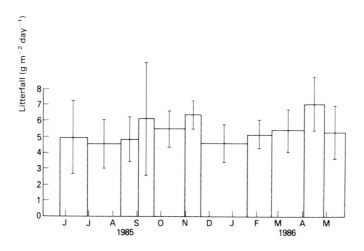

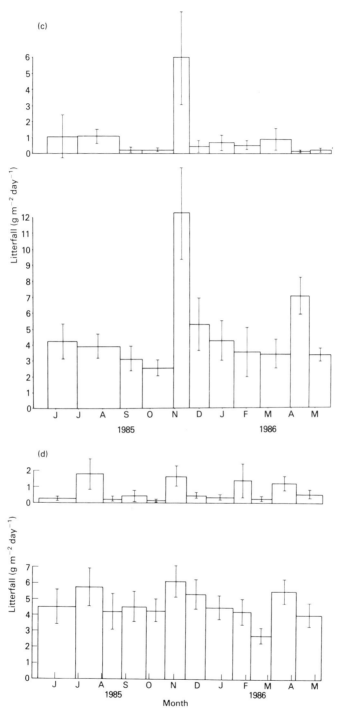

FIG. 2. Litterfall on forest plots at four altitudes, (a) 100 m, (b) 1000 m, (c) 2000 m and (d) 2600 m, on Volcán Barva, Costa Rica. The upper of each pair of histograms represents the woody litterfall and the lower the non-woody litterfall. The vertical bars show the 95% confidence limits.

TABLE 6. The concentrations ($\pm 95\%$ CL) of nitrogen, phosphorus, potassium, sodium, calcium and magnesium in the litterfall (oven dried at 105 °C) on four forest plots on Volcán Barva, Costa Rica. The values are means ($n = 12$) of analyses of monthly litterfall collections

Plot altitude (m)	N (mg g^{-1})	P (mg g^{-1})	K (mg g^{-1})	Na (mg g^{-1})	Ca (mg g^{-1})	Mg (mg g^{-1})
Non-woody litterfall						
100	14 ± 1.9	0.54 ± 0.07	2.0 ± 0.30	0.54 ± 0.18	8.3 ± 0.39	1.7 ± 0.07
1000	11 ± 2.0	0.45 ± 0.06	1.4 ± 0.18	0.44 ± 0.05	7.2 ± 0.69	1.9 ± 0.20
2000	9.0 ± 0.3	0.54 ± 0.06	2.2 ± 0.27	0.30 ± 0.05	11.0 ± 0.93	1.9 ± 0.15
2600	6.8 ± 0.4	0.53 ± 0.07	3.0 ± 0.36	0.20 ± 0.04	10.4 ± 0.48	2.3 ± 0.12
Woody litterfall						
100	6.0 ± 0.40	0.30 ± 0.07	1.4 ± 0.49	0.18 ± 0.08	6.6 ± 0.86	1.3 ± 0.12
1000	4.9 ± 0.40	0.14 ± 0.06	0.9 ± 0.50	0.14 ± 0.06	4.6 ± 0.43	1.2 ± 0.16
2000	3.4 ± 0.30	0.15 ± 0.07	1.3 ± 0.31	0.17 ± 0.07	8.3 ± 1.20	1.2 ± 0.18
2600	3.6 ± 0.30	0.23 ± 0.06	2.3 ± 0.50	0.19 ± 0.15	5.6 ± 0.74	1.2 ± 0.19

TABLE 7. The mean concentrations of nitrogen, phosphorus, potassium, sodium, calcium and magnesium in the litter layer (oven dried at 105 °C) from four forest plots on Volcán Barva, Costa Rica. Values are ±S.E. where $n = 3$ and without S.E. where $n = 2$. N.D. is not determined

Plot altitude (m)	N (mg g^{-1})	P (mg g^{-1})	K (mg g^{-1})	Na (mg g^{-1})	Ca (mg g^{-1})	Mg (mg g^{-1})
Non-woody litter						
100	15 ± 3.1	0.31 ± 0.08	1.0 ± 0.09	0.11 ± 0.03	9.6 ± 0.74	1.2 ± 0.06
1000	9.5 ± 0.47	0.09 ± 0.01	1.0	0.17	7.4	1.2
2000	8.5 ± 0.75	0.22 ± 0.04	1.5 ± 0.11	0.09 ± 0.02	10.5 ± 1.2	1.4 ± 0.12
2600	7.0 ± 1.4	0.20 ± 0.04	1.5	0.05	9.3	1.8
Woody litter						
100	6.1 ± 0.59	0.18 ± 0.04	0.60 ± 0.02	0.06 ± 0.01	6.3 ± 0.05	0.87 ± 0.04
1000	4.4 ± 0.69	N.D.	0.53	0.19	3.6	0.67
2000	4.2 ± 0.64	0.20 ± 0.01	1.2 ± 0.34	0.04 ± 0.001	6.5 ± 0.81	0.82 ± 0.19
2600	2.1 ± 0.94	0.09 ± 0.03	1.2	0.04	5.7	1.1

litterfall is the reduction in nitrogen concentration with altitude.

Litter input–litter layer quotients (k_L)

The k_L values for the litter components on the four sites are given in Table 8 and show a decline with altitude. Mean k_L values for small litter in the four sites are compared with the quotients for elements in the litterfall and litter layer in Table 9. Virtually all the values have higher quotients than the litter k_L and this indicates that there is no net immobilization of the elements during decomposition. Calcium and nitrogen are the least mobile elements at all altitudes, whilst the mobility of the others is ranked Na > K > P > Mg (100 m), P > Na > Mg > K (1000 m), Na > P > K > Mg (2000 m), Na > P > K > Mg (2600 m). The relatively high mobility of phosphorus should be noted.

TABLE 8. The values of k_L, a coefficient calculated by dividing the mass of annual litterfall (Table 4) by the mean mass of the litter layer (Table 5), for plots at four altitudes on Volcán Barva, Costa Rica

| | | k_L | |
| Plot altitude | | Small wood | |
(m)	Leaves	(≤2 cm diameter)	Total litterfall
100	3.30	1.12	2.53
1000	2.31	0.60	1.57
2000	1.47	0.52	1.12
2600	1.24	0.27	0.84

DISCUSSION

Mass of the litterfall and litter layer

The litterfall mass values (Table 4) fall within the ranges of those recorded for lowland rain forests (cf. the La Selva 100 m plot) and montane rain forests (cf. the plots at 1000, 2000 and 2600 m on Volcán Barva) elsewhere in the world (Table 10). Gessel *et al.* (1980) recorded a total small litterfall of 7.8 t ha^{-1} year^{-1} for a forest at an unspecified location near La Selva. Previous studies of montane forests in Costa Rica have found a low litterfall of 2.7 t ha^{-1} year^{-1} for a secondary lower montane forest at 1980 m (de la Cruz 1964) and an exceptionally high value of 27.0 t ha^{-1} year^{-1} (of which 15.5 t ha^{-1} year^{-1} were leaves) for a premontane secondary forest at 1200 m (Fournier & Camacho de Castro 1973). De la Cruz's study was made for too short a period (6 weeks), but that of Fournier & Camacho de Castro went on for 10 months and the high value is difficult to explain.

The mass of the litter layer in the 100 m plot is near the bottom of the range for lowland forests (Table 10). The mass of leaves in the litter layer of all the Barva montane plots is lower than recorded previously for montane forests.

TABLE 9. Estimated rate of addition (kg ha^{-1} year^{-1}) of elements in the small litterfall and their quantities (kg ha^{-1}) in the litter layer and in the soil at four forest sites on Volcán Barva, Costa Rica. Soil nitrogen and phosphorus are total amounts (from R. H. Marrs (personal communication)) and soil potassium, sodium, calcium and magnesium refer to exchangeable quantities (from Grieve et al. (1990)). The regression for bulk density on loss-on-ignition (Jeffrey 1970) was used to convert soil values from a weight to an area basis. The estimates for litterfall are obtained from the mean values in Tables 4 and 6, those for the litter layer from Tables 5 and 7

Fraction	N	P	K	Na	Ca	Mg	k_L
100 m forest							
Non-woody litter	110	4.1	15	4.1	63	13	
Woody litter	8.4	0.42	2.0	0.25	9.2	1.8	
(a) Total litterfall input	110	4.5	17	4.4	72	15	
(b) Litter layer	42	0.94	3.1	0.33	30	3.8	
Soil (top 15 cm)	3700	840	62	24	200	32	
Quotient (a)/(b)	2.6	4.8	5.5	13.3	2.4	3.9	2.53
1000 m forest							
Non-woody litter	60	2.5	7.7	2.4	40	10	
Woody litter	5.4	0.15	0.99	0.15	5.1	1.3	
(a) Total litterfall input	65	2.6	8.7	2.6	45	12	
(b) Litter layer	31	0.23	3.3	0.75	24	4.1	
Soil (top 15 cm)	8900	950	64	31	27	25	
Quotient (a)/(b)	2.1	11.3	2.6	3.5	1.9	2.9	1.57
2000 m forest							
Non-woody litter	43	2.6	11	1.4	53	9.1	
Woody litter	3.4	0.15	1.3	0.17	8.3	1.2	
(a) Total litterfall input	46	2.7	12	1.6	61	10	
(b) Litter layer	38	1.1	7.2	0.37	47	6.1	
Soil (top 15 cm)	10050	700	27	14	42	16	
Quotient (a)/(b)	1.2	2.5	1.7	4.3	1.3	1.6	1.12
2600 m forest							
Non-woody litter	31	2.4	14	0.92	48	11	
Woody litter	2.5	0.16	1.6	0.13	3.9	0.84	
(a) Total litterfall input	34	2.6	15	1.1	52	11	
(b) Litter layer	31	0.98	8.7	0.29	49	9.6	
Soil (top 15 cm)	12000	690	71	16	280	89	
Quotient (a)/(b)	1.1	2.7	1.7	3.8	1.1	1.1	0.84

TABLE 10. The ranges of mass of litterfall and litter layer from (a) lowland rain forests (>2000 mm year^{-1} rainfall) and (b) montane rain forests. The data are from Proctor (1984) and Anderson, Proctor & Vallack (1983), and montane forest litterfall include data from Weaver *et al.* (1986). Litterfall data are from studies which have been carried out for at least 12 months and have used at least ten litter traps. (Data for four plots within the same area in Papua New Guinea only.)

	Total litterfall (t ha^{-1} year^{-1})	Non-woody or leaf litterfall (t ha^{-1} year^{-1})	Total litter layer (t ha^{-1})	Non-woody or leaf litter layer (t ha^{-1})
(a)	3.4–13.2	2.9–8.2	3.2–11.2	1.7–5.1
(b)	3.1–10.0	2.4–7.3	6.1–7.7*	5.1–11.7

Litterfall chemistry

In all cases the Barva plots (Table 6) have non-woody or total litterfall element concentrations within the ranges of corresponding forests elsewhere (Table 11).

TABLE 11. The ranges of concentrations of elements in leaf litterfall from (a) lowland rain forests (>2000 mm year^{-1} rainfall) and (b) montane rain forests. The data are from Proctor (1984) and for montane forests include data from Weaver *et al.* (1986). Heath forests and forest-over-limestone are not included

	N (mg g^{-1})	P (mg g^{-1})	K (mg g^{-1})	Na (mg g^{-1})	Ca (mg g^{-1})	Mg (mg g^{-1})
(a)	9–18	0.11–1.6	1.3–9.1	0.05–0.74	1.5–2.4	1.1–4.6
(b)	6–13	0.17–0.74	1.4–5.9	0.04–1.3	1.9–13	1.8–4.2

Limiting nutrients on tropical mountains

The most useful comparisons can be made with litterfall values which have been recorded for forests at different altitudes on one mountain system. We do this in Fig. 3 for forests on Volcán Barva and in Puerto Rico, Sabah and Sarawak. The comparison here is restricted to nitrogen and phosphorus because they are the elements most likely to limit forest growth (Edwards 1982) and, since they are known to be retranslocated into perennial organs from senescing leaves, their litterfall concentrations are likely to reflect the abundance of their supply to the plant from the soil. Figure 3 shows a general decline in nitrogen concentrations with altitude, but no decline in phosphorus concentrations in leaf litterfall.

Nitrogen as a limiting nutrient on wet tropical mountains

Grieve *et al.* (1990) have collated soil data for several wet tropical mountains and conclude that for a range of characteristics the only consistent altitudinal trends are increases in soil organic matter and soil acidity. However, the characteristics that they measured did not include rates of nitrification and nitrogen mineralization. These were determined (on a soil unit weight basis) by Marrs *et al.* (1988) in

(a)   (b)

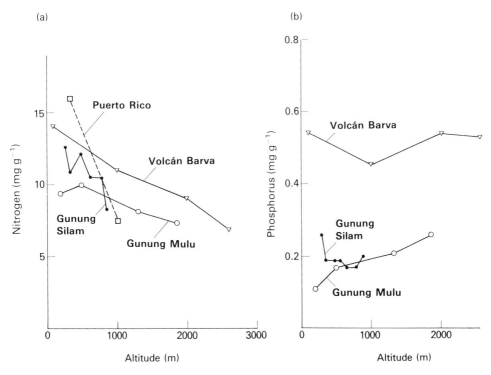

FIG. 3. Changes in (a) nitrogen concentrations and (b) phosphorus concentrations in leaf or non-woody litterfall in studies which have been made at a range of altitudes on one mountain. The Gunung Mulu data are from Proctor, Anderson & Vallack (1983); the Gunung Silam data are from Proctor *et al.* (1988); the Puerto Rican data (nitrogen only) are from Wiegert (1970) (420 m) and from Weaver *et al.* (1986) (1010 m); the data for Volcán Barva are from this work.

plots at 100 m, 500 m, 1000 m, 1500 m, 2000 m and 2600 m on Volcán Barva and showed a consistent decrease with altitude (Table 3). This reduction in soil nitrogen supply at least partly explains the decreasing nitrogen concentrations in litterfall (Table 4) and the increasing turnover times for this element (Table 8) with altitude.

The fundamental question remains of how a low supply of nitrogen might influence biomass, floristic composition, forest structure, and production in montane forests. There is little evidence that soil nutrients are related to biomass in primary forests. For example, some Malaysian dipterocarp forests with a large biomass are on soils with low nutrient concentrations, whilst forests on nutrient-rich soils may have a smaller stature (Proctor *et al.* 1983a). Relationships between floristic composition and nutrients are complex, although Whitmore (1984) has commented on similarities between Malaysian heath forests and upper montane forests, both of which are likely to be short of nitrogen (Proctor *et al.* 1983a, b, c). There is likely to be a correlation, albeit slight, between soil nutrients and litter production (Proctor *et al.* 1983b).

It is concluded that if nutrients are limiting ecosystem processes on tropical mountains, then nitrogen is the most likely element involved. Nitrogen limitation may be expressed in terms of floristic composition, forest structure, and production but a direct influence on biomass is less likely. The resolution of the question of nitrogen limitation requires more data from a range of wet tropical mountains and, more importantly, critical experiments.

ACKNOWLEDGEMENTS

We thank the National Parks Service of Costa Rica for permission to work in Braulio Carillo, OTS for permission to work in the grounds of La Selva Field Station, Operation Raleigh for support and its staff and venturers (particularly Miss Gleana Calva) for help of many kinds. Dr E. V. J. Tanner and Professor P. M. Vitousek are thanked for comments on the manuscript. The work was supported financially by the British Ecological Society, the Carnegie Trust, the Leverhulme Trust, the Natural Environmental Research Council and the National Geographic Society.

REFERENCES

Allen, S.E., Grimshaw, H.M., Parkinson, J.A. & Quarmby, C. (1974). *Chemical Analysis of Ecological Materials.* Blackwell Scientific Publications, Oxford.

Anderson, J.M., Proctor, J. & Vallack, H.W. (1983). Ecological studies in four contrasting lowland rain forests in Gunung Mulu National Park, Sarawak III. Decomposition processes and nutrient losses from leaf litter. *Journal of Ecology,* **71**, 503–527.

Atkin, L. & Proctor, J. (1988). Invertebrates in the litter and soil on Volcán Barva, Costa Rica. *Journal of Tropical Ecology,* **4**, 307–310.

Cruz, de la, A.A. (1964). A preliminary study of organic detritus in a tropical forest ecosystem. *Revista de Biologia Tropical,* **12**, 175–185.

Edwards, P.J. (1982). Studies of mineral cycling in a montane rain forest in New Guinea V. Rates of cycling in throughfall and litterfall. *Journal of Ecology,* **70**, 807–827.

Fournier, L.A. & Camacho de Castro, L. (1973). Producción y descomposición del mantillo en un bosque secundario húmedo de premontano. *Revista de Biologia Tropical,* **21**, 59–67.

Gessel, S.P., Cole, D.W., Johnson, D. & Turner, J. (1980). The nutrient cycles of two Costa Rican forests. *Progress in Ecology,* pp. 23–44. Today & Tomorrow's Printers & Publishers, New Delhi, India.

Grieve, I.C., Proctor, J. & Cousins, S.A. (1990). Ecological studies on rain forests at a range of altitudes on Volcán Barva, Costa Rica II. Soils. *Catena* (in press).

Grubb, P.J. (1971). Interpretation of the 'Massenerhebung' effect on tropical mountains. *Nature (London),* **229**, 44–45.

Grubb, P.J. (1977). Control of forest growth and distribution on wet tropical mountains. *Annual Review of Ecology and Systematics,* **8**, 83–107.

Heaney, A. & Proctor, J. (1990). Preliminary studies on forest structure and floristics on Volcán Barva, Costa Rica. *Journal of Tropical Ecology,* (in press).

Jeffery, D. W. (1970). A note on the use of ingnition loss as a means for the approximate estimation of soil bulk density. *Journal of Ecology,* **58**, 297–299.

Marrs, R.H., Proctor, J., Heaney, A. & Mountford, M.D. (1988). Changes in soils, nitrogen mineralization and nitrification along an altitudinal transect in tropical rain forest in Costa Rica. *Journal of Ecology,* **76**, 466–482.

O'Neill, J.V. & Webb, R.A. (1970). Simultaneous determination of nitrogen, phosphorus and potassium in plant material by automatic methods. *Journal of the Science of Food and Agriculture,* **21**, 217–219.

Proctor, J. (1983). Tropical forest litterfall I. Problems of data comparison. *Tropical Rain Forest: Ecology and Management* (Ed. by S.L. Sutton, T.C. Whitmore & A.C. Chadwick), pp. 267–273. Blackwell Scientific Publications, Oxford.

Proctor, J. (1984). Tropical forest litterfall II: the data set. *Tropical Rain-Forest: the Leeds Symposium* (Ed. by A.C. Chadwick & S.L. Sutton), pp. 83–113. Leeds Philosophical and Literary Society, Leeds.

Proctor, J., Anderson, J.M., Chai, P. & Vallack, H.W. (1983a). Ecological studies in four contrasting lowland rain forests in Gunung Mulu National Park, Sarawak I. Forest environment, structure and floristics. *Journal of Ecology*, **71**, 237–260.

Proctor, J., Anderson, J.M., Fogden, S.C.L. & Vallack, H.W. (1983b). Ecological studies in four contrasting lowland rain forests in Gunung Mulu National Park, Sarawak II. Litterfall, litter standing crop and preliminary observations in herbivory. *Journal of Ecology*, **71**, 261–283.

Proctor, J., Anderson, J.M. & Vallack, H.W. (1983c). Comparative studies on soils and litterfall in forests at a range of altitudes on Gunung Mulu, Sarawak. *Malaysian Forester*, **46**, 60–76.

Proctor, J., Philipps, C., Duff, G. K., Heaney, A. & Robertson, F.M. (1989). Ecological studies on Gunung Silam, a small ultrabasic mountain in Sabah, Malaysia II. Some forest processes, *Journal of Ecology*, **77** (in press).

Tanner, E.V.J. (1985). Jamaican montane forests: nutrient capital and cost of growth. *Journal of Ecology*, **73**, 553–568.

Weaver, P.L., Medina, E., Pool, D., Dugger, K., Gonzales–Liboy, J. & Cuevas, E. (1986). Ecological observations in the dwarf cloud forest of the Luquillo Mountains in Puerto Rico. *Biotropica*, **18**, 79–85.

Whitmore, T.C. (1984). *Tropical Rain Forests of the Far East*, 2nd edn. Clarendon Press, Oxford.

Wiegert, G.R. (1970). Effects of ionising radiation on leaf fall, decomposition and litter microarthropods of a montane rain forest. *A Tropical Rain Forest* (Ed. by H.T. Odum & R.I. Pigeon), pp. H-89–H-100. United States Atomic Energy Commission, Dale Ridge, Tennessee.

A bioassay study of soils in the Blue Mountains of Jamaica

J. R. HEALEY*

*Botany School, University of Cambridge,
Cambridge CB2 3EA*

SUMMARY

1 The fertility of two montane and two lowland soils was compared using the locally naturalized grass *Melinis minutiflora* as a bioassay species.

2 Total growth was similar on the montane and lowland soils. However, root growth was greater on the montane soils and shoot growth was greater on the lowland soils.

3 Lower availability of phosphorus in the montane soils was indicated by the mean foliar phosphorus concentrations of the montane soil bioassay plants which were 27% of those of the lowland soil plants.

4 Phosphorus and nitrogen fertilizer additions caused significant increases in growth of plants on the two montane soils. The largest percentage increase was in leaf growth.

5 Phosphorus addition greatly increased foliar phosphorus concentration. Addition of nitrogen, however, did not consistently cause an increase in foliar nitrogen concentration. Therefore, in this species foliar nitrogen concentration is a poor indicator of limitation to growth by low nitrogen availability.

6 Previous agricultural research using fertilizers provides evidence of limitations to growth by shortage of both phosphorus and nitrogen in Jamaican montane soils.

INTRODUCTION

The lower stature and productivity of most wet tropical montane forests compared with forests at lower altitudes have been the subject of much inconclusive research. Grubb (1977) reviewed the evidence that low availability of mineral nutrients limited growth at higher altitudes. This was the principal focus of Tanner's (1977) research in the Blue Mountains of Jamaica; however, he remained uncertain about the extent of the limitation to growth by low mineral nutrient availability.

Tanner compared four forest stands which were in close proximity, but on topographically different sites and which differed in their stature and productivity. He carried out three pot experiments which provided evidence that the rate of growth of the bioassay species was limited by shortage of phosphorus in the

---

*Present address: School of Agricultural and Forest Sciences, University College of North Wales, Bangor, Gwynedd, LL57 2UW.

montane forest soils. He found no evidence that growth was limited by shortage of any other mineral nutrient (including nitrogen).

Tanner also sampled the foliage of the tree species in his four forest sites. However, there were no consistent correlations between foliar concentrations of any mineral nutrient and the stature, rate of trunk growth or rate of litterfall of the forest at the site from which each sample was taken. Tanner (1986) compared his data of foliar mineral nutrient concentrations and of total mineral nutrient contents of the above-ground biomass with data from other tropical montane forests. On this basis he 'tentatively concluded' that "the relative impoverishment of the Jamaican Blue Mountain forests is probably not a result of poor mineral nutrient supply" (Tanner 1986).

It was decided to carry out a further bioassay experiment on the soils of these Blue Mountain forests because Tanner's bioassay studies, which had provided his strongest evidence for mineral nutrient (phosphorus) limitation to growth, had suffered from certain important shortcomings. As shown by Pigott & Taylor (1964), Rorison (1967) and Christie & Moorby (1975), the results of bioassays depend on the species used; the test plants used by Tanner were horticultural crops grown from New Zealand seed. The effects of differences in soil fertility on test plants are dependent on the environmental conditions under which an experiment is carried out (Lloyd & Pigott 1967; Peace & Grubb 1982); Tanner's bioassays were carried out at 170 m altitude in Kingston where the climate is different from the montane forests in temperature and humidity. Only a single lowland soil type was used in Tanner's bioassays and this was collected from a managed arboretum. The purpose of this study was to find out if a bioassay with an improved methodology would yield the same results.

The present bioassay differs from those of Tanner (1977) in that (a) a locally naturalized species was used that grows successfully in the Blue Mountains at a wide range of altitudes and on a wide variety of soil types, and (b) it was carried out in the Blue Mountains at a place where climatic conditions are similar to those in which the tested montane forest soils occur.

There were two objectives: (1) to compare the fertility for the test species of two montane soils with two lowland soils, and (2) to compare the extent to which the growth of the test species was limited by the availability of phosphorus and nitrogen in the soils from two types of montane forest which differed in stature and productivity. This was achieved by means of experimental phosphorus and nitrogen fertilizer additions. The results allowed an assessment to be made of the extent to which the differences in fertility between the lowland and montane soils were accounted for by the lower availability of nitrogen and phosphorus in the montane soils.

METHODS

Soils

The soils from four different locations in the Blue Mountain region were compared. The two montane soils were collected from Mull Ridge forest and Col forest on the eastern ridge of John Crow Peak (18°05′N, 76°40′W) at an altitude of 1550 m where the mean annual rainfall is about 2500 mm. Tanner (1977) described these two forest types and tested their highly organic, acid soils in his bioassays. Mull Ridge forest is an Upper Montane rain forest with a tree canopy height of 8–13 m. The nearby Col forest has a canopy height of 12–18 m, higher productivity and other features which allow it to be classified as impoverished Lower Montane rain forest (Grubb & Tanner 1976). The Col forest was referred to as Gap forest by Tanner (1977, 1980a,b, 1986). The term col (another English name for a topographical depression in a ridge) is used here instead of gap to avoid confusion with forest canopy gaps.

The two lowland soils were collected from locations at the base of the southern slopes of the Blue Mountains, both 13 km south-west of the montane sites and where the mean annual rainfall is about 1500 mm. The Hope soil was collected from disturbed hillside woodland at an altitude of 360 m in the Hope River Valley and the Mona soil was collected from the arboretum of the University of the West Indies at an altitude of 170 m on the Liguanea plain (this was the location from which Tanner (1977) collected lowland soil for his bioassays).

The two montane soils were derived from Purple Volcanic rocks of the Cretaceous Blue Mountain Volcanic group. The Hope soil was derived from rocks of the Wagwater Formation, which was formed by the deposition of Blue Mountain Volcanic rocks by fast flowing rivers in the Lower Eocene. The Mona soil was derived from Pleistocene alluvium deposited from the Blue Mountains (Geological Survey of Jamaica 1974). Characteristics of the four soils are given in Table 1.

TABLE 1. Characteristics of the four soils used in the bioassay experiment described in this paper. The last four rows are from Tanner (1977)

Soil type	Mona	Hope	Mull Ridge	Col
Altitude (m)	180	360	1550	1550
Mean pH	7.9	7.5	4.3	4.3
Soil density	1.39	1.28	0.51	0.47
(dry weight/fresh volume) (g ml^{-1})				
Organic carbon (% dry weight)	—	—	29.2	9.0
Total nitrogen (% dry weight)	—	—	1.67	0.52
Nitrogen mineralization after incubation for 40 days:				
NH$_4$ (mg N kg^{-1} day^{-1})	—	—	+0.60	−0.53
NO$_3$ (mg N kg^{-1} day^{-1})	—	—	+3.40	+1.30

The test species

The species used in the bioassay was *Melinis minutiflora* Beauv. (Poaceae), commonly known in Jamaica as Molasses Grass or Wynne Grass. This species is native to tropical Africa, principally on open hillsides between the altitudes of 950 m and 2500 m in Uganda and Tanzania (Snowdon 1953).

M. minutiflora is a useful high-yielding fodder grass (Eggeling 1947; Motta 1952) that introduced to Jamaica in 1920 (Barnett 1936) and it is now most abundant in the Blue Mountain region where it is dominant in cleared and abandoned areas between 600 m and 1700 m altitude.

M. minutiflora is a perennial with branched, leafy, spreading and ascending culms which often root from the lower nodes. Since it is a successful, fast-growing, early successional species it should be responsive to the availability of mineral nutrients (Parrish & Bazzaz 1982).

The location of the bioassay

The bioassay was carried out at Cinchona Botanic Garden, which is 2.5 km south-south-east of the montane forest sites, at an altitude of 1490 m, and has a mean annual rainfall of 2230 mm. The environmental conditions were within the range encountered at soil level between understorey and gaps in the forests.

Experimental procedure

Soil was collected from 0–10 cm depth at five sites at each of the four locations and immediately sealed in polythene sacks. Subsamples of the soil from each collection site were individually sealed in polythene bags and kept for later estimation of pH (following Allen, Grimshaw & Rowland (1976)) and soil density (dry weight/fresh volume). The rest of the soil was transported to Cinchona Botanic Garden where the soil from each of the four locations was separately mixed and sieved through a 0.5 cm mesh. Although this process undoubtedly affected soil fertility it was used to reduce variation within the test soils.

Within 3 days of collection, accurately measured 370 ml samples of each soil were placed to a depth of 10 cm in labelled polythene plant pots of 7 cm diameter. Seventeen pots were filled with each of the two lowland soils and 51 (17 × 3) with each of the two montane soils.

Horizontal stems of *M. minutiflora* were collected from the side of a track 1 km north of Cinchona Botanic Garden and cut into equal (10 cm) sections, each bearing one node with short roots (0.5–3 cm in length) and one node with a leaf. Two randomly selected cuttings were planted in each pot of soil. The pots were placed at random, on a wooden surface, under a single layer of fine-mesh shade cloth. They were watered daily with river water of pH 7.2 from the Cinchona supply, which is taken from a catchment underlain by Cretaceous volcanic and Tertiary igneous intrusive rocks. Boon, Jupp & Lee (1986) found that the concentrations of mineral ions in river water from another Blue Mountain catchment underlain by similar rock types were low. Furthermore, they found a very low concentration of soluble nitrate in water collected 5 km downstream of the Cinchona supply (0.043 mg l^{-1}).

After 4 and 12 days the pots were re-examined and if both cuttings in a pot appeared healthy one was removed. Twenty-three days after planting the number of cuttings was reduced to one in all the remaining pots. Then the pots of each of the two montane soils were randomly divided into three groups of 17; one group of each was left as an unfertilized control, one group was fertilized with phosphorus (50 mg Na_3PO_4 dissolved in 10 ml water per pot) and the other was fertilized with nitrate-nitrogen (100 mg $NaNO_3$ dissolved in 10 ml of water per pot). Ten millilitres of water were also added to each unfertilized pot. All the pots were re-randomized. These fertilizations and re-randomizations were repeated 15 days later.

The total fertilization rates were equivalent to 18.9 mg phosphorus per pot and 33.0 mg nitrogen per pot. These correspond to rates of 43 kg P ha^{-1} and 75 kg N ha^{-1} at a soil depth equal to that in the pots (10 cm).

The bioassay plants were harvested 94 days after planting (i.e. 71 days after initial fertilization). Soil was carefully washed off the roots and the plants were dried at 100 °C. The dry weights of the leaf blades, stems (including leaf sheaths) and roots of each plant were measured and the number of leaves counted.

None of the plants had sufficient leaf blade material for individual analysis of mineral nutrient concentrations. The leaf blades of each treatment group were bulked, mixed and divided into two samples, both of which were analysed for foliar phosphorus and nitrogen concentration (two was the maximum number of samples obtained for three of the eight groups). Each sample was dried at 105 °C, ground and digested in a sulphuric acid–peroxide mixture. In half of each sample the phosphate ion concentration was determined by colorimetry using an automated indophenol blue method. The other half was neutralized with sodium hydroxide and the ammonium ion concentration was determined using an automated colorimetric method which employed citrate buffer, salicylate and DIC (sodium dichloroisocyanurate and sodium hydroxide).

During the design of the experiment, particular contrasts between the different treatments were planned: firstly between the four locations using the unfertilized control plants (lowland versus montane, Mona versus Hope, Mull Ridge versus Col), and secondly between the nitrogen addition or phosphorus addition treatments and the control treatment for each of the two montane soils. The differences in numbers of replicates caused by mortality of the test plants defeated the objective of making these contrasts orthogonal. Therefore the contrasts were made by the modified t-test procedure specified for samples of unequal sizes (Snedecor & Cochran 1980). These contrasts were carried out on leaf, stem, root, total dry weights and leaf number.

RESULTS

Comparison of the unfertilized plants on the montane and lowland soils

The mean total weights of the unfertilized plants on the four soil types were similar (Table 2). However, the plants on the montane soils had a significantly greater root weight (Table 3) and consequently a much higher root weight ratio (Table 2). Conversely, the lowland soil plants had a significantly larger number of leaves, leaf weight (and therefore leaf weight ratio) and a larger stem weight.

An explanation for the biomass results seems to be provided by a comparison of the foliar mineral nutrient concentrations of the plants (Table 2). Although there was no clear difference in foliar nitrogen concentrations, the plants on the montane soils had much lower foliar phosphorus concentrations (on average 27% of those of the lowland soil plants) and much lower total weights of foliar phosphorus (on average 17% of those of the lowland plants). It is probable that the lower leaf weights of the montane soil plants were caused by phosphorus shortage and possible that their higher root weights were a response to phosphorus shortage.

TABLE 2. The dry weight yields (means and standard errors) and amounts of foliar mineral nutrients of the bioassay plants in the eight experimental groups. Foliar nitrogen and phosphorus concentrations were measured in two bulked samples per group; the mean concentration and the deviation of each of the two samples from this mean are shown

Region		Lowland		Montane					
Soil type		Mona	Hope	Mull Ridge			Col		
Treatment		Control	Control	Control	+P	+N	Control	+P	+N
Sample size (number of plants alive at harvest)		9	12	16	13	15	12	15	14
Dry weights (mg)									
Leaf blades	Mean	100	128	70	148	111	75	125	123
	SE	14	17	8	21	13	14	14	14
Stems and	Mean	567	593	472	728	519	473	607	616
leaf sheaths	SE	68	81	68	92	67	64	88	63
Roots	Mean	133	139	294	377	313	188	358	345
	SE	25	16	41	43	38	24	57	26
Total	Mean	800	860	836	1254	942	736	1091	1084
	SE	103	107	113	142	109	99	147	99
Leaf weight ratio		0.125	0.149	0.084	0.118	0.118	0.102	0.115	0.113
Stem weight ratio		0.709	0.690	0.565	0.581	0.551	0.643	0.556	0.568
Root weight ratio		0.166	0.162	0.352	0.301	0.332	0.255	0.328	0.318
Leaf number	Mean	6.6	8.0	5.0	9.9	6.0	5.8	9.5	6.3
	SE	0.5	1.1	0.4	1.2	0.4	0.7	0.8	0.6
Foliar P (% dry weight)	Mean	0.323	0.196	0.072	0.180	0.062	0.066	0.185	0.077
	Deviation from mean	0.008	0.002	0.001	0.017	0.010	0.008	0.005	0.000
Weight of foliar P (mg)	Mean	0.323	0.251	0.050	0.266	0.069	0.050	0.231	0.095
Foliar N (% dry weight)	Mean	1.74	1.61	2.05	1.63	1.95	1.75	1.82	1.89
	Deviation from mean	0.00	0.02	0.11	0.04	0.01	0.05	0.02	0.03
Weight of foliar N (mg)	Mean	1.74	2.06	1.44	2.41	2.16	1.31	2.28	2.32

TABLE 3. Statistical analysis of the results of the bioassay. The contrasts between the means were carried out by a modified *t*-test according to procedures specified for samples of unequal sizes (Snedecor & Cochran 1980) ($p < 0.05$ (∗), <0.01 (∗∗), <0.001 (∗∗∗))

(a) Sums of squares

	Degrees of freedom	Leaf weight	Stem weight	Root weight	Total weight	Leaf number
Treatment	7	0.070	0.689	0.826	2.801	319.9
Residual	98	0.276	7.534	1.961	18.604	808.0
Total	105	0.346	8.223	2.787	21.405	1127.9

(b) Contrasts between the four control treatments with no mineral nutrient additions

	Leaf weight	Stem weight	Root weight	Total weight	Leaf number
Montane vs Lowland	∗∗	N.S.	∗∗	N.S.	∗
Mona vs Hope	N.S.	N.S.	N.S.	N.S.	N.S.
Mull Ridge vs Col	N.S.	N.S.	∗	N.S.	N.S.

(c) Contrasts between the mineral nutrient addition and control treatments of the montane soils

	Leaf weight	Stem weight	Root weight	Total weight	Leaf number
Mull Ridge: +P > control	∗∗∗	∗	N.S.	∗	∗∗∗
Mull Ridge: +N > control	∗	N.S.	N.S.	N.S.	N.S.
Col: +P > control	∗∗	N.S.	∗∗	∗	∗∗
Col: +N > control	∗∗	N.S.	∗∗	∗	N.S.

The effects of mineral nutrient additions to the montane soils

Phosphorus addition significantly increased the total dry weight of the plants on both montane soils (Tables 2 and 3). The largest percentage increases were in leaf weight and leaf number (leaf weight ratio was also increased). Increasing the supply of phosphorus apparently reduced the constraint on leaf growth imposed by phosphorus shortage. Phosphorus addition significantly increased the root weight of the plants on the Col soil. However, the effect of phosphorus addition on root weight was less uniform than its effect on leaf weight: root weight ratio was increased on the Col soil but decreased on the Mull Ridge soil (Table 2).

Addition of nitrogen also increased the growth of the bioassay plants, especially on the Col soil (Table 2). Therefore shortage of nitrogen was limiting the growth of the plants on both montane soils. The most significant effect of nitrogen addition on both montane soils was the increase in leaf weight (Table 3).

The failure of phosphorus or nitrogen addition to reduce the root weight ratio of the montane soil plants to values close to those of the lowland soil plants provides no support for the hypothesis that the difference in root weight ratios was caused solely by a greater shortage of these two mineral nutrients in the montane soils. Other differences in soil properties do offer possible explanations: the greater density of the more mineral, lowland soils (Table 1) might have provided a physical constraint to root growth and the soils might have had very different water relations. Such factors might have limited the total biomass reached by the plants growing on the lowland soils, counteracting a greater availability of mineral nutrients.

Examination of the foliar nutrient concentrations of the fertilized montane soil plants showed that the promotion of growth by phosphorus addition was accompanied by a large increase in foliar phosphorus to concentrations of about two and a half times greater on average than the unfertilized plants (Table 2). This brought their concentrations and total amounts of foliar phosphorus close to those of the lowland soil plants. These results are compatible with the hypothesis that the low foliar phosphorus concentrations in the unfertilized plants on the montane soils were linked to the physiological limitation of their growth, e.g. by low concentrations of inorganic phosphate in photosynthesizing leaf cells. However, the promotion of growth by nitrogen addition was accompanied by no consistent change in foliar nitrogen concentration (Table 2). Foliar nitrogen concentration is a poor indicator for this species of the extent to which the growth of a plant is limited by nitrogen shortage. Therefore, for the comparison of the four soil types, there were no good grounds for rejecting the hypothesis that the growth of the plants on the montane soils was more limited by nitrogen shortage than the growth of the lowland soil plants.

Leaf blades consisted of less than 15% of the dry weight of the plants in all treatments (Table 2) and the foliar nitrogen concentrations may reflect the internal distribution of nitrogen between different organs ('allocation') as much as the total amount of nitrogen taken up by the plants. Many plant species closely regulate foliar nitrogen concentrations irrespective of soil nitrogen availability (Nye & Tinker 1969; Christie & Moorby 1975). In addition, as pointed out by Jarrell & Beverly (1981), differences in foliar mineral nutrient concentrations may not be linked to the amount of mineral nutrients taken up by plants because of 'dilution effects'. There is some evidence for this in the present study in the results of nitrogen and phosphorus fertilization of Mull Ridge soil plants (Table 2). The addition of one mineral nutrient produced an increase in the weight of the second mineral nutrient in the leaves, but it caused an even greater increase in total leaf weight, so the net effect was a decrease in the foliar concentration of the second mineral nutrient. The addition of nitrogen to the Mull Ridge soil even caused a dilution of foliar nitrogen in the bioassay plants.

The results support the suggestion by Jarrell & Beverly (1981) that mineral nutrient concentration data should not be used alone as evidence for the degree of limitation to growth by shortage of particular mineral nutrients. They should only be used in conjunction with evidence of the total amount of the mineral nutrient taken up by the plants and with evidence of the response of the plants to an increase in the availability of the mineral nutrient.

DISCUSSION

Comparison with earlier bioassay experiments

The results support the evidence for limitation to growth by phosphorus shortage in these montane soils found by Tanner (1977) in his bioassays. However, the results of the nitrogen addition experiment of the present study provide the first clear evidence for limitation to growth by nitrogen shortage in these montane soils. These results differ from those of Tanner (1977) which led him to conclude that, for his bioassay plants growing on the montane soils, "nitrogen shortage is not limiting their growth". *Amaranthus viridis* L. plants growing on Mull Ridge soil showed no response in shoot dry weight to the addition of nitrogen, and the foliar nitrogen concentrations of *Brassica pekinensis* skeels plants growing on lowland soil were only 30–45% of those of plants growing on montane soils. However, *B. pekinensis* reached a mean biomass on the lowland soil more than 17 times greater than on the montane soils and the total amount of nitrogen taken up by the lowland soil plants was between five and nine times greater than that taken up by plants on the montane soils. Therefore the difference in foliar nitrogen concentrations could be accounted for by a dilution effect. It is improbable that these two horticultural crop species had low nitrogen requirements.

The environmental conditions in which a bioassay is carried out could be expected to influence soil chemical and biological processes, especially the mineralization of nitrogen and its subsequent mobility (Lloyd & Pigott 1967). The pots of the present bioassay were watered daily and were in a similar cool, humid climate to that of the forests from which the montane soils were collected; it therefore seems improbable that soil dryness limited the availability of nitrogen.

The most probable explanation for the differences between the results of this bioassay and those of Tanner (1977) is that the large amounts of organic nitrogen in the montane forest soils (Table 1) underwent accelerated mineralization during Tanner's bioassays in Kingston where the mean annual temperature is 8 °C higher than in the montane forests.

The evidence of the present bioassay for limitation of growth by nitrogen availability in the montane forest soils supports Vitousek (1984). Based on a comparative study, in which he used the data of mineral nutrient concentrations in litterfall measured by Tanner, Vitousek implied that productivity in these Jamaican montane rain forests was limited by the availability of nitrogen.

Mycorrhizas

The uptake of mineral nutrients by bioassay plants could be severely limited by the absence of mycorrhizas. To investigate this possibility, small plants of *M. minutiflora* were collected from seven variously disturbed sites between Cinchona Botanic Garden and the forest from where the montane test soils were collected. All of the plants were found to have heavy mycorrhizal infections with copious vesicles or arbuscles or both .Vesicular-arbuscular mycorrhizas of similar appearance have been observed in 76% of a wide variety of tree seedlings sampled from the montane forest (J. R. Healey unpublished). Therefore it is unlikely that the montane forest test soils would have lacked appropriate mycorrhizal inocula for the *M. minutiflora* bioassay plants and unlikely that these plants were short of phosphorus because of lack of mycorrhizas.

Differences between the Mull Ridge and Col forest soils

The fertilizer addition treatments of this bioassay provide good evidence that the availability of nitrogen was more limiting to growth on the Col soil than on the Mull Ridge soil and that the availability of phosphorus was more limiting to growth on the Mull Ridge soil. Nitrogen fertilization caused a greater increase in the weights of stems, leaves and roots in the Col plants than in the Mull Ridge plants and phosphorus fertilization caused a greater increase in the weights of stems and leaves in the Mull Ridge plants (Table 2). These conclusions are supported by the following additional evidence.

For phosphorus: Following nitrogen addition the Col plants had a much greater total amount and concentration of foliar phosphorus than the Mull Ridge plants (Table 2).

For nitrogen:

1 Tanner's (1977) data show that the Mull Ridge soil has a much higher total nitrogen concentration and much higher rates of nitrogen mineralization than the Col soil (Table 1). Therefore the Mull Ridge soil would be expected to have more nitrogen available for plant growth.

2 The unfertilized Mull Ridge plants had a higher total weight of foliar nitrogen than the Col plants despite the fact that their total leaf weight was less.

3 Nitrogen addition caused a larger increase in the total weight and concentration of foliar nitrogen in the Col plants than the Mull Ridge plants (in which foliar nitrogen concentration was reduced).

The clearest difference in growth between the unfertilized Mull Ridge and Col plants was the significantly higher root weight of the Mull Ridge plants (Tables 2 and 3); they also had a much higher root weight ratio. Phosphorus addition to the Mull Ridge plants considerably reduced their root weight ratio, and therefore the high root weight ratio of the unfertilized Mull Ridge plants might have been primarily caused by phosphorus shortage.

The forest stands from which these two soils were collected occupy two of the four adjacent sites compared by Tanner (1977). The Mull Ridge forest is shorter in stature (it has a canopy height of 8–13 m compared with the 12–18 m of the Col forest (Grubb & Tanner 1976)), it has a lower rate of increase of above-ground tree biomass (0.10 kg m^{-2} year^{-1} compared with 0.35 kg m^{-2} year^{-1} of the Col forest (Tanner 1980a)) and it has a lower rate of litterfall (0.55 kg m^{-2} year^{-1} compared with 0.65 kg m^{-2} year^{-1} of the Col forest (Tanner 1980b)).

The present bioassay provides evidence that the availability of phosphorus for plant growth was less in the soil collected from the forest with lower stature and above-ground productivity (Mull Ridge forest). It can be argued, however, that the infertility of soils measured with an agricultural, bioassay species may have little relevance to the limitation of growth of the indigenous forest trees. If these trees are tolerant of low mineral nutrient availability they may not be responsive to variation in soil fertility (Mitchell & Chandler 1939; Bradshaw *et al.* 1960, 1964). However, higher soil fertility would selectively favour individuals of the same or different species that were more able to increase their growth in response to the increased availability of mineral nutrients. If such higher soil fertility were to persist for at least one regeneration cycle, this process of selection could result in increased productivity of the forest. In this case, the greater availability of phosphorus in the Col forest soil than the Mull Ridge forest soil indicated by this bioassay could be the cause of the higher productivity of the Col forest.

Tanner (1977) tentatively concluded that the differences between the two forest types in stature and above-ground productivity were not a result of differences in the availability of phosphorus or nitrogen. This conclusion was largely based on measurements of tree foliar mineral nutrient concentrations which, as has been shown above, provide weak evidence against the limitation of growth by the availability of mineral nutrients.

Existing knowledge of the fertility of Jamaican montane soils

Between 1945 and 1970 a large number of agricultural fertilizer experiments were carried out on a wide variety of Jamaican soil types. These showed that the degree of limitation of yield by particular mineral nutrients depends on soil type and ultimately on its parent material. Slow-growing, low-statured, upper montane forests in Jamaica occur on soils derived from both white limestone (John Crow Mountains) and shale, volcanic or igneous intrusive (Blue Mountains) rocks. None the less, the results of the agricultural experiments are consistent with the hypothesis that limitation to growth by the availability of nitrogen and phosphorus is greater at higher altitudes. Two of these studies were conducted on montane soils in the Blue Mountain region.

(a) At four locations with different soil types in the Yallahs Valley area on the south side of the mountains, experimental plots of *Daucus carota* L. (carrots) were fertilized with nitrogen, phosphorus and potassium in a fully factorial design (Sargeant 1954). The soil type at the highest altitude of the four (1100 m) was the shale-derived Hall's Delight Channery Clay Loam.

The Hall's Delight Channery Clay Loam was the most nitrogen limited of the four soil types (nitrogen fertilization caused a 150% increase in carrot yield) and also the most phosphorus limited (phosphorus fertilization caused a 140% increase in yield). This response to phosphorus fertilization was greater than all of those obtained with a wide variety of crops on soils derived from the same shale rock type (the Richmond Formation) at Orange River (34 km distant and at an altitude of 350 m). The only one of the four soil types to show an increase in carrot yield following potassium fertilization was that derived from limestone.

(b) The second montane fertilizer study was also carried out on Hall's Delight Channery Clay Loam soil. The study site was at and altitude of 1050 m and 1.5 km south-west of the Mull Ridge and Col forests. Coffee bushes were fertilized with nitrogen, phosphorus and potassium in a factorial design (Moss 1963; Moss & Brown 1973). During the first 4 years of bearing, the yield of coffee beans was greatly increased by nitrogen fertilization (the average increase was 320% and this was significant at the $p < 0.01$ level). This is by far the greatest response to nitrogen addition reported for field experiments on any soil type conducted in Jamaica. No effects of phosphorus or potassium fertilization on yield were detected in this study.

A pot bioassay comparison of six Jamaican soil types using *Lycopersicon esculentum* Miller (tomatoes) and *Oryza sativa* L. (hill rice cultivar) planted at a density of one plant per 200 g of soil was carried out by Hewitt (1950). One of the six soils was derived from the same volcanic rock type as the montane soils of the present bioassay and two of the other soils were derived from shales. The growth of the bioassay plants on these three soils was greatly increased by additions of nitrogen and phosphorus (but not by potassium) fertilizer.

The limitation of growth of *Melinis minutiflora* in the present bioassay by nitrogen and phosphorus shortage is consistent with the results of this previous work.

CONCLUSION

The present bioassay has provided new evidence for the limitation of plant growth in montane forest soils by the availability of phosphorus and nitrogen. It cannot, however, be emphasized too strongly that bioassay results are dependent on the species used and the methodology employed (the differences between the present results and those of Tanner (1977) amply demonstrate this point). Although the present study represents an improvement in methodology over previous investigations, there are still limits to the extent to which its results can be used to draw firm conclusions about the relative fertility of the tested soils. Therefore there is a clear need for further corroborative bioassay studies in which the responses of more than one species grown under the same conditions can be compared.

The primary requirement is for a comparison using indigenous tree species that are frequent in mature forests on a wide variety of soil types and at a wide range of altitudes in Jamaica. Such species would be predicted to be able to benefit from an increase in the fertility of an infertile forest soil. Of these widespread species, *Alchornea latifolia* Sw., *Clethra occidentalis* (L.) Kuntze and *Turpinia occidentalis* (Sw.) G. Don have the highest seedling growth rates in the montane forests (J. R. Healey unpublished) and would be the best candidates for a bioassay.

In order to compare properly the extents to which montane and lowland soils differ in their availability of phosphorus and nitrogen for plant growth, it would be necessary to carry out a bioassay experiment with a complete factorial design. This would require phosphorus and nitrogen fertilization treatments of all the soil types, which would permit the proper statistical testing of the interactions between phosphorus and nitrogen addition and soil type. The research carried out on Jamaican montane soils to date has not precluded the possibility that other mineral nutrients limit plant growth. Therefore a further bioassay should include a complete mineral nutrient fertilizer treatment to determine if this causes a greater increase in growth than the phosphorus and nitrogen treatment. The effects of mineral nutrient balance are complex and it would also be desirable to test the effects of different amounts of added mineral nutrients.

In the present bioassay with its limited replication the soil from each site was mixed and sieved in order to reduce within-treatment variability. However, soil fertility is considerably influenced by the physical structure of the soil as well as by its chemical and biological composition; disturbing the soil may accelerate mineralization. To minimize this source of error and to achieve a better sampling of the variation in the fertility of the soil within each forest type, a further study should use a larger number of randomly sampled, large, intact soil cores.

Finally, there should be a sufficient number of independent samples so that the analysis will not be weakened by the mortality of some bioassay plants. The equalization of the number of samples in each group by the random exclusion of excess samples would permit a simpler and more powerful statistical analysis of the data than was possible in the present study. Clearly a comprehensive bioassay study would be a large-scale undertaking.

In order to investigate properly the relationship between forest productivity and soil fertility it would be necessary to carry out fertilizer trials in the field. The four adjacent stands of montane forest with different above-ground productivity and stature that have been studied in detail by Tanner (1977, 1980a,b) would provide good sites for such an experiment. The value of the bioassay study proposed above would be greatly increased if the field trial was conducted using seedlings of the same species. It would be interesting to test the hypothesis arising from the *M. minutiflora* bioassay that the Mull Ridge forest has higher below-ground productivity than the Col forest and that this is a result of lower availability of phosphorus.

ACKNOWLEDGEMENTS

I thank Edmund Tanner for initiating and designing the experiment and for other guidance and practical assistance, Professor George Sidrak for making available facilities at the Department of Botany, University of the West Indies, Dale Hunter for harvesting and posting the plants, Lloyd Stamp for watering them, the Directors of the Forestry Department, Public Gardens Division and Cinchona Botanic Garden, Jamaica, for permission to carry out the study, and Adrian Newton, Lynn Davy and Peter Grubb for constructive criticism of the manuscript.

REFERENCES

Allen, S.E., Grimshaw, H.M. & Rowland, A.P. (1976). Chemical analysis. *Methods in Plant Ecology* (Ed. by P.D. Moore & S.B. Chapman), pp. 285–344. Blackwell Scientific Publications, Oxford.
Barnett, W.L. (1936). Wynne Grass. *The Journal of the Jamaica Agricultural Society*, **40**, 119–120.
Boon, P.J., Jupp, B.P. & Lee, D.G. (1986). The benthic ecology of rivers in the Blue Mountains

(Jamaica) prior to construction of a water regulation scheme. *Archiv für Hydrobiologie, Supplement Monographische Beiträge,* **74**, 315–355.

Bradshaw, A.D., Chadwick, M.J., Jowett, D., Lodge, R.W. & Snaydon, R.W. (1960). Experimental investigations into the mineral nutrition of several grass species. III. Phosphate level. *Journal of Ecology,* **48**, 631–637.

Bradshaw, A.D., Chadwick, M.J., Jowett, D. & Snaydon, R.W. (1964). Experimental investigations into the mineral nutrition of several grass species. IV. Nitrogen level. *Journal of Ecology,* **52**, 665–676.

Christie, E.K. & Moorby, J. (1975). Physiological responses of semi-arid grasses. 1. The influence of phosphorus supply on growth and phosphorus absorption. *Australian Journal of Agricultural Research,* **26**, 423–436.

Eggeling, W.J. (1947). *An Annotated List of the Grasses of the Uganda Protectorate.* Department of Agriculture, Uganda, Entebbe.

Geological Survey of Jamaica (1974). *Geology Sheet 25, "Kingston", Jamaica 1:50,000.* Ministry of Mining and Natural Resources, Kingston, Jamaica.

Grubb, P.J. (1977). Control of forest growth and distribution on wet tropical mountains: with special reference to mineral nutrition. *Annual Review of Ecology and Systematics,* **8**, 83–107.

Grubb, P.J. & Tanner, E.V.J. (1976). The montane forests and soils of Jamaica: a reassessment. *Journal of the Arnold Arboretum,* **57**, 313–368.

Hewitt, C.W. (1950). Fertility test in pots on the major soil types of Jamaica. *Bulletin of the Department of Agriculture, Jamaica (New Series),* **47**, 72–77.

Jarrell, W.M. & Beverly, R.B. (1981). The dilution effect in plant nutrient studies. *Advances in Agronomy,* **34**, 197–224.

Lloyd, P.S. & Pigott, C.D. (1967). The influence of soil conditions on the course of succession on the chalk of southern England. *Journal of Ecology.* **70**, 127–150.

Mitchell, H.L. & Chandler, R.F. (1939). The nitrogen nutrition and growth of certain deciduous trees of northeastern United States. *The Black Rock Forest Bulletin,* **11**, 1–94.

Moss, R.I. (1963). Coffee fertilizer trial, Chestervale. *Bulletin of the Ministry of Agriculture and Lands, Jamaica (New Series),* **62**, 74–75.

Moss, R.I. & Brown, G.E. (1973). Coffee fertilizer trial. *Bulletin of the Ministry of Agriculture and Fisheries, Jamaica (New Series),* **63**, 242–248.

Motta, M.S. (1952). Grass evaluation experiment. *Bulletin of the Department of Agriculture, Jamaica (New Series),* **50**, 46–48.

Nye, P.H. & Tinker, P.B. (1969). The concept of a root demand coefficient. *Journal of Applied Ecology,* **6**, 293–300.

Parrish, J.A.D. & Bazzaz, F.A. (1982). Responses of plants from three successional communities to a nutrient gradient. *Journal of Ecology,* **70**, 233–248.

Peace, W.J.H. & Grubb, P.J. (1982). Interaction of light and mineral nutrient supply in the growth of *Impatiens parviflora. New Phytologist,* **90**, 127–150.

Pigott, C.D. & Taylor, K. (1964). The distribution of some woodland herbs in relation to the supply of nitrogen and phosphorus in the soil. *Journal of Ecology,* **52** (supplement), 175–185.

Rorison, I.H. (1967). A seedling bioassay on some soils in the Sheffield area. *Journal of Ecology,* **55**, 725–741.

Sargeant, V.A.L. (1954). Soils and fertilizers, Yallahs Valley. *Bulletin of the Department of Agriculture, Jamaica (New Series),* **53**, 72–73.

Snedecor, G.W. & Cochran, W.G. (1980). *Statistical Methods,* 7th edn, Iowa State University Press, Ames, Iowa, USA.

Snowdon, J.D. (1953). *The Grass Communities and Mountain Vegetation of Uganda.* The Crown Agents for the Colonies, London.

Tanner, E.V.J. (1977). Four montane rain forests of Jamaica: a quantitative characterization of the floristics, the soils and the foliar mineral levels, and a discussion of the interrelations. *Journal of Ecology,* **65**, 883–918.

Tanner, E.V.J. (1980a). Studies on the biomass and productivity in a series of montane rain forests in Jamaica. *Journal of Ecology,* **68**, 573–588.

Tanner, E.V.J. (1980b). Litterfall in montane rain forests of Jamaica and its relation to climate. *Journal of Ecology*, **68**, 833–848.

Tanner, E.V.J. (1986). Forests of the Blue Mountains and the Port Royal Mountains of Jamaica. *Forests of Jamaica* (Ed. by D.A. Thompson, P.K. Bretting & M. Humphreys), pp. 15–30. The Jamaican Society of Scientists and Technologists, Kingston, Jamaica.

Vitousek, P.M. (1984). Litterfall, nutrient cycling, and nutrient limitation in tropical forests. *Ecology*, **65**, 285–298.

Nutrient effects of modification of shifting cultivation in West Africa

A. S. R. JUO AND B. T. KANG

International Institute of Tropical Agriculture (IITA),
PMB 5320, Oyo Road, Ibadan, Nigeria

SUMMARY

1 Recycling of plant residues, fertilizer use and inclusion of trees and perennials in crop fields are key components in systems for improved food crop production on infertile soils in the forest regions of West Africa.

2 On Alfisols of pH 5.5 or higher in the forest and forest–savanna transitional zones, systems including food crop–cover crop rotation, minimum tillage and the judicial use of fertilizer can sustain yields on small farms for 10 years or more without reverting land to bush fallow. Interplanting leguminous trees such as *Leucaena leucocephala* with annual food crops is shown to improve food crop yields. The leguminous trees fix atmospheric nitrogen, recycle mineral nutrients from the subsoil, and prevent soil erosion and run-off water on sloping land.

3 On strongly leached acid soils (i.e. Ultisols and Oxisols) in high-rainfall regions, nutrient cycling and green manuring are less effective because of subsoil infertility. Intensive food crop production on such soils requires costly inputs of fertilizer and lime. However, experiments have shown that periodic application of small dosages of lime can sustain a moderate crop yield. Gradual saturation of subsoil horizons with calcium is a prerequisite for effective recycling of nutrients in agricultural systems in the high-rainfall region.

INTRODUCTION

When land is plentiful, shifting cultivation is a stable form of agriculture in tropical forest ecosystems. In an ideal case, a small patch of forest is cleared and cropped for 1 or 2 years followed by a fallow of 15 years or more. Fields are cleared manually, and stumps and roots are left in place to help water infiltration and rapid regrowth after the cropping cycle. Plant residues are burned to enhance mineralization of soil organic matter and to make surface soils less acidic (Nye & Greenland 1960).

In West Africa, true shifting cultivation is rare. The system has broken down during the last 50 years because of increasing pressure on land and governmental efforts to modernize the region's food crop agriculture. Consequently, this has resulted in an increased rate of deforestation and land degradation (Lal, Sanchez & Cummings 1986). On small family farms there has been a trend to more intensive cropping, shorter periods of fallow and additional nutrient inputs to sustain crop yield. On large-scale commercial farms, their development has involved mechanical land clearing, soil conservation, the use of fertilizers, pesticides, herbicides and heavy machinery. In either case, sustainability of a modified system depends on an understanding of the soil and the wise application of economic and ecological principles.

Much effort has been made recently to improve soil management and food crop production systems in West Africa. The recycling of plant residues, judicial use of fertilizer and systematic inclusion of trees and perennials in food crop systems are key research issues (Jaiyebo & Moore 1964; Fore & Okigbo 1974; Juo & Lal 1977; Kang, Wilson & Sipkens 1981; Kang & Juo 1986). This paper attempts to highlight recent progress in this field with special reference to some long-term studies at the International Institute of Tropical Agriculture (IITA) in Nigeria. Socioeconomic assessments of agricultural development in West Africa including shifting cultivation are numerous but beyond the scope of this paper.

SOILS AND CROPPING SYSTEMS

Soil nutrient scarcity is characteristic of many tropical forest ecosystems (Proctor 1983; Jordan 1985). In much of the earth's tropical rain forests, soil nutrient concentrations are low and trees recycle mineral nutrients from decomposed litter to meet a major portion of their nutrient requirements. The widespread rain forest kaolinitic Ultisols and Oxisols often have (in the upper 100 cm of soil) effective cation exchange capacity (CEC) values of less than 4 m-equiv. 100 g^{-1} and contain less than 0.5 m-equiv. 100 g^{-1} of exchangeable calcium (Juo 1985). Any attempt to alter such ecosystems for agricultural use should give special consideration to long-term consequences (Golley 1983).

Two major soil groups dominate the forest regions of West Africa. The slightly acidic (i.e. pH 5.5) kaolinitic, low-CEC Alfisols occur widely in the wet-dry tropics with semi-deciduous forest. The acidic (pH 5.5) kaolinitic, low-CEC Ultisols and Oxisols are found mainly in the rain forest coastal regions. For more intensive cultivation, the major constraints for the low-CEC Alfisols are soil erosion, compaction and acidification, whereas those for the Ultisols and Oxisols are multiple nutrient deficiencies and aluminium toxicity (Ahn 1970; Dudal 1980; Juo 1980; Kang & Juo 1983; Lal 1985). Some properties of selected West African soils are given in Table 1.

Traditional and modified cropping systems in tropical Africa have been reviewed by Okigbo & Greenland (1976). In the forest regions, common cropping systems generally involve mixed cropping of root crops such as cassava (*Manihot esculenta* Crantz) and yams (*Discorea* spp.) with cereals such as maize (*Zea mays* L.) and upland rice (*Oryza sativa* L.) in rotation with a short-term bush fallow. In the Alfisol areas, cocoa (*Theobroma cacao* L.) is a common tree crop in small farms. In the high-rainfall Ultisol areas, oil palm (*Elaeis guineensis* Jacq.) becomes more common. Commercial plantations of cocoa, oil palm, coffee (*Coffea arabica* L. and *C. canephora* Pierre ex Froehner (syn. *C. robusta* Linden)), banana (*Musa paradisiaca* L.) and rubber (*Hevea brasiliensis* Muell.) were introduced to the region during the last century and their success relies on the

TABLE 1. Chemical and physical properties of selected upland soils in West Africa under natural bush or secondary forest (*mean annual rainfall)

Horizon	Depth (cm)	pH$_{H2O}$ (log units)	Clay (%)	Silt (%)	Ca	Exchangeable cations Mg (m-equiv. 100 g^{-1})	Al	CEC (m-equiv. 100 g^{-1})
*Alfisol derived from gneisses, Ibadan, Nigeria (1250 mm)**								
A$_1$	0–12	6.5	15	18	5.20	1.31	0	6.99
IIB$_{2t}$	42–92	6.4	54	8	3.05	0.89	0	4.33
*Ultisol derived from gneisses, Sefula, Liberia (4500 mm)**								
A$_{11}$	0–11	4.4	11	8	0.23	0.18	0.13	3.48
B$_{2t}$	55–108	4.7	21	8	0.12	0.02	0.36	1.16
*Ultisol derived from coastal sediments, Benin, Nigeria (1800 mm)**								
A$_{11}$	0–14	5.5	21	5	1.50	0.48	0.13	2.29
B$_{22t}$	75–125	4.7	48	3	0.33	0.12	0.85	1.35
*Ultisol derived from coastal sediments, Onne, Nigeria (2420 mm)**								
A$_1$	0–15	4.2	18	16	0.26	0.09	1.83	2.86
B$_{22t}$	60–115	4.3	36	5	0.16	0.02	1.88	2.33

availability and cost of material inputs and an increasingly competitive world market.

The agricultural systems in West Africa continue to be influenced by the poor soil resources of the region; thus nutrient management plays a critical role in the modification of traditional systems for more intensive or permanent agriculture.

MANAGEMENT OF SOIL ORGANIC MATTER

Although the chemistry of soil organic matter and its effects on soil management have long been studied, the dynamics of organic matter under tropical environments are little known. The rapid rate of decomposition of plant residues and the humified soil organic matter under tropical conditions suggests that in cultivated fields frequent additions of plant residue are required to maintain adequate soil organic matter (Nye 1961; Jenkinson & Ayanaba 1977; Mueller-Harvey, Juo & Wild 1985).

For tropical soils containing mainly kaolin and quartz in the organic fraction, the supply of plant nutrients depends largely on the mineralization of soil organic matter. The beneficial effect of crop residues on crop yield has been demonstrated in a long-term continuous cropping of maize at Ibadan, Nigeria (Fig. 1). The annual return of crop residues as mulch was 5–6 t ha^{-1} from two crops per year. Returning crop residues maintained more soil organic carbon in mulched plots as compared with plots where the residues were removed (Fig. 2). However, the beneficial effect of crop residues diminished gradually after the fifth year of continuous cultivation (Kang & Juo 1986). Continuous maize monoculture on the kaolinitic Alfisol investigated resulted in a decline in soil organic matter, pH, effective CEC and exchangeable calcium and magnesium (Figs 2 and 3).

Some workers have investigated experimentally crop rotations that include a

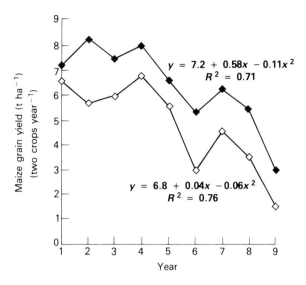

FIG. 1. Long-term effect of crop residue mulch on yield from continuous maize monoculture on a kaolinitic Alfisol cleared from secondary forest at Ibadan, Nigeria (a no-tillage system was used for seed bed preparation): ◆ maize stover was returned to the plot as mulch; ◇ maize stover was removed from the plot immediately after harvest (A. S. R. Juo unpublished).

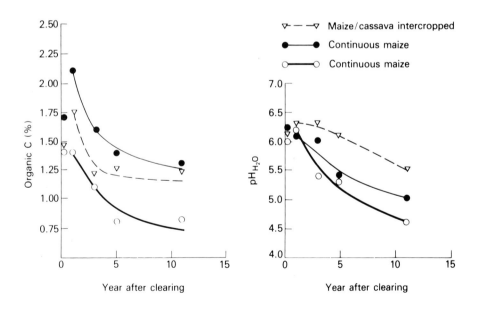

FIG. 2. Effect of continuous maize monoculture on soil pH and organic carbon content in an Alfisol cleared from secondary forest at Ibadan, Nigeria: ● maize stover was returned to the plot as mulch; ○ maize stover was removed from the plot after each harvest (A. S. R. Juo unpublished).

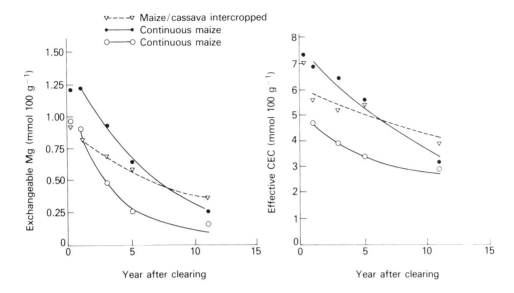

FIG. 3. Effect of continuous maize monoculture on exchangeable magnesium and effective CEC of an Alfisol cleared from secondary forest at Ibadan, Nigeria: ● maize stover was returned to the plot as mulch; ○ maize stover was removed from the plot after each harvest (A. S. R. Juo unpublished).

short period of managed fallow as alternative systems to shifting cultivation. Vine (1953), Jaiyebo & Moore (1964), Talineau *et al.* (1976), Juo (1981) and Wilson (1981) compared the effectiveness of leguminous cover crops (*Mucuna utilis* DC., *Pueraria phaseoloides* Benth., *Stylosanthes gracilis* Sw. and *Cajanus cajan* Millsp.), grasses (*Cynodon plectostachyus* L. and *Panicum maximum* Jacq.) and natural bush regrowth in restoring soil fertility of degraded Alfisols. The following conclusions may be drawn from these studies: (i) multi-species fallow, i.e. natural regrowth, is superior to fallow with single species; (ii) crop rotation including *Mucuna* and *Pueraria* as green manure can maintain a good crop yield (2–3 t ha^{-1} of maize) over 10 years or more without fertilizer application. However, additional nitrogen fertilizer for cereal crops such as maize is needed for higher yield (4–6 t ha^{-1}).

On the acid, leached soils in the high-rainfall region, the contributions of soil organic matter and green manuring to soil fertility are obscure. Organic matter on the surface of many Ultisols and Oxisols in rain forest ecosystems is predominantly aluminium-saturated at its cation exchange sites (Juo & Kamprath 1979). In traditional cultivation systems, the burning of plant residues is an essential practice to reduce soil acidity. Little is known regarding the accumulation, decomposition and mineralization of soil organic matter in acid, high-rainfall ecosystems and it is impossible to draw practical conclusions. Another major constraint to food crop agriculture on such soils is the low nutrient content of the subsoils. Field studies on Ultisols (pH 4.3) at IITA's substation at Onne (6°20'N.

7°30′E) in south-eastern Nigeria showed that as green manures or cover crops under an annual rainfall of 2420 mm, *Mucuna* and cowpea (*Vigna unguiculata* Walp.) are faster growing and produce better ground cover than *Pueraria*. Nevertheless, all three species have shallow and poor root growth because of the high acidity and low calcium in the subsoil. *Pueraria*, however, has the best nodulation in the acid soil (van der Kruijs *et al.* 1985).

EFFECTS OF FERTILIZERS AND LIME

To develop more intensive food crop production systems on the nutrient-depleted soil in West Africa, the use of chemical fertilizers is a necessity. Perhaps the most striking beneficial effects of fertilizers, lime and organic manure on crop yield were those demonstrated by Fore & Okigbo (1974) on an acid Ultisol at the Experimental Farm of the University of Nigeria at Nsukka (6°20′N, 7°30′E) in eastern Nigeria (Table 2). The surface layer of the soil (sandy loam) at the experimental site has 0.8% organic carbon, 0.25, 0.1 and 0.05 m-equiv. $100 \, g^{-1}$ of exchangeable calcium, magnesium and potassium, respectively and a pH of 4.6. Continuous cropping of maize and grain legumes on such poor soils would not be possible without the use of organic manure, lime and multi-element fertilizers.

TABLE 2. Effects of fertilizer, lime and farmyard manure on maize grain yield on an acid Ultisol in south-eastern Nigeria (Fore & Okigbo 1974)

Treatment	Grain yield $(t \, ha^{-1})$
Control	116
N, P, K, Mg	2214
N, P, K, Mg + lime	4037
N, P, K, Mg + manure	4857
N, P, K, Mg + lime + manure	7086

In cereals production systems, soil management practices consisting of crop rotation, minimum tillage and fertilizer can sustain crop yield on small farms for long periods without reverting the land to bush fallow. Results from two long-term trials conducted on an Alfisol (Fig. 4) and an Ultisol (Fig. 5) attest to these conclusions. For both soils, land was manually cleared from secondary bush fallow, and fertilizers were applied only to the main-season maize in a maize–cowpea rotation. At the Alfisol site (pH 6.5), nitrogen was limiting for maize after the second year and urea or calcium ammonium nitrate was applied at the rate of $60–120 \, kg \, N \, ha^{-1}$ to each maize crop during the second year and onward. Maintenance rates of phosphorus $(30 \, kg \, ha^{-1})$, potassium and $5 \, kg \, ha^{-1}$ sulphur were applied each year to the maize crop to ensure an adequate supply. Magnesium sulphate $(10 \, kg \, Mg \, ha^{-1})$ and zinc sulphate $(2 \, kg \, Zn \, ha^{-1})$ were added every 2 years. The nutrient inputs maintained good maize grain yield during the 12-year cropping period. At the high-rainfall Ultisol site (pH 4.3), lime was added to neutralize the acidity caused by high concentration of exchangeable

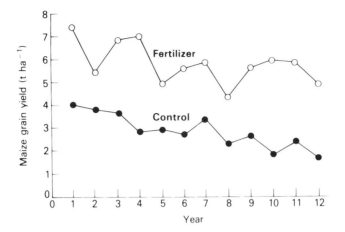

FIG. 4. Effect of nutrient inputs on maize yield in a maize–cowpea rotation on an Alfisol at Ibadan, Nigeria. Adequate rates of nitrogen, phosphorus, potassium, magnesium, sulphur and zinc were applied to each maize crop based on results from soil testing and plant nutrient analysis. The cowpea crop received no fertilizer (B. T. Kang unpublished).

aluminium and to supply calcium. Continuous maize–cowpea rotation with periodic applications of relatively small quantities of lime (i.e. 300–500 kg of calcium carbonate per hectare) maintained good levels of maize and cowpea yields (Fig. 5).

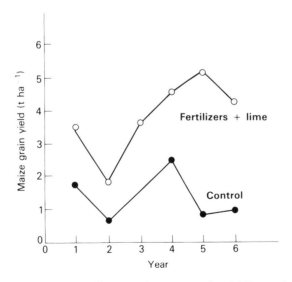

FIG. 5. Effect of nutrient inputs and lime amendments on maize yield in a maize–cowpea rotation on an acid Ultisol (typic paleudult) at Onne, Nigeria. Adequate rates of nitrogen, phosphorus, potassium, magnesium, sulphur and zinc fertilizers were applied to each maize crop based on results from soil testing and plant nutrient analysis. A small addition of ground limestone (0.5 t ha^{-1} calcium carbonate equivalent) was used every 2 years (B. T. Kang unpublished).

Cassava is a major food staple in West Africa grown either in a mixture with maize or upland rice or planted in a rotation as the last crop before bush fallow. The use of chemical fertilizers in such systems is rare, and yields from farmers' fields are generally low, ranging from 5 to 10 t ha^{-1} of fresh tubers (Ofori 1973). Cassava is known for its ability to survive and produce under a wide range of adverse conditions such as high soil acidity, low nutrient supply and drought. Improved cassava varieties, recently developed, are able to attain yields of 20–40 t ha^{-1} but require a nutrient input. In more intensive systems, potassium is probably limiting cassava production (Juo 1986). In continuously cropped fields, cassava generally shows no response to potassium application in kaolinitic soils until surface-soil exchangeable potassium drops below 0.15 m-equiv. 100 g^{-1} (Obigbesan 1977; Juo & Grimme 1980; Kang & Okele 1984). In the strongly acidic Ultisols in the high-rainfall regions, potassium and magnesium and the interaction between nitrogen and potassium are limiting. Field experiments on potassium-deficient Ultisols have shown that a best yield of 25 t ha^{-1} can be achieved at application rates of 50 kg N and 40 kg K ha^{-1} (Kang 1984; Juo 1986). When other nutrients are not limiting, a shortage of potassium often causes cassava to produce large amounts of leaves and stems but low tuber yield.

It should be emphasized that in the kaolinitic and sandy soils in West Africa, phosphorus deficiency is widespread. Phosphorus fixation is not a major constraint. Thus to sustain crop yield, an annual application of 10–30 kg P ha^{-1} is generally adequate (Juo & Fox 1977; Fox & Kang 1978).

The merit of liming in tropical agricultural systems deserves special attention. In temperate regions, liming has been an integral part of intensive cereal–legume rotation systems on acid soils. In West Africa, lime sources are scarce and it is too expensive for small-holders. On the other hand, as shifting cultivation is modified towards more intensive cropping, liming becomes essential to neutralize soil acidity and to supply plant calcium. For kaolinitic Ultisols in West Africa an initial rate of calcium addition of 0.5–1.0 t ha^{-1} reduces exchangeable aluminium saturation to 30% or less and an annual addition of 100–300 kg ha^{-1} sustains high crop yields (Friessen, Juo & Miller 1982). Surface application of lime at higher rates has little effect on subsoil acidity. Although calcium is leached from the limed surface layer, exchangeable aluminium saturation in the subsoil horizons is not appreciably affected by the downward movement of calcium (Fig. 6). Moreover, leaching of calcium from the limed and fertilized surface soil is accompanied by nitrate and chloride anions. Whilst over 90% of applied calcium may be found within 1 m of the soil surface after 3 years, recovery of that calcium would require a deep-rooting, acid-tolerant species (Pleysier & Juo 1981; Friessen *et al.* 1982).

NUTRIENT CYCLING IN TREE AND FOOD CROP MIXED SYSTEMS

Systematic inclusion of trees in food crop systems may be a sound approach to sustainable agriculture in tropical forest regions. The multistorey polyculture

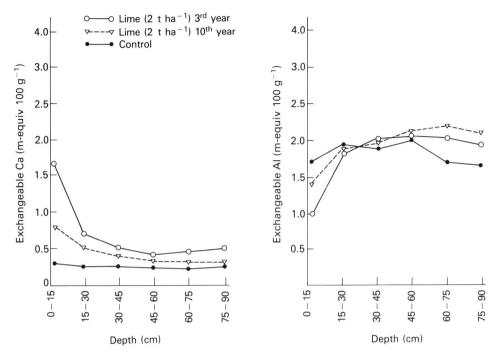

FIG. 6. Downward movement of calcium and aluminium in a limed Ultisol, Onne, Nigeria (powdered calcium carbonate lime was applied initially at a rate of 2 t ha^{-1} (A. S. R. Juo unpublished)).

systems of homestead gardens and self-sufficient unit farms in Sri Lanka and Indonesia are probably the best examples depicting man's ability to derive maximum benefits from forest ecosystems without altering them drastically. Although the multistorey systems have been well described (Terra 1954; Harwood & Price 1976; McConnell & Dharmapala 1978; Michon 1983), there have been no specific studies dealing with the effect of nutrient dynamics on plant production in those multi-component systems which include trees, perennials, annual food and vegetable crops, and in some instances, livestock and aquaculture. The effectiveness of nutrient cycling and biological fixation by leguminous trees and shrubs interplanted with annual food crops (the 'alley cropping' system) has been demonstrated for Alfisols in West Africa (Kang *et al.* 1981; Kang, Wilson & Lawson 1984; Wilson, Kang & Mulongoy 1986). In such systems annual food crops are planted between rows of deep-rooting and fast-growing leguminous trees such as *Leucaena leucocephala* Lam de Wit. and *Gliricidia sepium* Steud. The trees are generally pruned several times during the two cropping seasons of the year and the residues are returned to the soil as green manure for the accompanying food crop. Dry matter and nutrient content from five prunings of two leguminous species and two non-leguminous species grown at a spacing of 4 m × 0.5 m are given in Table 3. *Leucaena* is the best species in terms of annual dry-matter production and nutrient yields. It is capable of producing 7 t ha^{-1} of green manure including 247 kg ha^{-1} of nitrogen annually on non-acid soils. The leguminous species produce larger quantities of organic matter and have a higher nutrient content than the non-leguminous species (Table 3).

The effects of *Leucaena* and *Acioa barterii* Benth. on the yield of maize grown on a degraded Alfisol are given in Table 4 and demonstrate beneficial effects of interplanting with these trees. An experiment at Ibadan, Nigeria on interplanting with *Leucaena* showed that a maize yield of 2–3 t ha^{-1} could be sustained over 10 years without additional nutrients. However, for higher maize yields of 4–5 t ha^{-1} using improved varieties, an addition to each maize crop of 45–60 kg ha^{-1} of fertilizer nitrogen would be required.

The potential of interplanting with trees on strongly acidic, calcium-depleted soils in the high-rainfall regions has not been extensively studied. Preliminary observations at IITA's substation at Onne indicate that even for trees tolerant to a high degree of soil aluminium saturation or soil acidity, the root mass is concentrated in the relatively nutrient-rich surface layer of the soil. Hence, severe nutrient competition occurs between the woody species and the food crops. In such an environment, it may be worthwhile in the long run to establish suitable woody species during the first 2 years using fertilizer and subsoil liming. Then, a nutrient recycling system involving tree pruning, cropping and periodic fallow could be established.

TABLE 3. Biomass and nutrient content of leaves and twigs (from five prunings) of four woody species (grown in 4 m × 0.5 m spacing) on an Alfisol at Ibadan, Nigeria (B. T. Kang unpublished)

| Species | Biomass of leaves and twigs (t ha^{-1} year^{-1}) | Nutrient content of leaves and twigs | | | | |
| | | N | P | K | Ca | Mg |
			(kg ha^{-1} year^{-1})			
Acioa barterii (Chrysobalanaceae)	3.0	41	4	20	15	5
Alchornea cordiforlia Benth. (Euphorbiaceae)	4.0	85	6	48	42	8
Gliricidia sepium (Leguminosae)	5.5	169	11	149	66	17
Leucaena leucocephala (Leguminosae)	7.4	247	19	185	98	16

TABLE 4. Effects of nitrogen (urea) application and interplanting with *Leucaena leucocephala* or *Acioa barterii* on maize grain yield after 6 years continuous cropping on an Alfisol (pH 6.0) at Ibadan, Nigeria (S.E. (mean) = 0.31; L.S.D ($p < 0.05$) = 0.91) (B. T. Kang unpublished)

| N rate (kg ha^{-1}) | Yield (kg ha^{-1}) | | |
	Control	+*Leucaena*	+*Acioa*
0	1.41	3.16	1.86
45	1.91	4.27	3.54
90	3.22	–	–
135	3.18	–	–

CONCLUSIONS

1 Low soil fertility is one of the major factors limiting modification of shifting cultivation in West Africa. Mixed systems including food crops with leguminous trees or perennials are a promising approach in terms of nutrient cycling and land stabilization.

2 Adoption of improved nutrient management systems and practices will depend on social, economic and cultural conditions; however, increases in population and land pressures must lead to the development and adoption of new farming technologies which can sustain productivity of farm lands and prevent further deforestation.

REFERENCES

Ahn, P.M. (1970). *West African Soils.* Oxford University Press, Oxford.

Dudal, R. (1980). Soil–related constraints to agricultural development in the tropics. *IRRI, Priorities for Alleviating Soil-Related Constraints to Food Crop Production in the Tropics,* pp. 23–37. International Rice Research Institute (IRRI), Los Banos, Philippines.

Fore, R.E. & Okigbo, B.N. (1974). Yield response of maize to various fertilizers and lime on Nkpologu sandy loam. *Nigerian Agricultural Journal,* **9,** 124–127.

Fox, R.L. & Kang, B.T. (1978). Influence of phosphorus fertilizer placement and fertilization rate on maize nutrition. *Soil Science,* **125,** 34–40.

Friessen, D.K., Juo, A.S.R. & Miller, M.H. (1982). Residual value of lime and leaching of calcium in a kaolinitic Ultisol in the high rainfall tropics. *Soil Science Society of America Journal,* **46,** 1184–1189.

Golley, F.R. (1983). *Tropical Rainforest Ecosystems.* Elsevier Science, Amsterdam.

Harwood, R.R. & Price, E.C. (1976). Multiple cropping in tropical Asia. *Multiple Cropping, Special Publication No. 27,* pp. 11–40. American Society of Agronomy, Wisconsin.

Jaiyebo, E.O. & Moore, A.W. (1964). Soil fertility and nutrient storage in different soil–vegetation systems in a tropical rainforest environment. *Tropical Agriculture,* **41,** 129–139.

Jenkinson, D.S. & Ayanaba, A. (1977). Decomposition of carbon-14 labelled plant materials under tropical conditions. *Soil Science Society of America Journal,* **41,** 912–915.

Jordan, C. (1985). *Nutrient Cycling in Tropical Forest Ecosystems.* Wiley, Chichester.

Juo, A.S.R. (1980). Mineralogical characteristics of Alfisols and Ultisols. *Soils with Variable Charge* (Ed. by B.K.G. Theng), pp. 69–86. New Zealand Society of Soil Science, Lower Hutt.

Juo, A.S.R. (1981). Effect of fallow on maize yield. *Annual Report,* pp. 8–9. International Institute of Tropical Agriculture, Ibadan, Nigeria.

Juo, A.S.R. (1985). Cultivating tropical rainforest: methods and constraints. *Entwicklung Landlicher Raum (Germany),* **19,** 14–15.

Juo, A.S.R. (1986). Potassium response in tropical root and tuber crops (a review). *Potassium in Farming Systems in the Humid Tropics,* pp. 277–288. International Potash Institute, Bern, Switzerland.

Juo, A.S.R. & Fox, R.L. (1977). Phosphate sorption characteristics of some bench–mark soils in West Africa. *Soil Science,* **124,** 370–376.

Juo, A.S.R. & Grimme, H. (1980). Potassium status in major soils of tropical Africa with special reference to potassium availability. *Proceedings of the Potassium Workshop,* pp. 7–22. International Potash Institute, Bern, Switzerland.

Juo, A.S.R. & Kamprath, E.J. (1979). Copper chloride as an extractant for estimating the reactive Al pool in acid soils. *Soil Science Society of America Journal,* **43,** 35–38.

Juo, A.S.R. & Lal, R. (1977). Effects of fallow and continuous cultivation on chemical and physical properties of an Alfisol in southern Nigeria. *Plant and Soil,* **47,** 567–584.

Kang, B.T. (1984). Potassium and magnesium responses of cassava grown in an Ultisol in southern Nigeria. *Fertilizer Research,* **5,** 403–410.

Kang, B.T. & Juo, A.S.R. (1983). Management of low activity clay soils of tropical Africa for food crop production. *Proceedings of the International Soil Classification Workshop (Kigali, Rwanda)*, pp. 450–470. General Administration for Development & Cooperation, Brussels, Belgium.

Kang, B.T. & Juo, A.S.R. (1986). Effects of forest clearing on soil chemical properties and crop performance. *Land Clearing and Development in the Tropics* (Ed. by R. Lal, P. Sanchez & R.W. Cummings, Jr.), pp. 383–394. A.A. Balkema, Rotterdam.

Kang, B.T. & Okeke, J.E. (1984). Nitrogen and potassium of two cassava cultivars grown on an Alfisol in southern Nigeria. *Proceedings of the 6th Tropical Root Crop Symposium*, pp. 231–238. International Potato Institute, Lima, Peru.

Kang, B.T., Wilson, G.F. & Lawson, T.L. (1984). *Alley Cropping: a Stable Alternative to Shifting Cultivation*. Special Publication of the International Institute of Tropical Agriculture, Ibadan, Nigeria.

Kang, B.T., Wilson, G.F. & Sipkens, L. (1981). Alley cropping maize and *Leucaena* in southern Nigeria. *Plant and Soil*, **63**, 165–179.

Lal, R. (1985). Soil erosion and sediment transport research in tropical Africa. *Journal of Hydrological Science*, **30**, 239–256.

Lal, R., Sanchez, P.A. & Cummings, R.W. Jr. (Eds.) (1986). *Land Clearing and Development in the Tropics*. A.A. Balkema, Rotterdam.

McConnell, D.J. & Dharmapala, K.A.F. (1978). *The Forest-Garden Farms of Kandy, Sri Lanka*. Food & Agriculture Organization, Agricultural Diversification Project Paper. FAO, Rome.

Michon, G. (1983). Village–forest–gardens in Wet Java. *Plant Research and Agroforestry* (Ed. by P. Huxley), pp. 13–24. International Council for Research on Agroforestry (ICRAF), Nairobi.

Mueller-Harvey, I., Juo, A.S.R. & Wild, A. (1985). Soil organic C, N, S and P after clearance in Nigeria: mineralization rates and spatial variability. *Journal of Soil Science*, **36**, 585–591.

Nye, P.H. (1961). Organic matter and nutrient cycle under moist tropical forest. *Plant and Soil*, **13**, 333–345.

Nye, P.H. & Greenland, D.J. (1960). *The Soil Under Shifting Cultivation. Technical Communication 51*. Commonwealth Agricultural Bureau, U.K.

Obigbesan, G.O. (1977). Response of cassava to potassium fertilizer in western Nigeria. *Journal of Agricultural Science*, **89**, 23–27.

Ofori, C.S. (1973). Decline in fertility status in a tropical ochrosol under continuous cropping. *Experimental Agriculture*, **9**, 15–22.

Okigbo, B.N. & Greenland, D.J. (1976). Intercropping systems in tropical Africa. *Multiple Cropping*, pp. 63–101. American Society of Agronomy, Madison, Wisconsin.

Pleysier, J.L. & Juo, A.S.R. (1981). Leaching of fertilizer ions of an Ultisol: leaching through undisturbed soil columns. *Soil Science Society of America Journal*, **45**, 754–760.

Proctor, J. (1983). Mineral nutrients in tropical forests. *Progress in Physical Geography*, **7**, 422–443.

Richards, P.W. (1964). *The Tropical Rain Forest: An Ecological Study*. Cambridge University Press, Cambridge.

Talineau, J-C., Hainnaux, G., Bonzon, B., Filloneau, C., Picard, D. & Sicot, M. (1976). Quelques conséquences agronomiques de l'introduction d'une sole fourragère dans une succession culturale du milieu tropicale humide de Côte d'Ivoire. *Cahier: Organization de la Recherche Scientifique et Technique Outre Mer (ORSTOM), Serie Biologie*, **11**, 277–290.

Terra, G.J.A. (1954). Mixed gardens horticulture in Java. *Malaysian Journal of Tropical Geography*, **3**, 33–43.

Van der Kruijs, A., Hairiah, K., van der Noordwijk, M. & Kang, B.T. (1985). *Annual Report*, pp. 34–35. International Institute of Tropical Agriculture, Ibadan, Nigeria.

Vine, H. (1953). Experiments on the maintenance of soil fertility at Ibadan, Nigeria, 1922–51. *Experimental Agriculture*, **21**, 65–85.

Wilson, G.F. (1981). *Mucuna* mulch. *Annual Report*, p. 34. International Institute of Tropical Agriculture, Ibadan, Nigeria.

Wilson, G.F., Kang, B.T. & Mulongoy, K. (1986). Alley cropping: trees as sources of green manure and mulch in the tropics. *Biological Agriculture and Horticulture*, **3**, 251–267.

Role of weeds in nutrient cycling in the cropping phase of milpa agriculture in Belize, Central America

J. D. H. LAMBERT AND J. T. ARNASON

Ottawa-Carleton Centre for Graduate Studies and Research in Biology,
Carleton University, Ottawa K1S 5B6, Canada

SUMMARY

1 A study was made of shifting cultivation (milpa) in Belize, Central America. It was found that the destruction of the forest system and the imposition of a short agricultural cycle did not result in a dramatic decline in soil nutrient concentrations. Weeds were shown to play a positive role in limiting declines in soil nutrient concentrations in traditionally practised milpa agriculture.

2 Weeds accumulated a larger percentage of available nitrogen, phosphorus and potassium (per gram of dry matter) than corn or beans.

3 Weed biomass increased with each cropping during the first 12-month period and with each successive rainy season cropping.

4 Weeds were able to continue dry matter production under declining soil moisture. Under the same conditions, corn dry matter production declined, with the result that grain yields decreased sharply.

5 The traditional 2-year cropping cycle made best use of available nutrients and minimized competition from weeds.

6 Removal of cut forest biomass without burning prior to each rainy season planting did not lead to any significant decline in soil nutrient concentrations.

7 Experimental mulching of crop and weed residues in the second year without burning did not result in any rapid release of nutrients. The main beneficiary of the available nutrients was the herbaceous weeds.

INTRODUCTION

Milpa agriculture (which is synonymous with shifting or slash and burn agriculture) in the Americas has recently been judged as ecologically sound for forest areas (Sanchez 1976; Lambert & Arnason 1986; Jordan *et al.* 1987). The region of Central America which includes Mexico, Guatemala, Belize and northern Honduras had a substantial population during the Maya Civilization of one thousand years ago, and there is much evidence that milpa agriculture was then an important method of food production (Deevey *et al.* 1979; Lambert & Arnason 1983). One important feature of the area is that its soils are fertile Mollisols with a high base status which overlie limestone (Wright *et al.* 1959).

The cultivation period practised by modern Maya farmers is 2 years, embracing four plantings (Lambert & Arnason 1986). Crops (corn and beans) are often intercropped to exploit more efficiently both nutrient resources and microclimatic conditions. Seed, fruits and tubers are removed from the milpa and the remaining vegetative portion (stover) and non-crop production are left. Burning occurs once a year in late April–early May near the end of the dry season. In the present system, corn (*Zea mays* L.) stalks are left after the first harvest as support for climbing bean (*Phaseolus vulgaris* L.). At the second corn planting, before the beginning of the dry season, all standing plant growth (stover and weeds) is cut and left and the corn seed is planted in the mulch-covered soil. After harvesting in April, all growth is cut and burned and the second year's first corn crop is planted. Depending on the individual farmer and amount of weed growth, some weeding may take place during each cropping. If the initial burn has been successful, little weeding is required during the first corn crop.

In an earlier paper (Lambert & Arnason 1986) the role of weeds, including the prevention of nutrient loss by leaching, in the initial stages of secondary succession was described. For the purposes of this discussion we use the term weed to describe all non-crop species present in the milpas. In this paper we examine the division of nutrients between the crops and weeds and the role weeds play in nutrient cycling on land after clearing Cohune and High Bush.

MATERIALS AND METHODS

Study site

The study site was located at Indian Church, Belize (17°45'N, 80°40'W) and falls within the semi-evergreen seasonal forest zone according to Beard's classification (Beard 1955). Annual precipitation is 1500 mm with a distinct dry season from January to the end of May. The mean annual temperature is 25 °C.

Site preparation

Two forest types, seasonally dry hardwood (High Bush) and tropical palm (Cohune), are commonly used by farmers for milpa at Indian Church. The locations of the two milpas were selected by our two Mayan assistants who are experienced milpa farmers. Vegetation (trees, saplings and seedlings) was quantitatively sampled in twenty 10 m × 10 m plots in the High Bush (Lambert, Arnason & Gale 1980) and twenty 10 m × 10 m plots in the Cohune (Arnason & Lambert 1984). A 0.25 ha milpa in the High Bush in 1977 and a 1.25 ha milpa in the Cohune in 1978 were cut using machete and axe. Control plots were established in the adjacent undisturbed forest at both sites. Data collected in the forest sites included monthly samplings of litterfall, soil moisture, soil organic matter, percentage soil nitrogen, available phosphorus and exchangeable potassium.

Cropping schedule: High Bush

Under normal circumstances farmers use a milpa for only 2 years and only occasionally is corn planted in a third rainy season as in the High Bush milpa

(1977–1979). After cutting (January) and burning (May) the 0.25 ha milpa was divided into four 25 m × 25 m plots. In two plots a traditional planting schedule was followed. Corn was planted in late May and harvested in September and the stalks in one plot were cut and left. Climbing beans were planted in November in the uncut plot and were allowed to climb the standing corn stalks; they were harvested in January. A second corn planting was made, after cutting the remaining corn and bean stover in January, and harvested in April. The land was then prepared (cut and burned) for the second rainy season corn crop which was planted and harvested in September. The following May the weeds and corn stover were again cut and burned and a corn crop planted. After harvesting in September the milpa was abandoned.

Cropping schedule: Cohune

The Cohune milpa was used for only 2 years (1978–1979) and only the rainy season corn and weed data are presented. After cutting (January) and burning (May) the 1.25 ha milpa was divided into twenty 25 m × 25 m plots (5 × 4). In two plots the traditional planting schedule was followed. Two additional trials were carried out to determine if the system could be improved with the limited resources available to small farmers. In the first, to determine the effect on corn and weed production, all forest growth after cutting was removed from one 25 m × 25 m plot prior to planting. The following year all corn stover and weeds were again removed before planting. In the second trial, two 25 m × 25 m plots, following the normal cut, burn and planting sequence of the first year, were only cut the second year with the stover and weeds left unburned as a mulch.

Vegetation and soil sampling

Following local practice, four corn seeds were placed in holes made at 80 cm intervals using a planting stick. The planting density was about 20 000 ha^{-1}. For the beans, one seed was planted at the base of each corn stalk. At harvest in all corn plots in both milpas, five 3 m × 3 m plots (8 m from each corner plus one in the centre) were sampled to determine the number of individual stalks, grain yields and total corn biomass. Beans in the High Bush milpa were sampled with five similarly placed 1 m × 1 m plots to determine seed and total bean biomass. Weeds were sampled at all harvests from five 1 m × 1 m plots. All above-ground parts and roots were removed and separated by species for nutrient and total biomass.

Soil samples were collected at monthly intervals throughout the study period in each of the plots. Soil cores (0–12 cm deep) were taken from five locations within the plot and pooled to increase the reliability of sampling.

Analytical methods

All plant and soil samples were weighed, oven dried at 60 °C for 24 h and then reweighed to determine dry weight. Because of problems involved in removing soil from the root systems in the field without loss of root parts, nutrient data are not included. Plant and soil nutrient analyses were carried out using methods outlined by McKeague (1978). Total nitrogen was determined by micro-Kjeldahl techniques, available phosphorus colorimetrically and exchangeable potassium by atomic absorption spectrophotometry.

RESULTS

High Bush Forest

The removal of forest biomass results in a large loss of nutrients. The annual biomass increment of crops (13 144 kg ha^{-1}) and weeds (3321 kg ha^{-1}), even with the three plantings of the first year, is less than the forest biomass (64 577 kg ha^{-1}). Crop and weed yields at each harvest are plotted in Fig. 1. Corn growth following the initial burn had virtually no competition from weeds and there was an abundance of available nutrients in the ash. The weed biomass was small. The original forest woody species were present as coppice growth. Grasses were distinguished from other herbaceous species (forbs) because local milpa farmers consider them a greater problem than the forbs.

The relative amounts (as percentages) of total nitrogen, available phosphorus and exchangeable potassium present in all the biomass at each harvest are plotted in Figs. 2. At no time during the cropping period was the loss of the major nutrients from the system with the removal of grain greater than that returned in the stover and weeds. In all three rainy season corn harvests the amount of nitrogen in grain was greater than that in stover. However, the percentage of the total nitrogen in corn declined significantly each year (91% → 71% → 45%) with corresponding increases in nitrogen present in the weeds. There was significantly more phosphorus and potassium retained in corn stover than translocated to the grain, so that burning could have resulted in a release of readily available phosphorus and potassium.

Corn absorbed less of the major nutrients per hectare than the weeds, although it produced a larger amount of dry matter than the weeds in the High Bush milpa. The slower growing weeds absorbed less nitrogen, phosphorus and potassium, had a lower total biomass, but higher tissue concentrations (Table 1). Herbaceous and woody concentrations of total nitrogen and potassium were similar on a dry matter basis. Phosphorus concentrations were significantly higher in the herbs than in the woody life forms.

Cohune Forest

In the undisturbed Cohune Forest over the 2-year study period there was an accumulation of soil nitrogen towards the end of the dry season (Fig. 3(a)). Thereafter there was a general decline, possibly reflecting greater leaching and plant uptake during the wet season, as seen in the High Bush (Lambert & Arnason

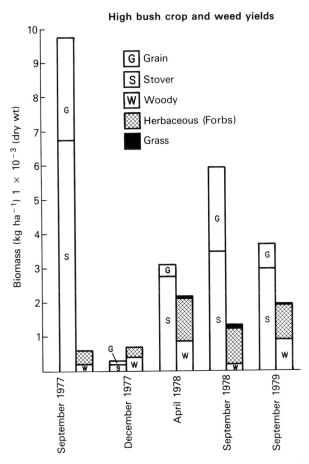

FIG. 1. Comparison of percentage biomass in crop and weed species at harvest. All crops are of corn except that harvested in December 1977 which is climbing beans.

1986). Available phosphorus and exchangeable potassium values (Fig. 3(a)) showed minimal seasonal variation, even though phosphorus concentrations were shown to be high in the Cohune litter (Arnason & Lambert 1984).

Major nutrient concentrations in the milpa plots reflect the different preparations. In the burned plots, available phosphorus and exchangeable potassium concentrations were significantly higher than in the undisturbed forest (Figs. 3(a) and (b)). Although the total annual input of major nutrients in the litterfall was lower in the Cohune Forest than in the High Bush, the concentrations were much higher (Arnason & Lambert 1984). With the first burn, significant amounts of phosphorus and potassium were added to the soil and were potentially available to crops and weeds. Nitrogen concentrations were similarly higher, but the soil concentrations following burning were not significantly different from the forest. A possible explanation might be the intense burn of the dry, highly suberized tissue which results in volatilization of the nitrogen.

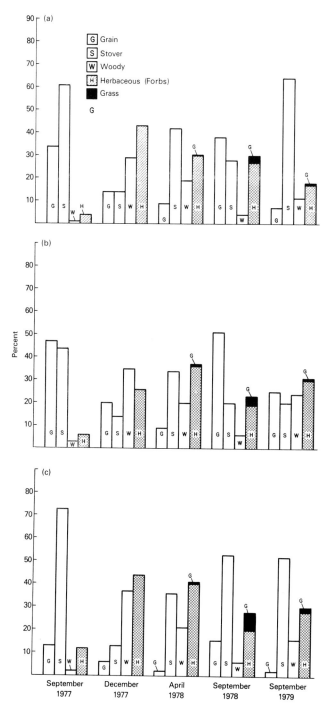

Fig. 2. Comparison of percentage available phosphorus (a), nitrogen (b) and exchangeable potassium (c) in crop and weed (woody, herbaceous (Forbs) and grass) species at harvest. All crops are of corn except that harvested in December 1977 which is climbing beans.

TABLE 1. Mean nutrient concentrations (% oven dry matter) in the above-ground biomass of corn and weeds (woody and herbaceous) over the five cropping periods in the High Bush milpa (within each column means followed by the same letter are not significantly different ($p \leqslant 0.05$ using Sheffe's Test) (SPSSX 1986))

	Nitrogen (%)	Phosphorus (%)	Potassium (%)
Corn	0.77 b	0.27 b	1.12 b
Woody weeds	1.69 a	0.41 a	2.79 a
Herbaceous weeds	1.62 a	0.30 a	2.49 a

Available phosphorus concentrations in the mulched milpa soils (Fig. 3(b)) declined significantly in the second year, an indication of uptake by the crops and weeds. However, they were still significantly higher than in the forest soil. Potassium concentrations in the unburned milpa (Fig. 3(c)) were similar to those of the forest soil. Nitrogen concentrations were significantly different from those of the forest soil. In both years available phosphorus and exchangeable potassium were significantly lower in the unburned plot than in the burned and mulched plots.

Corn yields (Table 2) in the burned Cohune milpa plots were similar to those in the High Bush milpa (Lambert & Arnason 1986). Weed biomass increased slightly.

In the mulched plot the corn grain yield was significantly lower than yields in the burned (68%) and unburned (55%) plots; conversely, weed biomass increased significantly (88%). Removing the original forest biomass without burning after cutting required enormous physical effort and had no positive effect on corn production. However, weed biomass increased by 68% (Table 2). Following the removal of all corn stover and weed biomass, the second year crop yields were only 22% lower than the burned milpa. Weed yields also declined by 24%.

The woody and herbaceous weeds held significantly higher concentrations of nitrogen (on a per kilogram basis) than the corn in the Cohune milpa (Table 2). Phosphorus concentrations were not significantly different between corn and weeds in the traditionally burned plots. However, in the unburned and mulched plots phosphorus concentrations were higher in the weeds. Herbaceous weeds generally had higher potassium concentrations than corn and woody species.

DISCUSSION

Although soil nutrient reserves in the High Bush milpa were not deficient, total corn biomass declined each year, while weed biomass increased over twofold. In the traditionally burned Cohune milpa, corn biomass did not decline in the second year and weed biomass increased by 63%. It was estimated that the High Bush site had been cleared for agriculture about 45 years earlier, whereas there was no evidence that the Cohune site had been used in the last 60 years. Although analyses were not carried out we concluded that the Cohune soils had a small weed seed bank as indicated by the lower weed biomass following burning. Weed species composition in the two milpa sites was similar.

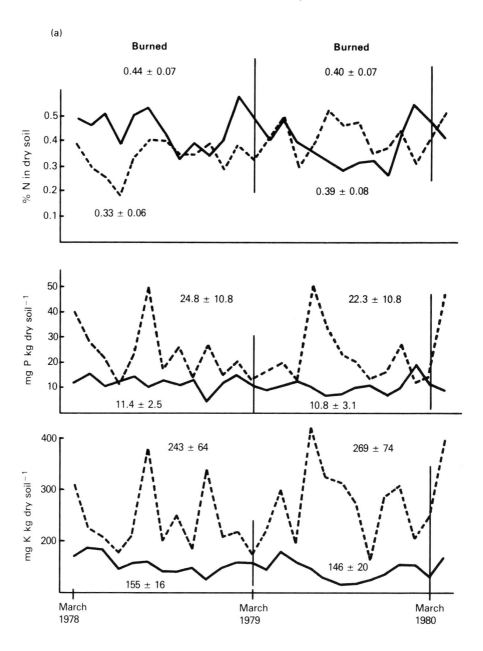

FIG. 3. Monthly percentage nitrogen and available phosphorus and potassium values in dry soil. All values with seasonal means and standard errors for forest amd milpa plots (———, forest; -----, milpa). (a) Milpa burned both years; (b) milpa burned first year, second mulch only with no burn; and (c) no burn either year, with all plant material removed.

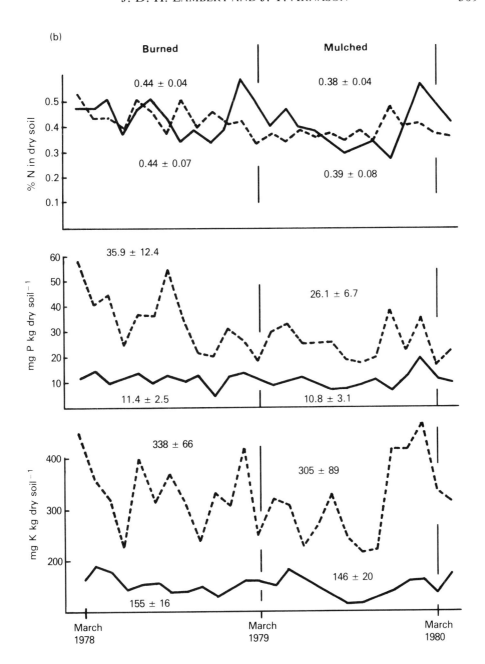

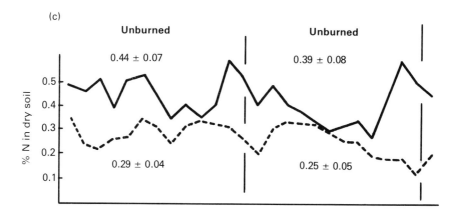

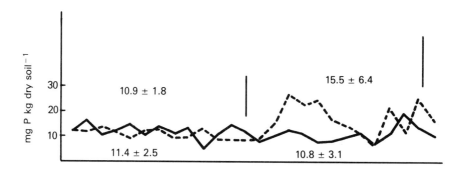

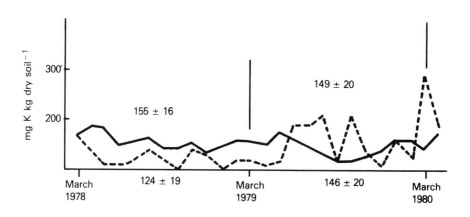

FIG. 3. *Continued.*

TABLE 2. Above-ground biomass (kg ha^{-1} dry weight) and nutrient concentrations (%) in corn and weed (woody and herbaceous) above-ground biomass at rainy season harvests from Cohune milpa (T = trace; within each column means followed by the same letter are not significantly different ($p \leqslant 0.05$ using Sheffe's Test) (SPSSX 1986))

	Biomass		Nitrogen (%)		Phosphorus (%)		Potassium (%)	
Burned	1978	1979	1978	1979	1978	1979	1978	1979
Corn	5772	6262	0.93 c	1.15 b	0.18 a	0.34 a	0.91 b	1.18 b
Woody weeds	140	130	1.86 b	1.54 a	0.21 a	0.23 a	0.86 b	0.85 b
Herbaceous weeds	76	223	2.76 a	1.5 a	0.26 a	0.22 a	1.31 a	2.15 a
Unburned								
Corn	6000	4928	0.79 b	0.85 b	0.14 b	0.23 a	0.68 a	0.64 b
Woody weeds	418	12	1.89 a	0.83 b	0.14 b	T	0.96 a	T
Herbaceous weeds	342	566	1.58 a	1.2 a	0.44 a	0.23 a	0.94 a	2.24 a
Mulched								
Corn	—	2788	—	0.68 b	—	0.17 b	—	0.57 b
Woody weeds	—	20	—	1.0 a	—	0.49 a	—	1.99 a
Herbaceous weeds	—	1902	—	1.2 a	—	0.26 b	—	2.39 a

Intraspecific differences and vigorous competitive ability of the weeds accounted for their success in both milpas over the cropping period. With each growth period the weed seed bank in the soil was increased so that crop planting in the third year was no longer economical. The traditional 2-year cycle with an annual burn therefore allowed the crop to make best use of available nutrients and in the rainy seasons to minimize weed competition.

With no nutrient input from the burning of the cut forest, soil nitrogen, phosphorus and potassium concentrations were significantly lower than the burned and mulched plots. After crop germination the major soil nutrients declined, rose during vegetative growth and declined again during reproductive growth. Corn yields were not significantly different from the traditionally burned plots in the first year but declined in the second year.

Mulching with animal manure and human refuse is common with subsistence farmers in Africa and Asia. However, Maya farmers do not generally have cattle or use human refuse. From an agronomic view the results of the mulching experiment were disappointing and contrasted with studies in Nigeria where mulched corn plots produced higher yields than unmulched plots (Lal 1978). We attribute the dramatic increase in weed biomass to the abundance of seeds shed during the previous 12 months by annual species, plus those brought in by animals and wind. Although burning resulted in high temperatures (200 °C), the fire was of short duration. Seeds on the soil surface would normally be killed by such temperatures while buried seeds would not. The absence of a burn plus the protective blanket of slowly decomposing mulch resulted in their successful germination and establishment. It seems that burning had no immediate effect on corn yield.

While the presence of weeds and mulch may inhibit nutrient loss by leaching or surface erosion, mulching without burning resulted in a 68% decline in corn grain yields when compared with the traditionally burned milpas. We have no precise figures on the total amount of mulch added, but it was estimated to be about 500 kg ha^{-1} oven dry weight (weeds and stover). It would appear that regardless of high ambient temperatures and abundant precipitation, decomposition is not rapid enough to produce a net benefit to the corn. Corn nitrogen, phosphorus and potassium yields were about one-quarter of those of the burned plot, while major nutrients available in the mulch were significantly greater than those returned in ash in the burned plot before cropping.

CONCLUSION

The following conclusions can be drawn from our preliminary study of weeds and their effect on crops and the soil system.

1 The above-ground parts of weeds had a higher concentration of nitrogen, phosphorus and potassium than the corn or beans even though corn yields were ten times greater.

2 Weed biomass increased with each cropping during the first 12 months and with each successive rainy season cropping.

3 Weeds showed greater dry matter production than corn under the declining soil moisture conditions of a dry season crop. Possibly as a result of competition for water, grain yields were significantly lower than in the rainy season crop.

4 The traditional 2-year cropping cycle seems to make best use of available nutrients and to minimize weed competition.

5 Experimental removal of the standing forest biomass without burning prior to the rainy season planting did not, in the first planting, result in any difference in corn yield. In the second year, corn yields were slightly lower, while herbaceous weed yield increased greatly.

6 Experimental mulching of crop and weed residues in the second year without burning led to very low grain yields. It did not apparently result in a rapid release of the major nutrients during the cropping applied. Possibly, the herbaceous weeds suppressed the corn through competition.

7 Soil nutrient concentrations in the unburned milpa did not differ significantly from the Cohune Forest during the 24-month study period.

The slash and burn system of cultivation has been considered inefficient by some workers (Watters 1971). The inefficiency is related to the loss of nutrients during and after burning and the quick appearance and inadequate control of weeds. With little capital available for mechanical clearing and cultivating or herbicide or fertilizer input, burning provides the best alternative for the subsistence farmer in terms of release of nutrients to the crops and weed control. In this study, mulching had a disastrous effect on crop yield, even though a no-burn approach might be considered more ecologically sound as a long-term practice. The benefits of burning are available to the farmer for at least a

2-year cropping period. While burning may lead to some loss of nutrients by leaching and volatilization, the large and increasing weed component in the cropping system is also clearly important in retaining nutrients in the vegetative growth. Further research is needed to find a way of exploiting the nutrient-retaining properties of the weeds for the benefit of the farmer.

REFERENCES

Arnason, J.T. & Lambert, J.D.H. (1984). Mineral cycling in a tropical palm forest. *Plant and Soil,* **79,** 211–225.

Beard, J.S. (1955). The classification of Tropical American vegetation types. *Journal of Ecology,* **56,** 827–844.

Deevey, E.S., Rice, D.S., Rice, P.M., Vaughan, H.H., Brenner, M. & Flannery, M.S. (1979). Mayan urbanism: impact on a tropical Karst environment. *Science,* **206,** 298–306.

Jordan, C.F. (1987). *Amazonian Rain Forest: Ecosystem Disturbance and Recovery.* Vol. 60. Springer, New York.

Lal, R. (1978). Influence of within– and between–row mulching on soil temperature, soil moisture, soil development and yield of maize (*Zea mays* L.) in a tropical soil. *Field Crops Research,* **1,** 127–139.

Lambert, J.D.H. & Arnason, J.T. (1983). Ancient maya land use and potential agricultural productivity at Lamanai, Belize. *Drained Field Agriculture in Central and South America* (Ed. by J.P. Darch), pp. 111–122. 44th International Congress of Americanists, Manchester, 1982.

Lambert, J.D.H. & Arnason, J.T. (1986). Nutrient dynamics in milpa agriculture and the role of weeds in initial stages of secondary succession in Belize, C.A. *Plant and Soil,* **93,** 303–322.

Lambert, J.D.H., Arnason, J.T. & Gale, J.L. (1980). Leaf litter and changing nutrient levels in a seasonally dry tropical hardwood forest, Belize, C.A. *Plant and Soil,* **55,** 429–443.

McKeague, J.E. (1978). *Manual on Sampling and Methods of Analysis.* Subcommittee on Methods of Analysis, Canadian Soil Survey Committee, Ottawa.

Sanchez, P.A. (1976). *Properties and Management of Soils in the Tropics.* Wiley, New York.

SPSSX (1986). *User's Guide: Statistics,* 2nd edn. McGraw-Hill, Chicago.

Watters, R.F. (1971). *Shifting Cultivation in Latin America, FAO Forestry Development Paper 17.* FAO, Rome.

Wright, A.C.S., Romney, D.H., Arbuckle, R.H. and Vial, V.E. (1959). *Land Use in British Honduras. Colonial Research Publications 24.* Colonial Office, London.

Mineralization of nutrients after forest clearance and their uptake during cropping

I. MUELLER-HARVEY[*†], A. S. R. JUO[**] AND A. WILD[*]

*Department of Soil Science, University of Reading, Reading RG1 5AQ, and
**International Institute of Tropical Agriculture, Ibadan, Nigeria

SUMMARY

1 A site under 15-year-old secondary forest in southern Nigeria was cleared and four crops were grown over a 22-month period. The soil was intensively sampled on four occasions during this period and analysed for carbon, nitrogen, total and organic phosphorus and sulphur.

2 The calculated half-lives for organic carbon, nitrogen, phosphorus and sulphur were 3.5, 3.3, 4.7 and 2.3 years, respectively. The decreases in nitrogen, organic phosphorus and sulphur from the top 10 cm of soil were 622, 53 and 79 kg ha^{-1}, respectively over the 22-month period. The decrease per year exceeded the uptake of nutrients by crops. The mineralized nitrogen and sulphur which were not taken up by the crops were assumed to have been lost mainly by leaching. It was calculated that the equivalent of 1 t ha^{-1} calcium carbonate would be required to replace the calcium leached with the nitrate and sulphate over 2 years.

3 The methods are discussed, especially in relation to the sources of variability in composition of the soil samples. Trees and clay content (hence total phosphorus) appear to be the main causes of short-range and long-range variability respectively.

4 Nitrate and ammonium concentrations in the top 10 cm of soil were measured over a 12-month period. Although the nitrate concentrations varied seasonally, they were consistently about twice as high on plots high in organic matter (1.6–2.7% carbon) than on plots low in organic matter (0.8–1.2% carbon).

INTRODUCTION

The traditional system of crop cultivation in the humid tropics is to use patches of land which have been under forest. The land is cleared by a combination of felling and burning, and is cultivated for a few years before being allowed to revert to forest fallow. This system, called rotational or shifting cultivation, has been described by several workers including Nye & Greenland (1965), Ruthenberg (1971) and Okigbo (1980). One of the main benefits of shifting cultivation is the accumulation of nutrients during the fallow period which become available to crops during the period of cultivation.

In this paper we describe a field experiment in southern Nigeria from which some results have previously been reported (Mueller-Harvey, Juo & Wild 1985).

---

†Present address: AFRC Institute for Grassland and Animal Production, Maidenhead SL6 5LR.

The aim was to measure the rate of mineralization of the organically held nitrogen, phosphorus and sulphur after secondary forest was brought into cultivation.

Two methods of investigation were considered. The first involved the measurement of the concentration of the three nutrients in inorganic form over the period of the experiment. This was rejected because no reliable methods could be found to measure the loss of nitrogen by leaching or in gaseous form, or to recover phosphate quantitatively. The second method, which was adopted, involved the measurement of the rates of decrease of organically held nutrients in the soil. This required intensive soil sampling; there were some inherent difficulties in the method which are described below.

METHODS

The experimental site was at the International Institute of Tropical Agriculture (IITA), Ibadan, Nigeria (7°30′N, 3°54′E, altitude 700 m), about 30 km south of the northern boundary of the West African lowland rain forest. Rainfall distribution is bimodal, permitting two cropping seasons each year, and the 20-year average is 1271 mm year^{-1}. The mean annual air temperature is 26.3 °C.

The site had been under secondary forest for about 15 years. Before clearing, trees were identified (Mueller–Harvey 1983). The understorey was first removed to provide access and to allow the first set of soil samples to be collected. All trees were cut and removed except for a few palm trees which were left standing. No vegetation was burned, and all operations were carried out manually.

After the site had been cleared in May 1979 it was cropped successively with soya bean (*Glycine max* L.), maize (*Zea mays* L.), maize and maize until August 1981. Cropping was conducted under zero-tillage conditions. No fertilizers were applied and crop residues were removed at harvest. Although the site was relatively flat, the soil surface was covered with perforated black plastic sheets to prevent splash erosion.

The cleared area was divided into 16 plots, each of 10 m × 10 m (Fig. 1). Two subplots, each of 2 m × 2 m, were located within each plot using random numbers; the same subplots were used throughout the period of the experiment. Sixteen soil cores (core diameter, 1.5 cm) were taken from each subplot on each sampling occasion, and two lots of eight cores were bulked and analysed separately. Therefore, on each sampling occasion, 64 samples were analysed, each sample containing eight bulked soil cores. (The bulking of soil cores was carried out to limit the number of analyses and to provide an adequate assessment of variability between subplots.) The depth of sampling was to 10 cm and 8 cm according to bulk density, as discussed below.

There were four sampling occasions at times 0, 10, 14 and 22 months to measure the concentrations of organic carbon and phosphorus, total nitrogen, phosphorus and sulphur, and bulk density. The analytical methods have been described by Mueller-Harvey *et al.* (1985). The measurements of total nitrogen

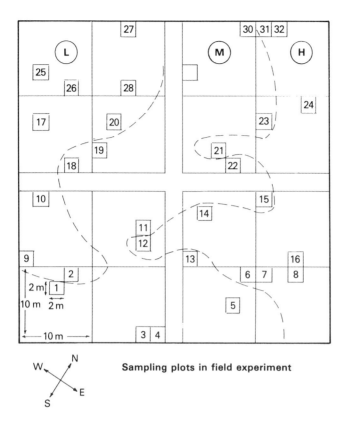

FIG. 1. Layout of plots in field experiment. The broken lines are the boundaries of low (L), medium (M) and high (H) organic matter subplots, where L = 0.80–1.19% carbon, M = 1.20–1.59% carbon and H = 1.60–2.67% carbon.

and total sulphur approximate to the organically held nitrogen and sulphur because the soils are freely drained and strongly leached. Bulk density was measured by pushing a 10 cm × 10 cm × 10 cm sampling box into the soil until it was flush with the soil surface; the soil was then dried and weighed. The analyses were used to calculate the rate of change of each constituent over a 22-month period.

Starting 9 months after the forest had been cleared, samples of soil (0–10 cm) were collected weekly over a 12-month period, extracted with 1 M KCl and analysed for NH_4–N and NO_3–N. The samples were collected from three low, three medium and three high organic matter plots (Fig. 1). Duplicate sets, each consisting of eight soil cores (diameter, 1.5 cm), were collected from each plot and each set was analysed separately. The same sampling method was used for plots covered with black plastic sheets and plots covered with crop residues, but results are reported here only for the plastic covered plots.

At crop harvest, plants were cut close to ground level, dried and weighed, and grain and stover were analysed separately for nitrogen and phosphorus using standard methods.

RESULTS AND DISCUSSION

Sample variability

Bulk density

During cultivation bulk density changed from 1.13 to 1.36 g cm^{-3}, an increase of about 20%. The values were variable. For example, on the first sampling occasion when 29 measurements were made the values ranged from 0.88 to 1.40 g cm^{-3} with a mean of 1.13 and a standard error of 0.03. Errors due to the variability of bulk density and its change during cropping were reduced by intensive sampling and by taking samples to a depth which gave a constant weight per unit land surface. Before the land was first brought into cultivation soil samples for chemical analysis were taken to a depth of 10 cm and later samples were taken to 8 cm.

Chemical analyses

Compared with the soil analyses summarized by Beckett & Webster (1971) the

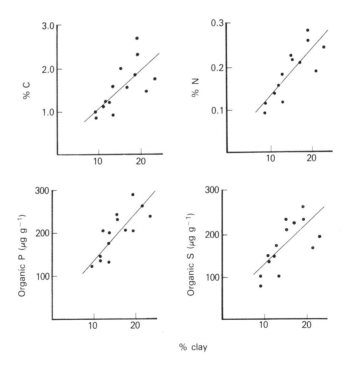

FIG. 2. Relationships between carbon (%), nitrogen (%), organic phosphorus (μg g^{-1}) and organic sulphur (μg g^{-1}) in soils and the percentage clay in samples taken immediately after forest clearance. Regression equations: C (%) = 0.086 (clay (%)) + 0.23 (R = 0.71); N (%) = 0.011 (clay (%)) + 0.018 (R = 0.82); organic P (μg g^{-1}) = 10.2 (clay (%)) + 38.9 (R = 0.82); organic S (μg g^{-1}) = 8.88 (clay (%)) + 33.8 (R = 0.70).

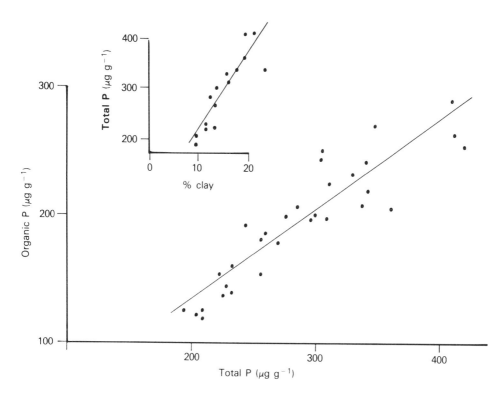

FIG. 3. Relationship between organic phosphorus and total phosphorus in soil samples taken after forest clearance. Inset shows the relationship between total phosphorus and clay in some of the samples. Regression equations: organic P (μg g^{-1}) = 0.69 (total P (μg g^{-1})) + 7.34 (R = 0.91); total P (μg g^{-1}) = 14.5 (clay (%)) + 75.5 (R = 0.89).

variability of the chemical analyses was low. The variability was not random and there was evidence that it could be accounted for, in the main, by the effects of particle size distribution and vegetation. Firstly, as shown in Fig. 2 and Fig. 3 (inset) there were significant linear relationships between percentage clay and organic carbon, nitrogen, phosphorus, sulphur and total phosphorus. Secondly, 50% or more of the variability of the organic carbon, nitrogen and sulphur concentrations occurred *within* sampling plots whereas most of the variability of organic and total phosphorus occurred *between* sampling plots (Table 1). The variability within plots can reasonably be attributed to the localized deposition of tree litter; the large variability of organic and total phosphorus between plots, which is longer range, can be attributed to the effect of clay content, which varied over the experimental area. Where clay content was low (mean value, 11.2%) the average total phosphorus concentration was 265 μg g^{-1}, and where it was comparatively high (mean value, 18.2%) the total phosphorus concentration was 422 μg g^{-1}.

TABLE 1. The source of variance of components of soil organic matter expressed as a percentage of total variance for samples from experimental plots near Ibadan, Nigeria collected as described in the text. The data are originally from Mueller-Harvey *et al.* (1985)

Source of variance	Carbon	Nitrogen	Organic phosphorus	Total phosphorus	Sulphur
Plots	20	35	79	64	37
Subplots	74	58	18	31	50
Samples	6	7	3	5	13

Of the three nutrients considered here, nitrogen can be fixed biologically and both nitrogen and sulphur can be added to the ecosystem in wet and dry deposition; however, most evidence indicates little accession of phosphorus from the atmosphere (Jordan 1985). The ecosystem thus has an almost fixed amount of phosphorus, but can increase its stock of nitrogen and sulphur. If tree growth is limited by the supply of phosphorus, litterfall and hence the soil organic components would be expected to be related to the total phosphorus content of the soil, and in turn to the percentage clay, as shown in Fig. 2. The suggestion is that the total phosphorus content of the soil determined the accumulation of organic carbon and organically held nutrients, a concept which may be valid for other ecosystems (McGill & Cole 1981).

Effect of tree species

Trees were identified before felling and soil organic matter contents could therefore be compared with the distribution of species. The contents were consistently higher under palm trees (*Elaeis guinensis* Jacq.), as has also been observed by Kang (1977). Leguminous trees (Mimosaceae and Papilionaceae) occurred most commonly on soils with high sand contents and these soils were low in organic matter. The soil C : N and C : S ratios were about the same where these trees had grown as elsewhere, but C : P ratios were slightly higher. The evidence, while by no means conclusive, suggests that the acquisition of nitrogen by non-symbiotic biological fixation had been of considerable importance elsewhere in the forest. This process needs to be better understood if fallow systems in the humid tropics are to be used effectively.

Nutrient availability

Mineral nitrogen

The NO$_3$–N analyses presented in Fig. 4 are 3-weekly averages on low, medium and high organic matter plots. The NH$_4$–N concentrations are shown for the medium organic matter plot only because they did not vary with the organic matter content of the soil; they were low and seasonal changes were small. By contrast, the NO$_3$–N concentrations were about twice as high on the high organic matter plots as on the low organic matter plots. There were also marked seasonal trends. The concentrations reached their peak during April with the onset of the rains. The first crop (maize) was planted on 24 April 1980 and the decrease in NO_3–N during May and June can be attributed to uptake by the crop, and loss by leaching or denitrification. The NO_3–N concentrations were low when the second crop was planted on 10 September.

On plots covered with crop residues, NH_4–N was about the same as on the plastic covered plots, but NO_3–N concentrations were generally lower. The results in Fig. 4 show the big influence of soil organic matter on the amount of

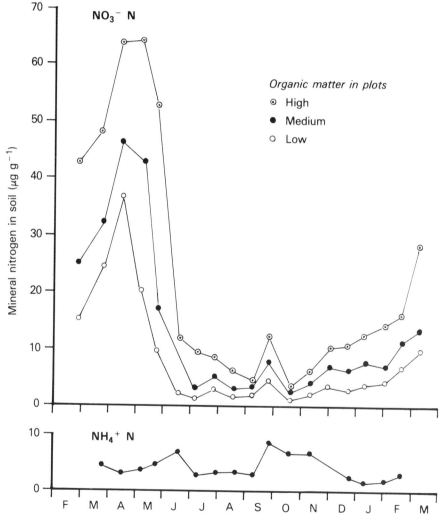

FIG. 4. Nitrate nitrogen in soil (0–10 cm) from high, medium and low organic matter plots, 1980–1981. Ammonium nitrogen did not differ between plots and analyses shown are for medium organic matter plots only.

nitrogen which becomes available to crops. The same will apply to sulphur and phosphorus.

Nutrient availability to crops

The amounts of nitrogen, phosphorus and sulphur in soil organic matter which mineralized over the 22-month period (June 1979–April 1981) were calculated from the changes in the concentrations of the organic components. As shown elsewhere (Mueller-Harvey *et al.* 1985) the decreases over the 22-month period in the top 10 cm of soil were 1.49 to 1.06%, 0.174 to 0.119%, 194 to 147 μg g^{-1} and 163 to 92 μg g^{-1} for carbon, nitrogen, organic phosphorus and total sulphur, respectively. For nitrogen, phosphorus and sulphur the reduction in the amounts in soil organic matter exceeded the amounts taken up by crops in the same period. The first crop was soya bean (which will possibly have added 50–100 kg ha^{-1} nitrogen to the system) and the stover of all crops was removed. If the stover had been returned to the soil and no leguminous crop had been grown, the differences given in Table 2 would have been greater. It should also be noted that the loss from soil organic matter is from the top 10 cm of soil only, and loss will also have occurred from greater depths.

The fate of the three nutrients after mineralization is not known. It is probable that most of the nitrate and sulphate not taken up by crops was leached out of the soil, nitrate being leached faster than sulphate because the latter may be adsorbed. The loss of nutrients is an economic loss, and for nitrogen alone the cost of replacement in fertilizer would amount to about £70 ha^{-1} at £0.3 per kilogram of nitrogen. Additionally, nitrate and sulphate ions will be leached with co-ions such as Ca^{2+}, Mg^{2+} and K^+. If Ca^{2+} was the only cation leached, the loss over the 22-month period would be 408 kg. For replacement this would require 1 t ha^{-1} of calcium carbonate. The estimate for leaching loss is not unreasonable, because after forest clearance at Onne near Port Harcourt (4°55′N, 7°0′E) the measured loss of calcium was 316 kg ha^{-1} in 1 year, averaged from drainage water analyses from eight lysimeters (T. F. Wong, personal communication). These losses have important implications for the nutrient balance of tropical ecosystems.

TABLE 2. Comparison of mineralization in soil (0–10 cm) of nitrogen, phosphorus and sulphur with the amounts in the above-ground parts of crops over a 22-month period at the experimental plots near Ibadan, Nigeria (*assumes N : S ratio in crops of 15 : 1 (Wild 1988))

	Mineralization from soil organic matter (kg ha^{-1})	Uptake by crops (kg ha^{-1})	Difference (kg ha^{-1})
N	622	382	238
P	53	43	10
S	79	25*	54

Rates of mineralization

The half-life values of each organically held element were 3.5, 3.3, 4.7 and 2.3 years for carbon, nitrogen, phosphorus and sulphur, respectively (Mueller-Harvey *et al.* 1985). The values show that the rate of mineralization of organic sulphur is greater than that of the other organically held elements; this led to a widening of the C : S and N : S ratios during cultivation. It is to be expected that because of the rapid mineralization of organic sulphur, especially in soils which adsorb sulphate weakly, deficiency of sulphur will occur early in the cropping sequence after forest clearance, which indeed has been observed by one of us (A. S. R. Juo).

The need for models of nutrient availability after fallows

Analysis of soil for organically held nutrients provides estimates of mineralized nutrients only indirectly. Furthermore, they cannot be obtained with sufficient frequency to allow mineralization rates to be compared with the time-course of nutrient uptake by crops. However, the data in Fig. 4 indicate that there is a high rate of mineralization at the start of the rains, as is commonly observed (Greenland 1958; Wild 1972; Haynes 1986). The concentrations are the differences between mineralization and losses (including uptake by the crop). More experimentation will be needed if the rates of mineralization and nutrient uptake are to be compared. Such experimentation would be useful because it appears that only part of the mineralized nutrients is taken up by crops.

The data from the present work provide some guidance to the length of period for which mineralized nutrients will be sufficient for a reasonable crop yield. It has, for example, been estimated that mineralization for 4 years after forest clearance will provide enough nitrogen and phosphorus to support two maize crops per year each yielding 1.5 t of grain (Mueller-Harvey *et al.* 1985). More sites need to be examined to test whether the patterns established at the site used here occur generally. If they do, there are good prospects for developing equations (models) to predict rates of mineralization, crop uptake and fertilizer requirements at other sites.

ACKNOWLEDGEMENTS

Financial support was provided through research fellowships to I. M-H by the International Institute of Tropical Agriculture and the Research Board of the University of Reading.

REFERENCES

Beckett, P.H.T. & Webster, R. (1971). Soil variability—a review. *Soils and Fertilizers*, **34**, 1–15.
Greenland, D.J. (1958). Nitrate fluctuations in tropical soils. *Journal of Agricultural Science*, **50**, 82–92.

Haynes, R. J. (1986). The decomposition process: mineralization, immobilization, humus formation, and degradation. *Mineral Nitrogen in the Plant–Soil System* (Ed. by R.J. Haynes), pp. 52–126. Academic Press, Orlando.

Jordan, C.F. (1985). *Nutrient Cycling in Tropical Forest Ecosystems.* Wiley, Chichester.

Kang, B.T. (1977). Effect of some biological factors on soil variability in the tropics II. Effect of oil palm tree (*Elaeis guinensis* Jacq.). *Plant and Soil,* **47,** 451–467.

McGill, W.B. & Cole, C.V. (1981). Comparative aspects of cycling of organic C, N, S and P through soil organic matter. *Geoderma,* **26,** 267–286

Mueller-Harvey, I. (1983). *A study of organic phosphorus and its transformations in soil and litter.* PhD Thesis, Reading University, U.K.

Mueller-Harvey, I., Juo, A.S.R. & Wild, A. (1985). Soil organic C, N, S, and P after forest clearance in Nigeria: mineralization rates and spatial variability. *Journal of Soil Science,* **36,** 585–591.

Nye, P.H. & Greenland, D.J. (1965). *The Soil under Shifting Cultivation. Technical Communication No 51.* Commonwealth Bureau of Soils, Harpenden, U.K.

Okigbo, B.N. (1980). Farming systems in West Africa. *Nitrogen Cycling in West African Ecosystems* (Ed. by T. Rosswall), pp. 131–156, SCOPE/UNEP. International Nitrogen Unit, Royal Swedish Academy of Sciences.

Ruthenberg, H. (1971). *Farming Systems in the Tropics.* Oxford University Press, Oxford.

Wild, A. (1972). Mineralization of soil nitrogen at a savanna site in Nigeria. *Experimental Agriculture,* **8,** 91–97.

Wild, A. (1988). Potassium, sodium, calcium, magnesium, sulphur, silicon. *Russell's Soil Conditions and Plant Growth* (Ed. by A. Wild), pp 743–779. Longman, Harlow.

Nutrient dynamics in forest fallows in South-East Asia

K. NAKANO* AND SYAHBUDDIN**

*The Kagoshima University Research Center for the South Pacific, Kagoshima 890, Japan, and
**Department of Biology, Faculty of Mathematics and Natural Sciences, Andalas University, Padang 25001, The Province of West Sumatra, Indonesia

SUMMARY

1 Quantitative studies on the nutrient dynamics of forest fallows in South-East Asia are reviewed. Most data are from Thailand and show that organic carbon, total nitrogen and cation exchange capacity of surface soil reach their lowest values 3 to 4 years after the beginning of the fallow, whilst exchangeable cations and pH values decline slowly throughout the fallow. For 'available' phosphorus, two studies indicate that the lowest point occurs around the fourth year after the beginning of the fallow period (during the 'bush' stage), whereas another study suggests a decline for many years until the stage of mature forest.

2 The present study was made on above-ground biomass and nutrients in the upper layer of soils (derived from volcanic ash) in young fallows (plots 1 and 2), a stable, anthropogenic fern community (plot 3), in 'bush' (plot 4) and in mature forest (plot 5) in a wet montane area (c. 1°S) at 1530–1800 m altitude in West Sumatra, Indonesia.

3 Total above-ground vegetation biomass increased from 0.21 kg m^{-2} (plot 1) to 1.20 kg m^{-2} (plot 4). The biomass in the mature forest (plot 5) was clearly higher than plots 1–4 but was not measured.

4 The contents of exchangeable bases in the upper layer of soils generally increased with above-ground biomass. Organic carbon and 'available' phosphorus were least in plot 4. The highest values of 'available' phosphorus and exchangeable potassium, sodium and magnesium were in plot 5.

INTRODUCTION AND REVIEW

This paper is mainly concerned with South-East Asian shifting cultivation where the most important crop is rice (Sasaki 1970); the following review does not include examples from New Guinea since rice is not the staple food of the shifting cultivators there (Barrau 1958).

There have been few quantitative and systematic studies on the nutrient dynamics of swidden cycles in South-East Asia and no study is completely satisfactory. The best data on vegetation recovery during fallow are from Thailand (Nakano 1978; Sabhasri 1978; Tsutsumi *et al.* 1983). In northern Thailand, the above-ground biomass was 27.7 t ha^{-1} after 6–7 years and 63.1 t ha^{-1} after 9–10 years (Sabhasri 1978). Much higher recovery rates have been reported by Moekiyat, Hitam & Wirakusumah (1980) in fallow near Balikpapan,

325

East Kalimantan. There the total biomass was 99.5 t ha^{-1} after 6 years and 164 t ha^{-1} after 10 years.

Comparing these data with those of Scott (1978), Uhl & Jordan (1984) and Jordan (1985), the recovery rate of the above-ground biomass of fallowed areas in Thailand is less than that in Africa or the neotropics, while the data from East Kalimantan show the highest or second-highest recovery rate. Considering the results of Sabhasri (1978) and Nakano (1978) for northern Thailand (and excluding values for the 4-monthly season after the abandonment of swiddens because this falls in a distinctly dry season there), there seems to be a roughly exponential rate of regrowth in the first 3 or 4 years of the fallow.

Drew, Aksornkoae & Kaitpraneet (1978) presented an example, in north-eastern Thailand, with an even lower rate of regrowth than that in northern Thailand. However, their study site was subject to burning "for an indeterminate period of many years" (Drew *et al.* 1978, p. 7). Simple comparison of regrowth in north-eastern Thailand (Tsutsumi *et al.* 1983) with other regions is inappropriate since the experimental plots of Tsutsumi *et al.* were not cropped. Nevertheless, the regrowth rate appears to be similar to that of northern Thailand.

Only Zinke, Sabhasri & Kunstadter (1978) and Tsutsumi *et al.* (1983) have given quantitative data on mineral nutrients in the regrowth vegetation. The first concerned almost an entire swidden cycle of 10 years, and the second almost the first 2 years after the clearing and burning of the primary forest.

Changes in soil chemical fertility have been investigated more frequently. However, difficulties of comparison have arisen because the samples have been taken from different areas with various fallow periods and because "the natural variability in soil properties within one field, or between fields of one soil series is a serious limitation in studying the effect of one or more external factors upon such properties" (Andriesse 1977, p. 10). The importance of experimental studies is frequently emphasized, but no one has yet attempted a complete study covering an entire swidden cycle in South-East Asia.

Nevertheless, some important points have emerged from the work so far. The trends in the quantitative changes of nutrients in the surface soils analysed by Nakano (1978) correspond well with those of the surface soils of Zinke *et al.* (1978) and Sabhasri (1978) despite some differences in the natural vegetation. Thus the contents of organic carbon, total nitrogen and cation exchange capacity reach their lowest points 3 to 4 years after the beginning of the fallow and gradually increase thereafter. This seems to support the popular view that ". . .soil humus increases in amount under the fallow" (Nye & Greenland 1960, p. 47). However, no studies on a series of samples in northern Thailand have indicated that the soils under mature forests have the highest contents of organic carbon. Except for the examples of Sabhasri (1978), exchangeable bases and pH slowly decline during the fallow. Both Sabhasri (1978) and Nakano (1978) indicated that, in so far as a swidden cycle is concerned, the lowest content of 'available' phosphorus occurs around the fourth year after the beginning of the fallow period, namely the 'bush' stage, whereas Zinke *et al.* (1978) suggested a continuous decline for many years up to mature forest.

Most of the more recent data (Andriesse 1977; Nakano 1978; Sabhasri 1978; Zinke *et al.* 1978) on soil fertility at the time of abandonment show that 'available' phosphorus, exchangeable calcium and pH values of surface soil are higher than those at the preclearing stage. Furthermore, Tulaphitak, Pairintra & Kyuma (1983) observed higher values of pH, 'available' phosphorus, exchangeable potassium and NO_3-N at the time of abandonment compared with the pre-clearing stage. Driessen, Buurman & Permadhy (1976) found higher concentrations of exchangeable potassium and NO_3-N in soils after a 2-year cropping compared with those of virgin forest.

Relatively higher values of pH and higher concentrations of NO_3-N, 'available' phosphorus and exchangeable cations at the beginning of the fallow phase must help the regrowth of fallow vegetation. One should note that the nutrient-utilization-efficiency of fallow vegetation is regarded as being higher than that of crops (Chapin 1980). To satisfy the yield requirements of shifting cultivators, even their low-potential varieties of crops require more fertile soils than the natural vegetation (Uhl 1987). Hence, researchers of shifting cultivation should keep in mind that the farmers usually select the most favourable sites (Dove 1985).

The roughly exponential (Nakano 1978; Sabhasri 1978) or surprisingly rapid (Moekiyat *et al.* 1980) regrowth rate at the initial stage of the fallow phase seems partly to reflect the following: the selection of comparatively fertile sites initially by shifting cultivators; the relative abundance of nutrients in the soils of abandoned swiddens; and the high nutrient-utilization-efficiency of recovering vegetation in spite of the possibly lowered soil organic matter during cropping (Soerianegara 1970). The rapid uptake of soluble nutrients from the soil by the fallow vegetation prevents their loss from the ecosystem (Vitousek & Reiners 1975). If further disturbances, such as fires, occur early on in the fallow, the most favourable opportunity for regrowth will be lost and soil erosion will remain severe (Kellman 1969). Moreover, the restoration of humus will be delayed (Coulter 1950; Kellman 1969; Satari 1969). On the other hand, if fallow vegetation is established soon after abandonment, humus re-accumulation may begin in about 5 years (Nakano 1978; Sabhasri 1978; Zinke *et al.* 1978).

The popular view that tropical forests store their nutrients in the vegetation rather than in the soils (Clarke 1976) is not necessarily correct. In the Thailand studies (Zinke *et al.* 1978; Tsutsumi *et al.* 1983), the quantities of phosphorus and exchangeable potassium held in the above-ground parts (including the components in the A_0 horizon) of mature forests were found to be higher than those held by the soils to a depth of 30 cm. However, Tsutsumi *et al.* (whose study site was not calcareous) found that the soil under the mature forest contained more calcium and magnesium than the above-ground parts. In both cases, the soils of 0–30 cm depth contained much more nitrogen than the above-ground parts.

Similar data are cited in Nye & Greenland (1960). Because most crops in swiddens in South-East Asia take up soil nutrients mainly from the upper 30 cm of soil, such comparisons are important, especially from the standpoint of shifting cultivators. As expected, Zinke *et al.* (1978) reported that the soils of 0–30 cm depth under the secondary forests had much higher proportions of all the important nutrient elements than the vegetation.

We now describe further work on nutrients and shifting cultivation from a montane area in West Sumatra, South-East Asia. Our study area is in phase III of Greenland 's (1974) development phase of land cultivation. This means that it does not lie in a typical forest-fallowed area.

SITE DESCRIPTION

The study site has been described in detail by Nakano *et al.* (1987). The site (*c.* 1°S, 101°E) is in the Barisan Mountains of the island of Sumatra, about 45 km east-south-east of Padang in the Province of West Sumatra. It is on a main and a subsidiary ridge along the south-western shore of Lake Diatas which has an area of 12 km^2 and is at an altitude of about 1530 m.

Meteorological data were obtained from a station on the eastern shore of the lake. There is no seasonal variation in temperature, and from 1983 to 1985, the daily maximum and minimum temperature ranges were between 22 °C and 26 °C and between 10 °C and 16 °C. The mean annual precipitation between 1978 and 1983 was 2437 mm. A relatively dry season occurs in June, July and August (Pusat Studi Lingkungan Hidup Universitas Andalas 1984). However, even in the driest month, July, the precipitation exceeds the evaporation (Pusat Studi Lingkungan Hidup Universitas Andalas 1984).

The soil is derived from volcanic ash (Anonymous 1974) produced by eruptions of the active volcano Mount Talang (2575 m) 14 km north-north-west of the study site.

The village at the foot of the subsidiary ridge (near plots 1–4) is encircled by wet paddy fields, very small orchards of sweet calabash (*Passiflora maliformis* L.) and upland fields for continual production of vegetables, such as potatoes (*Solanum tuberosum* L.), onions (*Allium cepa* L.) and tuber shallots (*Allium* sp.). The slopes of the subsidiary ridge are part of the area of shifting cultivation and are covered mainly by bracken (*Pteridium aquilinum* (L.) Kuhn), often with *Imperata cylindrica* (L.) Beauv. and *Chromolaena odorata* (L.) King & Robinson or *Eupatorium odoratum* L. Laumonier, Purnadjaja & Setiabudhi (1986) recognized this area as "grasslands or fernlands" on their vegetation map. As pointed out by Hagreis (1926), ferns are often as dominant in the apparently de-graded grassland of South-East Asia as the notorious *Imperata cylindrica* (L.) Beauu. and *Chromolaena odarata* (L.). The fallow periods in the study site are not necessarily short and sometimes last for a few decades. Nevertheless, the fallow vegetation rarely reaches the bush stage probably owing to frequent fires during the relatively dry season. It is probably true, however, that the stage of the fern community would often last for many years without fires.

The remnant forest is only on the upper part of the subsidiary ridges and on the main ridge, including a peak of 1815 m altitude. The forest is apparently mature, but with a little anthropogenic disturbance, and trees of species of *Ardisia*, *Castanopsis*, *Ficus*, *Lithocarpus*, *Litsea* and *Syzygium* are prominent.

MATERIALS AND METHODS

Sampling

Four sampling plots (numbers 1–4) were selected in a 200 m × 300 m area (1600–1650 m altitude) in the zone of shifting cultivation. In these plots the vegetation was sampled from four or five 2 m × 2 m quadrats in January 1985.

Plot 1 had been abandoned in August 1984. During the 10 months from October 1983 to August 1984, the farmer applied a small quantity of triple super-phosphate (TSP), which contains phosphorus and calcium, and had three potato harvests before abandonment. The field of plot 2 was abandoned in 1980 and the farmer had two potato harvests before abandonment. Plot 3 was in a semi-permanent stand of tall bracken with tall *Chromolaena odorata*. According to an old man living nearby, the vegetation there had remained as it was for nearly 30 years and rarely caught fire, although it might have undergone a light and non-destructive fire in 1978. Plot 4 was in an old field which had been abandoned 8–9 years before the sampling of the vegetation and had been used as a tobacco field for one harvest. No fertilizer had been applied. The vegetation of this plot was at the bush stage and included more than ten woody species; the predominant species was *Melastoma malabathricum* L. An additional plot (5) was chosen in the remnant forest at an altitude of about 1800 m on the main ridge 1.0 km south of plots 1–4. More details about plots 1–4 are given in Nakano *et al.* (1987).

The above-ground biomass of living vegetation in each 2 m × 2 m quadrat in plots 1–4 was measured as described by Nakano *et al.* (1987) who give full information on species composition and biomass. The quadrats were placed randomly, except in plot 2 where they were placed regularly (although the starting point was selected randomly).

Soil samples were collected from plots 1, 3, 4 and 5 in March 1986. No soil samples were collected from plot 2 since the field conditions changed too much during the 14 months between the sampling times of vegetation and soils. One pit was dug in each of plots 1, 4 and 5 for the collection of samples down to 95 cm depth (no data for the deep layers of these soils are discussed in this paper) after making profile descriptions. In addition, 15–20 samples of topsoil (0–5 cm depth) were randomly collected, using core samplers, from each of the plots 1, 3, 4 and 5. These topsoil samples were bulked for each plot.

Soil analyses

Analyses were made on air-dried soils sieved through a 2 mm mesh. Particle size distributions of the soils were determined using the following procedure. Ten grams of soil were treated with hydrogen peroxide and washed through a 70-mesh sieve with hot water. The remaining portion on the sieve was collected as the coarse sand fraction. The portion of suspension passing through the sieve was dispersed by adding 'Calgon' and shaking for 1 h. Clay and silt fractions were determined by the pipette method and the fine sand fraction was collected after decanting the silt and clay fractions.

pH was measured on a suspension of 10 g soil in 25 ml of de-ionized water or 1M potassium chloride solution. Organic carbon was measured by Allison's (1960) method. Total nitrogen was estimated by a semi-micro Kjeldahl technique using potassium sulphate and copper sulphate as catalysts. Available phosphorus was extracted from 1 g of soil with 200 ml of 0.002 N sulphuric acid for 30 min (the Truog method). Exchangeable cations were extracted from soil samples with 1 M ammonium acetate at pH 7.0 and analysed using atomic absorption spectroscopy.

RESULTS

The above-ground biomass of the vegetation and the chemical properties of the soils are summarized in Tables 1 and 2. The recovery of the above-ground biomass after abandonment is relatively slow. Plot 4, which had been abandoned for more than 8 years, had less than half the above-ground biomass of fallows of 3–4 years old in northern Thailand (Sabhasri 1978). However, plot 4 underwent a mild burning a few years after the beginning of the fallow (Nakano *et al.* 1987). It is remarkable that bracken (*Pteridium aquilinum*) should account for more than 90% of the above-ground biomass (Table 1) in plot 2 3–4 years after abandonment, although its absolute mean value is less than in plot 3 (Table 1). Its biomass is less in plot 4 where it is apparently disappearing.

The soils of plots 1, 3 and 4 show more or less the chemical reaction of allophane which characterizes Andosols. The soil from the forest (plot 5) is completely podzolized (T. Higashi, personal communication) and contains a

TABLE 1. Some details of the vegetation and the mean ($\pm$ S.E.) above-ground biomass (kg m^{-2} oven dry weight) of four plots in fallowed fields in West Sumatra, Indonesia (for biomass $n = 4$ (plot 1) or 5 (plots 2–4); *tentative S.E. (statistically incorrect because of the regular placing of quadrats) = 0.049; †tentative S.E. = 0.052)

Plot	1	2	3	4
Community type	Herbaceous	Fern-rich	Stable fern-rich	Bush
Length of fallow period	5 months	3–4 years	Not known	8–9 years
Above-ground biomass of *Pteridium aquilinum* (kg m^{-2})	0.09 $\pm$0.026	0.30*	0.33$\pm$0.057	0.17$\pm$0.025
Total above-ground biomass (kg m^{-2})	0.21$\pm$0.035	0.32†	0.47$\pm$0.028	1.20$\pm$0.372

TABLE 2. Chemical properties of soil samples collected from fallowed-field plots 1, 3 and 4 (Table 1) and a mature forest (plot 5) in West Sumatra, Indonesia. Samples (a) were bulked from 15–20 subsamples per plot collected from 0–5 cm depth; samples (b) are single collections per plot from 0–30 cm depth

Plot	Samples	pH_{H2O} (log units)	pH_{KCl} (log units)	Organic C (g m^{-2})	Total N (g m^{-2})	Available P (g m^{-2})	Exchangeable K (m-equiv. m^{-2})	Exchangeable Na (m-equiv. m^{-2})	Exchangeable Ca (m-equiv. m^{-2})	Exchangeable Mg (m-equiv. m^{-2})
1	a	4.85	3.92	3050	160	0.54	50	20	190	60
	b	—	—	10170	579	1.48	170	60	410	170
3	a	4.15	3.28	2390	137	0.42	80	20	250	60
	b	—	—	—	—	—	—	—	—	—
4	a	4.41	3.60	1750	110	0.24	80	10	300	100
	b	—	—	9360	671	1.11	370	80	730	360
5	a	3.72	2.58	3020	161	1.30	120	20	70	360
	b	—	—	10180	560	3.67	420	130	420	850

distinct A_2 horizon under the thick organic layer. The A_1 horizon of this soil is indistinguishable from the O_2 horizon. Therefore the soil data for plot 5 in Table 2 include a contribution from the O_2 horizon. The textures of these surface soils are: plot 1, light clay; plot 3, clay loam; plots 4 and 5, heavy clay.

All the soils are acidic and low in exchangeable cations, especially calcium and magnesium (Table 2). It should be noted that the contents of exchangeable bases generally increase as the biomass increases (Tables 1 and 2). Exceptions to this are sodium in the topsoils, and calcium in both the top and 0–30 cm layers of the soil in the mature forest. The TSP fertilization seems to have little influence on the surface-soil calcium in plot 1 at the time of sampling. Similar to the situation in northern Thailand referred to earlier, organic carbon and 'available' phosphorus are at a minimum at the bush stage (plot 4). Phosphorus is high in the soil in plot 1 following the TSP fertilization, but the fact that the phosphorus in plot 4 (bush) is far lower than in plot 3 (stable fern-rich community) is important. It is noteworthy that the soil (including O_2 horizon) from the forest at plot 5 has much soluble phosphorus. In the topsoils, the contents of organic carbon, total nitrogen and 'available' phosphorus are greater at plot 3 than at plot 4 and exchangeable calcium and magnesium contents are less.

Because the topsoil at plot 1, which did not support forest before its cropping phase, is rich in organic carbon, the data in Table 2 seem to give only partial support to the popular view that the soils of apparently degraded grassland or weedy vegetation are lower in humus than those of mature forests. However, the contents of organic carbon and most of the main plant nutrients in the topsoil of plot 3 are much lower than in plot 5.

DISCUSSION

Many forest fallow studies suggest declining contents of surface-soil exchangeable bases, particularly in the earlier stages of the fallow. This is probably due to erosion and leaching and to the uptake of immediately-available nutrients by the vegetation. When the fallow undergoes further disturbance and remains covered with depauperate herbaceous vegetation, the rate of erosion and leaching will go unchecked (Kellman 1969). Exchangeable bases, especially calcium and magnesium (Ahn 1974), are liable to be leached from the surface soil in regions with an ever-wet climate (or even where there is a distinctly dry season (Nakano 1978; Scott 1978)). Therefore, when the fallow vegetation remains sparse for a long time, exchangeable bases will be reduced.

In contrast with the typical cases of forest fallows, the data for plots 1 and 4 and mature forest in Table 2 imply that, when the fallow vegetation recovers in degraded circumstances, the contents of most of the exchangeable bases in surface soils increase with the restoration of the biomass. This process has some of the attributes of primary succession. In a study of the post-1883 succession of the vegetation of the Krakatau Islands, Higashi (1987) showed that the total contents of four kinds of exchangeable bases in the soils increased with the stages of vegetation succession.

The study in Irian Jaya (New Guinea) by Reynders (1961, p. 38) showed results apparently similar to those in Table 2 in that ". . . for all cations the lowest point falls at the beginning of the regeneration". However, Reynders studied the nutrient dynamics of the smooth progression from abandoned fields to forest in a forest-fallowed area, whereas the present study is concerned with the hindered succession of degraded vegetation. Furthermore, as pointed out by Andriesse (1977), Reynders' (1961) study was in an area with relatively fertile calcareous soils. In addition, the crops in the swiddens of his study site were sweet potato (*Ipomoea batatas* Lam.) and taro (*Colocasia esculenta* (L.) Schott), effectively root crops. The difference in the patterns of nutrient dynamics between Reynders (1961) and the studies of South-East Asian forest fallows cited earlier, may be attributable to the different kinds of the preceding crops.

An early decline of 'available' phosphorus during the fallow period has been recognized and has been attributed to the increased uptake of phosphorus by the recovering vegetation (Jordan 1985). However, as the root systems reach deeper layers, the deeper-lying available phosphorus may accumulate near the surface through the 'pumping effect' of the trees (Ewel 1986). The data in Table 2 are consistent with these ideas since the soluble phosphorus content in the surface soil of the bush (plot 4) is lower than that in both the stable fern-rich community (plot 3) and the mature forest (plot 5).

Table 2 shows that the stable fern-rich community (plot 3) is not markedly lower in nutrients than the bush (plot 4). This seems to agree with Scott's (1978, p. 136) view that the differences in the soils under the forest and the grassland "are not significant enough to inhibit the development of arboreal species in grassland given a long fire-free period".

CONCLUSION: ROLE OF NUTRIENTS IN FOREST FALLOWS

Recently, Ewel (1986) reviewed the ecological significance of fallow. Forest fallow is certainly much better than grass fallow in restoring soil conditions on degraded land. However, the recovery of nutrients in vegetation and surface soil is only one aspect of the restoration of the conditions for a satisfactory crop.

Except for extreme cases such as those in regions with heath forest, most abandoned swiddens are capable of recovery to forest if there is no further disturbance. The majority of quantitative studies suggest that a sufficiently fertile soil remains at the beginning of the fallow phase for the forest to recover. It may be biotic (including anthropogenic) or physical factors rather than nutrient conditions that slow the rate of succession. Uhl (1987) seems to support this idea. In particular, the utilization of a swidden for too long a period is harmful, since the coppicing ability of the stumps of felled trees is lost, and the surface soil may be physically degraded. Nakano (1978) and Tsutsumi *et al.* (1983) have indicated the important role of coppice shoots for the smooth recovery of secondary forests. The study by Juo & Lal (1977) showed the worsening of physical properties of tropical soils in the fields where consecutive croppings were carried out.

Dove (1985) also supports the consideration of a full range of factors. He showed that, in West Kalimantan, the mean yields of dry rice from swiddens in primary forests were much lower than those in secondary forests in the same area and year. The lower yields in the swiddens from primary forests were obtained despite a probably higher nutrient input due to a larger quantity of biomass burned and despite the probably less intense weed competition in the primary forest swiddens (Freeman 1970; Nakano 1978). Clearly, other important factors are at work.

These data and those cited earlier suggest that nutrients may actually be less important for shifting cultivators than has previously been believed.

ACKNOWLEDGEMENTS

A grant-in-aid from the Japan Society for the Promotion of Science, the Mitsubishi Foundation and the Tokyo Geographical Society promoted this work which is a contribution to the Project of Sumatra Nature Study. We thank Dr T. Higashi, Institute of Applied Biochemistry, University of Tsukuba, for his unstinting advice about the methods of soil survey and analyses used in this study, and technical staff of the Palyno Survey Co. Ltd, Japan, for help with soil analyses. Finally, we wish to express our gratitude to the anonymous referee and the editor for valuable comments and for the strenuous efforts to improve the English.

REFERENCES

Ahn, P.M. (1974). Some observations on basic and applied research in shifting cultivation. *Shifting Cultivation and Soil Conservation in Africa. FAO Soils Bulletin 24*, pp. 123–154. FAO, Rome.

Allison, L.E. (1960). Wet–combustion apparatus and procedure for organic and inorganic carbon in soil. *Soil Science Society of America Proceedings*, **24**, 36–40.

Andriesse, J.P. (1977). Nutrient level changes during a 20 year shifting cultivation cycle in Sarawak (Malaysia). *Paper Presented at the ISSN Conference 'CLAMATROPS', Kuala Lumpur, August 15–20, 1977*. Royal Tropical Institute, Amsterdam.

Anonymous (1974). *Peta Tanah Eksplorasi (Skala 1:1, 000, 000) Propinsi Sumatera Barat*. Lembaga Penelitan Tanah, Bogor, Indonesia.

Barrau, J. (1958). *Subsistence Agriculture in Melanesia. Bernice P. Bishop Museum Bulletin 219.* Bernice P. Bishop Museum, Honolulu.

Chapin, III, F.S. (1980). The mineral nutrition of wild plants. *Annual Review of Ecology and Systematics*, **11**, 233–260.

Clarke, W.C. (1976). Maintenance of agriculture and human habitats within the tropical forest ecosystem. *Human Ecology*, **4**, 247–259.

Coulter, J.K. (1950). Organic matter in Malayan soils. *Malayan Forester*, **13**, 189–202.

Dove, M.R. (1985). *Swidden Agriculture in Indonesia: the Subsistence Strategies of the Kalimantan Kantu.* Mouton, Berlin.

Drew, W.B., Aksornkoae, S. & Kaitpraneet, W. (1978). *An Assessment of Productivity in Successional Stages from Abandoned Swidden (Rai) to Dry Evergreen Forest in Northeastern Thailand. Forest Research Bulletin 56.* Faculty of Forestry, Kasetsart University, Bangkok.

Driessen, P.M., Buurman, P. & Permadhy (1976). The influence of shifting cultivation on a "podzolic" soil from Central Kalimantan. *Peat and Podzolic Soils and Their Potential for*

Agriculture. Proceedings of ATA 106 Midterm Seminar, Tugu, October 13–14, 1976. Soil Research Institute Bulletin 3, pp. 95–115. Soil Research Institute, Bogor, Indonesia.

Ewel, J.J. (1986). Designing agricultural ecosystems for the humid tropics. *Annual Review of Ecology and Systematics*, **17**, 245–271.

Freeman, D. (1970). *Report on the Iban. London School of Economics Monographs of Social Anthropology 41, University of London*. Athlone Press, London.

Greenland, D.J. (1974). Evolution and development of different types of shifting cultivation. *Shifting Cultivation and Soil Conservation in Africa. FAO Soils Bulletin 24*, pp. 5–13. FAO, Rome.

Hagreis, B.J. (1926). Rice culture on ladangs (dry fields). *Landbouw*, **2**, 50–53.

Higashi, T. (1987). Forest vegetation and the nutritional status of soils on the Krakatau Islands, Indonesia. *Soil Science and Plant Nutrition*, **33**, 103–122.

Jordan, C.F. (1985). *Nutrient Cycling in Tropical Forest Ecosystems*. Wiley, Chichester.

Juo, A.S.R. & Lal, R. (1977). The effect of fallow and continuous cultivation on the chemical and physical properties of an alfisol in western Nigeria. *Plant and Soil*, **47**, 567–584.

Kellman, M.C. (1969). Some environmental components of shifting cultivation in upland Mindanao. *Journal of Tropical Geography*, **28**, 40–56.

Laumonier, Y., Purnadjaja & Setiabudhi (1986). *Central Sumatra*. Institut de la Carte Internationale du Tapis Végétal, Toulouse and SEAMEO–BIOTROP, Bogor, Indonesia.

Moekiyat, W., Hitam, H. & Wirakusumah, R.S. (1980). Estimation of fallow period of the shifting cultivation practice, East Kalimantan. *Cita dan Fenomena Hutan Tropika Humida Kalimantan Timur* (Ed. by R.S. Wirakusumah), pp. 32–36. Pradnya Paramita, Jakarta.

Nakano, K. (1978). An ecological study of swidden agriculture at a village in Northern Thailand. *South East Asian Studies*, **16**, 411–446.

Nakano, K., Watanabe, T., Usman, R. & Syahbuddin (1987). A fundamental study of overall conservation of terrestrial and freshwater ecosystems in a montane region of western Sumatra: vegetation, land-use, and water quality. *Memoirs of the Kagoshima University Research Center for the South Pacific*, **8**, 87–124.

Nye, P.H. & Greenland, D.J. (1960). *The Soil Under Shifting Cultivation. Technical Communication No. 51*. Commonwealth Bureau of Soils, Harpenden, U.K.

Pusat Studi Lingkungan Hidup Universitas Andalas (Ed.) (1984). *Penelitan Air dan Biota Akuatik Danau Singkarak, Danau Maninjau, Danau Diatas dan Danau Dibawah Propinsi Sumatera Barat (Tahun 1983–1984)*. Departmen Pekerjaan Umum, Direktorat Jenderal Pengairan Dinas, Padang, Indonesia.

Reynders, J.J. (1961). Some remarks about shifting cultivation in Netherlands New Guinea. *Netherlands Journal of Agricultural Science*, **9**, 36–40.

Sabhasri, S. (1978). Effects of forest fallow cultivation on forest production and soil. *Farmers in the Forest: Economic Development and Marginal Agriculture in Northern Thailand* (Ed. by P. Kunstadter, E.C. Chapman & S. Sabhasri), pp. 160–184. University Press of Hawaii, Honolulu.

Sasaki, K. (1970). *Nettai no Yakibata*. Kokin–shoin, Tokyo.

Satari, A.M. (1969). Pengaruh vegetasi alang–alang dan belukar terhadap beberapa sifat tanah. *Communication of Agriculture*, **1**, 10–15.

Scott, G.A.J. (1978). *Grassland Development in the Gran Pajonal of Eastern Peru: a Study of Soil-Vegetation Nutrient Systems. Hawaii Monographs in Geography No. 1*. University of Hawaii at Manoa, Honolulu.

Soerianegara, I. (1970). *Soil Investigation in Mount Hondje Forest Reserve, West Java. Communication No. 93*. Departmen Pertanian, Direktorat Djenderal Kehutanan, Lembaga-Lembaga Penelitian Kehutanan, Bogor, Indonesia.

Tsutsumi, T., Yoda, K., Sahunalu, P., Dhanmanonda, P. & Prachaiyo, B. (1983). Forest: felling, burning and regeneration. *Shifting Cultivation: an Experiment at Nam Phrom, Northeast Thailand, and its Implications for Upland Farming in the Monsoon Tropics* (Ed. by K. Kyuma & C. Pairintra), pp. 13–62. Report of a research project, "Agroecological Studies on Shifting Cultivation and Its Transformation Process to Sustained Upland Farming", conducted as one of the overseas research projects with the grants of the Ministry of Education, Science and Culture, Japan.

Tulaphitak, T., Pairintra, C. & Kyuma, K. (1983). Soil fertility and tilth. *Shifting Cultivation: an*

Experiment at Nam Phrom, Northeast Thailand, and its Implications for Upland Farming in the Monsoon Tropics (Ed. by K. Kyuma & C. Pairintra), pp. 63–83.

Uhl, C. (1987). Factors controlling succession following slash-and-burn agriculture in Amazonia. *Journal of Ecology*, **75**, 377–407.

Uhl, C. & Jordan, C.F. (1984). Succession and nutrient dynamics following forest cutting and burning in Amazonia. *Ecology*, **65**, 1476–1490.

Vitousek, P.M. & Reiners, W.A. (1975). Ecosystem succession and nutrient retention: a hypothesis. *BioScience*, **25**, 376–381.

Zinke, P.J., Sabhasri, S. & Kunstadter, P. (1978). Soil fertility aspects of the Lua forest fallow system of shifting cultivation. *Farmers in the Forest: Economic Development and Marginal Agriculture in Northern Thailand* (Ed. by P. Kunstadter, E.C. Chapman & S. Sabhasri), pp. 134–159. University Press of Hawaii, Honolulu.

Nutrient cycling in forest fallows in north-eastern India

P. S. RAMAKRISHNAN*

School of Environmental Sciences, Jawaharlal Nehru University, New Delhi-110067, India

SUMMARY

1 This paper is based on intensive studies in north-eastern India of nutrient cycling processes in forest fallows following slash and burn agriculture (locally called *jhum*). Two sites, one at an altitude of 100 m and another at 1500 m, were considered.

2 In the slash and burn system, the fertility of the soil during the cropping phase is related to the nutrient cycling processes of the fallow phase.

3 During the cropping phase, nutrient losses occur through wind-blow, runoff and percolation water, and removal by crop harvest. Rapid depletion of soil nutrients occurs due to rapid transfer from soil to the living biomass during the first few years of fallow regrowth and is followed by subsequent net recovery through litterfall.

4 Partial weeding during the cropping phase and weeds of the early successional fallow phase help in the conservation of nutrients. An exotic weed such as *Mikania micrantha* H.B.K. conserves potassium in the system during the first few years of fallow regrowth.

5 Bamboos play an important role in nutrient conservation at the 100 m site from the tenth to the thirtieth year of fallow regrowth.

6 After the destruction of nutrient cycling by slash and burn, the system soon recovers through a quick succession, and the elements highly susceptible to leaching and runoff are conserved in the living biomass.

INTRODUCTION

The success of slash and burn agriculture (locally called *jhum*) in subtropical north-eastern India is to a large extent related to nutrient cycling patterns and processes of the forest fallow phase. Its success in the humid tropics generally depends on the same principles. Rapid regeneration of vegetation following clearing and burning reduces nutrient loss (Toky & Ramakrishnan 1981b; Mishra & Ramakrishnan 1983a), and allows a return to the steady state cycling characteristics of mature forest (Ramakrishnan & Toky 1981; Toky & Ramakrishnan 1983b; Jordan 1985; Vitousek & Sanford 1986). This paper is concerned with sites at 100 m and 1500 m altitude in north-eastern India (Ramakrishnan *et al.* 1981) and investigates the changing patterns of nutrient

---

*Present address: G.B. Pant Institute of Himalayan Environment and Development, Kosi, Almora 26343, U. P. India.

cycling during the forest fallow phase. The following aspects are studied: (i) the implication of the length of the fallow period for the nutrient budget under the cropping phase, (ii) the nutrient depletion pattern and recovery processes in the soil during secondary succession, (iii) nutrient turnover rates during early succession, (iv) key species and key processes contributing to nutrient conservation, and (v) the consequences related to nutrient cycling of biological invasion by exotic weeds.

SITE DESCRIPTION

The study site at lower altitude (100 m) is at Burnihat in the Khasi Hills of Meghalaya (26°0'N, 91°5'E) and supports semi-evergreen broadleaved forest. The climate is a subtropical monsoon with an average rainfall of 2200 mm year^{-1}; most rain falls from May to October. Average maximum and minimum temperatures are 25 °C and 12 °C for November to February and 32 °C and 23 °C for the remainder of the year. The soil is a red loamy oxisol (laterite) derived from metamorphic rocks. The surface soil has a high concentration of organic carbon and nitrogen but due to intense, leaching has low concentrations of cations. It has a surface pH of 7, but this declines to pH 5 at a depth of 40 cm (Ramakrishnan & Toky 1981).

The study site at higher altitude (1500 m) at Shillong in the Khasi Hills supports warm temperate montane forests with *Pinus kesiya*-dominated early successional forests; the mixed broadleaved forests of the climax phase are rare. The climate is monsoonal and the annual average rainfall is about 1800 mm. Average maximum and minimum temperatures are 17 °C and 8 °C for November to February and 28 °C and 16 °C for the remainder of the year.

During December and January the vegetation is slashed at the lower altitude site. Short stumps of the trees are left intact and there is no below-ground disturbance. Before the onset of the monsoon, towards the end of March or the beginning of April, the dried debris is burnt *in situ*. A mixture of six to thirteen crop species are sown together at the onset of the monsoon and the crops are harvested sequentially starting from July to December (Toky & Ramakrishnan 1981a).

The patterns of agriculture at the higher altitude site are a modified version of the typical type outlined above. The undergrowth vegetation of the pine forests and the lower branches of the sparsely distributed pine trees alone are slashed during December and January. The slash is arranged in parallel rows and the dried slash is topped over by a thin soil layer before a slow burn in May. The ridges so formed alternate with compacted furrows running along the slope. Crop mixtures are sown only on the ridges (Mishra & Ramakrishnan 1981).

At each of the 100 m and 1500 m sites there were agricultural plots under 2-, 5-, 10-, 15-, 20- and 30-year cycles. The data presented here are based on the means of three replicate subplots for each of the agricultural plots.

SLASH AND BURN AND SOIL NUTRIENTS

Nutrient depletion

After clear-cutting and burning of the forest, the ecosystem loses its ability to hold nutrients. Much ash is blown away by strong winds during the dry months of March and April (Toky & Ramakrishnan 1981b). Large losses also occur through volatilization of carbon and nitrogen during the burn so that there is a reduction in the quantity of these elements in the surface soil layers (Fig. 1). These losses continue during the early cropping phase. In contrast, available phosphorus and cations are added to the soil during the burn (Ramakrishnan & Toky 1981).

During the latter phases of the cropping period, carbon and nitrogen recovery occurs in the soil, partly because of the addition of organic matter through crop

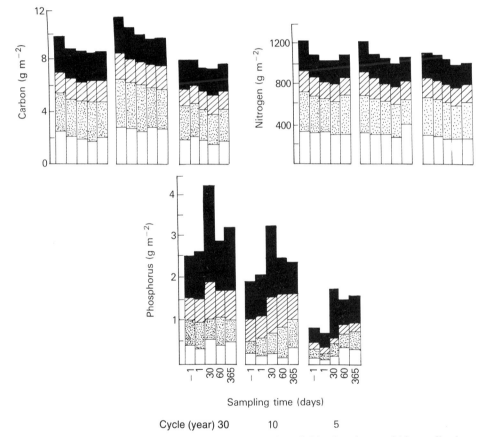

Fig. 1. Changes in total quantity of carbon, nitrogen and available phosphorus within a soil column of 40 cm depth after a burn for 30-, 10- and 5-year agricultural cycles. Dark column, 0–7 cm; hatched column, 7–14 cm; stippled column, 14–28 cm; open column, 28–40 cm (Ramakrishnan & Toky 1981).

and weed biomass and rapid nitrogen fixation by soil microbes. The depletion of organic carbon depends on the intensity of the cropping and the ratio of the cropping to the fallow period (Toky & Ramakrishnan 1981a). Under long agricultural cycles (a cycle is the length of the fallow phase between two successive croppings on the same site), adequate humus can be maintained in the soil even after many years of slash and burn agriculture (Coulter 1950; Birch & Friend 1956). Recovery of the available nitrogen lost during the burn occurs because of accelerated microbial activity following a rise in the pH and temperature of the surface soil (Moore & Jaiyebo 1963; Ahlgren & Ahlgren 1965). The increase in nitrification may be due to the removal of chemical inhibitors or to clear-cutting of intact vegetation and subsequent burning (Smith, Bormann & Likens 1968; Rice 1974). The activity of nitrifiers may also be closely linked to competitive interference by litter-decomposing heterotrophs in the humid tropics (Saxena & Ramakrishnan 1986).

After the slash and burn operation, the mixture of crop species is sown on plots of 2–2.5 ha on slopes of 30–40°. Nutrient losses occur through runoff and leaching during the early monsoon, particularly before the crop cover is established. A large proportion of the losses occurs in June as shown for cations in Fig. 2. The total losses through runoff and leaching can be considerable during

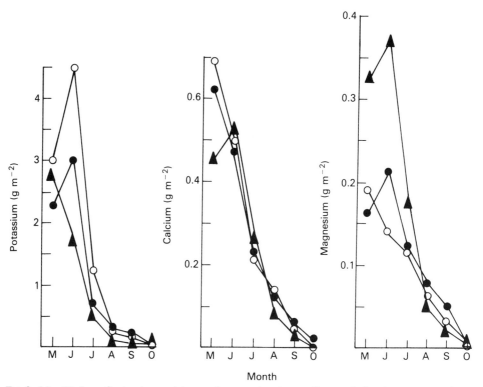

FIG. 2. Monthly loss of potassium, calcium and magnesium in runoff water during the monsoon of the cropping phase under following cycles of 30 (●), 10 (○) and 5 (▲) years (Toky & Ramakrishnan 1981b).

TABLE 1. Nutrient losses through runoff and percolation water collected in lysimeters at a site at 100 m altitude in Meghalaya, north-eastern India during cropping and fallow phases of slash and burn agriculture (values in parentheses are for percolation losses)

Nutrient	Cropping phase–agricultural cycle (years)			Fallow (years)	
(g m^{-2} year^{-1})	30	10	5	5	10
PO$_4$-P	0.11 (0.01)	0.13 (0.01)	0.09 (0.01)	0.01 (0.002)	0.01 (0.001)
NO$_3$-N	0.37 (0.88)	0.42 (1.06)	0.53 (0.92)	0.08 (0.11)	0.05 (0.05)
K	6.47 (1.51)	9.12 (2.12)	5.10 (1.37)	0.09 (0.05)	0.17 (0.02)
Ca	1.51 (0.53)	1.59 (0.48)	1.38 (0.46)	0.20 (0.27)	0.11 (0.16)
Mg	0.63 (0.25)	0.54 (0.21)	0.95 (0.23)	0.13 (0.09)	0.08 (0.05)

one cropping season (Table 1), particularly under a short agricultural cycle. The losses are impressive when totalled over 30 years. They are much greater for six croppings under 5-year cycles compared with three croppings under 10-year cycles; these, in turn, have much greater losses than those which occur for one 30-year cycle (Toky & Ramakrishnan 1981b).

Nutrient budget in agroecosystems

During a nitrogen budget analysis of a slash and burn system under cycles of 15, 10 and 5 years at the 1500 m site, Mishra & Ramakrishnan (1984) showed that a shortening of the cycle lowers the nitrogen content of the soil before burning as well as at the end of the 1- or 2-year cropping period (Table 2). Nitrogen loss under a 15-year agricultural cycle may be high because of the large quantities built up in the soil and vegetation after a longer fallow regrowth phase. Although the loss of nitrogen from a 5-year-cycle plot is lower after one cropping phase than that from a 15-year-cycle plot, the total loss is higher if the 5-year-cycle plot values are put on a time-scale of 15 years and multiplied by a factor of three.

We showed in this study that during one cropping phase, the agroecosystem loses about 600 kg ha^{-1} of nitrogen (the difference between the soil nitrogen capital before and after one cropping). If the plot under a 5-year cycle at the time of this study and during the previous 20 years (for which period land-use history was

TABLE 2. Net change in soil nitrogen (g m^{-2} year^{-1}) during cropping under slash and burn agriculture at a site at 1500 m altitude in Meghalaya, north-eastern India (Mishra & Ramakrishnan 1984) (*cropping was carried out for only 1 year under the 15-year and 10-year cycles and for 2 years under the 5-year cycle)

	Agricultural cycle* (years)			
	15	10	5	
			First-year crop	Second-year crop
Soil before burning (1)	768	774	640	598
Soil after the burn (2)	717	678	614	—
Soil at the end of cropping (3)	704	715	598	580
Net difference (1) minus (3)	64	59	42	18

known) had longer cycles preceding the 20-year period, then the system had lost 1.28×10^3 kg ha^{-1} of nitrogen from its initial capital of 7.68–6.40 $\times 10^3$ kg ha^{-1} (Table 2). While 10- or 15-year agricultural cycles are long enough to restore the original nitrogen status in the soil before the next cropping, it seems unlikely that the 600 kg ha^{-1} of nitrogen lost during one cropping could be restored under a 5-year cycle. One of the important disadvantages of a 5-year cycle lies in the reduced nitrogen capital (Mishra & Ramakrishnan 1983b, 1984). Increased frequency of fire and cropping with too short a fallow phase thus results in rapid site degradation (Ramakrishnan & Saxena 1984; Ramakrishnan 1985a, b; Saxena & Ramakrishnan 1986). For the agricultural system at the 100 m site we obtained broadly similar results, but with a net loss of 450 kg ha^{-1} of nitrogen and 14 kg ha^{-1} of phosphorus during one cropping under a 5-year cycle (Swamy & Ramakrishnan 1988a). This loss of nitrogen and phosphorus was accompanied by a net gain of all the cations (Swamy & Ramakrishnan 1987).

A comparative analysis of three weeding regimes showed that traditional weeding, where about 20% of the weed biomass is left behind by the forest farmer, has an important nutrient conservation role (Swamy & Ramakrishnan 1988b). Thus the loss of sediment and labile elements such as potassium through runoff is reduced by 20% when compared with total weeding. Traditional weeding has little effect on the yield potential of the crop mixture compared with total weeding. The harvested weed biomass traditionally put back into the system ensures efficient recycling of this resource. This weed management concept of the traditional farmer does not adversely affect the economic efficiency of the agroecosystem and suggests that the agriculture of the future should also have integrated weed management (Gliessman, Garcia & Amador 1981; Swamy & Ramakrishnan 1988a).

SECONDARY SUCCESSION FOLLOWING SLASH AND BURN AGRICULTURE

When a forest is converted to farm land, perturbations due to fire, the introduction of crop species, weeding, and other disturbances during crop harvest all result in a large reduction in the number of species. During secondary succession, the number of species increases gradually (Ross 1954; Odum 1969; Whitmore 1975; Toky & Ramakrishnan 1983a).

At both the 100 m site (Toky & Ramakrishnan 1983a) and the 1500 m site (Mishra & Ramakrishnan 1983c), a remarkably linear relation was observed during the first 15–20 years of succession with respect to species diversity and such processes as litter production and net primary productivity. The change in community structure was very marked at the lower altitude, from the initial weedy herbs, to a bamboo forest and, finally, to a mixed broadleaved forest. At the higher altitude, this change in community structure was less marked (Mishra & Ramakrishnan 1983c), because the slash and burn was not as complete as at the lower altitude (Toky & Ramakrishnan 1981a) since only the branches of the sparsely distributed trees and the ground vegetation were slashed. At the higher altitude, the *Pinus kesiya* Royle ex Gordon (Pinaceae) forest was the next stage in the succession after the herbaceous vegetation.

A steady increase in production in the first 5 or 6 years was due to the pioneer herbaceous species which effectively used the available light and nutrients (Saxena & Ramakrishnan 1983a, b; 1984a, b) and reproduced efficiently (Saxena & Ramakrishnan 1982). Subsequently, the shift to fast-growing bamboos (Rao & Ramakrishnan 1987) and to the early successional tree species (Ramakrishnan 1985a) also enhanced production.

NUTRIENT CYCLING IN FOREST FALLOWS

General patterns

With the rapid transfer of nutrients from the soil to the vegetation during the early phase of the fallow, rapid depletion of nutrients occurs in the soil even though losses by leaching and runoff are greatly reduced (Table 1). It is only after about 10 years of fallow that net transfer of nutrients back to the soil through litterfall becomes important and soil fertility recovers, as shown for phosphorus and potassium in Fig. 3. This is one of the reasons why a 10-year cycle for slash and burn agriculture is considered to be the shortest possible for the stability of the system (Ramakrishnan 1984), unless the fallow has an accelerated regrowth with species such as the introduced *Alnus nepalensis* Don. (Betulaceae) and other fast-growing early successional trees which improve soil fertility by rapid recycling of nutrients with a fast turnover of leaves (Ramakrishnan, Shukla & Boojh 1982; Baruah 1986).

At the 100 m site, the mineral nutrient content of the biomass increased during the first 20 years of fallow (Toky & Ramakrishnan 1983b). Starting with low enrichment quotients (content of element in the above-ground vegetation/ annual rate of uptake for that element) for potassium in younger fallows, a high value was attained in 15–20 years, because of the presence of the potassium-accu-mulating bamboo, *Dendrocalamus hamiltonii* Nees & Arnon (Gramineae) (Table 3). A similar role in Zäire for the early successional *Musanga cecropiodides* R. Br. was shown by Bartholomew, Mayer & Laudelout (1953). At the 100 m site, a sharp increase in the enrichment quotient for phosphorus was noted during the first 10 years of fallow regrowth because of selective accumulation by the herbaceous vegetation. Larger transfers of calcium and magnesium from soil to the tree biomass of an older fallow of 50 years resulted in a depletion of these two elements in the soil (Fig. 3). Matching our observations, Greenland & Kowal (1960) reported almost three times more calcium than potassium in the above-ground biomass in a 40-year-old fallow in Ghana. Similarly, Grubb & Edwards (1982) found higher concentrations of calcium and magnesium than potassium in the branches of older trees. Our own studies on a 50-year-old forest fallow in north-eastern India (Singh & Ramakrishnan 1982) and in the relict sacred grove

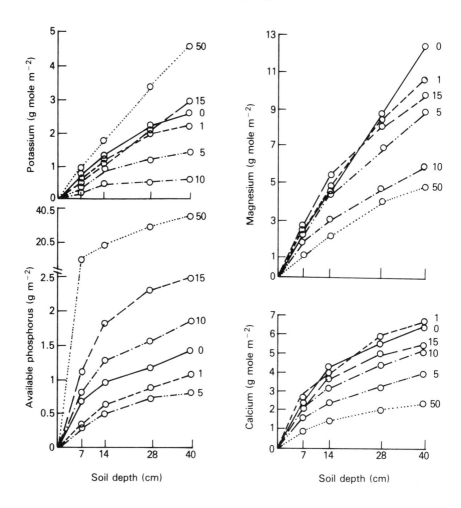

FIG. 3. Changes in the cumulative quantity of available phosphorus, potassium, calcium and magnesium within a soil column of 40 cm depth in fallows of different ages: O————O, 0 year; O – – –O, 1 year; O— ·· —O, 5 years; O—·—·—O, 10 years; O— —O, 15 years; O------O, 50 years (Ramakrishnan & Toky 1981).

TABLE 3. Rates of uptake of elements (g m^{-2} year^{-1}) in the above-ground biomass during 20 years succession following slash and burn agriculture in Meghalaya, north-eastern India (values in parentheses are the enrichment quotients (element held in vegetation/element uptake) of Woodwell, Whittaker & Houghton (1975) (Toky & Ramakrishnan 1983b))

Fallow age (years)	N	P	K	Ca	Mg
0–1	3.1 (0.9)	0.5 (1.0)	3.5 (0.9)	1.5 (0.9)	1.5 (1.0)
1–5	5.7 (2.5)	0.5 (4.0)	6.0 (3.0)	4.3 (1.8)	3.0 (2.1)
5–10	7.6 (2.5)	0.4 (6.2)	12.0 (4.5)	5.3 (3.1)	3.1 (2.8)
10–15	9.2 (3.7)	0.7 (6.3)	13.5 (7.2)	6.3 (4.5)	4.2 (3.7)
15–20	10.9 (4.5)	0.9 (7.1)	14.5 (9.5)	7.8 (5.6)	4.8 (4.7)

climax forests (Khiewtam 1986) have suggested that biomass storage of calcium and magnesium is much higher than that of potassium in older forest.

Fractional annual turnover (nutrient flux expressed as a percentage of the content of that nutrient in the vegetation and soil) (Reiners & Reiners 1970) of most elements in the soil increased with fallow age because of the rapid net up-take by the developing vegetation (Table 4). Phosphorus and potassium were exceptional in this respect and reached their highest annual turnover in the soil in the 1–5- and 10-year-old fallows, respectively. This was because of the rapid release of the selectively accumulated phosphorus by the herbs in 1–5-year-old fallows and potassium by *Dendrocalamus hamiltonii* in the 10-year-old fallow. The annual turnover of all elements in the vegetation followed a consistent pattern of decrease with age, suggesting net build-up in the biomass during the first 20 years.

With an early successional warm-temperate pine (*Pinus kesiya*) forest (Mishra & Ramakrishnan 1983c; Ramakrishnan & Das 1983) and climax mixed broadleaved forest (Khiewtam 1986) at the 1500 m site, lower temperatures, higher soil acidity and resinous pine litter (Das & Ramakrishnan 1985) all contribute to lower nutrient cycling rates during the forest fallow (Mishra & Ramakrishnan 1983d). For this reason the forest farmers merely cut off the lower branches of the sparse pine trees for agriculture (Mishra & Ramakrishnan 1981) rather than clear-felling as at lower altitudes.

Nutrient conservation through bamboos

Bamboos form an important component of the secondary succession of many tropical rain forests (Richards 1952; Whitmore 1975), including those of north-eastern India. Many of the species such as *Dendrocalamus hamiltonii* and *Neohouzeaua dulloa* A. Camus (Gramineae) decline after 25–30 years of fallow (Rao & Ramakrishnan 1987). In a recent study on the role of bamboos (Gramineae) (*Bambusa tulda, B. khasiana, Neohouzeaua dulloa*), we showed that they have much more nitrogen, phosphorus and potassium than the other species in the community (Table 5) (K. S. Rao & P. S. Ramakrishnan unpublished). We have already discussed the role of *Dendrocalamus hamiltonii* in accumulating potassium in the forest fallows. Nitrogen and potassium are highly labile and lost by runoff and leaching (Toky & Ramakrishnan 1983a); nitrogen is also lost through volatilization (Lloyd 1971; Mishra & Ramakrishnan 1984), whilst phosphorus is fixed by insoluble sesquioxides in the clay of soils rich in aluminium and iron (Gebhardt & Coleman 1974; Tinker 1977). The bamboos play a critical role in conserving these major nutrients in slash and burn agriculture.

Biological invasion and nutrient cycling properties

With the shortening of agricultural cycles, weeds become more abundant (Nye & Greenland 1960; Zinke, Sabhasri & Kunstadter 1978); we have quantified weeds

TABLE 4. The fractional annual turnover of elements (the weight leaving the vegetation or soil/the weight held in the vegetation or soil, expressed as a percentage) (Reiners & Reiners 1970) during 20 years succession following slash and burn agriculture in Meghalaya, north-eastern India (Toky & Ramakrishnan 1983b)

Fallow age (years)	N Soil	N Vegetation	P Soil	P Vegetation	K Soil	K Vegetation	Ca Soil	Ca Vegetation	Mg Soil	Mg Vegetation
1	0.3	42	50	10	3	20	1	64	1	40
5	0.5	29	50	11	10	16	5	39	3	32
10	0.6	32	20	12	46	9	5	23	4	29
15	0.8	20	35	10	11	6	6	15	3	20
20	1.0	17	30	8	12	5	7	11	4	16

TABLE 5. Annual nutrient accumulation (g m^{-2} year^{-1}) in the above-ground vegetation and in the bamboo component (in parentheses) of different forest fallows in north-eastern India (K. S. Rao & P. S. Ramakrishnan unpublished)

	Fallow age (years)						
	Garo Hills			Khasi Hills		Naga Hills	
	5	10	15	10	15	10	15
Nitrogen	1.20 (0.63)	2.07 (1.58)	1.74 (0.68)	2.63 (1.47)	1.99 (0.67)	2.66 (1.29)	2.52 (1.13)
Phosphorus	0.70 (0.03)	0.52 (0.46)	0.68 (0.33)	0.58 (0.52)	0.76 (0.45)	0.59 (0.14)	0.75 (0.62)
Potassium	5.36 (3.10)	11.82 (5.47)	13.37 (5.23)	7.55 (4.44)	10.50 (5.02)	9.95 (5.23)	9.14 (5.09)
Calcium	0.38 (0.03)	1.78 (0.57)	0.28 (0.57)	3.08 (0.64)	2.87 (1.29)	4.16 (0.52)	2.57 (0.43)
Magnesium	0.16 (0.02)	0.28 (0.05)	0.28 (0.07)	1.65 (0.41)	2.23 (0.33)	2.45 (0.46)	1.37 (0.18)

under slash and burn agriculture (Ramakrishnan 1984). The weed increase under short fallow cycles is due to the continuous presence of the same weed species in the cultivated plots and in the 4–6-year-long fallow plots. This allows a build-up of the soil banks of propagules.

Exotic weeds are important pioneers. In north-eastern India, there are species such as *Eupatorium odoratum* L. (Compositae) at lower altitudes, *E. adenophorum* Spreng. and *E. riparium* Regel. at higher altitudes (Dev & Ramakrishnan 1987) and *Mikania micrantha* H.B.K. (Asteraceae) (Swamy & Ramakrishnan 1987); all are native to the Latin American tropics. These were introduced to India about 100 years ago.

A series of perturbations occur during slash and burn agriculture resulting in the release of nutrients in a flush, followed by heavy losses during the agricultural operations. Under these conditions, when the high seasonal rainfall of over 2000 mm flows down the hill slope of 30–40°, the resultant soil is heterogeneous (Ramakrishnan 1985a). The availability of labile nitrogen in particular is uncertain. The pattern of C_3 and C_4 plants early in succession helps in the exploitation of nutrients from heterogeneous soils. C_4 species have a higher nitrogen-use efficiency and are restricted largely to nutrient-poor microsites, whilst the less efficient C_3 species occur in nutrient-rich microsites. It is also interesting that the C_3 species such as *Eupatorium* spp. and *Mikania micrantha* with a large biomass in the community are all exotic. All the important native grasses such as *Imperata cylindrica* Beauv., *Saccharum* spp., *Panicum* spp. and *Thysanolaena maxima* Kunze are all C_4 species. Native C_3 species do occur but they have a low biomass (Saxena & Ramakrishnan 1984c).

The consequences at the ecosystem level of biological invasion are considered in detail by Ramakrishnan & Vitousek (1989). In this paper only one salient consequence of biological invasion by the exotic species *Mikania micrantha* is discussed, which is often important in the first four years of fallow regrowth (Swamy & Ramakrishnan 1987). Potassium is accumulated rapidly in vegetation dominated by *Mikania micrantha* in the first four years of the fallow; this species' enrichment quotient for potassium was the highest observed (Table 6). What the bamboo *Dendrocalamus hamiltonii* does for potassium conservation under agricultural cycles of 10–25 years is done by *Mikania micrantha* under agricultural cycles of 4–5 years, which are now prevalent in north-east India.

LINKAGE BETWEEN CROPPING AND FALLOW PHASES OF SLASH AND BURN AGRICULTURE

Soon after the slash and burn operation, the soil nutrients differ, both quantitatively and qualitatively, between the short and long agricultural cycles. The quantitative differences are directly related to the biomass build-up during the fallow phase and the consequent slash load and ash release during the burn (Ramakrishnan & Toky 1981; Mishra & Ramakrishnan 1983b). Herbaceous communities of up to about 5 years of age generally have more phosphorus, and *Dendrocalamus hamiltonii* of 10–25 years of age has more potassium (Toky &

TABLE 6. Enrichment quotients (element held in vegetation/annual element uptake) of Woodwell, Whittaker & Houghton (1975) for *Mikania micrantha* and the total vegetation in successional fallows developed after shifting agriculture in north-east India (values in parentheses are for total vegetation) (Swamy & Ramakrishnan 1987)

Fallow age (years)	N	P	K	Ca	Mg
0–1	0.85	0.97	1.00	0.85	0.88
	(1.14)	(1.25)	(1.32)	(1.08)	(1.17)
1–2	1.03	1.12	1.18	1.03	0.98
	(1.42)	(1.74)	(1.60)	(1.33)	(1.29)
2–4	1.19	1.30	1.61	1.22	1.07
	(2.12)	(2.67)	(2.74)	(1.90)	(2.41)
4–8	1.85	1.94	2.55	2.44	1.46
	(2.63)	(5.62)	(4.01)	(2.64)	(3.20)
8–12	1.93	2.19	2.81	2.47	1.52
	(3.08)	(4.64)	(6.15)	(3.58)	(3.34)

Ramakrishnan 1983b), so that different quantities of these elements are released in ash under short and long agricultural cycles. We have seen how fallows dominated by *Mikania micrantha* also conserve potassium under short cycles. Thus qualitative differences in the nutrients after slash and burn are related to the vegetation structure of the fallow phase. Recently we have shown (P. S. Ramakrishnan unpublished) that there is an increased proportional release of calcium and magnesium when agricultural cycles are long (60 years or clearing of virgin forest) as in the Arunachal Pradesh in north-eastern India.

CONCLUSIONS

The nutrient cycling patterns of the slash and burn agricultural system in north-eastern India reveal some important points.

1 Compared with the cropping phase, the nutrient losses from the system are greatly reduced in the early fallow phase of the weedy herbaceous community.

2 In the initial 15 years or so of fallow regrowth, there can be rapid shifts in the nutrient pool between the soil and the vegetation compartments when the community structure changes from herbaceous to bamboo/pine dominated and, finally and more slowly, to a mixed broadleaved forest.

3 From a nutrient cycling viewpoint, a 10-year cycle for agriculture is the minimum for cropping because, among other reasons, soil fertility recovery is adequate at this stage.

4 A few species such as *Mikania micrantha* or *Dendrocalamus hamiltonii* may have a dominant role in nutrient cycling.

5 Biological invasion by exotics need not always be viewed as undesirable as they may have useful attributes, e.g. *Mikania micrantha* helps to conserve potassium.

REFERENCES

Ahlgren, I.F. & Ahlgren, C.E. (1965). Effects of prescribed burning on soil microorganisms in a Minnesota jackpine forest. *Ecology*, **46**, 304–310.

Bartholomew, W.V., Mayer, J. & Laudelout, H. (1953). Mineral nutrient immobilization under forest and grass fallow in the Yangambi (Belgian Congo) region. *Publications de l' Institut National pour l'Etude Agronomique du Congo Belge, Serie Scientifique*, **57**, 1–27.

Baruah, U. (1986). *Studies on ecological adaptation of shrub species in successional forest communities.* PhD Thesis, North-Eastern Hill University, Shillong, India.

Birch, H.F. & Friend, M.T. (1956). The organic matter and nitrogen status of east African soils. *Journal of Soil Science*, **7**, 156–167.

Coulter, J.K. (1950). Organic matter in Malayan soils: a preliminary study of the organic matter content in soil under virgin jungle, forest plantations and abandoned cultivated land. *Malayan Forester*, **13**, 189–202.

Das, A.K. & Ramakrishnan, P.S. (1985). Litter dynamics in Khasi pine (*Pinus kesiya* Royle ex Gordon) of north-eastern India. *Forest Ecology and Management*, **10**, 135–153.

Dev, P. & Ramakrishnan, P.S. (1987). Coexistence of closely related *Eupatorium* species. I. *Eupatorium odoratum* L. versus Eupatorium adenophorum Spreng. versus *Eupatorium riparium* Regel. at different altitudes. *Proceedings of the Indian Academy of Sciences (Plant Sciences)*, **97**, 165–176.

Gebhardt, H. & Coleman, N.T. (1974). Anion adsorption by allophanic tropical soils. III. Phosphate adsorption. *Soil Sciences Society of America, Proceedings*, **38**, 255–261.

Gliessman, S.R., Garcia, E.R. & Amador, A.M. (1981). The ecological basis for the application of traditional agricultural technology in the management of tropical agroecosystems. *Agro-Ecosystems*, **7**, 173–185.

Greenland, D.J. & Kowal, J.M.L. (1960). Nutrient content of the moist tropical forest of Ghana. *Plant and Soil*, **12**, 154–174.

Grubb, P.J. & Edwards, P.J. (1982). Studies of mineral cycling in a montane rain forest in New Guinea, III. The distribution of mineral elements in the above–ground material. *Journal of Ecology*, **70**, 623–648.

Jordan, C.F. (1985). *Nutrient Cycling in Tropical Forest Ecosystems.* Wiley, New York.

Khiewtam, R.S. (1986). *Ecosystem function of protected forests, Cherrapunji and adjoining areas.* PhD Thesis, North-Eastern Hill University, Shillong, India.

Lloyd, P.S. (1971). Effect of fire on the chemical status of herbaceous communities of the Derbyshire Dales. *Journal of Ecology*, **59**, 261–273.

Mishra, B.K. & Ramakrishnan, P.S. (1981). The economic yield and energy efficiency of hill agroecosystems at higher elevations of Meghalaya in north-eastern India. *Acta Oecologica-Oecologia Applicata*, **2**, 369–389.

Mishra, B.K. & Ramakrishnan, P.S. (1983a). Slash and burn agriculture at higher elevations in north-eastern India. I. Sediment, water and nutrient losses. *Agriculture, Ecosystem and Environment*, **9**, 69–82.

Mishra, B.K. & Ramakrishnan, P.S. (1983b). Slash and burn agriculture at higher elevations in north-eastern India. II. Soil fertility changes. *Agriculture, Ecosystem and Environment*, **9**, 83–96.

Mishra, B.K. & Ramakrishnan, P.S. (1983c). Secondary succession subsequent to slash and burn agriculture at higher elevations of north-east India. I. Species diversity, biomass and litter production. *Acta Oecologica–Oecologia Applicata*, **4**, 95–107.

Mishra, B.K. & Ramakrishnan, P.S. (1983d). Secondary succession subsequent to slash and burn agriculture at higher elevations of north-east India. II. Nutrient cycling. *Acta Oecologica-Oecologia Applicata*, **4**, 237–245.

Mishra, B.K. & Ramakrishnan, P.S. (1984). Nitrogen budget under rotational bush fallow agriculture (jhum) at higher elevations of Meghalaya in north-eastern India. *Plant and Soil*, **81**, 37–46.

Moore, A.W. & Jaiyebo, E.O. (1963). The influence of cover on nitrate and nitrifiable nitrogen content of the soil in a tropical rain forest environment. *Empire Journal of Experimental Agriculture*, **31**, 189–198.

Nye, P.H. & Greenland, D.J. (1960). *The Soil Under Shifting Cultivation. Technical Communication No. 51.* Commonwealth Bureau of Soils, Harpenden, U.K.

Odum, E.P. (1969). The strategy of ecosystem development. *Science*, **164**, 262–270.

Ramakrishnan, P.S. (1984). The sciences behind rotational bush fallow agriculture systems (jhum). *Proceedings of the Indian Academy of Sciences (Plant Sciences)*, **93**, 379–400.

Ramakrishnan, P.S. (1985a). *Research on Humid Tropical Forests*. Regional Meeting of the National MAB Committees of Central and South Asian Countries, New Delhi, India.

Ramakrishnan, P.S. (1985b). Tribal man in the humid tropics of the north-east. *Man in India*, **65**, 1–32.

Ramakrishnan, P.S. & Das, A.K. (1983). Studies on pine ecosystem function in Meghalaya. *Tropical Plant Science Research*, **1**, 15–24.

Ramakrishnan, P.S. & Saxena, K.G. (1984). Nitrification potential in successional communities and desertification of Cherrapunji. *Current Science*, **53**, 107–109.

Ramakrishnan, P.S. Shukla, R.P. & Boojh, R. (1982). Growth strategies of trees and their application in forest management. *Current Science*, **51**, 448–455.

Ramakrishnan, P.S. & Toky, O.P. (1981). Soil nutrient status of hill agro–ecosystems and recovery patterns after slash and burn agriculture (jhum) in north-eastern India. *Plant and Soil*, **60**, 41–65.

Ramakrishnan, P.S., Toky, O.P., Mishra, B.K. & Saxena, K.G. (1981). Slash and burn agriculture in northeastern India. *Fire Regimes and Ecosystem Properties* (Ed. by H.A. Mooney, T.M. Bonnieksen, N.L. Christensen, J.E. Lotan & W.A. Reiners), pp. 570–586. United States Department of Agriculture, Forest Service General Technical Report, Wo-26, Honolulu, Hawaii.

Ramakrishnan, P.S. & Vitousek, P. (1989). Ecosystem-level processes and the consequence of biological invasions. *Ecology of Biological Invasions* (Ed. by H.A. Mooney). Wiley, New York (in press).

Rao, K.S. & Ramakrishnan, P.S. (1989). Comparative analysis of the population dynamics of two bamboo species, *Dendrocalamus hamiltonii* Nees. & Arn. and *Neohozeoua dulloa* A.. Camus in a successional environment. *Forest Ecology and Management*, **21**, 177–189.

Reiners, W.A. & Reiners, N.M. (1970). Energy and nutrient dynamics of forest floors in three Minnesota forests. *Journal of Ecology*, **58**, 497–519.

Rice, E.L. (1974). *Allelopathy*. Academic Press, New York.

Richards, P.W. (1952). *The Tropical Rain Forest*. Cambridge University Press, London.

Ross, R. (1954). Ecological studies on the rain forest of southern Nigeria. III. Secondary succession in the Shasha forest reserve. *Journal of Ecology*, **42**, 259–282.

Saxena, K.G. & Ramakrishnan, P.S. (1982). Reproductive efficiency of secondary successional herbaceous population subsequent to slash and burn of sub-tropical humid forests in north-eastern India. *Proceedings of the Indian Academy of Sciences (Plant Sciences)*, **91**, 61–68.

Saxena, K.G. & Ramakrishnan, P.S. (1983a). Growth and allocation strategies of some perennial weeds of slash and burn agriculture (jhum) in north-eastern India. *Canadian Journal of Botany*, **61**, 1300–1306.

Saxena, K.G. & Ramakrishnan, P.S. (1983b). Growth, resources, allocation pattern and nutritional status of some dominant annual weeds of shifting agriculture (jhum) in north-eastern India. *Acta Oecologica–Oecologia Plantarum*, **4**, 323–333.

Saxena, K.G. & Ramakrishnan, P.S. (1984a). Herbaceous vegetation development and weed potential in slash and burn agriculture (jhum) in N.E. India. *Weed Research*. **24**, 135–142.

Saxena, K.G. & Ramakrishnan, P.S. (1984b). Growth and patterns of resource allocation in *Eupatorium odoratum* in the secondary successional environment following slash and burn agriculture (jhum). *Weed Research*, **24**, 135–142.

Saxena, K.G. & Ramakrishnan, P.S. (1984c). C_3/C_4 species distribution among successional herbs following slash and burn in north-eastern India. *Acta Oecologica–Oecologia Plantarum*, **5** 335–346.

Saxena, K.G. & Ramakrishnan, P.S. (1986). Nitrification during slash and burn agriculture (jhum) in north-eastern India. *Acta Oecologica-Oecologia Plantarum*, **7**, 319–331.

Singh, J. & Ramakrishnan, P.S. (1982). Structure and function of a sub–tropical humid forest of Meghalaya. I. Vegetation biomass and its nutrients. *Proceedings of the Indian Academy of Sciences (Plant Sciences)*, **97**, 241–253.

Smith, W.H., Bormann, F.H. & Likens, G.E. (1968). Response of chemotrophic nitrifiers in forest cutting. *Soil Science*, **106**, 471–473.

Swamy, P.S. & Ramakrishnan, P.S. (1987). Weed potential of *Mikania micrantha* H.B.K. and its control in fallows after shifting agriculture (jhum) in north-east India. *Agriculture, Ecosystem and Environment*, **18**, 195–204.

Swamy, P.S. & Ramakrishnan, P.S. (1988a). Nutrient budget under slash and burn agriculture (jhum) with different weeding regimes in north-eastern India. *Acta Oecologica-Oecologia Applicata*, **9**, 85–102.

Swamy, P.S. & Ramakrishnan, P.S. (1988b). Ecological implications of traditional weeding and other imposed weeding regimes under slash and burn agriculture (jhum) in north-eastern India. *Weed Research*, **28**, 127–136.

Tinker, P.B. (1977). Economy and chemistry of phosphorus. *Nature (London)*, **270**, 103–104.

Toky, O.P. & Ramakrishnan, P.S. (1981a). Cropping and yields in agricultural systems of the north-eastern hill region of India. *Agro-Ecosystems*, **7**, 11–25.

Toky, O.P. & Ramakrishnan, P.S. (1981b). Run-off and infiltration losses related to shifting agriculture in north-eastern India. *Environmental Conservation*, **8**, 313–321.

Toky, O.P. & Ramakrishnan, P.S. (1983a). Secondary succession following slash and burn agriculture in north-eastern India. I. Biomass, litterfall and productivity. *Journal of Ecology*, **71**, 735–745.

Toky, O.P. & Ramakrishnan, P.S. (1983b). Secondary succession following slash and burn agriculture in north-eastern India. II. Nutrient cycling. *Journal of Ecology*, **71**, 747–757.

Vitousek, P.M. & Sanford, Jr., R.L. (1986). Nutrient cycling in moist tropical forest. *Annual Review of Ecology and Systematics*, **17**, 137–169.

Whitmore, T.C. (1975). *Tropical Rain Forests of the Far East*. Oxford University Press, Oxford.

Woodwell, G.M., Whittaker, R.H. & Houghton, R.A. (1975). Nutrient concentration in plants in Brookhaven oak–pine forest. *Ecology*, **56**, 318–332.

Zinke, P.J., Sabhasri, S. & Kunstadter, P. (1978). Soil fertility aspect of the 'Lua' forest fallow system of shifting cultivation. *Farmers of the Forest* (Ed. by P. Kunstadter, E.C. Chapman & S. Sabhasri), pp. 134–159. East–West Center, Honolulu, Hawaii.

The use of mathematical models in the development of shifting cultivation systems

B. R. TRENBATH*

*Agro-Ecological Consultancies,
12 New Road, Reading RG1 5JD*

SUMMARY

1 Three models of contrasting type predict how variation in some of the practices used in shifting cultivation affects soil fertility.

2 Model 1 uses five management and five biological variables to calculate the effect on soils and food production of varying the number of crops taken per cycle and the time under fallow. Intensification is predicted to lead to immediate increases in food production at the expense of corresponding longer-term declines in soil fertility. Assuming an initial fertility level of 67% of that under primary forest, steady state systems on 10 ha provide subsistence for about four man-equivalents, i.e. a population of about 50 km^{-2}.

3 Using three of the biological variables which can be manipulated by management, and considering a typical degrading system, Model 1 predicts the size of the changes in the variables required to stop the decline of soil fertility. The three variables considered represent the rate of decline of fertility during cropping, the rate of recovery under fallow, and how well the ash, at present lost by erosion, is conserved. Interventions which affect all three variables act synergistically.

4 Model 2 is based on graphs in which soil fertility after a cropping cycle is plotted as a function of fertility before cropping. The steady states identified by Model 1 appear to be stable equilibria, given constant management.

5 A hypothesis is proposed which suggests that erosion losses of nutrients are disproportionately large in early fallows on plots already depleted of most of their fertility. When the graphs are modified to take this into account, the equilibrium properties of the system are radically changed. The model now mimics the situation in which intensification beyond a certain level causes non-regeneration of forest and potentially permanent low fertility.

6 Model 3 simulates changes through time in three variables, namely biomass of a grass weed, biomass of trees and soil fertility. Runs show how, without considering erosion, interaction between these three variables is sufficient to produce the same threshold effect as was mimicked with Model 2. Intensification of cropping beyond a certain level causes forest regrowth to give way to permanent grass, with minimal restoration of fertility.

---

*Present address: Department of Agricultural Botany, University of Reading, Whiteknights, Reading RG6 2AS.

353

7 Possible applications of Model 1 include mapping of estimated rates of fertility decline from minimal ground survey data and estimating how much the improvable elements of a system have to be changed to bring it into a non-degrading steady state. Models 2 and 3 provide interpretations of the collapse of intensified systems to permanent grassland, triggered respectively by erosion and weed–tree competition. Models 1 and 3 could be used as simulators for training environmental managers.

INTRODUCTION

Shifting cultivation is a form of husbandry in which the soil of individual cultivated plots is subjected to alternating depletive and restorative phases. Farmers relying on it for subsistence in the forest and savanna areas of the tropics are under pressure to feed increasing populations on shrinking areas of land of declining fertility (UNESCO 1978; Greenland & Okigbo 1983).

By virtue of their isolation and relative poverty, these farmers, numbering more than 250 million in humid tropical Africa alone (Bene, Beall & Cote 1977), are necessarily the world's largest group of 'organic' farmers. Attempting to provide them with options for development, institutions and agricultural scientists are searching for ways of improving the various aspects of the system (Kyuma & Pairintra 1983; Ramakrishnan 1984; Schelhaas, Koopmans & Andriesse 1984; FAO 1985; IITA 1985, 1986). Some are trying to reduce the rate of yield decline during the cropping phase. For this, they have developed several ways of retaining plant nutrients against removal by water, wind and weeds, of conserving organic matter and other fertility-promoting factors, and of restoring soil reserves of available nitrogen by means of biological fixation of atmospheric nitrogen in the root systems of intercropped leguminous bushes and trees. Where such approaches can indefinitely prevent soil degradation, the shifting cultivators have the option of engaging in 'permanent field' agriculture, seldom needing a traditional fallow (IITA 1985).

Aware that most of the marginal land at present under shifting cultivation will probably always need some kind of fallow phase (Grandstaff 1980), other researchers are continuing to aim at improving shifting cultivation, in particular by improving the restorative capacity of the fallow. Their work involves the search for widely-adapted, fast-growing tree or bush species with deep roots; spreading canopies and abundant litter production to protect the soil against erosion, to act as nutrient pumps to bring up leached nutrients from the subsoil, to recharge the pool of soil organic matter, and to regenerate the biological life of the soil (Högberg 1986; IITA 1986).

In order to develop the system as a whole, researchers are trying to obtain higher levels of efficiency in the use of plant nutrients and other resources by means of an understanding of the nutrient, carbon and hydrological cycles. Particularly promising for this purpose are multiple cropping techniques (Francis 1986), new approaches to animal husbandry which complement the novel methods of tree cropping (Sumberg, Okali & Attah-Krah 1984), and detailed mathematical models of agro-forestry systems which may be general enough to be applied usefully to shifting cultivation (Young, Cheatle & Muraya 1987).

Within the research institutions, many developments of the shifting cultivation system thus seem to be awaiting large-scale trials. However, outside these institutions the prospects for widespread implementation are much less hopeful. Paralysing political, cultural and socio-economic constraints express themselves in many ways (Jackson 1984; Joyce & Burwell 1985). Nevertheless, awareness of impending catastrophe may force large investments and consequent effort such as recently proposed in the Tropical Forestry Action Plan (FAO 1985). The urgent need for the success of such last-ditch efforts suggests that planning tools are needed which will indicate a range of appropriate ameliorative measures from which local people can select acceptable ones for local testing and adaptation. The need for institutions to be responsive to local aspirations and flexible in the support they offer is evident from the diversity of soils, climates and cultures present in the areas they serve. This need is especially pressing in the uplands where most of the shifting cultivation is practised (Sajise & Baguinon 1981).

The present paper outlines three sorts of modelling approach which could help planners identify sustainable forms of shifting cultivation for areas where other suitable, more productive options do not exist. In particular, it shows how a systems analysis view which represents the crop–fallow cycle in mathematical terms can help formulate critical questions for research, suggest best avenues for development effort, and evaluate, at least crudely, the likely effect of proposed improvements.

MODELS OF THE SHIFTING CULTIVATION SYSTEM

Three contrasting models (Models 1–3) are described which predict the consequences of shifting cultivation carried on in different ways. They build on the pioneering models of Greenland & Nye (1959). Because the full range of development options is so great (Grandstaff 1980), especially when compared with the research input so far, attention is mostly focussed on the most obvious control variables of the system, namely the lengths of the cropping and fallow phases.

1. Simple empirical model

In order to address a wide range of general questions, a model has been developed (Trenbath 1984) which estimates soil fertility change and level of subsistence food production in relation to five biological and five management variables (Table 1). The effect on the soil (S) is given percentage change in fertility per cycle of $t_c + t_f$ years and the human food production (H) is given in man-equivalent-years/year (MEy/y). Calculations of labour requirement and labour

TABLE 1. Symbols for variable parameters in Model 1, and the values used to generate Fig. 1 (Trenbath 1984). The first five items are 'biological' parameters and the second five are 'management' parameters (MEy = man-equivalent-years)

Symbol	Meaning	Value
F_{oc}	Soil fertility at start of cropping phase	2 t ha^{-1} of unhusked rice
F_∞	Soil fertility in primary forest	3 t ha^{-1} of unhusked rice
x	Rate of proportional reduction of yield (and soil fertility) in cropping phase	0.3/crop
b	Subsistence requirement of unhusked rice	0.517 t/MEy
K_F	Time under fallow for soil fertility to reach $F_\infty/2$ from an initial value of zero ('half-recovery time')	11 years
n	Number of crops taken in a year of cropping	1 per year
A	Total area of land in the system	10 ha
t_c	Duration of cropping phase (varied)	years
t_f	Duration of fallow phase (varied)	years
a	Area of individual plot within the available area = $A/(t_c + t_f)$ (varied)	ha

efficiency presented with the original model are not considered here.

The model considers an idealized system in which the available area is equally divided into $t_c + t_f$ plots, each representing one of the stages through which a given plot passes in the course of the $t_c + t$ years of a complete cycle.

The single state variable, soil fertility F, is considered for a representative 're-ference' plot. This variable is an empirical one, combining the various effects on crop yield of soil factors and the populations of weeds, pests and diseases in the plot. Its value at any annual time point is the yield of upland rice (in MEy) that could be hypothetically obtained from the plot using standard procedures. During the fallow phase, the standard procedures would involve slash and burn of the regrowth before planting; during the cropping phase, they would simply involve planting.

Assuming that, within one cycle, all plots start their cropping phase with the same initial soil fertility F_{oc}, the food production in any year is calculated by supposing that the sequences of changes in time and in space are equivalent. The yield of the whole system of plots in 1 year is thus supposed to be the same as the sum of the yields of a single plot followed through time. The estimates of yield through time are based on observations showing that successive yields can be represented as a decreasing exponential function of crop number. Food production in MEy/y is then found by summing the yields expected from the reference plot in the course of its cropping phase:

$$H = a F_{oc} \sum_{i=1}^{nt_c} (1 - x)^{i-1}/b$$

with the meanings of the symbols as given in Table 1.

In the absence of data indicating directly the effect of length of fallow on the yield of the first crop taken after the fallow, the form of the time-course of regeneration of soil fertility during the fallow is based on that of a rough proxy, the total nitrogen content of the soil. Based on data of soil nitrogen from the moist forest zone of Nigeria (Aweto 1981; Trenbath 1984), the regeneration of soil fertility in the fallow phase is modelled as a rectangular hyperbola rising asymptotically to the value F_∞ found in primary forest. The value of F_∞ is the yield of a first crop grown after an infinitely long fallow. The initial gradient of this curve is F_∞/K_F where K_F is the time estimated from Aweto's data for soil nitrogen to attain half of its final value (Table 1).

At the end of the cropping phase, the plot's 'position' on the curve is found as a point according to its residual soil fertility. The abscissa of the point is the time required for the plot to gain that level of soil fertility, starting from zero; this is the 'time-equivalent' t_f' of the residual fertility. The level of fertility at the end of the fallow is found by reading off the value at $t_f' + t_f$. This new level of fertility is the initial level F_{oc}' for the next cropping cycle. The percentage change in F over the whole cycle is therefore given by

$$S = -100 (1 - F_{oc}' /F_{oc})$$
$$= -100 \left(1 - \frac{F_\infty (t_f + t_f')}{F_{oc} (K_F + t_f + t_f')}\right)^*$$

with

$$t_f' = \frac{F_{oc} (1 - x)^{nt_c} K_F}{F_\infty - F_{oc} (1 - x)^{nt_c}}$$

When the parameter set in Table 1 is used, the behaviour of the model with respect to changes in nt_c and t_f (Fig. 1) seems broadly to match the experience of farmers trying to intensify their shifting cultivation systems. Thus, if fallows are long enough (e.g. in Fig. 1(a), if $t_f = 12$ and $nt_c = 1$), the system can remain indefinitely in steady state (Hinton 1978). From this state, any decrease in t_f, with or without increase in nt_c, increases production in the short term but causes long-term declines due to falling soil fertility. In many parts of the tropical uplands, fallows have been shortened to less than 5 years, with catastrophic declines in yield (e.g. Kushwaha, Ramakrishnan & Tripathi 1981; Jackson 1984). Given the

---

*In Trenbath (1984), F_{oc} in the denominator was omitted in error. The results presented were, however, correct.

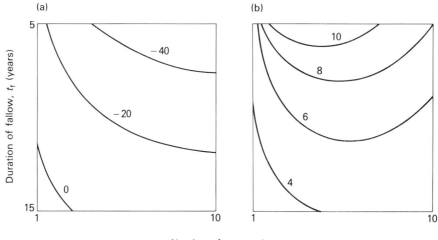

FIG. 1. Contours fitted to surfaces generated by shifting cultivation Model 1 to show response of soil fertility and food production to variation in durations of fallow and cropping phases. Because one crop is assumed to be taken each year, the number of years in cropping is the number of crops taken before abandonment of plots. (a) Contours of rate of change of soil fertility (%/cycle); (b) contours of subsistence food production (man-equivalent-years year^{-1}). Parameter values are as given in Table 1.

initial level of $F_{oc} = 2/3F_\infty = 2$ t ha^{-1}, the steady state systems identified in Fig. 1 are expected to provide subsistence for only about 4 ME, i.e. a family of five, on a total area of 10 ha. This implies a population carrying capacity of 50 km^{-2}; interestingly, this is exactly the threshold population density beyond which it has been suggested (UNESCO 1978) that yield declines occur.

If the model was validated and refined by experimentation, the information, such as that contained in Fig. 1, could provide useful guidelines for administrators trying to match their levels of intervention in different localities to the likely rates of soil degradation there. Furthermore, if satellite imagery was used to estimate nt_c and t_f, and ground survey was used to measure mean F_{oc} and the variables needed for a submodel to estimate local values of x, then contours of approximate degradation rates could be drawn over maps of the area concerned. Such maps could help identify the parts where priority intervention might best be targeted.

Another possible application of the model is in indicating the research and extension topics most likely to provide ways of bringing degrading systems into steady state. In Fig. 2, three variables which could be significantly influenced by cultural practice have been varied over a wide range. To generate this figure, an intensified system was assumed with $n = 2$, $t_c = 2$ and $t_f = 5$; the parameter set in Table 1 was used except that F_{oc} was set to 1.5 t ha^{-1} in order to moderate the rate of soil degradation. The first variable, the rate of yield decline during cropping (x), is known to be strongly affected by interventions such as

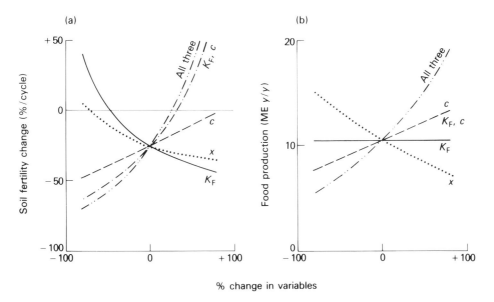

FIG. 2. Response curves, calculated by shifting cultivation Model 1, of (a) soil fertility and (b) food production to changes (from −100% to +100%) in three variables: x, rate of yield decline during cropping; K_F, time under fallow needed for soil fertility to reach $F_\alpha/2$, i.e. the half-recovery time; c, ash conservation factor (see text). Simultaneous improvements in two or three variables ('K_F, c' and 'all three') test for synergisms among the effects of the variables. In (a) a 0% change in soil fertility signifies a system in steady state. The changes needed to attain this state are read off from the horizontal axis. The parameter values are given in the text.

applications of compost/fertilizer, anti-erosion measures and more effective weeding. Similarly, the second variable, the time under fallow needed for fertility to reach half of the totally recovered level ($F_\alpha/2$), can be affected by the many ways of encouraging regrowth of trees, especially of leguminous species.

The third variable is a new and more speculative one. It is introduced here as an 'ash conservation' factor c which affects F_{oc} at all points where it appears in the model. Its use derives from statements in the literature which suggest that, at least under some conditions, the initial yield in a cropping phase depends strongly on the amount of ash nutrients present when the crop is planted (Nakano 1978; Andriesse & Schelhaas 1985). Assuming that yield is strictly proportional to the amount of a limiting nutrient such as phosphorus available to the crop in the soil and ash, and that the ash contains half the fallow's total resource of the nutrient (Koopmans & Andriesse 1982, 1983), then loss of half of the ash by blow-off and erosion (Toky & Ramakrishnan 1981; Kyuma & Pairintra 1983) would lower the first crop yield by a quarter. Seen in reverse, complete conservation of that lost half would raise the F_{oc} value by 33%. To produce this effect in the model, a factor z is applied to F_{oc} throughout the model, calculated as $z = (2 + c)/3$; when $c = 1$, then $z = 1$ and F_{oc} has the original input value; complete conservation of ash ($c = 2$) gives a z value of 1.33.

In Fig. 2(a), the responses to variation in the three variables show that the system can be brought into steady state by changes in x, K_F and c within the range tested. The changes required are -70%, -43% and $+85\%$, respectively. This result means that soil fertility decline could be stopped by such improvements as a cut in annual rate of yield decline (x) from 0.3 to 0.09, a cut in the 'half-recovery time' (K_F) from 11 to 6.3 years, or an 85% conservation of the blown-off ash.

In order to test for interactions among simultaneous improvements in the three factors, the predicted soil fertility changes and food productions were calculated over the same range of changes, considering pairs of factors and all three at a time. Eighty per cent improvement in all three simultaneously led to a 71% increase in fertility per cycle as opposed to the predicted 27% increase if the factors had simply behaved additively (all compared with the 25% decline predicted for the unimproved system). As shown in Fig. 2(a), a steady state is expected from a 22% improvement in all three factors together. The best combination for pairwise improvement seems to be K_F and c, giving a steady state if both are improved by 31%.

Food production is similarly increased by improvements in the factors, singly or in combination (Fig. 2(b)). With an 80% improvement in all three factors simultaneously, the system is predicted to support 19.2 ME, that is, nearly double the subsistence provided by the unimproved system.

Predictions such as these suggest profitable lines of research, especially into the exploitation of synergisms among individual improvements. Simple models such as this would appear to be helpful in devising research policy.

2. Simple graphical model

Farmers practising shifting cultivation in forest areas have often found, as intensification proceeds, that the land no longer reverts to forest when cropping ends. Worse than this, even when the land is rested, the forest may not reappear. This non-regeneration is seen on land that has been heavily disturbed, in particular by a long cropping phase or too short a fallow, by serious erosion or by being burned repeatedly (Nakano 1978; Sabhasri 1978; Ramakrishnan & Mishra 1981). There seems to be a threshold of disturbance beyond which non-regeneration occurs. Since forest cover during the fallow provides such a convenient and cheap means of restoring soil fertility for future cropping, its replacement by herbaceous weeds is a calamity for people depending on the land for subsistence (Greenland & Okigbo 1983).

By way of introduction to the third model, which addresses the biological basis of this disturbance threshold, a simple model (Model 2) is now described which represents the dynamics of the shifting cultivation system in terms of equilibrium points, stability domains and thresholds between them. We first establish the forms of the key relationships in the model.

Concerning the cropping phase, data on cropping sequences (Trenbath 1984) show that, as a rule of thumb, crop yield, and thus soil fertility as defined above, declines exponentially with crop number. A regular decrease of 30% per crop has been taken as a standard expectation (Table 1). If soil fertility in one year is plotted against that a year later (for $n = 1$), this situation is represented by a straight line of slope 0.7 passing through the origin (Fig. 3(a)).

Concerning the fallow phase, the existence of a high-level equilibrium of soil fertility under forest has been well established (Greenland & Nye 1959). It was referred to earlier as F_∞. Asymptotic approach to it from below is implied by many sets of data on soil characters in fallows of different ages; there seem to be no data showing approach to it from above.

When fertility levels are moderate to high, the rate of approach to F_∞ in a forest fallow often appears to be roughly proportional to how far the fertility is from F_∞; for instance, early in a fallow, the rate of accumulation of nutrients in the biomass and in the soil is at a maximum (Greenland & Nye 1959; Aweto 1981). If nutrients are limiting fertility, the rate of increase of soil fertility (measured as potential crop yield) is thus probably also at a maximum. Plotting now for fallow a graph of fertility in one year against that a year later gives the curve in Fig. 3(a). Between fertility values p and q, increase in fertility will be constant with time, but above q the rate of increase will fall to zero as F_∞ is approached. The point at which the curve intersects the 45° line is the single stable equilibrium (steady state) point of the forest system. (Zero fertility is also an equilibrium point, but here it is unstable since any slight departure from it leads to further departure.)

The general level of fertility around which some West African systems were operating about 30 years ago was quoted by Greenland & Nye (1959) to be about $3/4 F_\infty$. Yields as low as 60 kg ha^{-1} in contemporary intensified systems in Thailand (Jackson 1984) suggest that they may be operating at something less than $F_\infty/10$. At such low fertility levels, the initial rate of increase in the fallow is likely to be slower. A reasonable guess might be that, at these low levels, the rate of fertility increase is limited by the current level and is proportional to it. Such an exponential increase in fertility with time at low levels is implicit in Greenland & Nye's (1959) model. In line with this hypothesis, increasing rates of nutrient accumulation in biomass have certainly been reported (Ramakrishnan & Toky 1983). An assumption that the hypothesis is correct allows the curve in Fig. 3(a) to be completed by the addition of a dotted straight line indicating rate proportionality at low values of fertility.

For given values of n, t_c and t_f, the curves shown in Fig. 3(a) can be entered and used recursively the necessary number of times to arrive at curves which show the change in fertility over a whole cycle of $t_c + t_f$ years. In Fig. 3(b), such curves are presented for the values $t_c = 1$ year and t_f either 10 or 2 years (n fixed hereafter at 1 crop year^{-1}). Inspection of the upper curve shows that there is still only one stable equilibrium so close to F_∞ as to be indistinguishable from it. At least with respect to soil fertility, this system is not intensive enough to progressively degrade the environment.

However, inspection of the lower curve shows that with intensification, the

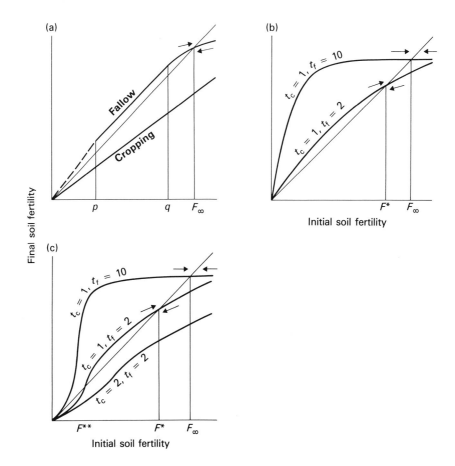

FIG. 3. Graphical model (Model 2) of soil fertility change under shifting cultivation. (a) Hypothetical relationships between soil fertility in successive years, during cropping and during fallow; initial fertility is plotted horizontally and final fertility, one year later, is plotted vertically using the same scale. The 45° line thus represents 'no change'. Note the yearly decrease in fertility during cropping, and the yearly increase during fallow (providing the fertility is less than the high-level equilibrium value, F_∞). Non-zero equilibrium levels of fertility are indicated by arrows (converging for stable points, and diverging for unstable points). (b) Hypothetical relationships as in (a) but over the time interval of a whole cycle. The curves were derived from those in (a) by using the cropping and fallow curves recursively. The cycle consists of 1 year of cropping ($t_c = 1$ year) followed by either 10 or 2 years of fallow ($t_f = 10$ or 2 years); the lower curve represents the greater degree of intensification. (c) As in (b), but soil erosion has strongly affected the curves at low fertility. The lowest curve ($t_c = 2$, $t_f = 2$) represents still further intensification. See text for further explanation.

stable equilibrium value of fertility (marked F^*) is forced down below F_∞. The significance of this equilibrium value in the model is that, for a given set of parameter values, whatever the initial level of fertility, the fertility will always approach the equilibrium value asymptotically. In a similar way, a system will return to it after being perturbed away from equilibrium. A further consequence of the model is that as the value of nt_c/t_f rises with intensification, F^* is depressed, even approaching zero.

A possible reason for the disturbance threshold now presents itself. As intensification proceeds, progressive lowering of the line in Fig. 3(b) will lead to a situation where just a small further lowering will very rapidly reduce the value of F^* towards zero. The slight extra intensification responsible could perhaps be viewed as having carried the system beyond the threshold and so caused it to 'collapse'.

However, this model is unrealistic in that the collapse is freely reversible. Any time that the farmer could afford to lower nt_c/t_f, even slightly, F^* would rise again. Its new level would simply depend on nt_c/t_f. A small reduction in the intensity of land use would give a relatively large increase in F^*.

The element missed from this interpretation of the collapse seems to be a detail of the dynamics of soil fertility (as measured by potential crop yield) early in the fallow phase on low fertility soils. The soils of early fallows show a further net loss of organic matter, and a continued depletion of nutrients due to uptake into the biomass of vigorously growing weeds and regrowth, and to continued erosion (Palmer 1972; Ramakrishnan & Toky 1981; A. C. Millington, personal communication). At a site where nutrients are deficient and are limiting fertility, compared with a high nutrient situation, a plot in early fallow has a higher percentage of its total nutrient resource in plant biomass, and thus a higher percentage of this resource subject to the great losses during burning and early cropping. In addition, because the regrowth's canopy in such plots will take longer to close, erosion will remove a larger percentage of nutrient-rich topsoil than in a plot with higher fertility. Unintentional fire and attendant extra erosion on such low fertility plots would similarly magnify this effect.

The consequence of including these effects in Model 2 is shown in Fig. 3(c) where the low fertility parts of the previous curves have been lowered. In the non-intensive system (top curve), there is still only one stable equilibrium at F_∞. With moderate intensification (middle curve), the implications of the lowered part of the curve are now seen: a second non-zero equilibrium point (F^{**}) has appeared at low fertility, which inspection shows is an unstable point. This equilibrium point has the properties of a disturbance threshold. As in a real shifting cultivation system, provided that no plot falls below this threshold, any fertility trend in the system will be towards the upper equilibrium point. However, as soon as plots fall below it, their long-term trend is predicted to be towards zero. Zero is now a second stable equilibrium point. According to the model, this change of behaviour and the downward trend are irreversible unless special efforts are made to bring the fertility back above the threshold or, alternatively, to relax the intensity of land use enough to force the threshold down below the current level of fertility.

Further intensification (bottom curve in Fig. 3(c)) is expected to lead to a situation where the only stable point is at zero fertility; the fertility trends will be uniformly downward.

This simple graphical model provides an apparently new interpretation, based on soil fertility, of the problem of non-regeneration of forest. In the hypothesis represented by Fig. 3(c), increasing intensification generates a situation where the state variable has two stable equilibrium points, one at a high level and one at a low level, with an unstable point between them. The unstable point thus separates two 'stability domains' of fertility level. By definition, the system will always move towards the stable equilibrium that dominates the stability domain in which it is located. A sufficiently strong perturbation of the system can cause it to cross over the threshold into another stability domain and so be attracted towards a different stable point. In the shifting cultivation system, it is this behaviour that has such serious consequences. Supporting the appropriateness of the model, the effects of intense perturbation, i.e. of excessive disturbance of a plot, have indeed been found to be reversible only with difficulty.

The discussion leading to the form of model shown in Fig. 3(c) has focussed attention on a possibly key aspect of the shifting cultivation cycle, namely rates of restoration of potential crop yields in fallows on degraded soil, on which no data seem to be available.

If further research confirms the form of curves in Fig. 3(c), this simple model could offer an easily understood teaching tool for administrators and extension personnel. It could make it clear that sustainability of production depends not only on the nature of the production system, but also on how it is driven.

3. Complex process-oriented model

The last model to be described illustrates how, in the absence of erosion and fire, competitive interaction between forest trees and weeds could explain the existence of the disturbance threshold considered in the previous section. To take account of this interaction and how it depends on fertility level, the model calculates simultaneous changes in three state variables: the biomasses of weed (*Imperata* grass) and of trees, and the soil fertility. Since detailed justification and parameter values are published elsewhere (Trenbath, Conway & Craig 1989), its structure is described only in outline. Examples of output are presented to establish the model's credibility, to help develop a more general view of the system's stability domains, and to suggest that the model could be useful in predicting outcomes of different levels of intensification or types of intervention.

In the course of a simulation of the changes through time in a single plot of the shifting cultivation system, two submodels, one relating to the cropping phase and the other to the fallow, are referred to alternately. In the cropping phase, biomass of the grass weed (G) rises sigmoidally to a maximum. Biomass of the trees (T) falls sharply at first due to cutting and then more gradually as a result of death of roots, respiration of reserves etc. The change in soil fertility and the gradual fall in tree biomass are modelled as exponential declines, each with its own rate constant. The cropping phase submodel uses analytical equations to calculate the biomasses and soil fertility after t_c years of cropping. These values provide the starting conditions for the differential equations simulating the fallow phase.

The fallow phase submodel calculates rates of change of the three state variables. Simultaneous solution of the equations through t_f years of time shows the consequences of the varying rates of change. The rates of change of the two sorts of biomass are modelled by Lotka–Volterra equations of the form

$$\dot{x}_1 = x_1 \, r_1 \, (1 - a \, x_1 - b \, x_2)$$

where x_1 is the biomass of species 1 and $\dot{x}_1$ is its rate of change (dx_1/dt), r_1 is the potential relative growth rate of species 1, x_2 is the biomass of species 2 with which species 1 is growing, and a and b incorporate the 'competition' coefficients. To provide simple logistic growth in pure stands, the coefficient a is in each case the reciprocal of the species' own maximum biomass.

To match observations that the trees' influence on the rate of grass growth increases greatly as their taller canopy becomes dense enough to significantly shade the grass, in the equation for grass growth, the coefficient b increases linearly with T up to its maximum value (T_{max}), at which the presence of a unit of tree biomass has ten times the influence of a unit of grass biomass. (Thus, when $T = T_{max}/10 = 42$ t ha^{-1}, the effect of tree biomass equals that of grass; below this, its 'competitive' effect reduces, because of being shaded itself, to zero.) Correspondingly, in the equation for tree growth, the coefficient b falls linearly with increasing T. To produce an asymptotic increase in relative growth rates of both species towards potential rates at 'infinite' fertility, a factor is applied to each of the equations, depending on F. The factors cause grass growth to be relatively favoured at low fertility and tree growth at high fertility.

Considering fertility change, the rate of change at low levels of fertility is taken to be a linear function of the sum of grass and tree biomasses but with a weighting that makes tree biomass five times more effective in restoring fertility than grass biomass. The fertility thus rises at an increasing rate. At higher fertilities, increase is gradually reduced by a factor which is linearly dependent on how far the current level is from F_x; hence, F_x is reached asymptotically.

Using a preliminary set of parameter estimates, a series of runs has been made, each starting with a single cropping phase in primary forest but with various numbers of crops taken. The results of tree biomass are compared (Fig. 4) with published data of forest regrowth. The conditions of climate, soil type, fertility, duration of cropping etc, before abandonment are not standardized, and so the comparison cannot be used to validate the model. Nevertheless, the exercise shows that observations exist which match rather well the different kinds of regrowth curve generated by the model.

In the same figure, as the number of crops taken is increased, the forest regrows more slowly. This response agrees with observations by Nakano (1978) (who described it as 'a widely recognized effect', p. 428) and also with

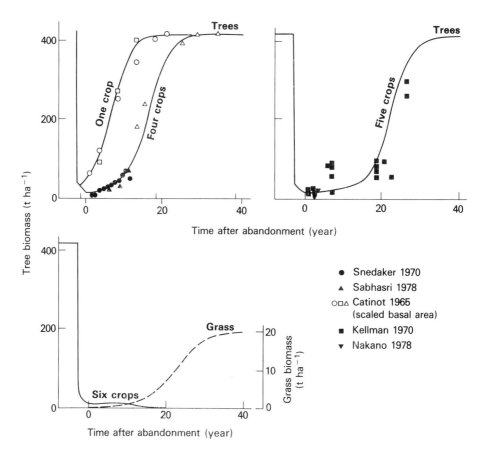

FIG. 4. Recovery of forest during the fallow phase of shifting cultivation, simulated by Model 3. After an initial loss of biomass due to clearing and then cropping, forest tends to regenerate. After one to five crops, forest regenerates successfully, but after six or more, grass weeds (broken line) suppress regrowth of the trees (full line). Forest biomass data and basal areas are plotted on the curve which they match best; basal areas were re-scaled vertically to reach the same maximum value. Data of Snedaker (1970), Kellman (1970) and Catinot (1965) are cited from UNESCO (1978, pp. 224 and 541). See text for parameter values (Trenbath, Conway & Craig 1989).

observations reported in UNESCO (1978). In Fig. 4, the response to increasing disturbance of the plot is seen to change abruptly when six crops are taken. Rather than the delayed regeneration seen after five crops, after six crops the slowly regrowing forest is suppressed by the grass weed. This agrees with many qualitative observations (e.g. '*Imperata* grass tends to invade as fertility declines' (Ivens 1983), and see also Keen (1978) and Greenland & Okigbo (1983)). (The parameters governing grass growth in this run have since been refined, and now give a faster approach to a lower maximum biomass.)

When these results were plotted as a three-dimensional graph (Fig. 5) and some exploratory runs were started in various parts of the 'state' space (i.e. that defined by the state variables' axes), it became apparent that the disturbance threshold was two-dimensional, represented by an inclined and curved plane

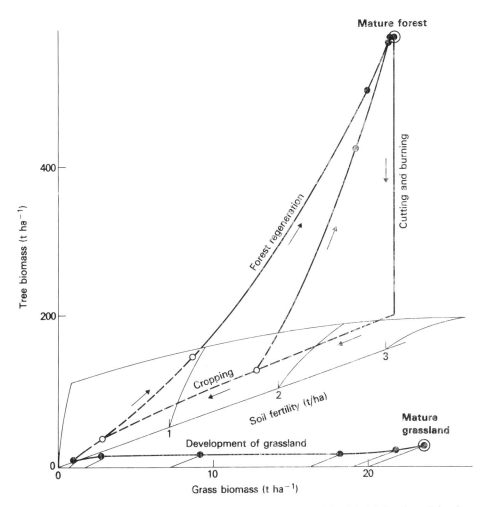

FIG. 5. Trajectories of a shifting cultivation system simulated by Model 3, plotted in three-dimensional state space. A curved plane representing a disturbance threshold for forest regeneration rises from the soil fertility axis. Trajectories and points hidden by this plane are shown as broken lines and open symbols, respectively. Starting with mature forest, either one, four or eight crops have been taken, followed by a fallow of indefinite length. After one and four crops, the system state moves back towards that of mature forest; points on the trajectories after abandonment indicate progress at 10-year intervals. After eight crops, having passed through the threshold plane, the system state moves towards mature grassland (Trenbath, Conway & Craig 1989).

through the space. This plane is shown in the figure as arising from the fertility axis. It divides the state space into two stability domains, each with its own stable equilibrium point, either mature forest or mature grassland. These points were found to attract all fallow phase plots within their own domain. Starting from a point within the forest stability domain, the number of crops taken (i.e. the level of disturbance) decides whether the trajectory of the system penetrates the threshold plane. If it does so, grassland develops. If it does not, then the forest regenerates.

Although the parameter set and functions used in the model need further refinement, the interpretation of the system's dynamics given in Fig. 5 suggests some plausible novel forms of intervention. For instance, if a plot which has just passed through the threshold plane is abandoned to fallow, grass invasion might be prevented by application of either compost/fertilizer or extra weeding effort/selective herbicide. After slight elaboration of the model to calculate crop yields and labour requirements, the model could be used to estimate the net return on cash invested in interventions. It would be entirely feasible to evaluate the benefits of a full range of options, and not only of the 'obvious' approaches such as putting fertilizer or herbicide on the crops. When the cash and labour costs of the system developments considered by Grandstaff (1980) and others have been estimated, models of the types described in this paper may be able to help policy makers and research managers to target funds for system stabilization into the projects with the biggest payoffs.

REFERENCES

Andriesse, J.P. & Schelhaas, R.M. (1985). *Monitoring Project of Nutrient Cycling in Soils used for Shifting Cultivation under Various Climatic Conditions in Asia: Nutrient Changes in the Cropping Period at Vanathavillu, Sri Lanka and at Semongkok (Sarawak), Malaysia. Progress Report No. 3.* Royal Tropical Institute, Amsterdam.

Aweto, A.O. (1981). Secondary succession and soil fertility restoration in south-western Nigeria. II. Soil fertility restoration. *Journal of Ecology*, **69**, 609–614.

Bene, J.G., Beall, H.W. & Cote, A. (1977). *Trees, Food and People.* International Development Research Center, Ottawa.

FAO (1985). *Tropical Forestry Action Plan.* Committee on Forest Development in the Tropics, FAO, Rome.

Francis, C.A. (Ed.) (1986). *Multiple Cropping Systems.* Macmillan, New York.

Grandstaff, T.B. (1980). *Shifting Cultivation in Northern Thailand: Possibilities for Development.* Resource Systems Theory and Methodology Series, No. 3, United Nations University.

Greenland, D.J. & Nye, P.H. (1959). Increase in the carbon and nitrogen contents of tropical soils under natural fallows. *Journal of Soil Science*, **10**, 284–299.

Greenland, D.J. & Okigbo, B.D. (1983). Crop production under shifting cultivation and the maintenance of soil fertility. *IRRI Symposium on Potential Productivity of Field Crops under Different Environments, 22-26 September, 1980*, pp. 505–524. International Rice Research Institute, los Banos, Philippines.

Hinton, P. (1978). Declining production among sedentary swidden cultivators: the case of Pwo Karen. *Farmers in the Forest* (Ed. by P. Kunstadter, E.C. Chapman & S. Sabhasri), pp. 185–198. University Press of Hawaii, Honolulu.

Högberg, P. (1986). Nitrogen-fixation and nutrient relations in savanna woodland trees (Tanzania). *Journal of Applied Ecology*, **23**, 675–688.

IITA (1985). *Farming Systems Program Research Highlights 1981–1984.* International Institute of Tropical Agriculture, Ibadan, Nigeria.

IITA (1986). *Annual Report and Research Highlights.* International Institute of Tropical Agriculture, Ibadan, Nigeria.

Ivens, G.W. (1983). *Imperata cylindrica*, its weak points and possibilities of exploitation for control purposes. *Mountain Research and Development*, **3**, 372–377.

Jackson, J.K. (1984). Constraints on the introduction of an agro-forestry element into traditional forms of shifting cultivation. *Social, Economic, and Institutional Aspects of Agro-forestry* (Ed. by J.K. Jackson), pp. 72–74. United Nations University.

Joyce, S. & Burwell, B. (1985). *Community-level Forestry Development: Options and Guidelines for*

Collaboration in PL 480 Programs. Peace Corps/Agency for International Development, Washington, DC.

Keen, F.G.B. (1978). Ecological relationships in a Hmong (Meo) economy. *Farmers in the Forest* (Ed. by P. Kunstadter, E.C. Chapman & S. Sabhasri), pp. 210–221. University Press of Hawaii, Honolulu.

Koopmans, T.T. & Andriesse, J.P. (1982). *Baseline Study Monitoring Project of Nutrient Cycling in Shifting Cultivation, Vanathavillu, Sri Lanka and Semongkok (Sarawak), Malaysia. Progress Report No. 1*. Royal Tropical Institute, Amsterdam.

Koopmans, T.T. & Andriesse, J.P. (1983). *Baseline Study Monitoring Project of Nutrient Cycling in Shifting Cultivation: Report on Mae Muang Luang Site, Thailand. Addendum to Progress Report No. 1*. Royal Tropical Institute, Amsterdam.

Kushwaha, S.P.S., Ramakrishnan, P.S. & Tripathi, R.S. (1981). Population dynamics of *Eupatorium odoratum* in successional environments following slash and burn agriculture. *Journal of Applied Ecology*, **18**, 529–535.

Kyuma, K. & Pairintra, C. (Eds.) (1983). *Shifting Cultivation: an Experiment at Nam Phrom, Northeast Thailand, and its Implications for Upland Farming in the Monsoon Tropics*. Faculty of Agriculture, Kyoto University.

Nakano, K. (1978). An ecological study of swidden agriculture at a village in northern Thailand. *South East Asian Studies*, **16**, 411–446.

Palmer, I. (1972). *Science and Agricultural Production. Report No. 72.8*. United Nations Research Institute for Social Development, Paris.

Ramakrishnan, P.S. (1984). The science behind rotational bush fallow agriculture system (jhum). *Proceedings of the Indian Academy of Science (Plant Sciences)*, **93**, 379–400.

Ramakrishnan, P.S. & Mishra, B.K. (1981). Population dynamics of *Eupatorium adenophorum* Spreng. during secondary succession after slash and burn agriculture (jhum) in north-eastern India. *Weed Research*, **22**, 77–84.

Ramakrishnan, P.S. & Toky, O.P. (1981). Soil nutrient status of hill agro-ecosystems and recovery pattern after slash and burn agriculture (jhum) in north-eastern India. *Plant and Soil*, **60**, 41–64.

Ramakrishnan, P.S. & Toky, O.P. (1983). Secondary succession following slash and burn agriculture in north-eastern India. II. Nutrient cycling. *Journal of Ecology*, **71**, 747–757.

Sabhasri, S. (1978). Effects of forest fallow cultivation on forest production and soil. *Farmers in the Forest* (Ed. by P. Kunstadter, E.C. Chapman & S. Sabhasri), pp. 160–184. University Press of Hawaii, Honolulu.

Sajise, P.E. & Baguinon, N.T. (1981). Some facets of upland development in the Philippines. *Program on Environmental Science and Management (University of the Philippines, los Banos, Philippines) Bulletin*, **1**, 4–10.

Schelhaas, R.M., Koopmans, T.T. & Andriesse, J.P. (1984). *The Effect of Burning on Fertility Level: Monitoring Project of Nutrient Cycling in Shifting Cultivation; Vanathavillu, Sri Lanka, Semongok (Sarawak), Malaysia and Mae Muang Luang, Thailand. Progress Report No. 2*. Royal Tropical Institute, Amsterdam.

Sumberg, J., Okali, C. & Attah-Krah, A.N. (1984). Nigeria launches pilot development project based on ILCA/IITA research. *International Livestock Centre for Africa Newsletter*, **3**(3), 1–3.

Toky, O.P & Ramakrishnan, P.S. (1981). Run-off and infiltration losses related to shifting agriculture (Jhum) in north-eastern India. *Environmental Conservation*, **8**, 313–321.

Trenbath, B.R. (1984). Decline of soil fertility and the collapse of shifting cultivation systems under intensification. *Tropical Rain-Forest: the Leeds Symposium* (Ed. by A.C. Chadwick & S.L. Sutton), pp. 279-292. Leeds Philosophical and Literary Society, Leeds.

Trenbath, B.R., Conway, G.R. & Craig, I.A. (1989). Threats to sustainability in intensified agricultural systems: analysis and implications for management. *Research Approaches in Agricultural Ecology* (Ed. by S.R. Gliessman). Springer, New York (in press).

UNESCO (1978). *Tropical Forest Ecosystems: a State-of-Knowledge Report*. Natural Resources Research XIV, United Nations Educational, Scientific and Cultural Organisation, Paris.

Young, A., Cheatle, R.J. & Muraya, P. (1987). *The Potential of Agroforestry for Soil Conservation. Part III. Soil Changes under Agroforestry (SCUAF): a Predictive Model. Working Paper No. 44*. International Council for Research in Agroforestry, Nairobi.

Nutritional constraints in secondary vegetation and upland rice in south-west Ivory Coast

H. VAN REULER* AND B. H. JANSSEN

*Department of Soil Science and Plant Nutrition,
Agricultural University, Wageningen, The Netherlands*

SUMMARY

1 The Tai National Park (330 000 ha) in south-west Ivory Coast is the last extensive area with undisturbed forest in Africa west of the Dahomey Gap. The annual rainfall is about 1800 mm.

2 The indigenous people practise shifting cultivation with upland rice as the main food crop. Due to immigration, there is a shortage of land outside the Park and therefore the crop yields need to increase.

3 The nutrient status of secondary vegetation is discussed. Phosphorus is the limiting nutrient.

4 In on-farm trials with rice the effects of nitrogen, phosphorus and potassium fertilizers and lime were studied. The yields varied between sites and between treatments from 0.9 to 5.0 t ha^{-1}. A significant positive response was obtained to phosphorus fertilizers only.

5 The response of upland rice to phosphorus fertilizer application was related to the extractable soil phosphorus concentrations (modified Olsen method). An application of 50 kg phosphorus fertilizer resulted in a yield increase of about 600 kg grain.

6 The yields of the plots without fertilizer in the trials were between 1.5 and 3.3 t ha^{-1}, considerably higher than the local farmers' yields (0.8–1.0 t ha^{-1}). This was mainly caused by differences in management, including more thorough clearing of the fields, regular weeding, fencing of the fields to limit the damage by rodents, and guarding against bird damage.

INTRODUCTION

The Tai National Park in the south-western part of Ivory Coast is the last extensive area with undisturbed forest in Africa west of the Dahomey Gap. Until the mid 1960s the region was largely uninhabited. The small population living along a few roads and on the coast practised subsistence shifting cultivation. In 1965 the Government decided to develop the region by timber exploitation to be followed by the creation of major agro-industrial projects to provide employment and trade after the timber harvest and the setting up of viable industries to ensure

---

*Present address: Centre Néerlandais-ORSTOM, 01 BP V51, Abidjan 01, Ivory Coast.

the region's economic development (Dosso, Guillaumet & Hadley 1981).

The Government also aimed to increase the population density by migration mainly from central Ivory Coast. Additional to the planned development, the region has attracted spontaneous immigration from other parts of Ivory Coast and neighbouring countries such as Burkina Faso and Mali (Dosso *et al.* 1981). This immigration was enforced by poor climatic conditions in the Sahelian zone (Lena 1984). The majority of the immigrants settled and started to grow crops, particularly coffee and cocoa. The overall consequence of these developments is that the area of undisturbed forest is decreasing very quickly. To safeguard the forest, the Tai National Park (330 000 ha) was established in 1972. In a few years time the primary forest outside the Park boundaries will have vanished. Each year the farmers have to clear fields with younger secondary vegetation. To safeguard the Park from disturbance, the areas cleared for agriculture outside have to be more intensively farmed.

The Agricultural University of Wageningen, The Netherlands has a project to study this, and work is in progess on forestry, agro-forestry, vegetation succession, soils and soil fertility. This paper deals with the nutrients in different land-use systems.

PHYSICAL AND BIOTIC ENVIRONMENT

The Tai National Park is situated between the Sassandra river in the east and the Cavally river in the west (Fig. 1). The study area is located on the western side of the Park.

The mean annual rainfall at the village of Tai is 1833 mm with a standard deviation of 338 mm (Casenave *et al.* 1980). According to Fritsch (1980) four seasons can be distinguished: (i) a long rainy season from March to July accounting for 45% of the total rainfall, (ii) a short relatively dry season from July to September, (iii) a short rainy season from September to November accounting for 30% of the total rainfall, and (iv) a long dry season from November to March in which the potential evapotranspiration exceeds the rainfall. The mean monthly temperature varies from 24.7 °C to 27.4 °C. In Fig. 2 the average climatic data and the calculated potential evapotranspiration according to the Turc formula are presented.

The rocks in the study area belong to the Precambrian Basement complex (Papon cited in Van Kekem (1986)). The main rock type is metamorphic migmatite, rich in biotite. Granite occurs locally. The region consists of uplands (up to 200 m altitude) with an undulating to rolling relief. The slopes tend to be long and are mostly convex. Valleys are relatively narrow and the streams have few meanders. The average local relief is 20 to 25 m.

A soil map of the south-western part of Ivory Coast at a scale of 1 : 200 000 has been prepared by the Development and Resources Corporation (1967). Near the village of Tai, more detailed studies have been carried out (Fritsch 1980; Fraters 1986; Van Kekem 1986). Figure 3 presents a representative transect near Tai and Table 1 shows the soil classification according to different systems. The

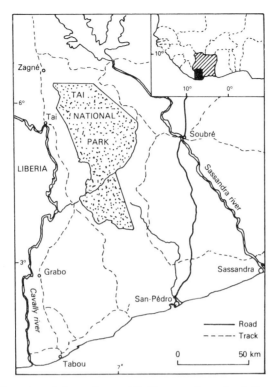

Fig. 1. Location of the study area (Guillaumet, Couturier & Dosso 1984).

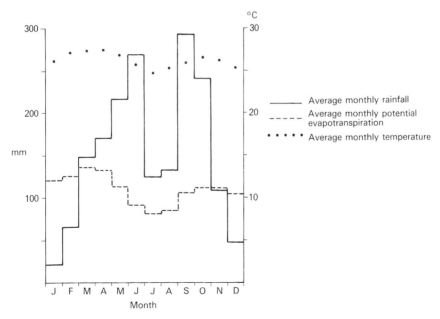

Fig. 2. Climatic data of the Tai meteorological station. Records from 1944 to 1959 and from 1966 to 1979.

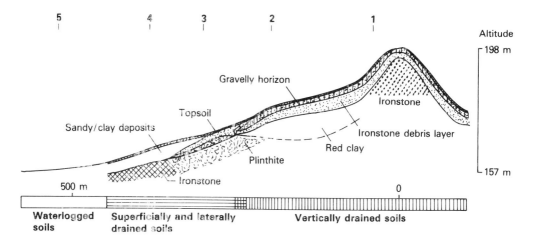

FIG. 3. Transect of soils representative of the Tai region (Fritsch 1980; Vooren 1985). Vertical scale is exaggerated. The numbers refer to the soils analysed by Fraters (1986) and Borst (1987).

soils on the slopes are strongly leached and chemically poor. The wet soils in the valley bottoms are presently not used for agriculture.

According to Vooren (1985) the vegetation type is tropical lowland evergreen seasonal forest in the UNESCO (1973) world classification. In the forest over 150 endemic woody species occur. The biomass varies from 350 t ha^{-1} in the valleys to 560 t ha^{-1} on the higher parts of the slopes (Huttel 1977). In the Park a great variety of monkeys is found as well as chimpanzees. Other animal species include elephant, pigmy hippopotamus, panther and buffalo.

The indigenous people, Guéré and Oubi, traditionally clear the forest and cultivate the land for one or two crop cycles with upland rice as the main crop.

TABLE 1. Classification of the soils of the transect presented in Fig. 3. The soils are classified according to Commission de Pédologie et de Cartographie des Sols (CPS) (1967), FAO/UNESCO (1974) and Soil Survey Staff (1975) (Fraters 1986)

Position on transect	CPS	FAO/UNESCO	Soil Survey Staff
1	Sol ferrallitique fortement désaturé, remanié, modal	Ferric Acrisol	Orthoxic Palehumult
2	Sol ferrallitique fortement désaturé, remanié, faiblement apprauvi	Ferric Acrisol	Orthoxic Palehumult
3	Sol ferrallitique fortement désaturé, à recrouvement plus ou moins apprauvi	Ferric Acrisol/ Plinthic Ferralsol	Plinthudult/ Plinthic Haplorthox
4	Sol ferrallitique fortement désaturé, induré apprauvi, hydromorph	Xanthic Ferralsol	Tropeptic Haplorthox
5	Sol hydromorph, peu humifère, à amphigley à nappe phreatique	Dystric Gleysol	Tropaquent

Thereafter the fields are either left fallow for a period of at least 15 years, or cash crops such as coffee and cocoa are planted. Hunting and gathering of forest products are often important activities (Moreau & De Namur 1978; De Rouw 1979). The immigrants, like the Baoulé people, also cultivate food crops after forest clearance, but they always plant coffee or cocoa thereafter.

SOIL NUTRIENTS

The soils in the Tai region are chemically poor. Fraters (1986) and Borst (1987) studied soil samples collected under primary forest from the transect presented in Fig. 3. Generally the nutrient concentrations of the soils in the positions 1 and 2 are higher than those of the profiles in the positions 3 and 4. It should be taken into account, however, that these data are always determined on the fine earth fraction (<2 mm) only. In soils with high gravel (>2 mm) contents the fertility is volumetrically diluted. The soils in the positions 1 and 2 have gravel mass contents of about 75% by weight. If the data are corrected for this content, the differences in fertility between the soils disappear. Borst (1987) studied these soils in a glasshouse experiment, using the double-pot technique in which plants can take up nutrients from the soil and from a nutrient solution simultaneously (Janssen 1974). He found that compared with a set of reference soils, the Tai soils were very low in phosphorus, low to medium in potassium, and medium in magnesium, except the valley bottom soil which was low.

Jaffré (1985) studied the forest regrowth on fields abandoned after one crop of upland rice. The above-ground phytomass and its nutrient contents were measured in a rice field at harvest (time 0) and at sites with secondary regrowth at 14, 26, 48, 78 and 180 months. Fritsch (1982) found that the soils at these sites did not differ greatly and when they differed it was mainly in pH and exchangeable bases (Table 2). All the soil properties indicate that the chemical fertility of the soils is low.

TABLE 2. Analytical data of topsoil samples (0–20 cm) from sites with secondary vegetation of varying age (Fritsch 1982). Gravel is expressed as a fraction of the whole soil, other chemical data (except pH) are expressed as a fraction of the fine earth (<2 mm). (*Modified Olsen extraction: 0.5 M NaHCO$_3$ + 0.5 M NH$_4$F, adjusted to pH 8.5. [†]CEC, pH 7.0. [‡]Corrected data for the percentage gravel on the basis of specific gravity for gravel = 3, bulk density of fine earth = 1.3)

Age of vegetation (months)	Gravel (%)	pH$_{HO}$ (log units)	Organic C	N (g kg^{-1})	Total P	Extractable P* (mg kg^{-1})	Ca	Mg	K	Na	CEC[†]
								(m-equiv. kg^{-1})			
0	4	4.7	9.0	0.7	96	9.0	5.5	3.0	0.7	0.2	37.4
14	1	5.2	10.0	0.9	103	9.5	12.2	4.8	0.7	0.1	41.8
26	7	4.9	11.9	0.9	120	10.0	9.0	4.0	0.4	0.1	50.2
48	7	4.9	10.3	0.9	103	9.5	11.0	3.5	0.5	0.1	48.6
78	1	5.3	11.4	1.0	170	9.5	10.9	8.0	1.0	0.2	43.8
180	20	4.5	13.5	1.1	127	13.5	6.4	3.0	1.0	0.2	56.9
180			12.2	0.9	114	12.2	5.8	2.7	0.9	0.1	51.2

The data in Table 3 show that the above-ground phytomass increased more or less linearly with an annual rate of about 5 t ha^{-1}. The rate of increase of the nutrient content of the phytomass was less than linear. This does not necessarily mean that the nutrient uptake rates decreased. The annual uptake of nutrients is equal to the sum of the annual net increase in total nutrient content of the phytomass plus the amount of nutrients returned in the litterfall and decaying roots. Since these returns increase with time, the net increase in nutrient content of the phytomass gradually decreases until it is zero at equilibrium. Then the annual uptake equals the amount of nutrients returned (Noij, Janssen & van Reuler 1988).

TABLE 3. Total above-ground phytomass (t ha^{-1}) of secondary vegetation of varying age, and its contents of nitrogen, phosphorus and potassium (kg ha^{-1}) (Jaffré 1985)

Age of vegetation (months)	Phytomass (t ha^{-1})	N	P (kg ha^{-1})	K
0	1.3	21.6	1.56	25.4
14	8.9	78.9	4.59	92.2
26	14.1	97.2	6.88	130.1
48	21.6	141.0	10.53	176.4
78	38.4	236.4	14.37	243.6
180	77.7	464.9	20.71	273.9

That the availability of nutrients probably did not decrease with time is reflected in the concentrations of nutrients in the leaves (Table 4). These were highest initially, but from 14 months onwards there was no consistent change with time.

The ratios of the nutrient concentrations in the leaves were calculated and compared with the ratios found in the leaves of primary forest in Surinam (Ohler 1980) and of a number of agricultural tree crops at optimum nutrition (De Geus 1973). Agricultural research in Surinam showed that after clearing, phosphorus was the major limiting nutrient for agricultural crops on these soils (Boxman & Janssen 1988). Because the N/P and K/P quotients are similar in Tai and Surinam, it is probable that phosphorus is also limiting in the Tai region. This is supported by the comparison with the data for agricultural tree crops in Table 4, which all have lower N/P and K/P quotients than the leaves in Tai. This indicates that in the Tai region phosphorus is the least available nutrient and therefore that the rate of forest regrowth may be limited by the availability of phosphorus.

No systematic research on the availability of nutrients for agricultural crops had been carried out in the Tai area. Therefore field trials were started in 1987.

FIELD TRIALS

Materials and methods

Fertilizer trials with upland rice (*Oryza sativa*, cultivar IDSA 6) were conducted on farms in six fields in an area from 20 km north to 10 km south of Tai in the growing season (March–August) of 1987.

Table 4. Leaf mass (t ha^{-1}) of secondary vegetation of varying age, leaf concentration of nitrogen, phosphorus and potassium (g kg^{-1}) and the ratios of these concentrations (Jaffré 1985) compared with the nutrient concentrations and ratios in the leaves of primary forest trees on phosphorus-deficient soils in Surinam (Ohler 1980) and in leaves of a number of agricultural tree crops at optimum nutrition (various authors cited by De Geus (1973))

Age of vegetation (months)	Leaf mass (t ha^{-1})	N	P (g kg^{-1})	K	N/P	K/P	N/K
0	0.30	30.4	1.70	21.2	17.9	12.5	1.4
14	1.19	22.9	1.04	13.7	22.0	13.2	1.7
26	1.17	24.9	1.40	15.1	17.8	10.8	1.7
48	1.30	25.2	1.54	13.0	16.4	8.4	1.9
78	1.48	24.8	1.28	14.7	19.4	11.5	1.7
180	3.85	25.2	1.00	13.4	25.2	13.4	1.9
Mean 14–180		24.6	1.25	14.0	19.7	11.2	1.8
Surinam primary forest	16.6	13.1	0.77	9.9	17.0	12.9	1.3
Cacao		24	1.8	16	13.3	8.9	1.5
Citrus		27	1.8	17	15	9.4	1.6
Coconut		19	1.25	9	15.2	7.2	2.1
Oil palm		26	1.68	11	15.5	6.5	1.7
Pecan		27	2.1	8.5	13	4.0	3.2
Rubber (Malaysia)						15.1	5.9	2.6
Rubber (Vietnam)						14.4	3.9	3.9

The relative position of the fields on the transect in Fig. 3 and some characteristics of the topsoil (0–20 cm) before the trials started are presented in Table 5. Some data on the vegetation before clearing are given in Table 6. The fields were cleared by slash and burn and as much unburnt wood as possible was removed by hand. This resulted in a 5–20% increase in the net surface to be planted compared with the farmers' fields. The rainfall was recorded at or near each site.

The experimental design was a 2^4 factorial in three replicates, that is 48 plots per trial field. Each of the six fields consisted of three blocks, each of sixteen 5 m × 4 m plots. The factors investigated were nitrogen, phosphorus, potassium and lime. Application rates were 0 and 50 kg N ha^{-1} as urea ($CO(NH_2)_2$, 46% N), 50 kg P ha^{-1} as triplesuperphosphate (mainly $Ca(H_2PO_4)_2.H_2O$, 20% P), 50 kg K ha^{-1} as potassium chloride (KCl, 50% K) and 400 kg $Ca(OH)_2$ ha^{-1}.

Lime was applied before sowing. The nitrogen and potassium applications were split into two equal parts and broadcast at 9–14 days and 44–54 days after sowing, except at field IV where the applications were made at 30 and 62 days after sowing. Triplesuperphosphate was placed in holes of 1 cm diameter at a distance of about 7 cm from the plant and at a depth of less than 12 cm, at 9–14 days (at field IV, 30 days) after sowing.

The rice was sown in the traditional way with a planting stick or machete. The average density of planting holes was about 90 000 ha^{-1} with five to ten grains in each hole. The fields were fenced and when necessary, weeded by hand, leaving the weed remains as surface mulch. During the maturing stage the fields were

TABLE 5. The relative positions of the trial fields on the transect of Fig. 3 and the analytical data of the topsoil (0–20 cm). Gravel content is expressed as a fraction of the whole soil, other chemical data (except pH) are expressed as a fraction of the fine earth (<2 mm) (*Modified Olsen extraction: 0.5 M NaHCO$_3$ + 0.5 M NH$_4$F, adjusted to pH 8.5. †CEC, pH 7.0)

Trial field	Position on transect	Gravel	Sand	Silt	Clay	pH$_{H2O}$	Organic C	N	Total P	Extractable P*	Exchangeable cations				
			(%)			(log units)	(g kg^{-1})			(mg kg^{-1})	Ca	Mg	K	Na	CEC†
											(m-equiv. kg^{-1})				
I	4–3	29	70.3	7.0	18.9	3.9	16.1	1.4	73	18	8.7	5.2	2.2	0.3	76.2
II	4	2	67.7	6.1	22.8	4.1	11.2	1.1	98	11	7.7	4.4	2.0	0.2	57.4
III	3–4	4	69.2	6.6	21.2	4.1	9.0	0.9	137	10	6.4	3.5	2.2	0.2	46.6
IV	3–4	20	74.1	7.5	14.9	4.9	11.6	1.3	129	13	15.3	7.3	2.6	0.2	48.9
V	5–4	1	67.3	8.5	21.4	4.4	10.5	1.2	134	22	8.2	6.0	2.3	0.3	56.5
VI	5–4	1	76.9	10.3	10.5	4.3	8.6	0.8	80	17	8.2	4.5	1.2	0.2	34.5

TABLE 6. Effects of fertilizer treatments on rice grain yields (t ha^{-1}). The values are the average yields of 24 experimental plots with (+) or without (−) the respective nutrient. Before clearing, the vegetation on fields I and II consisted of primary forest and on the other fields of secondary regrowth of the indicated age. The shade produced by remaining and surrounding trees is also indicated. (**.*Significant difference at 0.01 and 0.05 level, respectively. †Estimated shade: + + = much; + = intermediate; 0 = none. ‡Average yields of 16 experimental plots. §Average yields of 3 experimental plots)

Trial field	Age of regrowth (years)	Shade†	Yield (t ha^{-1})								No fertilizer§
			−N	+N	−P	+P	−K	+K	−L	+L	
I		+ +	2.16	2.16	1.63	2.68**	2.13	2.18	2.06	2.26	1.49
II‡		+ +	1.66	1.85	1.50	2.01*	1.85	1.66	1.68	1.82	1.55
III	34	+	2.54	2.17**	2.10	2.61**	2.42	2.30	2.36	2.35	2.57
IV	23	0	3.21	3.29	2.70	3.81**	3.22	3.29	3.33	3.17	2.50
V	23	0	3.76	3.99	3.87	3.89	3.75	4.00	3.88	3.88	3.11
VI	1	0	3.15	3.40	3.09	3.46*	3.37	3.16	3.32	3.23	3.14

guarded against bird damage. The rice was harvested after 114–131 days. The harvested plot size was 3 m × 4 m. The yield data refer to grains with a moisture content of 14%.

Results

Rice yields varied between sites and between treatments from 0.9 to 5 t ha^{-1} on individual plots. The variation in yield between replicates of the same treatment was large. The average yields of the main treatments varied from 1.5 to 4.0 t ha^{-1} (Table 6). Each yield figure is the average of 24 items unless indicated otherwise. For example '−N' means the average of all plots that did not receive nitrogen fertilizer irrespective of the application of other nutrients or lime. At all fields, except V, there was a significant positive response to phosphorus but not to nitrogen, potassium and lime. At field III nitrogen application had a significant negative effect.

The yields on the control plots were about the same as those on the nitrogen–potassium–lime fertilized plots without phosphorus (with again field III as an exception), another indication that possible effects of nitrogen, potassium and lime were very small.

It was observed that during the vegetative growth, the rice often responded to nitrogen, provided that phosphorus was also applied. This positive nitrogen–phosphorus interaction was not observed in the final grain yields.

Lowest yields were obtained on fields cleared from primary forest. This is in contrast to the generally accepted assumption that such sites produce more than sites cleared from secondary vegetation due to the higher nutrient content of the primary forest.

DISCUSSION

The results of the field trials confirm the conclusions drawn from the data on the secondary vegetation that phosphorus availability is a major growth-limiting factor.

The rice yields of the $-P$ treatments were clearly related to the extractable phosphorus content at the fields IV, V and VI, but not elsewhere. At similar values of extractable phosphorus the yields of both the $-P$ and the $+P$ treatments of fields I, II and III were considerably lower than those of fields IV, V and VI. Compared with the other fields, the following adverse conditions were present in fields I, II and III: a lower pH, more shade, a higher position on the slopes and they had been cleared from an older and probably heavier forest.

A possible negative effect of a low pH seems to contradict the absence of a significant effect of liming. However, the lime was broadcast and not worked into the soil and therefore had probably not yet affected the yields. This hypothesis is supported by the fact that the second crop (maize grown from August to December 1987) showed a positive response to lime, especially on the fields which originally had the lowest pH values.

The higher position on the slope may have negatively influenced the yield via the moisture supply.

The presence of shade may have caused a decrease in solar irradiation but, in view of the yield levels concerned, it is questionable whether this can have played an important role.

The influence of the former forest vegetation is through the quantity and quality of the slashed material and the presence of the remaining roots. The decomposition of woody material results in immobilization of inorganic phosphorus and nitrogen, thus lowering the amounts that are available for uptake by plants (Noij *et al.* 1988). With the presently available knowledge it is difficult to say which factors were most important.

The yields of the plots without fertilizer application were higher than those obtained by local farmers, which vary from about 0.8 to 1.0 t ha^{-1} (A. De Rouw, personal communication). There are several reasons for this difference: the experimental plots were almost completely covered by the crop, while on farmers' fields a considerable part may be occupied by fallen trees and branches; unlike farmers' plots the experimental plots were fenced (limiting the damage by rodents), regularly weeded and guarded against bird damage at the maturing stage of the rice; the farmers' fields may be affected by shade. For a number of reasons some selected tree species are not felled or burnt during the clearing of primary and old secondary forest (De Rouw 1987). As well as trees left in the fields, the surrounding vegetation may produce shade, especially if the clearings are of a limited size. The effect of shade on farmers' fields may be stronger in clearings from primary forest where more solid trees occur than in secondary forest.

CONCLUSION

An important way of lowering the population pressure on the last remaining forest area in south-west Ivory Coast is to increase the yields of agricultural crops.

The results given in this paper indicate that in the Tai area phosphorus can be considered as the major limiting nutrient for the secondary vegetation as well as for upland rice. An application of 50 kg phosphorus to rice resulted in an average yield increase of 600 kg ha^{-1}. With the present prices of rice and phosphorus fertilizer in Ivory Coast this is economically viable. However, further research with varying application rates of phosphorus and other nutrients will be necessary over a number of years to determine the most economic rates.

The results also indicate that the low yields per hectare generally obtained in the local shifting cultivation systems are not only due to low soil fertility. Other reasons may be poor management, the fact that the net area planted is relatively small due to fallen trees and branches, and shading.

ACKNOWLEDGEMENTS

We thank the Ministry of Scientific Research of Ivory Coast for granting permission to carry out the study, the farmers in the Tai region for their cooperation and hospitality and M. A. Muilenburg and R. Postma for much help with the field trials.

REFERENCES

Borst, A.P. (1987). *Study on the availability of some nutrients in soils of the Tai region, Côte d'Ivoire.* MSc Thesis, Agricultural University, Wageningen, The Netherlands.

Boxman, O. & Janssen, B.H. (1989). Availability of nutrients and fertilizer use. *Mechanized Annual Cropping on Low Fertility Soils in the Humid Tropics. A Case Study in Suriname* (Ed. by B.H. Janssen & J.F. Wienk), Section 6.5. Agricultural University Papers, Wageningen, The Netherlands.

Casenave, A., Flory, J., Guiguen, N., Ranc, N., Simon, J.M., Toilliez, J. & Tourne, M. (1980). *Etude Hydrologique des Bassins de Tai. Campagnes 1978–1979.* Office de la Recherche Scientifique et Technique Outre-Mer, Centre d'Adiopodoumé, Côte d'Ivoire.

Commission de Pédologie et de Cartographie des Sols (1967). *Classification des Sols.* Laboratoire Pédologie-Géologie, Ecole Nationale Supérieure d'Agriculture, Grignon, France.

De Geus, J.G. (1973). Fertilizer Guide for the Tropics and Subtropics, 2nd edn. Centre d'Etude de l'Azote, Zurich.

De Rouw, A. (1979). *La Culture Traditionelle dans le Sud-ouest de la Côte d'Ivoire (région de Tai): le Système Oubi Confronté aux Pratiques Agricoles Baoulés Immigrés.* Office de la Recherche Scientifique et Technique Outre-Mer, Centre d'Adiopodoumé, Côte d'Ivoire.

De Rouw, A. (1987). Tree management as part of two farming systems in the wet forest zone (Ivory Coast). *Acta Oecologica, Oecologia Applicata,* **8**, 39–51.

Development and Resources Corporation (1967). *Soil Survey of the South-West Region.* Report prepared for the Government of Ivory Coast, New York.

Dosso, H., Guillaumet, J.L. & Hadley, M. (1981). The Tai project: land use problems in a tropical rain forest. *Ambio,* **10**, 120–125.

FAO/UNESCO (1974). *Soil Map of the World (1:5.000.000), Vol.1 Legend.* UNESCO, Paris.

Fraters, D. (1986). *A study of a catena in Tai forest, Ivory Coast.* MSc Thesis, Agricultural University, Wageningen, The Netherlands.

Fritsch, E. (1980). *Etude Pédologique et Représentation Cartographique à 1:50.000 d'une Zone de 1600 ha, Représentative de la Région Forestière du Sud-ouest Ivoirien. Rapport d'élève.* Office de la Recherche Scientifique et Technique Outre-Mer, Centre d'Adiopodoumé, Côte d'Ivoire.

Fritsch, E. (1982). *Evolution des Sols sous Recrû Forestier Après Mise en Culture Traditionelle dans le*

Sud-ouest de la Côte d'Ivoire. Office de la Recherche Scientifique et Technique Outre-Mer, Centre d'Adiopodoumé, Côte d'Ivoire.

Guillaumet, J.L., Couturier, G. & Dosso, H. (1984). *Recherche et Aménagement en Milieu Forestier Tropical Humide: Le Projet Tai de Côte d'Ivoire. Notes Techniques du MAB 15.* UNESCO, Paris.

Huttel, Ch. (1977). *Etude de Quelques Caractéristiques Structurales de la Végétation du Bassin Versant de l'Audrénisrou.* Office de la Recherche Scientifique et Technique Outre-Mer, Centre d'Adiopodoumé, Côte d'Ivoire.

Jaffré, T. (1985). Composition minérale et stocks de bioéléments dans la biomasse épigée de recrûs forestiers en Côte d'Ivoire. *Acta Oecologica, Oecologia Plantarum,* **6**, 233–246.

Janssen, B.H. (1974). A double pot technique for rapid soil testing. *Tropical Agriculture (Trinidad),* **51**, 233–246.

Lena, Ph. (1984). Le développement des activités humaines. *Recherche et Aménagement en Milieu Forestier Tropical Humide: Le Projet Tai de Côte d'Ivoire. Notes Techniques du MAB 15* (Ed. by J.L. Guillaumet, G. Couturier & H. Dosso), pp. 59–113. UNESCO, Paris.

Moreau, R. & De Namur, Ch. (1978). Le système cultural traditionnel des Oubis de la région de Tai. *Cahier ORSTOM, Série Biologique,* **12**, 191–197.

Noij, I.G.A.M., Janssen, B.H. & Van Reuler, H. (1988). Modelling nutrient cycling in tropical forest areas. A case study of Tai, Côte d'Ivoire. *Proceedings Second International Tropenbos Seminar* pp. 122–128. The Tropenbos Programme, Ede, The Netherlands.

Ohler, F.M.J. (1980). *Phytomass and Mineral Content in Untouched Forest. Centrum voor Landbouwkundig Onderzoek in Suriname, Rapport 132.* Landbouwhogeschool Wageningen, The Netherlands.

Soil Survey Staff (1975). *Soil Taxonomy. A Basic System of Soil Classification for Making and Interpreting Soil Surveys. Agricultural Handbook 436.* Department of Agriculture, Washington, U.S.A.

UNESCO (1973). *International Classification and Mapping of Vegetation. Ecological Conservation No. 6.* UNESCO, Paris.

Van Kekem, A.J. (1986). Tai Biosphere reserve, Ivory Coast. *Guidelines for Soil Survey and Land Evaluation in Ecological Research. MAB Technical Note 17* (Ed. by R.F. Breimer, A.J. Van Kekem & H. van Reuler), pp. 105–108. UNESCO, Paris.

Vooren, A.P. (1985). *Patterns in Tree and Branch-Fall in a West African Rain Forest. Report D 85–05.* Department of Silviculture, Wageningen Agricultural University.

Nutrient cycling in moist tropical forests: the hydrological framework

L. A. BRUIJNZEEL

Department of Hydrogeology and Geographical Hydrology,
Free University, PO Box 7161, 1007 MC Amsterdam,
The Netherlands

SUMMARY

1 There is considerable diversity in the hydrological behaviour of moist tropical forest areas, especially with respect to runoff patterns, which mainly relates to variations in geological (and therefore geomorphological and pedological) settings.

2 Apart from forests at specific locations, such as coastal fog belts or cloud belts in mountainous areas, or forests of very large areas (e.g. the Amazon basin), tropical forests most probably do not influence local amounts of rainfall significantly.

3 Annual evapotranspiration (ET) for tropical lowland forests that rarely or never experience serious soil moisture shortages (as determined by the water balance method) averages 1425 mm (range 1230–1550 mm) ($n = 17$); this value may fall to 900 mm in the case of seasonal forest.

4 Corresponding values for montane forests (excluding 'cloud forests') converge at 1250 mm year^{-1} (range 1145–1380 mm year^{-1}) ($n = 8$), with no clear trends with altitude or annual precipitation.

5 'Cloud forests' (Stadtmuller 1987) represent a special case, showing very low ET rates as a result of low radiation inputs, low atmospheric vapour pressure deficits and the process of 'cloud stripping'; available data suggest 'gross' (i.e. including contributions by cloud stripping) values for ET of 310–450 mm year^{-1}.

6 Of the two main components of ET, rainfall interception (Ei) has frequently been overestimated because of inadequate sampling designs for measuring net precipitation; relatively large numbers of gauges that are relocated at regular time intervals at random locations on the forest floor are required for reliable estimates.

7 The best studies of net precipitation in tropical forests suggest an average value of 86% (range 77–93%) of incident precipitation (on an annual basis) for lowland forests ($n = 13$) and 82% (range 75–86%) for lower montane forests ($n = 5$); as stemflow usually constitutes 0.5–2% of rainfall, average interception values for the two groups of forests amount to 14% (range 4.5–22%) and 18% (range 10–24%) of incident precipitation, respectively.

8 The second major component of ET, transpiration (Et), is often only known indirectly (Et = ET – Ei) and unreliably. Values so determined converge around 1045 mm year^{-1} (range 885–1285 mm year^{-1}) ($n = 9$) for lowland forests never severely short of water to about 600 mm year^{-1} for (semi)deciduous forest; estimates for lower montane forests (excluding 'cloud forests') do not correlate with site elevation and vary considerably (560–830 mm year^{-1}); estimates available for 'cloud forest' range from 285 to 515 mm year^{-1} (values corrected for cloud stripping).

9 Rates of the release of nutrients through chemical weathering may be evaluated by means of the small-catchment mass balance technique, except for phosphorus which is too immobile; few reliable tropical studies exist and great care should be exercised in interpreting rates of weathering in terms of root network accessibility to released nutrients.

10 Weathering rates for moist tropical forest sites are mainly governed by the nature of the geological substrate and range from extremely low in the case of highly weathered deposits to considerable in the case of relatively young volcanic strata; rates differ between elements as a function of rock mineralogy as well.

11 The hydrological and biogeochemical patterns of a variety of tropical forest ecosystems, such as peat swamp forest, forest on ultrabasic rocks, and to a slightly lesser extent, montane forests, are still poorly known.

12 It is suggested that more effort be directed to the development of models describing hydrological and biogeochemical processes in those forests for which a good data set is available, rather than to start at new locations; such modelling is considered essential in improving our ability of predicting environmental consequences of forest conversions.

13 The majority of studies in tropical forests have been conducted more or less on an individual basis, although there has been an increasing tendency towards more integrated research since the initiation of the IBP and MAB programmes. Finally, the suggestion is made that the major contributions that 'physical' scientists may make to the study of nutrient flows in tropical forest ecosystems are the following: (1) detailed (hydro-)pedological surveys enabling the choice of truly regionally representative study sites, (2) a proper quantification of pathways followed by the water through the ecosystem, and (3) a quantification of the supply of nutrients by chemical weathering.

INTRODUCTION

The link between the hydrological cycle and fluxes and cycling of nutrients in the more humid regions of the earth has been recognized for several decades (Ovington 1962; Bormann & Likens 1967). Yet, there have been few comprehensive studies on tropical forest nutrient dynamics that have quantified the nutrients in the various ecosystem compartments and fluxes and have combined these with a proper quantification of the hydrological variables involved (Bruijnzeel 1983a; Vitousek & Sanford 1986; Proctor 1987). Because water is a transporting agent, solvent and catalyst, quantitative hydrological data are vital in understanding forest nutrient cycles (Likens *et al.* 1977).

This paper aims to review the hydrological information on moist tropical forests and to look at those nutrient pathways that involve water as the principal transport medium.

Moist tropical forests as defined here include montane forests and (1) lie between 23°N and 23°S, (2) receive at least 1600 mm of rainfall annually and (3) experience no more than 4 dry (following Schmidt & Ferguson (1951), i.e. with rainfall < 60 mm) months, or (4) experience a longer dry season in combination with an annual rainfall exceeding 4000 mm and adequate soil moisture storage opportunities.

THE FOREST HYDROLOGICAL CYCLE

Although most tropical ecologists will be familiar with the outline of the forest hydrological cycle, there is still some semantic confusion about terms such as 'runoff' and 'interception loss'. Therefore, a brief description will be given of a simple forest hydrological system (Fig. 1). Since forest ecosystems are generally part of larger landscape units drained by one or more streams, this is followed by a discussion of how different parts of a drainage basin are linked hydrologically (Fig. 2).

Apart from specific locations, such as coastal fog belts or cloud belts, rain is the precipitation input to forests in the humid tropics. A small part reaches the forest floor directly without touching the canopy: the so-called 'direct' or 'free' throughfall (Rutter et al. 1971). Of the rainfall that strikes the vegetation, a substantial portion is intercepted and evaporates back into the atmosphere during and immediately after the storm (Bruijnzeel & Wiersum 1987). Many hydrologists therefore like to refer to this component as 'interception loss'. However, if it is assumed that leaves covered with a film of water do not transpire (the energy necessary for transpiration largely being consumed to evaporate the water on the leaves), then while intercepted water is being evaporated there should be a saving in water taken up for transpiration (Rutter 1975). Burgy & Pomeroy (1958) therefore introduced the distinction between 'gross' interception loss (gross rainfall minus net rainfall) and 'net' interception loss (the gross loss minus the saving in transpired water). Since the latter is difficult to determine, the use of these terms does little more than create confusion. In the present review rainfall interception is taken as gross rainfall minus net rainfall (see below).

The remainder of the rain falls as crown drip and along branches and trunks as stemflow after the storage capacities of the canopy and trunks have been filled respectively (Leyton, Reynolds & Thompson 1967). The sum of direct throughfall, drip and stemflow is commonly called net precipitation (Helvey & Patric 1965).

Although direct throughfall and crown drip cannot be determined separately in the field, the distinction between the two is useful in modelling the process of rainfall interception (Rutter et al. 1971; Gash 1979). Furthermore, it helps to clarify the complexities of dry deposition and exchange of nutrients in the canopy (Parker 1983; Lovett & Lindberg 1984).

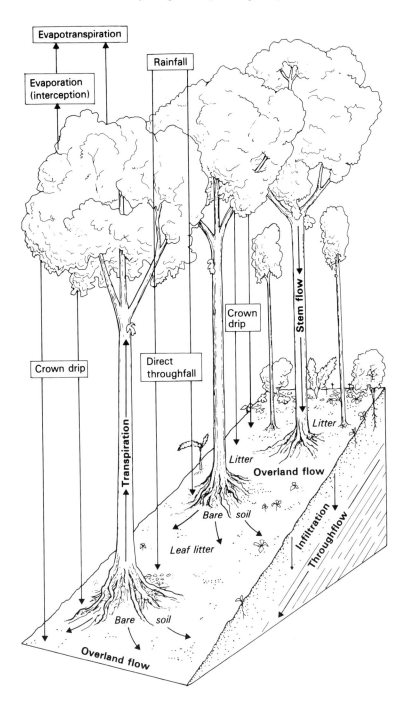

FIG. 1. The hillslope forest hydrological cycle (adapted from Douglas (1977)).

Normally, amounts of precipitation measured within tropical forests are substantially less than outside, but in coastal fog belts and montane cloud belts the reverse sometimes applies because of 'occult precipitation', the stripping of fog/clouds by the vegetation (Zadroga 1981; Stadtmuller 1987).

The rainfall arriving at the forest floor encounters a filter that determines the path to reach the stream channel (Fig. 2). The water in the various pathways may be characterized by solute concentrations which reflect differences in residence time (Bruijnzeel 1983b) and the prevailing hydrological pattern influences the amounts of nutrients leached from the system (Burt 1986). In addition, this may influence forest structure (e.g. Lescure & Boulet 1985) and determines the fate of the land following forest clearing (Nortcliff & Thornes 1981).

Since precipitation inputs are discrete and sometimes, especially in the more seasonal tropics, widely separated in time, streamflows exhibit periods of suddenly increased discharge associated with rainfall and longer periods of slowly decreasing flow of water stored in the catchment. The immediacy of streamflow response suggests that part of the rainfall follows a rapid route to the stream channel, thereby producing 'quickflow'. The water travelling more slowly emerges as 'baseflow' (Ward 1984).

If rainfall intensities below the forest exceed the infiltration capacity of the soil, the unabsorbed excess runs off as 'Hortonian' or 'infiltration excess' overland flow (Horton 1933; flow path Q_o in Fig. 2(a)). The remainder infiltrates into the soil and, depending on vertical and lateral hydraulic conductivities, local soil moisture patterns and slope steepness, may take one of several routes to the stream channel (Fig. (2a)). In the (relatively rare) case of deep, permeable and uniform deposits, the water will tend to travel vertically downwards to the zone of saturation and will then follow a curving path to the stream channel (flow path Q_g in Fig. 2(a)). Generally, however, permeability decreases with depth. Part of the water then percolates vertically until it meets an obstruction and is deflected

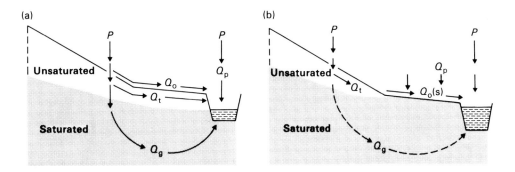

FIG. 2. Flow paths of the sources of streamflow (Ward 1984). Q_p is direct precipitation on the water surface, Q_o is 'Hortonian' overland flow, Q_t is throughflow, Q_g is groundwater flow and $Q_o(s)$ is saturation overland flow.

laterally (e.g. Weyman 1973; Guehl 1983); however, during and immediately after rainstorms some water may flow more or less parallel to the slope surface as so-called 'subsurface stormflow' (Zaslavsky & Rogowski 1969; Harr 1977; Cales 1982; flow path Q_t in Fig. (2a)).

Usually lateral flow in the soil profile is referred to as 'throughflow' (Kirkby & Chorley 1967; cf. Fig. 1). The bulk of it generally travels relatively slowly through the soil matrix, feeding near-saturated sections around stream channels and in topographic depressions, thereby maintaining the baseflow of the stream (Hewlett 1961; Kirkby & Chorley 1967). These near-saturated zones in a catchment may act as a major source of quickflow during rainstorms (Dietrich, Windsor & Dunne, 1982; Nortcliff & Thornes 1984).

The mechanism of quickflow production reflects the prevailing climatic, geomorphological and pedological setting (Walsh 1980; Ward 1984; Burt & Butcher 1985). In the case of the situation depicted in Fig. 2(b), quickflow is often generated through the formation of what has been called a 'riparian groundwater ridge' (Ward 1984), which may rise to the surface and induce 'saturation overland flow' (Dunne 1978; flow path $Q_o(s)$ in Fig. 2(b)). In such cases a significant portion of the quickflow consists of freshly fallen water with relatively low solute concentrations (Bruijnzeel 1983b) and stormflow patterns will reflect differences in rainfall intensity as they occur (Dunne 1978).

However, where deep permeable soils overlie impermeable bedrock and where steep hillslopes border a narrow floodplain, there will be little saturation overland flow. Rather, quickflow will then be dominated by (rapid) throughflow contributions (Dunne 1978). Depending on the depth and initial moisture status of the soil and the size of the storm, a peak in streamflow may occur shortly after the storm or up to several days later (Hewlett & Nutter 1970). It has often been suggested (e.g. Whipkey 1965; Mosley 1982) that part of the throughflow travels through soil macropores quickly enough to reach the stream channel during the storm (hence the term 'subsurface stormflow'), whilst others have proposed a 'push-through' mechanism to explain the rapid response of streams to rainfall in areas without any type of overland flow (Hewlett & Hibbert 1967).

Despite the emphasis which has been placed on the role of macropores in soil hydrology (Sollins *this volume*; Nortcliff & Thornes *this volume*), recent work on stormflow generation in areas of high rainfall, short and steep slopes and highly permeable soils, using natural isotope and chemical tracers, has shown the importance of the push-through mechanism (Pearce, Stewart & Sklash 1986; Sklash, Stewart & Pearce 1986).

Not all water infiltrating into the soil emerges as streamflow; a large part of it is taken up by the forest and returns to the atmosphere through transpiration. In the present context the term forest evapotranspiration will be used to denote the sum of transpiration (i.e. evaporation from a dry canopy) and interception (i.e. evaporation from a wet canopy). Evaporation from the litter and soil surface has been shown to be negligible in humid tropical forests (Jordan & Heuveldop 1981; Roche 1982).

HYDROLOGICAL PATTERNS IN TROPICAL FORESTS

Generally speaking, infiltration capacities of forest soils are high (Douglas 1977; Pritchett 1979) and infiltration excess overland flow in forests is therefore a rare phenomenon, even under intense rainfall. However, where the soil becomes exposed through treefall (Ruxton 1967) or landslips on steep slopes (Imeson & Vis 1982), effects of overland flow may be important. In the Colombian Andes, Imeson & Vis (1982) found that the amount of bare soil varied greatly within and between forest types. They reported an average value of 6% (range 0–21%) of bare soil with a slight trend to lower values in montane forests.

A rather extreme case has been reported by Herwitz (1986a) for a forest in Queensland with an annual rainfall of about 6500 mm. There the combination of high intensity rainfall and its funnelling by the trees produced large volumes of water around the trunk bases and often exceeded local infiltration capacities with the result that water flowed downhill over the surface for varying distances. However, work in other tropical forests has shown that this type of runoff is usually less than 1% of the rainfall (Nortcliff, Thornes & Waylen 1979; Lundgren 1980; Roose 1981; Cales 1982; Hatch 1983). On the other hand, on forested slopes underlain by soils with an impermeable horizon relatively close to the surface, substantial (up to 47% of total streamflow) volumes of saturation overland flow have been reported (Bonell & Gilmour 1978; Walsh 1980; Dietrich et al. 1982; Sarrailh 1983).

Estimates of the amounts of dissolved nutrients in overland flow in the tropics are scarce and range from quite small (rain forest on a steep sandy slope in Ivory Coast (Roose 1981)) to considerable (80-year-old plantation of cacao on a moderate slope on an alfisol in Brazil (De Oliveira Leite 1985)), despite only slight differences in their Hortonian runoff volumes. The quantities of dissolved nutrients will be less than the quantities of nutrients contained in the sediment transported by the overland flow (Leigh 1978).

As stated earlier, for a given rainfall regime, hillslope flow patterns are dependent on the nature of the substrate (Fig. 2). At one end of the spectrum there are those substrates which are sufficiently permeable to prevent the occurrence of either type of overland flow on the hillside (Nortcliff et al. 1979; Walsh 1980; Roose 1981; Bruijnzeel 1983b). Streamflow during storms is then either dominated by rapid throughflow in the case of narrow valley bottoms (e.g. Walsh 1980; Bruijnzeel 1983b) or by localized saturation overland flow generated in the wide valley bottoms (e.g. Nortcliff et al. 1979; see also Fig. 2(b)). At the other extreme, for soils which have a sudden decrease in permeability at shallow depths, there is the widespread occurrence of saturation overland flow on the slopes (as opposed to the valley bottom) dominating the stream's storm hydrograph (Bonell & Gilmour 1978; Dietrich et al. 1982). A whole array of situations (freely draining soils versus soils of restricted drainage) has been described for rain forests in French Guyana (Cales 1982; Guehl 1983; Lescure & Boulet 1985; Fritsch, Dubreuil & Sarrailh 1987).

THE HYDROLOGICAL CYCLE IN MOIST
TROPICAL FOREST

Rainfall

Mineral nutrients enter a forest through wet deposition (i.e. dissolved in precipitation) and as dry deposition. As the relative importance of these inputs depends on amount and distribution of rainfall, it is of interest to investigate to what extent tropical forests are able to influence the amount of rainfall they receive. There is no conclusive evidence that, except for special cases, forests in the humid zones of the world have an important effect in this respect (Bruijnzeel 1986). Two such special cases, the vast forested surface of the Amazon basin and the so-called 'cloud forests', will be discussed further.

In the Amazon basin, measurements of natural oxygen-18 and deuterium concentrations in precipitation suggest that recycling of water vapour through forest evapotranspiration may constitute an important source of atmospheric moisture for rainfall in the area (Salati *et al.* 1979). A descriptive model was developed which subdivided the Central Amazon basin into 3° longitudinal segments. The observed gradient in isotopic concentration of rainfall (when going from the coast to the headwater area in the west) could then reasonably be explained by assuming that in each segment rainfall was derived for one half of the segment from evapotranspirational recycling within the segment itself, with the remainder produced from water vapour derived from the neighbouring eastern segment (Dall'Olio *et al.* 1979). The geoclimatic setting of the Amazon basin — a horseshoe-shaped plain open to the moisture-bearing eastern trade winds and effectively sheltered by mountains and high plateaus to the west, north and south — is conducive to this hypothesis. Additional support comes from small-scale water balance studies in the region, which suggest that 74–81% of incident precipitation returns to the atmosphere via forest evapotranspiration, the remainder running off as streamflow (Leopoldo *et al.* 1982a,b).

Similarly, Crozat (1979) and Delmas & Servant (1983) have suggested that an important part of the potassium and sulphur inputs for rain forest in Ivory Coast is generated by the forest itself. One can merely speculate as to what will be the long-term effect of large-scale removal of tropical forest on atmospheric nutrient inputs.

The issue of the decline in rainfall often ascribed to 'deforestation' in the humid tropics was recently reviewed by Bruijnzeel (1986), who concluded that it is unwise to expect firm conclusions in the absence of unanimously accepted climatic models. However, as a first approximation, a decrease in annual rainfall of about 10% has been suggested by Henderson-Sellers & Gornitz (1984) and Shuttleworth (1988) for a hypothetical conversion of the Amazon rain forest to grassland.

The amount of rainfall reaching the soil surface in 'cloud forests' (defined as 'forests frequently covered in clouds or mist' by Stadtmuller (1987)), is undisputedly greater than in 'non-cloud' forests (Stadtmuller 1987). Although occurring in restricted physiographic and climatic situations, such as coastal fog belts and at high elevations with frequent cloud incidence, these forests cover about 500 000 km^2 or almost 5% of the total area of closed moist tropical forests (Persson 1974). Such increases in total precipitation can be sizeable, hundreds of millimetres per year being contributed by occult precipitation in forests subjected to persistent wind-driven fog and clouds. Typical values for the humid tropics range between 7 and 18% of ordinary rainfall during rainy seasons to over 100% of the rainfall during dry seasons (Hermann 1970; Vogelmann 1973; Juvik & Ekern 1978; Vis 1986). Therefore, conversion of cloud forests to certain types of agricultural land use not using trees may reduce streamflow and groundwater recharge. However, experimental evidence is lacking to date.

Evapotranspiration

Shuttleworth (1979) and Stewart (1984) have reviewed the techniques for estimating evapotranspiration (ET). A general distinction can be made between water balance methods and micrometeorological techniques. The former find ET by difference and involve measurements of precipitation, streamflow or drainage and changes in soil moisture storage and are commonly applied to (presumably watertight) catchment areas (Lee 1970). Micrometeorological methods, on the other hand, require sophisticated instrumentation at various levels within and above the forest canopy and have therefore been much less widely used (Shuttleworth et al. 1984). The majority of published estimates for ET in moist tropical forests have been made by the water balance method on catchment areas ranging in size from less than 1 ha to the entire Congo basin.

Catchment leakage may limit the application of the water balance method, especially in small headwater catchments, where streams lose water through the weathering mantle, whereas large streams may also lose considerable amounts of water to their floodplains. In both cases ET will be overestimated. In addition, areal precipitation estimates are frequently unreliable for larger tropical basins, especially forested ones (Aitken, Ribeny & Brown 1972). Theoretically the best estimates could be obtained from carefully selected catchments of small size (up to a few square kilometres) monitored for a number of years to account for climatic variability. However, even under these conditions a precision of 15% is already difficult to achieve for ET with the catchment water balance method (Lee 1970; Bruijnzeel 1988). Shuttleworth et al. (1984) reported systematic errors of 5–10% for energy flux measurements above a rain forest in Central Amazonia.

Sometimes information on ET may be required for a specific part of a forest (e.g. on the ridges) rather than the lumped estimate given by the catchment-based approach. This introduces the practical problem of estimating the deep drainage component, which cannot be evaluated by the regular measurement of changes in soil moisture storage alone (Huttel 1975). This component can be estimated by the hydraulic conductivity–potential gradient method (Cooper 1979; Bruijnzeel 1987), which involves continuous or at least daily observations of subsoil moisture tensions.

ET of lowland forests

Published results are variable. For example, estimated annual values of ET of lowland and hill dipterocarp forests on granitic substrates in peninsular Malaysia — all receiving more than 2000 mm of rain annually — range from about 1000 mm (Low & Goh 1972) to almost 1800 mm (Rahim & Kasran 1986). Much of this variation is explicable in terms of leakage or errors of methodology. Values from the more reliable studies are given in Fig. 3.

The scatter of the points in Fig. 3 is partly due to the inclusion of a few studies, such as those referred to as ●7, ▲4 and ▲5, made during dry years. The wettest location included (the Guma basin in Sierra Leone, ▲3) experiences a severe dry season of 5 months, despite a high annual precipitation, which may account for its relatively low ET value (Ledger 1975). The area experiences an annual deluge of some 4500 mm within 3 months, a situation similar to that reported for the Western Ghats in India (Rai & Proctor 1986). Indeed, the two areas should make an interesting ecological and hydrological comparison.

The rest of the data in Fig. 3 and Table 1 converge around an average figure of 1425 mm year^{-1} (range 1230–1550 mm year^{-1}; $n = 17$). However, annual ET for a particular forest tends to be correlated with annual rainfall as a result of increased rainfall interception in wet years and a limiting of transpiration by soil

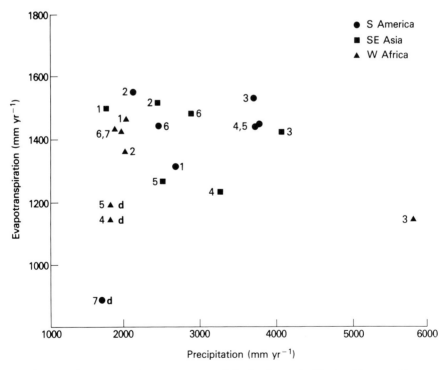

FIG. 3. Annual evapotranspiration versus precipitation in tropical lowland forests. d is dry year. See Table 1.

Table 1. Annual evapotranspiration versus percipitation in tropical lowland forests (Bruijnzeel 1988b). d is dry year.

Site		Precipitation (mm year⁻¹)	ET (mm year⁻¹)	Period (year)	Location	Reference
S America (●)	1	2648	1311	2	Ducke Reserve, Brazil	Shuttleworth (1988)
	2	2089	1548	1	Bacia Modelo. Brazil	Leopoldo et al. (1982a)
	3	3676	1528	8	Grégoire I	Roche (1982)
	4	3697	1437	8	Grégoire II } French Guyana	Roche (1982)
	5	3751	1444	8	Grégoire III	Roche (1982)
	6	2425	1440	2	Barro Colorado Panama	Dietrich et al. (1982)
	7	1684	886	1	Barro Colorado, Panama	Dietrich et al. (1982)
SE Asia (■)	1	1727	1498	6	Sungei Tekam, Malaysia	Anonymous (1986)
	2	2410	1516	3	Sungei Lui I, Malaysia	Low & Goh (1972); Anonymous (1977)
	3	4037	1421	6	Babinda, Queensland	Gilmour (1977)
	4	3236	1232	6	Angat, Philippines	Baconguis (1980)
	5	2482	1267	1	Ulu Langat, Malaysia	Low & Goh (1972)
	6	2851	1481	1	Janlappa, Indonesia	Calder et al. (1986)
W Africa (▲)	1	2003	1465	1	Tai (I), Ivory Coast	Collinet et al. (1984)
	2	1986	1363	7	Tai (II), Ivory Coast	Collinet et al. (1984)
	3	5795	1146	3	Guma, Sierra Leone	Ledger (1975)
	4	1800	1145	3	Banco, Ivory Coast	Huttel (1975)
	5	1800	1195	2	Banco, Ivory Coast	Huttel (1975)
	6	1950	1425	1	Yapo, Ivory Coast	Huttel (1975)
	7	1860	1433	1	Yangambi, Congo	Focan & Fripiat (1953)

moisture deficits in dry years (Blackie 1979b; Shuttleworth 1988). Nothing meaningful can be stated at present on differences between the three major rain forest blocks and more studies are necessary, particularly to shed more light on some of the low values recorded in South-East Asia (Fig. 3, Table 1).

On physical grounds, Calder, Wright & Murdiyarso (1986) suggested that the evaporation equivalent of the net radiation received by a lowland rain forest canopy would provide a good first estimate of ET. Shuttleworth (1988) reported for an Amazonian rain forest that on fine days typically 75–80% of energy was used for transpiration, but that on rainy days evaporating water from the wet canopy absorbed energy in excess of that locally available as radiation (i.e. a downward flux of sensible heat existed at such times above the forest). Over a period of 2 years, ET accounted for almost 90% of the net radiant energy measured above the canopy at this site.

Annual values of ET in the tropics apparently fall with a decrease in annual rainfall on a broad regional scale (Solomon 1967; Rodier & Vuillaume 1970), but reports on local variations, e.g. for a single forest as the dry season progresses, are rare. In his work on several forest types in seasonal western Venezuela, Franco (1979) showed annual ET values from 900 to 1300 mm for deciduous to seasonal evergreen forests. He presented evidence that the water holding capacity of the soils not only governed the spatial distribution of forest types, but also the rate at which ET changed during the dry season. Relevant data were also collected for three lowland rain forests in Ivory Coast by Huttel (1975) using neutron probe equipment. Maximum moisture depletion rates occurred at the onset and end of the main rainy season, whilst minima were observed at the height of the dry season. Huttel's data were published in a graphical form and an opportunity has been missed to construct a mathematical model describing transpiration rates as a function of soil moisture for these forests.

Alternatively, the so-called zero flux plane method, a variant of the site water balance technique and applicable in seasonal climates (Cooper 1979), could be used to derive the relationship between transpiration and soil moisture status.

ET of montane forests

The small data set for montane forests contains some of the best long-term records available for forested basins in the tropics (Fig. 4 and Table 2).

ET in montane forests is not correlated with altitude or rainfall. Apart from the anomalously high value reported by Richardson (1982) for a lower montane forest in Jamaica and attributed by her to high rainfall and breezy conditions, ET values for other montane forests (excluding 'cloud forests') are about the overall mean of 1250 mm year^{-1} (range 1145–1380 mm year^{-1}; $n = 8$). This average value is surprisingly close to the mean of 1425 mm for lowland forests, especially in view of the large difference in average altitude — about 100 m versus about 1900 m — between the two groups. There are no data on radiation for many of the forests in Fig. 4 and Table 2, and it is not possible to compare radiant

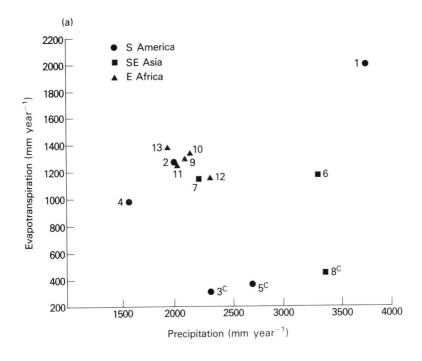

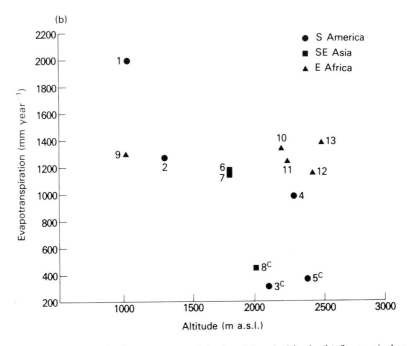

FIG. 4. Annual evapotranspiration versus precipitation (a) and altitude (b) for tropical montane forests (Bruijnzeel 1988b). c is 'cloud forest'. See Table 2.

TABLE 2. Annual evapotranspiration, precipitation and altitude for tropical montane forests (Bruijnzeel 1988b). (Symbols refer to Fig. 4)

Site	Precipitation (mm year^{-1})	ET (mm year^{-1})	Altitude (m)	Duration (year)	Location	Reference
S America (●)						
1	3746	1998	1020	1	Blue Mts, Jamaica	Richardson (1982)
2	1983	1265	1300	1	Sierra Nevada, Colombia	Hermann (1970)
3	2316	308[c]	2100	1	Sierra Nevada, Colombia	Hermann (1970)
4	1576	980	2300	1	San Eusebio, Venezuela	Steinhardt (1979)
5	2697	366[c]	2400	15	Rio Macho, Costa Rica	Calvo (1986)
SE Asia (■)						
6	3306	1170	1800	7	Ciwidey, Indonesia	Gonggrijp (1941)
7	2210	1145	1800	8	Ramu, Papua New Guinea	Ribeny & Brown (1968)
8	3370	450[c]	2000	2	Mt Data, Philippines	De los Santos (1981)
E Africa (▲)						
9	2081	1295	1010	8	Périnet, Madagascar	Bailly *et al.* (1974)
10	2130	1337	2200	13	Kericho, Kenya	Blackie (1979a)
11	2013	1240	2250	12	Kericho, Kenya (sub-basin)	Blackie (1979a)
12	2307	1156	2440	16	Kimakia, Kenya	Blackie (1979b)
13	1924	1381	2500	10	Mbeya, Tanzania	Edwards (1979)

energy in the montane and lowland environments. Schmidt (1950) showed that in Java, although sunshine duration decreased strongly with altitude, the effect was lessened by a concurrent increase in radiation intensity. Interestingly, Körner & Cochrane (1985) reported a statistically significant increase in stomatal conductance with altitude for eucalypt forests in south-eastern Australia.

The few examples of 'cloud forest' (3, 5, 8 and, to a lesser extent, 4 in Fig. 4 and Table 2) exhibit considerably lower values of ET, which must be attributed to the combined effects of low transpiration rates under the prevailing climatic conditions (Gates 1969; Weaver, Byer & Bruck 1973) and to increased precipitation inputs through cloud stripping (Zadroga 1981). As such these low values are apparent only and should be 'corrected' by adding corresponding amounts of occult precipitation. No direct estimates of contributions by occult precipitation to the 'cloud forests' of Fig. 4 and Table 2 are available, but in two cases such measurements have been made in similar forests nearby, namely by Vis (1986) in Colombia and Caceres (1981) in Costa Rica. By combining corresponding figures, values of 570 and 775 mm are obtained for the Colombian and Costa Rican forests, respectively.

Our hydrological knowledge of montane tropical forests in general and of 'cloud forests' in particular is still fragmentary, even though they have received considerable attention from plant ecologists and physiologists trying to explain their often peculiar stature (Howard 1968, 1969; Gates 1969; Weaver *et al.* 1973, 1986; Tanner 1977, 1985; Medina, Cuevas & Weaver 1981; Kapos & Tanner 1985; Proctor *et al.* 1988).

It is of interest to examine the magnitude of the two major components of ET, namely water vapour transfer from a wet canopy (interception Ei) and from a dry canopy (transpiration Et). The former governs the amount of rainfall reaching the soil, and hence the amount of water available for transpiration.

Throughfall, stemflow and rainfall interception

Although no other component of the hydrological cycle in tropical forests has received so much attention as measurement of net precipitation, the results from over 100 'tropical' interception studies, more than 70 from natural forests, are diverse and differ in their reliability, mainly for climatic, vegetative and procedural reasons (L. A. Bruijnzeel unpublished) (cf. a similar conclusion about studies on litterfall in tropical forests by Proctor 1983).

The highly complex nature of the processes involved (Leonard 1967; Jackson 1975) and the high spatial and sometimes temporal heterogeneity of tropical forest canopies require elaborate sampling designs, which have been rarely used (Lloyd & Marques Filho 1988). Out of the 75 throughfall studies listed by L. A. Bruijnzeel (unpublished), only 18 can be considered to have sampled net precipitation more or less adequately (i.e. with confidence limits of 10–15%). Whereas statistical evaluations of the number of gauges required for a certain level of precision have been available for deciduous (Czarnowski & Olszewski

1970) and coniferous (Kimmins 1973) forests in the temperate zone, such information was lacking for tropical rain forests until the work of Lloyd and Marques Filho (1988).

Figure 5 suggests that to estimate mean throughfall in a tropical lowland rain forest with confidence limits of 10%, one would need about 40 (standard) rain gauges in a fixed arrangement. Thus far only Pereira (1952), working in a montane bamboo forest in Kenya, has used such a large number of gauges. However, the reliability of the estimate improves rapidly if the gauges are relocated at regular time intervals at random locations on the forest floor (Lloyd & Marques Filho 1988; Fig. 5).

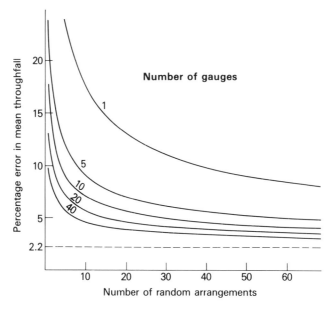

FIG. 5. Probable standard errors of the mean of measured throughfall in lowland rain forest near Mandus, Brazil, for increasing sample size and numbers of gauge relocations (Lloyd & Marques-Filho 1988).

Few investigators of throughfall in tropical forests have practised relocation (e.g. Ducrey & Finkelstein 1983; Collinet, Monteny & Pouyard 1984; Vis 1986; Lloyd & Marques Filho 1988) and it is difficult to assess the deviation from the 'true' mean for the numerous fixed-gauge studies. Some workers have approached the problem of spatial heterogeneity by increasing their sampling surface through the use of large metal plates, elongated gutters or plastic sheets (e.g. Gonggrijp 1941; Clements & Colon 1975; Jordan & Heuveldop 1981; Calder *et al.* 1986). However, the use of a large collecting surface is no guarantee of a good estimate. This was demonstrated indirectly by Bruijnzeel & Wiersum (1987), who used 10–12 trough-type gauges (with an equivalent surface of 140–168 standard gauges) to estimate throughfall in a young plantation of *Acacia auriculiformis* A. Cunn. in Indonesia. Their measurements were made during two consecutive rainy seasons with fixed trough arrangements that differed between both periods as the troughs were removed during the dry season. Although both estimates of seasonal throughfalls had standard errors of less than 5%, the means were significantly ($p < 0.001$) different. Since the difference was only partially explicable in terms of increases in canopy storage capacity or storm patterns, it had to be concluded that the two trough configurations sampled the spatial variation in throughfall differently (Bruijnzeel & Wiersum 1987). Therefore, the majority of throughfall studies in tropical forests must be considered as more or less inadequate.

Choosing only those investigations which both lasted for at least a year (to account for seasonal variations in storm patterns or vegetation status) and used a gauge-relocation technique or a fixed arrangement of at least 20 gauges, an average annual throughfall of 85% (range 77–93%) of incident rainfall was obtained for lowland forests ($n = 13$) and 80% (range 75–86%) for montane forests ($n = 5$). The highest percentages were often recorded by those studies in which the gauges were randomly relocated at regular time intervals (cf. Fig. 5), probably because of the inclusion of a more representative number of 'drip points' where throughfall is concentrated and exceeds incident precipitation (Shuttleworth 1988). Therefore, these average estimates should be regarded as conservative.

All this has a bearing on the quantification of nutrients in throughfall. It is likely that the net retention of nutrients by the tropical forest canopy (e.g. Manokaran 1980) may be an artefact of this underestimation. Although net precipitation estimates for the San Carlos forest (where the idea of 'nutrient scavenging' by the canopy as an adaptation to oligotrophic conditions originated (Jordan *et al.* 1980)) seem reliable, the quality of the analytical data is questionable (Galloway *et al.* 1982; Vitousek & Sanford 1986). Indeed, the majority of studies of throughfall quality in tropical forests (including the colline forest in Puerto Rico where the canopy was shown to retain certain isotopes (Witkamp 1970)) report a net leaching of nutrients from the canopy regardless of soil fertility (Vitousek & Sanford 1986). There is a need for more good studies of throughfall quality in the tropics.

For stemflow in lowland tropical forests there are many reports that it accounts for about 1–2% of incident rainfall (L. A. Bruijnzeel unpublished). Overall contributions of stemflow to soil water may be small, but it is important compared with the amount of rainfall intercepted by the forest. In addition, stemflow carries substantial amounts of nutrients to the bases of individual trees (Herwitz 1986b). Also, stemflow measurements should take into account the large spatial variability of tropical forests (Lloyd & Marques Filho 1988). Stemflow is usually determined volumetrically and the amounts are subsequently converted to millimetres of water by dividing them by projected crown area (Freise 1936). However, given the difficulties associated with estimating crown areas in tropical rain forests, it is advisable to sample every tree within a sufficiently large plot and to divide the sum of stemflow volumes by the area of the plot (Helvey & Patric 1965).

Several investigators have reported that stemflow for large-diameter trees is less than that for smaller-stemmed trees (Weaver 1972; Jordan 1978; Lloyd & Marques Filho 1988). This may be ascribed to differences in branching patterns as well as to the fact that drip from the higher trees may become funnelled again upon hitting trees lower down. This could possibly enhance nutrient availability for smaller trees and could perhaps be part of an explanation for the many-stemmed pole habit of trees in many heath forests or montane forests where nutrients may be limiting.

A related aspect is the erosive power of both stemflow and crown drip. Since stemflow represents a concentration of water at the base of the stem, in certain climatic and topographic conditions it may take on dramatic proportions (Herwitz 1986a; see also the section on hydrological patterns).

Several recent studies suggest that, contrary to common belief (e.g. UNESCO 1978), the kinetic energy of throughfall in natural and man-made forests in the tropics is higher, because of increases in drop size, than for rainfall in the open (Wiersum 1985; Vis 1986; Brandt 1988). The change in drop size was shown to be greater under a multiple canopy than under a single canopy, but the lack of height in the former case meant that kinetic energy gained through the drop-size changes was lost in low terminal velocities (Brandt 1988). The amount of splash erosion is governed by the degree to which the ground surface is covered by litter or undergrowth, rather than by the kinetic energy of the rain drops (Wiersum 1985).

Williamson (1981) suggested that drip tips on leaves tend to produce smaller drops, thereby decreasing the risk of splash erosion. Later, Williamson *et al.* (1983) tentatively explained the vertical distribution of drip tips in the canopy (Richards 1952) in these terms. Phytomorphological and erosion surveys at a number of contrasting sites, together with further experimental work along the lines indicated by Wiersum (1985) and Brandt (1988), could throw more light on this problem.

The rainfall intercepted by the forest (Ei) can be derived from measurements of incident rainfall and net precipitation. Not surprisingly in the light of the above remarks on the reliability of most throughfall studies, reported estimates of Ei in tropical forests vary between 4.5% (Jordan & Heuveldop 1981) and 45% (Read 1977). Concentrating on the more reliable studies of throughfall used previously suggests average annual values for Ei of 14% (range 4.5–22%) of incident rainfall in the case of lowland forests ($n = 13$) and of 18% (range 10–24%) for montane forests ($n = 5$). The higher value for montane forests may reflect the generally lower rainfall intensities prevailing on mountains (e.g. Braak 1921), but may be an artefact of the small data set.

Annual Ei for 'cloud forests' ranges from about 10% (Caceres 1981; Vis 1986) to negative values due to cloud stripping (Weaver 1972). Again it should be remembered that these average values of Ei are probably overestimates as the throughfall figures on which they are based must be considered as conservative.

Transpiration

In contrast with the many studies of rainfall interception (i.e. evaporation from a wet canopy), there are few accounts of evaporation from a dry canopy (i.e. transpiration) for moist tropical forests (Bruijnzeel 1988b). Several techniques can be used to estimate transpiration rates, namely hydrological, micrometeorological, plant physiological and 'empirical' methods (Shuttleworth 1979).

The hydrological technique basically combines data on ET (usually obtained from a plot or catchment water balance) with information on Ei, finding Et by difference (for weekly or longer periods) and neglecting evaporation from the forest floor (e.g. Leopoldo *et al.* 1982a,b). The estimate must be regarded as potentially crude due to the possibility of accumulating errors and basin leakage (cf. Lee 1970; Lloyd & Marques-Filho 1988). Thus the annual transpiration values for two similar forests in Central Amazonia obtained by this method were 987 mm and 1280 mm (Leopoldo *et al.* 1982a,b). As we shall see, most estimates have been made in this way and should be interpreted with care.

A perhaps more reliable variant of the hydrological technique involves the monitoring of changes in soil water during (extended) periods of low rainfall (Huttel 1975; Cooper 1979; Calder *et al.* 1986). Such measurements should be carried out to a depth of at least 300 cm if the soil is as deep or deeper than that, as trees are known to extract water from depths of at least 150 cm in lowland rain forests (Huttel 1975; Guehl 1983; Calder *et al.* 1986) and occasionally (e.g. during droughts) down to a depth of about 5 m (Eeles 1979; Poels 1987).

Short-term measurements of vapour transfer from a dry canopy using micrometeorological methods in the same forest as that studied by Leopoldo *et al.* (1982b) yielded very similar estimates of Et (Shuttleworth *et al.* 1984). However, in view of the cost of instrumentation and problems of maintenance, micrometeorological techniques are not likely to become widely used in tropical forests.

Several plant physiological techniques, such as the injection and monitoring of isotope tracers (Kline *et al.* 1970; Jordan & Kline 1977), the heat pulse method (Kenworthy 1969; Yoshikawa, Ogino & Maiyus 1986) and potometry (Coster 1937; Wanner & Soerohaldoko 1979), have also been used to gain an idea of transpiration rates in tropical forests. Since such measurements are made on individual trees, the problem of extrapolation to the forest as a whole remains. Jordan & Kline (1977) reported a high correlation between transpiration volumes (litres per day) and sapwood cross-sectional area for a set of 20 trees in a lowland rain forest in Venezuela. Similarly, from the data on dbh and sap flow rates reported for a Sumatran rain forest by Yoshikawa *et al.* (1986), a highly significant linear regression equation could be computed between sap flow rates ($cm^3\ h^{-1}$) and total cross-sectional area (L. A. Bruijnzeel unpublished).

The Venezuelan data were used later to derive an estimate of 2186 mm year^{-1} for Et (Jordan & Heuveldop 1981), but this value is clearly an overestimation (cf. Fig. 3). Nevertheless, the potential of the isotope injection technique was demonstrated by Waring & Roberts (1979) and Waring, Whitehead & Jarvis (1980) who found good agreement between rates of water uptake as determined by isotope tracers on the one hand, and whole-tree potometry and the Penman–Monteith transpiration model on the other, for *Pinus sylvestris* in Scotland. Further work is desirable and should be backed up by independent estimates of Et.

Lastly, a more 'empirical' approach is the use of the physically-based combination formula developed by Penman (1948, 1956) as extended by Monteith (1965) to describe evaporation from a vegetated surface. The Penman–Monteith model has proved to be a powerful tool in the prediction of evaporation from both wet and dry canopies in the temperate zone (Calder 1977; Gash & Morton 1978) and recently it has been shown to be capable of producing plausible results for tropical forests as well (Whitehead, Okati & Fasehun 1981; Calder *et al.* 1986; Institute of Hydrology 1988). A major difficulty with the application of the Penman–Monteith formula, however, is associated with the 'canopy resistance' parameter (i.e. the stomatal resistance to water vapour transfer divided by leaf area index), which is not only difficult to estimate for a species-rich forest, but is also a strong determinant of the formula's output (Beven 1979). A team from the Institute of Hydrology (1988) made extensive measurements of stomatal resistance throughout the canopy of a rain forest near Manaus, Brazil. They found the stomatal resistance of leaves in the upper half of the canopy to decrease with increasing solar radiation, whilst a positive correlation existed with atmospheric humidity deficit. Seasonal differences in resistance were ascribed to effects of soil moisture deficit and seasonal differences in leaf age. When Et was calculated using measured stomatal resistances in the Penman–Monteith formula, the results compared closely with independent estimates by a micrometeorological technique (Institute of Hydrology 1988).

Most of the studies on lowland forest ET (Fig. 3) have also reported estimates of Ei which were used to compute approximate annual values for Et of 885–1285 mm (mean 1045 mm, $n = 9$).

Transpiration for markedly seasonal forests in Fig. 3 (●6, Panama; ■3, Queensland) was below 500 mm year^{-1}. This low value may partly be caused by the application of relatively high interception values (Gilmour 1975; Read 1977), but Franco (1979) observed a similarly low value (630 mm) in semi-deciduous forest in western Venezuela. Values of Et for montane forests (excluding 'cloud forests') varied between 560 and 830 mm year^{-1} with no relation to elevation. The data set, however, is small ($n = 4$).

In 'cloud forests', the available information is limited to instantaneous estimates via physiological techniques for forests in Puerto Rico (Gates 1969; Weaver *et al.* 1973), which in combination with a leaf area index value of 2 (reported by Weaver *et al.* (1986)) and extrapolated to a year, suggest a value for Et of less than 75 mm year^{-1} (0.2 mm day^{-1}). Alternatively, one can gain an idea of 'cloud forest' Et by combining the data on ET and Ei for Colombian and Costa Rican forests collected by Hermann (1970) and Vis (1986) and by Calvo (1986) and Caceres (1981), respectively. Correcting for occult precipitation inputs, annual values for Et of about 285 mm (0.7 mm day $^{-1}$) for the Colombian forest and about 510 mm (1.4 mm day^{-1}) for the Costa Rican forest are obtained. These values are very similar to those recently obtained for a 'cloud forest' in East Malaysia (L. A. Bruijnzeel, M. J. Waterloo & B. Kotterink unpublished).

Such low values are probably caused by the weather conditions in these forests (Baynton 1968; Weaver et al. 1973), rather than by high stomatal resistances (Cintron 1970; Kapos & Tanner 1985). Also in view of the fact that water stress rarely, if at all, occurs in 'cloud forest' trees (Hermann 1970; Kapos & Tanner 1985), their low stomatal resistance may be adaptive in that it may enable the trees to rapidly increase transpiration rates whenever weather conditions permit. Several workers (reviewed by Leigh (1975)) have suggested that persistent fog may cause forest stunting by blocking transpiration and, consequently, nutrient uptake. Grubb (1977) provided arguments against this idea and suggested that, if nutrient uptake is inhibited by cloudy conditions, it is much more likely to be due to low light intensities and reduced supply of metabolites to the roots. Similarly, leaves of undergrowth species in forests in Indonesia and Hawaii were shown to have low evaporative resistance by Wanner & Soerohaldoko (1979) and Pearcy & Calkin (1983) respectively, a finding they interpreted as an adaptation to sporadic exposure to sunlight.

Summarizing, we have relatively little quantitative knowledge of transpiration rates in tropical forests.

RATES OF CHEMICAL WEATHERING IN MOIST TROPICAL FOREST

Apart from providing a quantification of the various flows of water in a forest ecosystem as a preliminary to the estimation of nutrient fluxes, hydrologists may also contribute to the study of chemical weathering rates of the substratum, which is often an important supplier of nutrients to the ecosystem.

Clayton (1979) reviewed techniques for the estimation of chemical weathering rates and concluded that mass balance nutrient studies would provide the best estimates. Such studies can be conducted on small watertight catchment areas or with large lysimeters and should last for several years in view of climatic variability (Likens et al. 1977). The use of lysimeters poses problems of spatial variability and, in the case of large constructions in remote rain forest areas, severe technical problems. Therefore, the use of small watertight catchment areas drained by perennial streams and underlain by a homogeneous geological substrate is preferred.

Basically the method entails the quantification of the amounts of nutrients entering the ecosystem via bulk precipitation and leaving it in streamflow. If the forest is in a steady state with respect to the uptake and return of nutrients, the difference between outputs and inputs on a catchment scale (the elemental flux) equals the amount of nutrients released by weathering of the substrate minus amounts consumed in the formation of secondary compounds like clay minerals, etc. (Bormann & Likens 1967). As long as there is a net increase in biomass, a portion of the elements released by weathering will be incorporated in the vegetation and the chemical flux will be an underestimation of the weathering rate (Likens *et al.* 1977; Bruijnzeel 1983c).

At least on a catchment scale many primary and old secondary forests in the humid tropics have approached a steady state with respect to their biomass (cf. Lieberman *et al.* 1985). It follows that the small-basin mass balance technique may be especially suitable for them, given the right geological setting. A word of caution is needed, however: although the small-basin mass balance technique may provide a good estimate of rock weathering rate, it remains to be seen to what extent the nutrients released are accessible to tree roots. Burnham (*this volume*) has given a good example of this from peninsular Malaysia, where a deep soil on a granitic substratum showed a very sharp transition between the fresh rock (occurring at a depth of 10 m) and the overlying thoroughly weathered material. Yet streams draining this type of terrain carry considerable amounts of calcium, magnesium and potassium (Kenworthy 1971; Douglas 1977). To a large extent such solutes may be expected to derive from the narrow zone of active weathering, which in this particular instance must be considered out of reach of the root network. However, experimental evidence is lacking.

Baillie (*this volume*) has made the important distinction between 'open' and 'closed' nutrient cycles. Root systems in ecosystems with 'open' cycles penetrate the zone of weathering activity and are not concentrated in the surface layers of the soil. The 'closed' type of cycle operates in situations where nutrient input from weathering materials is negligible. Such losses as do occur must be compensated by atmospheric inputs and the roots tend to be highly concentrated in the surface layers of the soil (cf. Herrera *et al.* 1978).

From the above it will be clear that a small-catchment mass balance study should be accompanied by proper pedological and pedo-hydrological surveys. In addition, the chemical aspects of hillslope soil moisture should be included in order to complete the picture. This type of integrated study is rare in tropical forests (Roose 1981; Bruijnzeel 1983a; Brinkmann 1985; Nortcliff & Thornes *this volume*) and more work is needed.

Of the well over 60 studies of elemental fluxes in forested basins published to date, very few pertain to the tropics. Unfortunately the bulk of these 'tropical' studies suffer from a variety of shortcomings, such as a limited sampling period or major gaps in the underlying hydrological records (Kenworthy 1971; Turvey 1974; Golley *et al.* 1975), a crude approximation of the drainage component (Steinhardt 1979; Jordan 1982), or a limited representativity of the analytical data set, especially so for precipitation (e.g. Kenworthy 1971; Turvey 1974; Poels 1987). Bruijnzeel (1989) noted that average elemental concentrations of bulk precipitation at a number of stations in the humid tropics seemed to reflect the rigidity of sampling procedures rather than environmental factors such as proximity to the sea, volcanism or climatic seasonality. Most studies of elemental fluxes in tropical forests have overestimated nutrient inputs via bulk precipitation.

However, this is offset to some extent by the lack of estimates of dry deposition rates on tropical forest canopies (cf. Mathieu 1976; Crozat 1979; Roose 1981). Further work on dry deposition is as desirable as difficult (White & Turner 1970), although recently promising techniques have been suggested by Gosz, Brookins & Moore (1983) and Lovett & Lindberg (1984) which could be tested in the tropics.

Studies on input–output budgets for tropical forests have been listed by Vitousek & Sanford (1986) and Proctor (1987), although they were not used to evaluate weathering rates. Their lists could be extended by the investigations conducted in various forested basins in the Ivory Coast (Mathieu 1976; Roose 1981), southern China and Taiwan (Lam 1978; King & Yang 1984), Indonesia (Bruijnzeel 1983c) and Surinam (Boxman et al. 1985; Poels 1987).

Vegetation effects may also have influenced estimates of weathering rates in some tropical studies. For example, the Puerto Rican forest studied by Jordan, Kline & Sasscer (1972) may still be acquiring biomass as the area is disturbed by hurricanes. Similarly, although the actual uptake of nutrients by the fast-growing plantation forest covering the Indonesian basin studied by Bruijnzeel (1983c) was explicitly taken into account, it cannot be excluded that uptake rates were such that soil reserves of calcium and potassium were being depleted, implying an overestimation of the weathering rate (cf. Clayton 1979). Since, in addition, virtually all of these studies were conducted over a relatively short time (often a year), there is also the problem of climatic variations (Likens et al. 1977).

In spite of the shortcomings of the data set, a few tentative generalizations are possible (mainly based on catchment studies).

1 For areas receiving more or less similar annual rainfall totals (say 2000–3000 mm), catchment lithology is the dominant factor determining net solute losses.

2 Some infertile sites exhibit extremely low losses or even slight accumulations for calcium, magnesium and potassium, suggesting low weathering contributions (Franken & Leopoldo 1984; Brinkmann 1985; Poels 1987).

3 Relatively large amounts of nutrients are released from more fertile substrates, such as andesitic materials (Jordan et al. 1972; Turvey 1974; Bruijnzeel 1983c) or certain sedimentary substrates (Golley et al. 1975; King & Yang 1984).

4 Sites of intermediate fertility show variable results, suggesting differences in the degree of weathering (cf. granites in Hong Kong versus Malaysia (Kenworthy 1971; Lam 1978; Manokaran 1980)) or in parent material (e.g. granite versus schists (Lam 1978; Roose 1981)).

5 The low precipitation surplus of more seasonal environments results in a net accumulation of nutrients (e.g. Mathieu 1976; Steinhardt 1979).

6 Incorporation of macro-nutrients, such as calcium, magnesium or potassium, in secondary compounds (clay minerals) is of minor importance in most humid tropical situations; phosphorus, however, 'accumulates' in virtually all studies (regardless of the fertility of the substrate) indicating the very low mobility of the element. It has been suggested that most of the phosphorus released by weathering becomes tied up in organic and ferroaluminium compounds in the soil (Sanchez 1976; Clayton 1979).

In view of the geological diversity of tropical forest environments and the limited number of studies of solute behaviour in soil water and stream water, it is clear that this is a major area for further work. The inclusion of mineral stability theory may prove particularly valuable in the study of water–rock interactions. Examples using this approach in 'tropical' weathering studies have been given by Dirven, van Schuylenborgh & van Breemen (1976), Roose (1981) and Bruijnzeel (1983a).

CONCLUSION

At present the findings on water and nutrient dynamics in tropical forests exhibit understandable, but regrettable, diversity. Understandable, as individual subjects are easily picked (e.g. litter production, rainfall interception), especially by narrow specialists; regrettable, as often results cannot be linked together to provide an overall view.

Fortunately, there are a few rain forest sites where scientists from various disciplines have worked together and where a general picture has begun to emerge (Vitousek & Sanford 1986). However, in virtually none of these sites has the full potential of the physical sciences (pedology, forest hydrology and meteorology, hillslope hydrology) been realized completely. Likewise, nowhere has the flow of water and the nutrients contained in it been fully described or modelled.

Nevertheless, since the beginning of the International Biological Programme there has been a trend towards increased integration, e.g. in the Man and Biosphere project at San Carlos de Rio Negro, Venezuela (Brünig *et al.* 1978; Medina & Cuevas *this volume*) and the Ecologie Erosion Experimentation (ECEREX) project in French Guyana (Bailly 1983). In addition, the work carried out at Reserva Ducke and surroundings, Central Amazonas, over the last two decades in a number of more or less individually operating projects on forest biomass (Klinge 1976), litterfall (e.g. Klinge & Rodrigues 1968), catchment hydrology (Nortcliff & Thornes 1981, 1984; Leopoldo *et al.* 1982b), forest micrometeorology (Shuttleworth *et al.* 1984; Shuttleworth 1988), plant physiology (Institute of Hydrology 1988) and overall biogeochemistry (Brinkmann 1985) has resulted in an impressive data set for this location.

On the other hand, few reliable data are available on hydrochemical pathways in South-East Asian rain forests: work is essentially limited to the throughfall studies of Manokaran (1980) and Crowther (1987a) and observations on streamwater chemistry (Douglas 1967; Kenworthy 1971; Turvey 1974; Walsh 1982; Rahim & Yusof 1986; Crowther 1987b).

Although biogeochemical information is still far from complete, or almost lacking, for a variety of tropical vegetation types (e.g. peat swamp forest, forest on ultrabasic substrates), it would seem in the light of current forest conversion rates that a much greater proportion of our efforts should be directed at modelling hydrological and biogeochemical processes in those forests for which a basic set of data is already available, so as to improve our ability of predicting the environmental impacts of such conversions (cf. Jordan 1985; Bruijnzeel 1986). As such the recently initiated Tropical Soil Biology and Fertility programme of the International Union of Biological Sciences (Swift 1985) is to be regarded as a welcome contribution. However, the lesson to be learned from the ECEREX project in French Guyana, namely that plot and small-catchment studies should be carried out within a framework of (hydro-)pedological surveys if representative results are to be obtained, should not be forgotten (Fritsch *et al.* 1987).

Together with the study of the mode and rate of nutrient release through chemical weathering, it is perhaps in this field that the greatest scope for contributions by hydrologists and pedologists to the study of nutrient flows in tropical forest ecosystems can be found.

ACKNOWLEDGEMENTS

I wish to thank Dr J. M. Fritsch and Dr J. H. C. Gash for making available in press material, Romée de Vries for typing the manuscript, Kees Bons for introducing me to the world of 'Quattro', Dr John Proctor for editorial surgery and Irene Sieverding for support.

REFERENCES

Aitken, A.P., Ribeny, F.M.J. & Brown, J.A.H. (1972). The estimation of mean annual runoff over the territory of Papua New Guinea. *Civil Engineering Transactions (Australia),* **14**, 49–56.

Anonymous (1977). Sungai Lui representative basin report no. 1 for 1971/72 to 1973/74. *Water Resources Publication No. 7.* Drainage & Irrigation Department, Kuala Lumpur, Malaysia.

Anonymous (1986). Sungai Tekam experimental basin transition report July 1980 to June 1983. *Water Resources Publication No. 16.* Drainage & Irrigation Department, Kuala Lumpur, Malaysia.

Baconguis, S. (1980). Water balance, water use and maximum water storage of a dipterocarp forest watershed in San Lorenzo, Norzagaray, Bulacan. *Sylvatrop,* **2**, 73–98.

Bailly, C. (1983). *Le Projêt Ecologie Erosion Experimentation.* Centre Technique Forestier Tropical, Nogent-sur-Marne, France.

Bailly, C., Benoit de Coignac, G., Malvos, C., Ningre, J.M. & Sarrailh, J.M. (1974). Etude de l'influence du couvert naturel et de ses modifications à Madagascar; expérimentations en bassins versants élémentaires. *Cahiers Scientifiques Centre Technique Forestier Tropical,* **4**, 1–114.

Baynton, H.W. (1968). The ecology of an elfin forest in Puerto Rico, 2. The microclimate of Pico del Oeste. *Journal of the Arnold Arboretum,* **49**, 419–430.

Beven, K. (1979). A sensitivity analysis of the Penman–Monteith actual evapotranspiration estimates. *Journal of Hydrology,* **44**, 169–190.

Blackie, J.R. (1979a). The water balance of the Kimakia catchments. *East African Agricultural and Forestry Journal,* **43**, 155–174.

Blackie, J.R. (1979b). The water balance of the Kericho catchments. *East African Agricultural and Forestry Journal,* **43**, 55–84.

Bonell, M. & Gilmour, D.A. (1978). The development of overland flow in a tropical rainforest catchment. *Journal of Hydrology,* **39**, 365–382.

Bormann, F.H. & Likens, G.E. (1967). Nutrient cycling. *Science,* **155**, 424–429.

Boxman, O., De Graaf, N.R., Hendrison, J., Jonkers, W.B.J., Poels, R.L.H., Schmidt, P. & Tjon Lim Sang, R. (1985). Towards sustained timber production from tropical rain forests in Suriname. *Netherlands Journal of Agricultural Science,* **33**, 125–132.

Braak, C. (1921). Het klimaat van Nederlandsch Indië. *Verhandelingen van het Koninklijk*

Magnetisch en Meterologisch Observatorium te Batavia, **8**(1), 497.

Brandt, J. (1988). The transformation of rainfall energy by a tropical rain forest canopy in relation to soil erosion. *Journal of Biogeography*, **15**, 41–48.

Brinkmann, W.L.F. (1985). Studies on hydrobiogeochemistry of a tropical lowland forest system. *Geojournal*, **11**, 89–101.

Bruijnzeel, L.A. (1983a). *Hydrological and biogeochemical aspects of man-made forests in south-central Java, Indonesia*. PhD Thesis, Free University, Amsterdam.

Bruijnzeel, L.A. (1983b). Evaluation of runoff sources in a forested basin in a wet monsoonal environment: a combined hydrological and hydrochemical approach. *International Association of Hydrological Sciences Publication*, **140**, 165–174.

Bruijnzeel, L.A. (1983c). The chemical mass balance of a small basin in a wet monsoonal environment and the effect of fast-growing plantation forest. *International Association of Hydrological Sciences Publication*, **141**, 229–239.

Bruijnzeel, L.A. (1986). Environmental impacts of (de)forestation in the humid tropics: a watershed perspective. *Wallaceana*, **46**, 3–13.

Bruijnzeel, L.A. (1987). Soil physical techniques: an alternative to (paired) watershed studies in evaluating water use of tropical vegetation? *Future Directions for Watershed Research in the Asia–Pacific Region* (Ed. by P.W. Adams & L.S. Hamilton), pp. 35–36. Proceedings of the Taipei Workshop 1987. Taiwan Forestry Research Institute, Taipei, Taiwan, and Environment and Policy Institute, Honolulu, Hawaii.

Bruijnzeel, L. A. (1988). Estimates of evaporation in plantations of *Agathis dammara* warb. in south-central Java, Indonesia. *Journal of Tropical Forest Science*, **1**, 145–161.

Bruijnzeel, L.A. (1989). Nutrient content of bulk precipitation in south-central Java, Indonesia. *Journal of Tropical Ecology*, **5**, 187–202.

Bruijnzeel, L.A. & Wiersum, K.F. (1987). Rainfall interception by a young *Acacia auriculiformis* A. Cunn. plantation forest in West Java, Indonesia: application of Gash's analytical model. *Hydrological Processes*, **1**, 309–319.

Brünig, E.F., Herrera, R., Heuveldop, J., Jordan, C.F., Klinge, H. & Medina, E. (1978). The international Amazon project coordinated by Centro de Ecologia, Instituto Venezolano de Investigaciones Cientificas: organization and recent advances. *Chair of World Forestry Special Report No. 1*, pp. 104–131. Chair of World Forestry, Hamburg-Reinbek.

Burgy, R.H. & Pomeroy, C.R. (1958). Interception loss in grassy vegetation. *Transactions of the American Geophysical Union*, **39**, 1095–1100.

Burt, T.P. (1986). Runoff processes and solutional denudation on humid temperate hillslopes. *Solute Processes and Landforms* (Ed. by S.T. Trudgill), pp. 193–249. Wiley, Chichester.

Burt, T.P. & Butcher, D.P. (1985). On the generation of delayed peaks in stream discharge. *Journal of Hydrology*, **78**, 361–378.

Caceres, G. (1981). *Importancia hidrologica de la intercepcion horizontal en un bosque muy humedo premontano en Balalaica, Turrialba, Costa Rica*. MSc Thesis, University of Costa Rica, Turrialba.

Calder, I.R. (1977). A model of transpiration and interception loss from a spruce forest in Plynlimon, central Wales. *Journal of Hydrology*, **33**, 247–265.

Calder, I.R., Wright, I.R. & Murdiyarso, D. (1986). A study of evaporation from tropical rainforest—West Java. *Journal of Hydrology*, **89**, 13–31.

Cales, G. (1982). Premières observations sur l'installation d'une case ERLO. *ECEREX Bulletin de Liaison du Groupe de Travail No. 6*. Délégation Générale à la Recherche Scientifique et Technique, Paris.

Calvo, J. (1986). An evaluation of Thornthwaite's water balance technique in predicting stream runoff in Costa Rica. *Hydrological Sciences Journal*, **31**, 51–60.

Cintron, G. (1970). Variation in size and frequency of stomata with altitude in the Luquillo Mountains. *A Tropical Rain Forest* (Ed. by H.T. Odum & R.F. Pidgeon), pp. H133–135. United States Atomic Energy Commission, Washington.

Clayton, J.L. (1979). Nutrient supply to soil by rock weathering. *Impact of Intensive Harvesting on Forest Nutrient Cycling* (Ed. by A.L. Leaf), pp. 75–96. New York State University, Ithaca, New York.

Clements, R.G. & Colon, J.A. (1975). The rainfall interception process and mineral cycling in a montane rain forest in eastern Puerto Rico. *Mineral Cycling in Southeastern Ecosystems* (Ed. by F.G. Howell, J.B. Gentry & M.H. Smith), pp. 813–823. Technical Information Center, Energy Research Development and Administration, Washington.

Collinet, J., Montény, B. & Pouyaud, B. (1984). Le milieu physique. *Recherche et Aménagement en Milieu Forestier Tropical Humide: le Projet Tai de Côte d'Ivoire. Notes Techniques du MAB 15.* (Ed. by J.L. Guillaumet, G. Couturier & H. Dosso), pp. 35–58. UNESCO, Paris.

Cooper, J.D. (1979). Water use of a tea estate from soil moisture measurements. *East African Agricultural and Forestry Journal*, **43**, 102–121.

Coster, C. (1937). De Verdamping van verschillende veetatievormen op Java. *Tectoria*, **30**, 1–102.

Coster, C. (1938). Oppervlakkige afstroming en erosie op Java. *Tectona*, **31**, 613–728.

Crowther, J. (1987a). Ecological observations in tropical karst terrain, West Malaysia. II. Rainfall interception, litterfall and nutrient cycling. *Journal of Biogeography*, **14**, 145–155.

Crowther, J. (1987b). Ecological observations in tropical karst terrain, West Malaysia. III. Dynamics of the vegetation–soil–bedrock system. *Journal of Biogeography*, **14**, 157–164.

Crozat, G. (1979). Sur l'émission d'un aérosol riche en potassium par la forêt tropicale. *Tellus*, **31**, 52–57.

Czarnowski, M.S. & Olszewski, J.L. (1970). Number and spacing of rainfall-gauges in a deciduous forest stand. *Oikos*, **21**, 48–51.

Dall'Olio, A., Salati, E., Azevedo, C.T. & Matsui, E. (1979). Modelo de fracionamento isotopico da agua na Bacia Amazônica. *Acta Amazonica*, **9**, 675–687.

De los Santos, A.E. (1981). *Water budget and nutrient fluxes in mossy forest on Mt. Data, Mt. Province.* MSc Thesis, University of the Philippines at Los Banos, Laguna, Philippines.

De Oliveira Leite, J. (1985). Interflow, overland flow and leaching of natural nutrients on an alfisol slope of southern Bahia, Brazil. *Journal of Hydrology*, **80**, 77–92.

Delmas, R. & Servant, J. (1983). Atmospheric balance of sulphur above an equatorial forest. *Tellus*, **353**, 110–120.

Dietrich, W.E., Windsor, D.M. & Dunne, T. (1982). Geology, climate, and hydrology of Barro Colorado Island. *The Ecology of a Tropical Forest: Seasonal Rhythms and Long-term Changes* (Ed. by E. Leigh, A.S. Rand & D.M. Windsor), pp. 21–46. Smithsonian Institution, Washington DC.

Dirven, J.M.C., van Schuylenborgh, J. & van Breemen, N. (1976). Weathering of serpentinite in Matanzas province, Cuba: mass transfer calculations and irreversible reaction pathways. *Soil Science Society of America Journal*, **40**, 901–907.

Douglas, I. (1967). Erosion on granite terrains under tropical rain forest in Australia, Malaysia and Singapore. *International Association of Hydrological Sciences Publication*, **75**, 31–39.

Douglas, I. (1977). *Humid Landforms*. The Massachusetts Institute of Technology Press, Cambridge, Massachusetts.

Ducrey, M. & Finkelstein, D. (1983). Contribution à l'étude de l'interception des précipitations en forêt tropicale humide de Guyane. *Le Projet ECEREX. Analyse de l'Ecosystème Forestier Tropical Humide et des Modifications Apportées par l'Homme* (Ed. by C. Bailly), pp. 305–326. Centre Technique Forestier Tropical, Nogent-sur-Marne, France.

Dunne, T. (1978). Field studies of hillslope flow processes. *Hillslope Hydrology* (Ed. by M.J. Kirkby), pp. 227–293. Wiley, New York.

Edwards, K.A. (1979). The water balance of the Mbeya experimental catchments. *East African Agricultural and Forestry Journal*, **43**, 231–247.

Eeles, C.W.O. (1979). Soil moisture deficits under montane rain forest and tea. *East African Agricultural and Forestry Journal*, **43**, 128–138.

Focan, A. & Fripiat, J.J. (1953). Une année d'observation de l'humidité du sol à Yangambi. *Bulletin des Séances de l'Institut Royal Colonial Belge*, **24**, 971–984.

Franco, W. (1979). Die Wasserdynamik einiger Waldstandorte der West-Llanos Venezuelas und ihre Beziehung zur Saisonalität des Laubfalls. *Göttinger Bodenkundliche Berichte*, **61**, 1–201.

Franken, W. & Leopoldo, P.R. (1984). Hydrology of catchment areas of Central-Amazonian forest streams. *The Amazon. Limnology and Landscape Ecology of a Mighty Tropical River and its Basin* (Ed. by H. Sioli), pp. 501–519. W. Junk, The Hague.

Freise, F. (1936). Das Binnenklima von Urwäldern im subtropischen Brasilien. *Petermanns Geographische Mitteilungen*, **1936**, 301–304.

Fritsch, J.M., Dubreuil, P.L. & Sarrailh, J.M. (1987). De la parcelle au petit bassin-versant: effêt d'échelle dans l'écosystème forestier amazonien. *International Association of the Hydrological Sciences Publication*, **167**, 131–142.

Galloway, J.N., Likens, G.E., Keene, W.C. & Miller, J.M. (1982). The composition of precipitation in remote areas of the world. *Journal of Geophysical Research*, **87**, 8771–8786.

Gash, J.H.C. (1979). An analytical model of rainfall interception by forests. *Quarterly Journal of the Royal Meterological Society*, **105**, 43–55.

Gash, J.H.C. & Morton, A.J. (1978). An application of the Rutter model to the estimation of the interception loss from Thetford forest. *Journal of Hydrology*, **38**, 49–58.

Gates, D.M. (1969). The ecology of an elfin forest in Puerto Rico, 4. Transpiration rates and temperatures of leaves in cool humid environment. *Journal of the Arnold Arboretum*, **50**, 93–98.

Gilmour, D.A. (1975). *Catchment water balance studies on the wet tropical coast of north Queensland.* PhD Thesis, James Cook University, Townsville, Australia.

Gilmour, D.A. (1977). Effect of rainforest logging and clearing on water yield and quality in a high rainfall zone of north-east Queensland. *Proceedings of the Brisbane Hydrology Symposium 1977*, pp. 156–160. Institution of Engineers Australia, Canberra.

Golley, F.B., McGinnis, J.T., Clements, R.G., Child, G.I. & Duever, M.J. (1975). *Mineral Cycling in a Tropical Moist Forest Ecosystem.* University of Georgia Press, Athens.

Gonggrijp, L. (1941). De verdamping van het gebergtebosch in West Java op 1750–2000 m zeehoogte. *Tectona*, **34**, 437–447.

Gosz, J.R., Brookins, D.G. & Moore, D.I. (1983). Using strontium isotope ratios to estimate inputs to ecosystems. *BioScience*, **33**, 23–30.

Grubb, P.J. (1977). Control of forest growth and distribution on wet tropical mountains: with special reference to mineral nutrition. *Annual Review of Ecology and Systematics*, **8**, 83–107.

Guehl, J.M. (1983). La dynamique de l'eau dans le sol mesurée in situ dans un système mixte en forêt primaire. *Le Projêt ECEREX* (Ed. by C. Bailly), pp. 53–71. Centre Technique Forestier Tropical, Nogent-sur-Marne, France.

Harr, R.D. (1977). Water flux in soil and subsoil on a steep forested slope. *Journal of Hydrology*, **33**, 37–58.

Hatch, T. (1983). Soil erosion and shifting cultivation in Sarawak. *Proceedings of the Regional Workshop on Hydrological Impacts of Forestry Practices and Reafforestation* (Ed. by A. Kamis, F.S. Lai, S.S. Lee & A.R.M. Derus), pp. 51–60. Universiti Pertanian Malaysia, Serdang, Malaysia.

Helvey, J.D. & Patric, J.H. (1965). Canopy and litter interception of rainfall by hardwoods of eastern United States. *Water Resources Research*, **1**, 193–206.

Henderson-Sellers, A. & Gornitz, V. (1984). Possible climatic impacts of land cover transformations, with particular emphasis on tropical deforestation. *Climatic Change*, **6**, 231–257.

Hermann, R. (1970). Vertically differentiated water balance in tropical high mountains—with special reference to the Sierra Nevada de Sa. Marta, Colombia. *International Association of Hydrological Sciences Publication*, **93**, 262–273.

Herrera, R., Jordan, C.F., Klinge, H. & Medina, E. (1978). Amazon ecosystems : their structure and functioning with particular emphasis on nutrients. *Interciencia*, **3**, 223–232.

Herwitz, S.R. (1986a). Infiltration-excess caused by stemflow in a cyclone-prone tropical rainforest. *Earth Surface Processes and Landforms*, **11**, 401–412.

Herwitz, S.R. (1986b). Episodic stemflow inputs of magnesium and potassium to a tropical forest floor during heavy rainfall events. *Oecologia*, **70**, 423–425.

Hewlett, J.D. (1961). Soil moisture as a source of baseflow from steep mountain watersheds. *South-Eastern Forest Experimental Station Paper, 132.* U.S. Forest Service. Asheville, North Carolina.

Hewlett, J.D. & Hibbert, A.R. (1967). Factors affecting the response of small watersheds to precipitation in humid areas. *International Symposium on Forest Hydrology* (Ed. by W.E. Sopper & H.W. Lull), pp. 275–290. Pergamon Press, Oxford.

Hewlett, J.D. & Nutter, W.L. (1970). The varying source area of streamflow from upland basins. *Proceedings of the Symposium on Interdisciplinary Aspects of Watershed Management*, pp. 65–83. Boseman, Montana, U.S.A.

Horton, R.E. (1933). The role of infiltration in the hydrologic cycle. *Transactions of the American Geophysical Union*, **14**, 446–460.

Howard, R.A. (1968). The ecology of an elfin forest in Puerto Rico, 1. Introduction and composition studies. *Journal of the Arnold Arboretum*, **49**, 381–418.

Howard, R.A. (1969). The ecology of an elfin forest in Puerto Rico, 8. Studies of stemgrowth and form and of leaf structure. *Journal of the Arnold Arboretum*, **50**, 225–267.

Huttel, Ch. (1975). Recherches sur l'écosystème de la forêt subéquatoriale de basse Côte d'Ivoire. IV Estimation du bilan hydrique. *La Terre et la Vie*, **29**, 192–202.

Imeson, A.C. & Vis, M. (1982). A survey of soil erosion processes in tropical forest ecosystems on volcanic ash soils in the central Andean Cordillera, Colombia. *Geografiska Annaler, Series A*, **64**, 181–198.

Institute of Hydrology (1988). Amazon experiments. *Research Report 1984–87*, pp. 19–21. Institute of Hydrology, Wallingford, UK.

Jackson, I.J. (1975). Relationships between rainfall parameters and interception by tropical forest. *Journal of Hydrology*, **24**, 215–238.

Jordan, C.F. (1978). Stemflow and nutrient transfer in a tropical rain forest. *Oikos*, **31**, 257–263.

Jordan, C.F. (1982). The nutrient balance of an Amazonian rain forest. *Ecology*, **63**, 647–654.

Jordan, C.F. (1985). *Nutrient Cycling in Tropical Forest Ecosystems*. Wiley, New York.

Jordan, C.F., Golley, F.B., Hall, J. & Hall, J. (1980). Nutrient scavenging of rainfall by the canopy of an Amazonian rain forest. *Biotropica*, **12**, 61–66.

Jordan, C.F. & Heuveldop, J. (1981). The water budget of an Amazonian rain forest. *Acta Amazonica*, **11**, 87–92.

Jordan, C.F. & Kline, J.R. (1977). Transpiration of trees in a tropical rain forest. *Journal of Applied Ecology*, **14**, 853–860.

Jordan, C.F., Kline, J.R. & Sasscer, D.S. (1972). Relative stability of mineral cycles in forest ecosystems. *American Naturalist*, **106**, 237–254.

Juvik, J.O. & Ekern, P.C. (1978). *A Climatology of Mountain Fog on Mauna Loa, Hawaii Island. Technical Report No. 118*, Water Resources Research Centre, University of Hawaii.

Kapos, V. & Tanner, E.V.J. (1985). Water relations of Jamaican upper montane rain forest trees. *Ecology*, **66**, 241–250.

Kenworthy, J.B. (1969). Water balance in the tropical rain forest: a preliminary study in the Ulu Gombak forest reserve. *Malayan Nature Journal*, **22**, 129–135.

Kenworthy, J.B. (1971). Water and nutrient cycling in a tropical rain forest. *The Water Relations of Malesian Forests* (Ed. by J.R. Flenley), pp. 49–65. University of Hull, Department of Geography, Miscellaneous Series 11.

Kimmins, J.P. (1973). Some statistical aspects of sampling throughfall precipitation in nutrient cycling studies in British Columbian coastal forests. *Ecology*, **54**, 1008–1019.

King, H.B. & Yang, B.Y. (1984). Precipitation and stream water chemistry in Pi-Lu Chi watersheds, January 1981–December 1982. *Taiwan Forestry Research Institute Bulletin, 427*. Taiwan Forestry Research Institute, Taipei, Taiwan.

Kirkby, M.J. & Chorley, R.J. (1967). Throughflow, overland flow and erosion. *Bulletin of the International Association of Scientific Hydrology*, **12**, 5–21.

Kline, J.R., Martin, J.R., Jordan, C.F. & Koranda, J.J. (1970). Measurement of transpiration in tropical trees with tritiated water. *Ecology*, **51**, 1068–1073.

Klinge, H. (1976). Bilanzierung von Hauptnährstoffen im Oekosystem tropischer Regenwald (Manaus)—Vorläufige Daten. *Biogeographica*, **7**, 59–76.

Klinge, H. & Rodrigues, W.A. (1968). Litter production in an area of Amazonian terra firme forest. II. Mineral nutrient content of the litter. *Amazoniana*, **1**, 303–310.

Körner, Ch. & Cochrane, P.M. (1985). Stomatal responses and water relations of *Eucalyptus pauciflora* in summer along an elevational gradient. *Oecologia*, **66**, 443–455.

Lam, K.C. (1978). Soil erosion, suspended sediment and solute production in three Hong Kong catchments. *Journal of Tropical Geography*, **47**, 51–62.

Ledger, D.C. (1975). The water balance of an exceptionally wet catchment area in West Africa. *Journal of Hydrology*, **24**, 207–214.

Lee, R. (1970). Theoretical estimates versus forest water yield. *Water Resources Research*, **6**, 327–1334.

Leigh, C.H. (1978). Slope hydrology and denudation in the Pasoh forest reserve. 1. Surface wash: experimental techniques and some preliminary results. *Malayan Nature Journal*, **30**, 179–197.

Leigh, E.G. (1975). Structure and climate in tropical rain forest. *Annual Review of Ecology and Systematics*, **6**, 67–86.

Leonard, R.E. (1967). Mathematical theory of interception. *International Symposium on Forest Hydrology* (Ed. by W.E. Sopper & H.W. Lull), pp. 131–136. Pergamon Press, Oxford.

Leopoldo, P.R., Franken, W., Matsui, E. & Salati, E. (1982a). Estimativa de evapotranspiràçào de floresta amazônica de terra firme. *Acta Amazonica*, **12**, 23–28.

Leopoldo, P.R., Franken, W. & Salati, E. (1982b). Balanço hidrico de pequena bacia hidrografica en floresta amazônica de terra firme. *Acta Amazonica*, **12**, 333–337.

Lescure, J.P. & Boulet, R. (1985). Relationships between soil and vegetation in a tropical rainforest in French Guiana. *Biotropica*, **17**, 155–164.

Leyton, L., Reynolds, E.R.C. & Thompson, F.B. (1967). Rainfall interception in forest and moorland. *International Symposium on Forest Hydrology* (Ed. by W.E. Sopper & H.W. Lull), pp. 163–168. Pergamon Press, Oxford.

Lieberman, D., Lieberman, M., Peralta, R. & Hartshorn, G.S. (1985). Mortality patterns and stand turnover rates in a wet tropical forest in Costa Rica. *Journal of Ecology*, **73**, 915–924.

Likens, G.E., Bormann, F.H., Pierce, R.S., Eaton, J.S. & Johnson, N.M. (1977). *Biogeochemistry of a Forested Ecosystem.* Springer, New York.

Lloyd, C.R. & Marques Filho, A. de O. (1988). Spatial variability of throughfall and stemflow measurements in Amazonian rain forest. *Agricultural and Forest Meteorology*, **42**, 63–73.

Lovett, G.M. & Lindberg, S.E. (1984). Dry deposition and canopy exchange in a mixed oak forest as determined by analysis of throughfall. *Journal of Applied Ecology*, **21**, 1013–1027.

Low, K.S. & Goh, G.C. (1972). The water balance of five catchments in Selangor, West Malaysia. *Journal of Tropical Geography*, **35**, 60–66.

Lundgren, L. (1980). Comparison of surface runoff and soil loss from runoff plots in forest and small-scale agriculture in the Usambara Mts., Tanzania. *Geografiska Annaler, Series A*, **62**, 113–148.

Manokaran, N. (1980). The nutrient contents of precipitation, throughfall and stemflow in a lowland tropical rainforest in peninsular Malaysia. *The Malaysian Forester*, **43**, 266–289.

Mathieu, Ph. (1976). Influence des apports atmosphériques et du pluviolessivage forestier sur la qualité des eaux de deux bassins versants en Côte d'Ivoire. *Cahiers ORSTOM, Série Géologie*, **8**, 11–32.

Medina, E., Cuevas, E. & Weaver, P.L. (1981). Composición foliar y transpiración de espécies leñosas de Pico del Este, Sierra de Luquillo, Puerto Rico. *Acta Científica Venezolana*, **32**, 159–165.

Monteith, J.L. (1965). Evaporation and environment. *Symposium of the Society of Experimental Biology*, **19**, 205–234.

Mosley, M.P. (1982). Subsurface flow velocities through selected forest soils, South Island, New Zealand. *Journal of Hydrology*, **55**, 65–92.

Nortcliff, S. & Thornes, J.B. (1981). Seasonal variations in the hydrology of a small forested catchment near Manaus, Amazonas, and the implications for its management. *Tropical Agricultural Hydrology* (Ed. by R. Lal & E.W. Russell), pp. 37–57. Wiley, New York.

Nortcliff, S. & Thornes, J.B. (1984). Floodplain response of a small tropical stream. *Catchment Experiments in Fluvial Hydrology* (Ed. by T.P. Burt & D.E. Walling), pp. 73–85. Geo-Abstracts, Norwich.

Nortcliff, S., Thornes, J.B. & Waylen, M.J. (1979). Tropical forest systems: a hydrological approach. *Amazoniana*, **6**, 557–563.

Ovington, J.D. (1962). Quantitative ecology and the woodland ecosystem concept. *Advances in Ecological Research*, **1**, 103–192.

Parker, G.G. (1983). Throughfall and stemflow in the forest nutrient cycle. *Advances in Ecological Research*, **13**, 57–133.

Pearce, A.J., Stewart, M.K. & Sklash, M.G. (1986). Storm runoff generation in humid headwater catchments. 1. Where does the water come from? *Water Resources Research*, **22**, 1263–1272.

Pearcy, R.W. & Calkin, H.C. (1983). Carbon dioxide exchange of C3 and C4 tree species in the understorey of an Hawaiian forest. *Oecologia*, **58**, 26–32.

Penman, H.L. (1948). Natural evaporation from open water, bare soil and grass. *Proceedings of the Royal Society of London, Series A*, **193**, 120–146.

Penman, H.L. (1956). Evaporation: an introductory survey. *Netherlands Journal of Agricultural Science*, **4**, 9–29.

Pereira, H.C. (1952). Interception of rainfall by cypress plantations. *East African Agricultural Journal Kenya*, **18**, 73–76.

Persson, R. (1974). *World Forest Resources*. Royal College of Forestry, Stockholm.

Poels, R. (1987). *Soils, water and nutrients in a forest ecosystem in Suriname*. PhD Thesis, Agricultural University, Wageningen, The Netherlands.

Pritchett, W.L. (1979). *Properties and Management of Forest Soils*. Wiley, New York.

Proctor, J. (1983). Tropical forest litterfall. I. Problems of data comparison. *Tropical Rain Forest: Ecology and Management* (Ed. by S.L. Sutton, T.C. Whitmore & A.C. Chadwick), pp. 267–273. Blackwell Scientific Publications, Oxford.

Proctor, J. (1987). Nutrient cycling in primary and old secondary rain forests. *Applied Geography*, **7**, 135–152.

Proctor, J., Philipps, C., Duff, G.K., Heaney, A. & Robertson, F.M. (1988). Ecological studies on Gunung Silam, a small ultrabasic mountain in Sabah, Malaysia II. Some forest processes. *Journal of Ecology* (in press).

Rahim, A. & Kasran, B. (1986). Hydrologic regime of dipterocarp forest catchments in peninsular Malaysia. *Hydrological Workshop, Kota Kinabalu, 1986*, p. 20. Universiti Kebangsaan Malaysia, Kota Kinabalu, Sabah, Malaysia.

Rahim, A. & Yusof, Z. (1986). Stream water quality of undisturbed forest catchments in peninsular Malaysia. *Impact of Man's Activities on Tropical Upland Forest Ecosystems* (Ed. by Y. Hadi, K. Awang, N.M. Majid & S. Mohamed), p. 19. Universiti Pertanian Malaysia Press, Serdang, Malaysia.

Rai, S.N. & Proctor, J. (1986). Ecological studies on four rain forest sites in Karnataka, India. I. Environment, structure, floristics, and biomass. *Journal of Ecology*, **74**, 439–454.

Read, R.G. (1977). Microclimate as background environment for ecological studies of insects in a tropical forest. *Journal of Applied Meteorology*, **16**, 1282–1291.

Ribeny, F.M.J. & Brown, J.A.H. (1968) The application of a rainfall runoff–model to a wet tropical catchment. *Civil Engineering Transactions (Australia)*, **10**, 65–72.

Richards, P.W. (1952). *The Tropical Rain Forest*. Cambridge Universiy Press, Cambridge.

Richardson, J.H. (1982). Some implications of tropical forest replacement in Jamaica. *Zeitschrift für Geomorphologie Neue Folge, Supplement Band*, **44**, 107–118.

Roche, M.A. (1982). Evapotranspiration réelle de la forêt amazonienne en Guyane. *Cahiers ORSTOM, Série Hydrologie*, **19**, 37–44.

Rodier, J. & Vuillaume, G. (1970). Interprétation des résultats sur quelques bassins représentatifs tropicaux. *International Association of Hydrological Sciences Publication*, **96**, 443–454.

Roose, E.J. (1981). Dynamique actuelle des sols ferrallitiques et ferrugineaux tropicaux d'Afrique occidentale. *Travaux et Documents de l'ORSTOM 130*. L'Office de la Recherche Scientifique et Technique Outre-Mer, Paris.

Rutter, A.J. (1975). The hydrological cycle in vegetation. *Vegetation and the Atmosphere* (Ed. by J.L. Monteith), pp. 111–154. Academic Press, London.

Rutter, A.J., Kershaw, K.A., Robins, P.C. & Morton, A.J. (1971). A predictive model of rainfall interception in forests. I. Derivation of the model from observations in a plantation of Corsican pine. *Agricultural Meteorology*, **9**, 367–384.

Ruxton, B.P. (1967). Slopewash under mature primary rainforest in northern Papua. *Landform Studies from Australia and New Guinea* (Ed. by J.N. Jennings & J.A. Mabbutt), pp. 85–94. Australian National University Press, Canberra.

Salati, E., Dall'Olio, A., Matsui, E. & Gat, J.R. (1979). Recycling of water in the Amazon Basin: an isotopic study. *Water Resources Research*, **15**, 1250–1258.

Sanchez, P.A. (1976). *Properties and Management of Soils in the Tropics*. Wiley, New York.

Sarrailh, J.M. (1983). Les parcelles élémentaires d'étude du ruissellement et de l'érosion. *Le Projet ECEREX* (Ed. by C. Bailly), pp. 394–403. Centre Technique Forestier Tropical, Nogent-sur-Marne, France.

Schmidt, F.H. (1950). On the distribution of sunshine in Java. *Verhandelingen van het Meteorologisch en Geofysisch Observatorium, Djakarta*, **40**, p.18.

Schmidt, F.H. & Ferguson, J.H.A. (1951). Rainfall types based on wet and dry period ratios for Indonesia and Western New Guinea. *Verhandelingen van het Meteorologisch en Geofysisch Observatorium, Djarkarta*, **42**, p.7.

Shuttleworth, W.J. (1979). *Evaporation. Report No. 56*. Institute of Hydrology, Wallingford, U.K.

Shuttleworth, W.J. (1988). Evaporation from Amazonian rain forest. *Proceedings of the Royal Society of London, Series B* (in press).

Shuttleworth, W.J., Gash, J.H.C., Lloyd, C.R., Moore, C.J., Roberts, J., Marques Filho, A., Fisch, G., De Paula Silva Filho, V., De Nazaré Góes Ribeiro, M., Molion, L.C.B., De Abreu Sá, L.D., Nobre, J.C.A., Cabral, O.M.R., Patel, S.R. & Carvalho de Moraes, J. (1984). Eddy correlation measurements of energy partition for Amazonian forest. *Quarterly Journal of the Royal Meteorological Society*, **110**, 1143–1162.

Sklash, M.G., Stewart, M.K. & Pearce, A.J. (1986). Storm runoff generation in humid headwater catchments. 2. A case study of hillslope and low-order stream response. *Water Resources Research*, **22**, 1273–1282.

Solomon, S. (1967). Relationships between precipitation, evaporation and runoff in tropical-equatorial regions. *Water Resources Research*, **3**, 163–172.

Stadtmuller, T. (1987). *Cloud Forests in the Humid Tropics. A Bibliographic Review*. The United Nations University, Tokyo, and Centro Agronomico Tropical de Investigación y Enseñanza, Turrialba, Costa Rica.

Steinhardt, U. (1979). Untersuchungen über den Wasser- und Nährstoffhaushalt eines andinen Wolkenwaldes in Venezuela. *Göttinger Bodenkundliche Berichte*, **56**, 1–185.

Stewart, J.B. (1984). Measurement and prediction of evaporation from forested and agricultural catchments. *Agricultural Water Management*, **8**, 1–28.

Swift, M.J. (Ed.) (1985). *Tropical Soil Biology and Fertility (TSBF): Planning for research. Biology International Special Issue No. 9*. International Union of Biological Sciences, Paris.

Tanner, E.V.J. (1977). *Mineral cycling in montane rain forests in Jamaica*. PhD Thesis, University of Cambridge.

Tanner, E.V.J. (1985). Jamaican montane forests: nutrient capital and cost of growth. *Journal of Ecology*, **73**, 553–568.

Turvey, N.D. (1974). *Nutrient Cycling under Tropical Rain Forest in Central Papua. Occasional Paper, 10*. Department of Geography, University of Papua New Guinea.

UNESCO (1978). *Tropical Forest Ecosystems, a State of Knowledge Report*. UNESCO, Paris.

Vis, M. (1986). Interception, drop size distributions and rainfall kinetic energy in four Colombian forest ecosystems. *Earth Surface Processes and Landforms*, **11**, 591–603.

Vitousek, P.M. & Sanford, R.L. (1986). Nutrient cycling in moist tropical forest. *Annual Review of Ecology and Systematics*, **17**, 137–167.

Vogelmann, H.W. (1973). Fog precipitation in the cloud forests of Eastern Mexico. *BioScience*, **23**, 96–100.

Walsh, R.P.D. (1980). Runoff processes and models in the humid tropics. *Zeitschrift für Geomorphologie Neue Folge Supplement Band*, **36**, 176–202.

Walsh, R.P.D. (1982). Hydrology and water chemistry. *Sarawak Museum Journal Special Issue*, **2**, 121–181.

Wanner, H. & Soerohaldoko, S. (1979). Transpiration types in montane rain forest. *Berichte der Schweizerische Botanische Gesellschaft*, **89**, 193–210.

Ward, R.C. (1984). On the response to precipitation of headwater streams in humid areas. *Journal of Hydrology*, **74**, 171–189.

Waring, R.H. & Roberts, J. (1979). Estimating water flux through stems of Scots pine with tritiated water and phosphorus-32. *Journal of Experimental Botany*, **30**, 459–471.

Waring, R.H., Whitehead, D. & Jarvis, P.G. (1980). Comparison of an isotopic method and the Penman–Monteith equation for estimating transpiration from Scots pine. *Canadian Journal of Forestry Research*, **10**, 355–358.

Weaver, P.L. (1972). Cloud moisture interception in the Luquillo Mountains of Puerto Rico. *Caribbean Journal of Science*, **12**, 129–144.

Weaver, P.L., Byer, M.D. & Bruck, D.L. (1973). Transpiration rates in the Luquillo Mountains of Puerto Rico. *Biotropica*, **5**, 123–133.

Weaver, P.L., Medina, E., Pool, D., Dugger. K., Gonzales-Liboy, J. & Cuevas, E. (1986). Ecological observations in the dwarf cloud forest of the Luquillo Mountains of Puerto Rico. *Biotropica*, **18**, 79–85.

Weyman, D.R. (1973). Measurements of the downslope flow of water in a soil. *Journal of Hydrology*, **20**, 267–288.

Whipkey, R.Z. (1965). Sub-surface stormflow from forested slopes. *Bulletin of the International Association of Scientific Hydrology*, **10**, 74–85.

White, E.J. & Turner, F. (1970). A method of estimating income of nutrients in a catch of airborne particles by a woodland canopy. *Journal of Applied Ecology*, **7**, 441–461.

Whitehead, D., Okali, D.U.U. & Fasehun, F.E. (1981). Stomatal response to environmental variables in two tropical forest species during the dry season in Nigeria. *Journal of Applied Ecology*, **18**, 571–587.

Wiersum, K.F. (1985). Effects of various vegetation layers of an *Acacia auriculiformis* forest plantation on surface erosion at Java, Indonesia. *Soil Erosion and Conservation* (Ed. by S.A. El-Swaify, W.C. Moldenhauer A. Lo), pp. 79–89. Soil Conservation Society of America, Ankeny, Iowa.

Williamson, G.B. (1981), Driptips and splash erosion. *Biotropica*, **13**, 228–231.

Williamson, G.B., Romero, A., Armstrong, J.K., Gush, T.J., Hruska, A.J., Klass, P.E. & Thompson, J.T. (1983). Driptips, dropsize and leaf drying. *Biotropica*, **15**, 232–234.

Witkamp, M. (1970). Mineral retention by epiphyllic organisms. *A Tropical Rain Forest* (Ed. by H.T. Odum & R.F. Pidgeon), pp. H177–179. United States Atomic Energy Commission, Washington.

Yoshikawa, K., Ogino, K. & Maiyus, M. (1986). Some aspects of sap flow rate of tree species in a tropical rain forest in West Sumatra. *Diversity and Dynamics of Plant Life in Sumatra. Part 1* (Ed. by M. Hotta), pp. 45–59. Kyoto University, Kyoto, Japan.

Zadroga, F. (1981). The hydrological importance of a montane cloud forest area of Costa Rica. *Tropical Agricultural Hydrology* (Ed. by R. Lal & E.W. Russell), pp. 59–73. Wiley, New York.

Zaslavsky, D. & Rogowski, A.S. (1969). Hydrologic and morphologic implications of anisotropy and infiltration in soil profile development. *Soil Science Society of America Proceedings*, **33**, 594–599.

The role of mineral nutrients in the tropics: a plant ecologist's view

P. J. GRUBB

Botany School, University of Cambridge,
Downing Street, Cambridge CB2 3EA

SUMMARY

1 The problems of determining the extent of nutrient limitation on growth are discussed, and the results of recent experimental studies are briefly reviewed.

2 The extent to which forest stature and physiognomy parallel nutrient supply in the tropics is considered, and the few quantitative studies comparing limitations by nutrient shortage and by water shortage in the one community are assessed.

3 The various definitions of nutrient-use efficiency (NUE) given in the literature are reviewed, and it is proposed that contrary to expectation, plants in forests and savannas on richer soils may often have higher values of NUE.

4 The importance of studies on the influences of plants on soil fertility is spelt out, and emphasis is placed on recent studies which question the extent of 'nutrient pumping' from the subsoil to the topsoil by woody plants.

5 The importance of mineral supply for plant–microbe and plant–animal relations is briefly considered.

6 Some general comments are made on research to date on mineral nutrients in tropical forests and savannas, and in particular on the contributions to this Symposium, together with suggestions for future work.

INTRODUCTION

The greater part of this paper is devoted to an overview of five main issues. First, the question 'How may we prove that mineral nutrients are limiting?' is considered, and the available evidence on which elements are limiting in various tropical communities is summarized. Secondly, the question 'To what extent does nutrient supply determine the structure and physiognomy of vegetation in the tropics?' is asked, and the relative importance of limitation by nutrient supply and by other factors is considered. Thirdly, the concept of 'nutrient-use efficiency' is examined, and some of the difficulties in making useful comparisons between systems are pointed out. Fourthly, the influence of plants on soil fertility is investigated, and particularly the question of 'nutrient pumping' from the subsoil to the topsoil by woody plants. Fifthly, the role of symbionts and the involvement of mineral nutrients in plant–herbivore relations are briefly considered. The final part of the paper is devoted to general comments on the limitations of the work carried out so far, and the needs for future work.

417

HOW MAY WE PROVE THAT MINERAL NUTRIENTS ARE LIMITING?

It is important to refine this question. It is now widely appreciated that when a soil is deficient in its supply of one or more mineral nutrients, and because of this plants of many species grow at a rate far below their full capacity (or fail totally) on the soil, the plants which predominate on the soil naturally may have little capacity to respond to greater quantities of nutrients. The experimental studies which have demonstrated this have been those carried out with temperate perennial herbs grown in a glasshouse or a controlled-environment cabinet, beginning with those of Bradshaw *et al.* (1960, 1964). Species associated naturally with soils which were known to be infertile for crop plants were found to show a smaller proportional response in relative growth rate to increasing supply of nitrogen or phosphorus than plants associated with soils known to be fertile for crop plants. In fact, this point was clearly established in the classical studies of Mitchell & Chandler (1939) on forest trees, long before the comparative studies on herbs were begun. Additions of nitrogen to spontaneous stands of mixed deciduous species on grey–brown podzolic soils in New York State brought about smaller responses in girth increment in species characteristic of soils which were less base-rich and 'less fertile', and larger responses in species characteristic of soils which were more base-rich and 'more fertile'. A logical conclusion from all these studies is that if we add a given amount of a certain fertilizer to stands of natural vegetation on two soils, one strongly nutrient deficient and another of intermediate nutrient status, we may well find a smaller response in growth rate in the vegetation on the poorer soil. This kind of result has been discussed by Chapin, Vitousek & Van Cleve (1986), using examples from recent work in boreal forest.

It is now easy to see that the question of nutrient limitation has to be treated in two parts. First, is it the case that the supply of a certain nutrient limits the growth of the plants in a certain community? This can be answered simply by increasing the supply of the nutrient concerned. Secondly, is it the case that plants which are absent from the community in question could grow there (and persist through successive regeneration cycles) if the supply of one or more nutrients was increased? This can be answered only by introducing seeds or seedlings into clearings or high forest or intact savanna (depending on the natural pattern of regeneration of the species in question) and increasing the supply of nutrient(s). Although we do now have some answers to questions of the first type, and these are reviewed in the next two sections, it seems that there is not a single published study dealing with an experiment of the second type for non-crop species.

It may be that soil toxicity provides the first limitation to growth of species that are naturally absent, rather than shortage of nutrients. This situation has been well studied with regard to crops on strongly acidic peat in the lowlands of south-east Asia by Polak (1948) and others. Most crop species cannot tolerate the high concentration of hydronium ions; after liming the effective deficiencies depend on the crop (reviewed by Grubb & Tanner (1976)). Mor humus from montane forest in Jamaica has proved to be similarly toxic for crop plants (Tanner 1977), but we still lack experiments in which relevant forest tree species are shown to fail because of hydronium-ion toxicity on tropical peat or mor. The position is exactly similar for strongly acidic ancient soils rich in aluminium ions known to be toxic to crop plants (cf. Lathwell & Grove 1986), although Fölster (1986) confidently interprets the behaviour of the roots of certain woody plants in the field as evidence of the impact of aluminium toxicity.

Returning to the first question, the results of experiments on temperate grasslands (Thurston 1969) and herbs in temperate forest (Ellenberg 1978, p. 186) lead us to expect that different species in a community will prove to be limited by different nutrients. Furthermore, the degree of response to a single major limiting nutrient, or to a combination of limiting nutrients, may differ widely between species, even among those commonly found together. Thus, at an old-field site in Costa Rica, Harcombe (1977) found the herb *Phytolacca rivinoides* to be very much more responsive to an application of nitrogen, phosphorus and potassium than the tree *Cecropia obtusifolia*. However, I do not believe that we should expect all herbs to be more responsive than all trees. By analogy with the temperate zone, we should expect a spectrum of responses in both life forms (cf. Ellenberg 1978). Within savannas on nutrient-poor soils, it may be predicted that short-lived plants associated with overgrazing and other forms of disturbance will generally respond more than the long-lived perennials typical of less disturbed sites, in the same way as annuals of very poor soils in the northern temperate zone can be very responsive to added nutrients while the perennials — as emphasized above — tend not to be (Boorman 1982; Rozijn 1984). It seems that no comparison of the two groups is available for one savanna, but it is notable that Penning de Vries & Djiteye (1982) reported increases in yield of up to 500% with additional nitrogen and phosphorus in largely annual-dominated grasslands of the overgrazed Sahel, while Garcia-Miragaya, San Jose & Hernandez (1983) found an increase of only 10–20% in the biomass of perennial grass-dominated savanna on 'infertile' soil in Venezuela.

Even within a species, there may be variation in responsiveness dependent on the age of the plant and its light supply — not to mention genetically determined differences. We may guess that young plants will prove to be more responsive than old, as found for temperate plantation crops (cf. Miller 1984). As for the light supply, J. R. Healey (unpublished), working in montane forest in Jamaica, has found that the response of spontaneous seedlings to addition of nitrogen may be positive in the bright light of a clearing, but non-significant in the shade, and even possibly negative in some species in shade. These results are consistent with those of an unpublished experiment on ten species of tall shrub, all widespread in Britain, carried out by W. G. Lee and myself; we found a wide range of responses when plants were grown on two soils of different nitrogen and phosphorus supplying power at different radiant fluxes, provided by neutral shade screens. One species did not respond to the increased nutrient supply even in bright light, two responded only in bright light, and another showed the same proportional response in relative growth rate at high and low light; yet others showed an interaction of light and nutrient effects. Most species were less productive, or died more quickly, on the more fertile soil in deep shade. Some of the earliest experiments on the interaction of shade and nutrient supply on yield were carried out with tropical crops such as cacao and coffee (summarized by Murray & Nichols 1966); addition of nutrients is necessary to prevent such crops being less productive in bright light.

We are now in a position to review the few results available on two classical problems: the distinction between montane and lowland forests with regard to nutrient supply, and the separation of different types of lowland forest.

Montane rain forests versus lowland rain forests in the tropics

A decline in forest stature and an increase in scleromorphism with an increase in altitude is found all over the tropics (Richards 1952; Grubb 1977; Whitmore 1984), and the available evidence also points to a decline in productivity, particularly in the rate of trunk growth (Grubb 1977; Tanner 1980; Gerrish & Bridges 1984). The decline in productivity is likely to be primarily a result of decreased irradiance and lower temperatures, but it has been argued elsewhere that another important factor is likely to be a significant reduction in the rate of supply of nitrogen in the soil — a result of the decreased rate of decomposition of organic matter in montane soils (Grubb 1971, 1977; Edwards & Grubb 1982). Studies on the concentration of nitrogen in the leaves and in the whole above-ground biomass (Grubb 1977; Tanner 1985), and on the amounts of nitrogen cycling via litterfall (Edwards 1982; Vitousek 1984; Tanner 1985; Heaney & Proctor *this volume*), have provided support for this hypothesis, but all these observations can be explained in other ways, as pointed out by Edwards & Grubb (1982). Various agricultural experiments with fertilizers in Jamaica (summarized by Healey (*this volume*)) have suggested that nitrogen limitation is greater in montane soils, and very recent papers have provided direct evidence from field incubations that there is much less mineralization in montane forest soils than in lowland forest soils (Matson & Vitousek 1987; Marrs *et al.* 1988).

Evidence for limitation of growth by nitrogen supply is also beginning to accumulate. Vitousek *et al.* (1987) have shown that girth increment (but not litterfall) in a natural Hawaiian upper montane rain forest, composed mainly of *Metrosideros polymorpha*, is significantly increased by addition of nitrogen, but not phosphorus or all known nutrients other than nitrogen and phosphorus. Gerrish & Bridges (1984) showed that girth increment was significantly increased after addition of a 'complete fertilizer'. In an unreplicated experiment, Tanner *et al.* (1989) have found that both nitrogen and phosphorus applied singly appear to increase girth increment in upper montane forest in Jamaica, and in a replicated experiment, E. V. J. Tanner (unpublished) has found that addition of nitrogen and phosphorus together did not lead to an increase in litterfall in upper montane forest in Venezuela. J. R. Healey (unpublished) has shown that in the Jamaican upper montane forest, addition of nitrogen increases height growth of seedlings of certain tree species, but not others, in experimentally created forest gaps. All these recent results constitute an important step forward. However, it remains to be established (a) whether the growth of most trees in most montane forests is more limited by nitrogen supply than that of most trees in most lowland forests (or are the trees 'adapted' by evolution to the undoubtedly reduced supply in such a way that they are less responsive?), and (b) whether the reduced supply of nitrogen interacts in a significant way with reduced irradiance and/or lower temperatures in setting the upper altitudinal limits of various species.

Perhaps the most surprising development with respect to nitrogen relations and altitude has been the finding that in intraspecific and intrageneric comparisons in both northern and southern temperate zones the concentration of nitrogen in the leaves of both trees and herbs tends to increase with altitude (Körner, Bannister & Mark 1986) — the opposite of the trend found in community-level comparisons within the forest zones on tropical mountains (Grubb 1977). The trend on temperate mountains occurs despite an undoubted decrease in the amount of available nitrogen in the soil, and is paralleled by a marked upward trend in the maximum rate of photosynthesis per unit leaf area (Körner & Diemer 1987). It would be particularly fascinating to obtain information on intraspecific comparisons for tropical montane forest species, and to find out what is happening in the leaves of plants above the tree line in the tropics where temperate genera commonly predominate (see note added in proof, p. 439).

The exclusion of lowland forest trees from low-stature upper montane forests at low altitudes — those showing the 'strong *Massenerhebung* effect' of Grubb & Stevens (1985) — may well be a result of hydronium-ion toxicity in the associated peat rather than shortage of any nutrient as such. On the other hand, the low stature and the presumed low growth rate of the species that can tolerate the potential toxicity are likely to be limited by an extremely small supply of nitrogen or some other nutrient(s). Plants in temperate bogs often show a greater response to potassium than to nitrogen or phosphorus (references in Grubb & Tanner (1976)).

Nutrient limitation in different kinds of lowland rain forest

Vitousek (1984), on finding very high dry mass : P ratios in the litterfall of lowland tropical forests, and a positive correlation between the amount of fine litterfall in these forests and the phosphorus concentration in the litter, has argued that phosphorus rather than nitrogen may be the primary limiting nutrient for forest growth in the lowland wet tropics generally. He has contrasted this situation with a primary limitation by nitrogen in the temperate zones and on tropical mountains. Certainly, the rates of nitrogen mineralization in lowland forest soils can be extremely high (De Rham 1970; Vitousek & Denslow 1986). However, in an experiment carried out in Costa Rica with seedlings of the non-mycorrhizal herb *Phytolacca* and rooted cuttings of six shrubs (three *Miconia* spp.

and three *Piper* spp.), grown in intact cores of soil from a forest site with moderate phosphorus-supplying power (as judged by chemical analysis), it was found that addition of a complete fertilizer solution increased growth significantly and very appreciably, whereas addition of phosphorus (as NaH_2PO_4) affected only the *Phytolacca* significantly (Denslow, Vitousek & Schultz 1987). No species responded significantly to addition of nitrogen (as NH_4NO_3), but there is always a problem with assessing the effect of added nitrogen in pots where the volume of soil supplying unit length of root is initially very large (Cornforth 1968; Peace & Grubb 1982). This is a very important piece of work that needs to be followed up with seedlings rather than cuttings, and with trees rather than shrubs, at a number of lowland sites.

The finding by Denslow *et al.* that elements other than phosphorus and nitrogen are important is in agreement with the ideas of Baillie (*this volume*) and Furch & Klinge (*this volume*) and the results of work in the forests on the extremely nutrient-deficient soils of the Rio Negro region reported by Medina & Cuevas (*this volume*). In the forests on oxisols, derived largely from lateritic gravel but partly from sand, the amounts of the cations potassium, calcium and magnesium in the biomass and in the litterfall are extraordinarily small. Most significantly, the fine roots in the 'root mat', which invade the fresh litter, have been found by experiment to take up calcium and magnesium much more than phosphorus (Cuevas & Medina 1983), and the change with age in the nitrogen concentration of the litter (Medina & Cuevas *this volume*) suggests that not much of this element is taken up either. The remarkable development of not only the 'root mat' in the forest floor, but also masses of fine roots that thoroughly occupy fallen logs, and climb at least 1.5 m up standing dead stems, strongly suggests that the shortage of cations is so limiting to growth that a net benefit is to be gained from investment of resources in a thorough nutrient-scavenging system.

In a world context, the Rio Negro region is also especially interesting because of the contrast between the forest on oxisols and the 'tall *caatinga*' forest on groundwater podzols. Within the generally flat landscape the podzols are formed on deep sand at slightly lower sites, and are thus flushed with bases; this is shown by the analyses of the soil and the plants, and by the amounts in circulation via litterfall. The *caatinga* also tends to have a higher phosphate status (Medina & Cuevas *this volume*). On the other hand, the *caatinga* has a much more meagre supply of nitrogen, as judged by whole-plant analyses and the amounts circulating by litterfall. We thus find a case of a forest on a flushed, more base-rich site-type having a significantly smaller supply of nitrogen — quite the reverse of the position found so widely in the northern temperate zone (cf. Gorham 1953).

The possible significance of micro-nutrients in the *caatinga* would also be worth studying, partly because of the large accumulation of highly acidic peat-like organic matter which is likely to complex copper, and partly because on deep, strongly leached sands outside the tropics, for example in Australia, it has been shown that there are deficiencies for crop plants in boron, copper, molybdenum and zinc (summarized by Specht & Rayson 1957).

Although no experiment has been carried out on the impact of added nutrients on the growth of whole plants in either the oxisol-forest or the *caatinga*, Cuevas & Medina (1983) have tried the novel approach of measuring the responses of fine-root growth to nutrient additions. As one would forecast from the data on the amounts of nutrients in circulation, growth was most enhanced by calcium and phosphorus in the oxisol-forest and by nitrogen in the tall *caatinga*.

TO WHAT EXTENT IS VEGETATION TYPE DETERMINED BY NUTRIENT SUPPLY?

In his introduction to this Symposium, Whitmore threw out a challenge, suggesting that the role of nutrient supply in determining the characteristic features of, say, heath forest or montane forest could be exaggerated, especially in comparison with the part played by periodic shortage of water. In the next two sections of this paper the extent to which forest stature and physiognomy do parallel nutrient supply is investigated, and such evidence as there is on the relative importance of nutrient shortage and other factors is examined. Because of the limitation on space only forests are considered.

The correlation between soil nutrient status and forest stature and physiognomy

There are two types of case where we see a strong correlation between nutrient status and forest form. The first is typically found in the lowlands; here we see a marked contrast between low-stature, thin-stemmed forest, poor in buttresses and vines and rich in trees with relatively small, hard leaves on soils that are very infertile for herbaceous crops (derived from deep sand or concretionary lateritic material) and tall, thick-stemmed forest, rich in vines and in buttressed trees with larger, less extremely hard leaves on soils of moderate to high fertility for agriculture (derived from a great variety of parent materials). In the case of the low-statured forests in the Rio Negro region of South America, there is no doubt that they have a smaller working capital of most mineral nutrients per unit area than taller forests on more fertile soils, and smaller amounts cycling through unit area of forest each year (Cuevas & Medina 1986; Vitousek & Sanford 1986; Medina & Cuevas *this volume*). For the similar low-statured forests in South-East Asia, the preliminary information available suggests that the same is true there (Peace & McDonald 1981).

The second case is seen typically in the mountains; here we often find lower-stature, smaller-leaved, vine-poor forest on leached ridge-top soils (some of which develop a covering of mor humus or peat) and taller, larger-leaved, vine-rich forests on flushed soils in gullies. In a very detailed study of one such case — in the Blue Mountains of Jamaica — Tanner (1977, 1985) has shown that the amounts of nutrients cycling through the forest each year are again smaller in the lower-stature, smaller-leaved, vine-poor forest. Preliminary data from foliar analyses for forests in Malaya suggest a similar position there (Grubb 1977).

We may also see in the mountains an analogue of the effect of soil type described above for the lowlands. The montane forests on strongly acidic low-phosphate soils in Jamaica studied by Grubb & Tanner (1976) and Tanner (1977, 1985) may be usefully compared with those on basic, more phosphate-rich soils in Papua New Guinea studied by Edwards & Grubb (1977), Edwards (1982) and Grubb & Stevens (1985). In the Jamaican study area, there is a marked contrast between low-stature, vine-poor forests on leached ridges (pH 3.5–4.0 at 0–10 cm depth) and taller forests quite rich in vines in the flushed gullies (pH 4.4–5.0); still lower-stature forest with still smaller leaves is found on occasional mor-capped knolls (pH 2.8–3.5). In contrast, in the study area in Papua New Guinea, there is no marked differentiation in forest form or composition or in soil profile between ridges and gullies (pH 5.6–6.6 at 0–10 cm depth at ridge-top sites and at slope and valley sites). Despite being found at a lower altitude, the whole suite of forests in the Jamaican study area is much shorter than that in Papua New Guinea (range 5–23 m compared with 27–33 m plus emergents to 37 m). There is no doubt that the amounts of nutrients cycling through the forest each year are greater in the New Guinean forests (Tanner 1985).

Certainly we should not expect a perfect correlation between forest form and soil nutrient status. For one thing, soil stability may have an overriding effect. Where mountain slopes are very steep and the slope soils very unstable, it is common to find the trees of greatest stature and girth on ridge soils despite the fact that these are more leached (Grubb & Stevens 1985, p. 83). More interestingly, the general trend is broken by 'superplants' which defy our expectations. The best examples with respect to nutrient supply are found towards the edge of the tropics or just outside: *Agathis* and *Eucalyptus*. Both dominate forest on soils known to be infertile for agricultural crops, but grow to much greater heights and girths than the trees that dominate forest on adjacent soils of greater fertility for crop plants (Cockayne 1928, p. 157; Webb 1968). Even in the case of *Agathis* and *Eucalyptus*, the forests are notably scleromorphic and lacking in vines. Within the tropics, notable examples of massive stature on soils very poor in mineral nutrients are provided by *Shorea albida* on raised domes of highly acidic peat (Anderson 1964; Whitmore 1984) and by some of the marginal, taller types of *kerangas* or heath forest, also dominated by dipterocarps (Proctor *et al.* 1983a). Without doubt some of the dipterocarps must be admitted to the category of superplant.

The existence of plants which defy the general trend in mature height or trunk girth is not confined to series of communities defined in terms of nutrient availability. Nobody will deny that in the tropics forests generally decline in height with altitude, but in Papua New Guinea some lower montane forests dominated by *Nothofagus* are taller than many lowland forests and a few 40 m tall *Nothofagus* species even penetrate the upper montane zone (Grubb & Stevens 1985). In Colombia, the tallest palm in the world, *Ceroxylon andicola*, which grows to a height of more than 60 m, is confined to montane forest and reaches altitudes of at least 3000 m (Cuatrecasas 1958, fig. VIII-I; Corner 1966). Similarly, it must be agreed that in the tropics it is usual to find a decline in forest height with decreasing rainfall (cf. Beard 1955; Hall & Swaine 1976), and yet in parts of Queensland and Papua New Guinea sites with lower rainfall or excessively drained soils often carry the tallest trees (Webb 1968; Gray 1975), in this case species of *Araucaria*, another genus of superplant.

Clearly any balanced and complete treatment of the relationship between plant form and an environmental factor — be it mineral nutrient supply, water supply, irradiance or warmth — must take into account both the general trend and the notable exceptions.

Relative importance of nutrient shortage and other environmental factors

The best investigated case is that of low-stature ridge-top forest in the mountains. Some ecologists may be inclined to attribute the reduction in tree height on ridges to wind effects or reduced water supply rather than to leached soils. In certain cases, wind does seem to be the most important factor (Lawton 1982; Sugden 1986), but on most large tropical mountains there is no obvious directional wind-shearing of the canopy on ridges. P. Bellingham and J. R. Healey (personal communication) have suggested that the whole suite of forests on the ridge of the Blue Mountains in Jamaica described by Grubb & Tanner (1976) is reduced in stature relative to that only a few hundreds of metres lower down as a result of exposure to wind; however, it is certainly not the case that the ridge-top forests there suffer constant strong winds as does the ridge in Venezuela described by Sugden (1986). Whether or not a modest overall reduction in stature by wind occurs at the Jamaican site (presumably through some kind of temperature effect), there seems little doubt that the differentiation between mor ridge, mull ridge and col ('gap') forests is primarily the result of differences in soil nutrient status. The differences in soil fertility and in the amounts of nutrients in circulation have been documented by Tanner (1977, 1985). A prolonged and critical study by Kapos & Tanner (1985) on the water status of the plants and soils, including a markedly dry spell, did not reveal evidence of significant shortage of water in the smaller-stature forest. Earlier, less sophisticated studies showed a lack of desiccation tolerance in the shoots of scleromorphic upper montane forest trees in Jamaica and Malaya (Buckley, Corlett & Grubb 1980). If water shortage is not responsible for dwarfing ridge-top forests in Jamaica, where mor humus forms, it seems even less likely to be responsible in areas where there is a sufficiently constant soil wetness for peat to form on the ridges, as in Malaya (Whitmore & Burnham 1969) and the Solomon Islands (Lee 1969; Whitmore 1969).

In the case of low-stature forests on infertile soils of the lowlands, wind effects are not of concern, but drought may be, especially where the soils are deep sands. However, in the Rio Negro area, measurements by W. Franco and N. Dezzeo over a period of 10 months, including the 'dry season' (fig. 2 in Medina & Cuevas *this volume*), show no appreciable water deficit in the soil of one of the two major forest types (tall *caatinga* on deep sand) and in the soil of the other major type (mixed forest on oxisol) much smaller deficits than would be found in the soil of a tropical deciduous forest. On the other hand, the amounts of mineral nutrients in circulation are certainly very low in both *caatinga* and mixed forest (Medina & Cuevas *this volume*). Drought periods of the type emphasized by Bruenig (1969) for Sarawak may commonly reduce growth or increase the rate of litterfall, and in extreme cases be associated with extensive fires (cf. Sanford *et al.* 1985), but the case for considering that shortage of water rather than shortage of nutrients has been responsible for the evolution of the peculiar features of the forests in the Rio Negro region seems to me to be very weak. In other areas, where the deep sandy soils are not characteristically low-lying and do not have a high water table, the position may be different. On the other hand, it is surely suggestive that while the forests of nutrient-poor soils in the Rio Negro region with an annual rainfall of about 3500 mm have a peculiar form, those of richer soils with a rainfall marginal for rain forest (say 1800 mm year^{-1} as in eastern Brazil and Queensland) have a fairly typical rain forest physiognomy (Richards 1952; Webb 1968).

The persistence of an adequate water supply throughout the year in the tall *caatinga* forest contrasts with the undoubtedly precarious water supply in the soil of the slight domes of sand carrying '*bana*' vegetation ('short *caatinga*'), in which the treelets of 1–2 m have a decidedly bonsai appearance. In their case the water table can be at a depth of only 20 cm much of the year, and then sink by 1 m in just 5 days of dry weather; the plants certainly shut their stomata in response to the loss of water supply, and it is arguable that the strikingly near-vertical inclination of the leaves of many species is important in minimizing the risk of overheating under these conditions (Medina, Sobrado & Herrera 1978).

Certainly further critical measurements of nutrient status and water status, and new experiments involving additions of water and nutrients, are needed to establish without any doubt the relative importance of nutrient shortage and water shortage in the cases reviewed; however, the evidence to date places the emphasis on nutrients.

EFFICIENCY OF USE OF MINERAL NUTRIENTS

Cuevas & Medina (1986) and several contributors to this volume consider their results in terms of 'nutrient-use efficiency'. It is necessary to dissect the nature of this concept, and the dangers of its unqualified use, very carefully.

Investigators concerned with this issue have produced a remarkable array of terms (Table 1). These have been defined on very different scales of space and time. Ideally, it seems to me, the ecologist interested in mechanisms should start from the larger scales of space and time, and work down to smaller scales to see how the phenomena found at larger scales can be explained. Unfortunately, most of the proposed definitions at the scale of community (or stand) and year are defective. The 'ideal' definition proposed by Vitousek (1982) omits the issue of uptake of nutrients followed by leaching. In any thorough cost analysis this issue is important because of the cost to the plant of active absorption of the nutrients through the roots in the first place. Gray's (1983) definition copes with this issue (and he made valuable comparative measurements of leaching in two mediterranean-climate communities), but his inclusion of only canopy tissue on the production side of the equation is a serious limitation. The same criticism applies to Ågren's (1983) 'nitrogen productivity', and the measure used in practice by Vitousek (1982, 1984), i.e. dry weight of litterfall/nutrient content. The deficiency of these definitions is serious because of the different patterns of allocation to leaf and stem tissue at different levels of total productivity, which are dealt with further below. Rundel's (1982) definition, which omits consideration of roots, is of very limited value for the kind of comparison of more- and less-fertile sites that he was attempting.

Although not in itself a felicitous term, the 'nitrogen utility index' of Hirose (1971), broadened to the 'resource utility index' by Hirose (1975), has the definition of greatest general value: rate of dry matter production/rate of uptake of nutrient. It is concerned with whole-plant production, and in theory allows both for the uptake and leaching of nutrients, and for the less obvious losses of dry matter. Here I have in mind the losses to herbivores that are so difficult to measure accurately, the losses through nectar (up to 37% of current assimilation in one temperate herb (Southwick 1984)) and pollen, the organic matter which is lost to the soil by diffusion or excretion from the roots (variously estimated as equal to 0.1–18% of the total production of shoots and roots (cf. Newman 1978)), and that lost to the extramatrical hyphae of mycorrhizal fungi. The link between efficiency of net production and the efficiency of photosynthesis may be loose as a result of the very wide range of values found for the ratio between the rate of respiration and the relative growth rate (Lambers 1985). The link between efficiency of net production and the efficiency of photosynthesis under light-saturated conditions may be particularly loose, because much photosynthesis occurs under conditions of rapidly changing radiant flux (Pearcy 1987), and little is known about the pattern of variation in efficiency under these conditions. Hirose's definition also allows for uptake of nutrients to the shoot, followed by return to the roots via the phloem, which has been documented for potassium (Armstrong & Kirkby 1979), nitrogen (Simpson, Lambers & Dalling 1982) and sulphur (Saker, Clarkson & Purves 1988), with the possibility of leakage back into the soil (cf. Ritz & Newman 1985).

In the forseeable future, ecologists working with tropical forests and savannas are unlikely to be able to cope with movements of carbon or recycled mineral nutrients from root to soil, or losses through nectar and pollen on large plants. However, efforts should be made to cover total production of shoots and roots, herbivory and leaching of nutrients. The definition of nutrient-use efficiency (NUE) accepted here is 'rate of production of shoots (including trunks, branches, flowers and fruits) plus roots/rate of uptake of nutrient'.

Setting aside the issue of definition, there are real problems in comparing communities. These arise from variation in NUE with age of plant. Agricultura-

TABLE 1. A range of definitions of nutrient-use efficiency (and similar terms) ordered by the scales of time and space

Temporal scale	Spatial scale	Term	Authors	Definition
Instantaneous	Leaf	Nitrogen-use efficiency Potential photosynthetic nitrogen-use efficiency	Field & Mooney (1983) Field & Mooney (1986)	Photosynthetic rate at light saturation and favourable temperature and humidity Unit of nitrogen in the leaf
Instantaneous	Plant	Nitrogen-use efficiency	Brown (1978)	Biomass produced (or CO_2 fixed) Unit of nitrogen in the plant
Hour	Plant	Nitrogen productivity	Ingestad (1979)	Rate of dry matter production Unit of nitrogen in the plant
Day	Plant	Net assimilation rate on basis of leaf protein-N (or total-N)	Williams (1939)	Rate of dry matter production Unit of protein-N (or total-N) in leaves
Week or month	Plant	Utilization quotient	Steenbjerg & Jakobsen (1963)	Accumulated production Unit of nutrient accumulated (i.e. taken up and retained)
Year	Leaf	Potential photosynthate per unit nitrogen	Small (1972)	Maximum net photosynthetic rate (leaf weight basis) × leaf-life length (seasons) Concentration of nitrogen in leaf
Year	Population or community	Nitrogen utility index	Hirose (1971)	Rate of dry matter production Rate of nitrogen uptake
Year	Population	Nitrogen-use efficiency	Berendse & Aerts (1987)	Dry matter production per unit nitrogen in plant Mean residence time of nitrogen

Term	Stand/Community	Time	Author	Definition
Nitrogen productivity	Stand	Year	Ågren (1983)	Dry mass of new leaves / Nitrogen in all leaves at end of season
Nitrogen-use efficiency quotient	Community	Year	Gray (1983)	Dry mass of new canopy tissue (i.e. leaves flowers and fruits) / Unit of nutrient returned to soil in litter fall, throughfall and stemflow
Nitrogen utilization efficiency	Community	Year	Rundel (1982)	Total production (dry mass) above ground / Unit of nitrogen invested in leaves and not withdrawn at senescence
Nutrient-use efficiency	Community	Year	Vitousek (1982)	(a) *Ideal* Dry mass of new living tissue + above-ground litterfall + roots that die / Content of nutrient in these three fractions (b) *In practice* Dry mass of litterfall / Nutrient content of litterfall

lists have long known that annual crops accumulate major nutrients relatively faster than dry weight (Gregory 1953), and there is evidence for the same trend in spontaneous populations of short-lived plants (Gay, Grubb & Hudson 1982). Similarly, the uptake of mineral nutrients by plantations of conifers declines with age much more than the rate of accumulation of dry matter (Switzer & Nelson 1972; Miller 1984), and the same is found in natural coniferous forest subject to periodic destruction by fire (Fahey & Knight 1986). Thus, in general, NUE increases with plant age. Now, tropical forests and savannas suffer disturbance and regenerate on very various scales of space and time. Therefore we should be careful to compare communities at various stages of development, and remember that within the mixed-age populations of most communities there are likely to be individuals (even within one species) showing a wide range of values of NUE. The issue of sampling communities is vitally important; for sampling to be adequate, it must be designed in relation to the scale of the regeneration patches in the communities concerned.

It is commonly accepted that, if natural communities of poorer and richer soils are compared, the former appear to have a higher NUE, as judged by the in-adequate criterion of dry weight of above-ground material per unit of nutrient. This was the case in a comparison of six tropical forests made by Grubb (1977, table 5), and this trend has been largely confirmed as more data have become available (Tanner 1985; Vitousek & Sanford 1986). However, some forests have not fitted neatly into this pattern, e.g. the large-stature lowland rain forests on soils of moderate fertility in the Ivory Coast studied by Bernhard-Reversat, Huttel & Lemée (1978); they have as much dry weight per unit of certain major nutrients (phosphorus and potassium) as the forests that have been studied on soils which are poor when judged by crop plants. I believe that the clue to this finding is the fact that trees produce less wood relative to leaf when total production is lower (whether limited by lack of mineral nutrients, water or warmth (Grubb 1977)), and wood has much lower concentrations of mineral nutrients than leaf material. For a woody plant under unfavourable conditions, the first priority, it seems, is to maintain its leafy canopy which is active in pro-duction, and perhaps in shading competitors. If conditions are rather more favourable, more stem tissue can be produced and thus a taller and/or wider crown; in this way the plant keeps above its competitors and in many cases shades them. As relatively more stem tissue is produced, the NUE goes up!

In this way we can understand how the '(nutrient) cost to grow' — the inverse of NUE — was found by Tanner (1985) to be greater in low-stature forest on mor humus than in taller forest (on mull humus) which had a greater mean annual girth increment. The same phenomenon has been found by Saverimuttu (1987) in a comparison of two grassland types on limestone in England, one on soil that provides a poor supply of nitrogen and phosphorus and one on richer soil. The latter has about 80% of the above-ground material in stems and leaf sheaths at the time of peak standing crop (as opposed to 20%), and both have much lower con-centrations of nitrogen and phosphorus in the stems-plus-leaf-sheaths fraction than in leaf blades. In this way the grassland on richer soil accumulates more above-ground dry weight each year per unit of nitrogen and phosphorus in it. Presumably the same is likely to be found in comparing savanna grasses on poorer and richer soils. This is a special instance of the general case, emphasized by Hirose (1984), that if the plant has a substantial potential carbon sink, its NUE can be very much improved. An agricultural example is the greater NUE of crops which produce starch-rich tubers compared with those which produce protein-rich seeds (cf. Ramakrishnan *this volume*).

Whatever the pure ecologists' approach to NUE, a major practical issue in the next few decades is going to be the question of how much wood can be produced per unit of nutrient in that tissue by a given forest-type or given plantation species under a regime of continual exploitation. Bruijnzeel (1984) found, for example, a higher production of wood per unit of nitrogen or phosphorus in the wood in plantations of *Pinus merkusii* compared with nearby plantations of *Agathis dammara* in Java. A major factor in the production of large quantities of wood with low nutrient content seems to be the astonishingly complete withdrawal of certain nutrients, particularly phosphorus and potassium, from older wood in some kinds of tree, first emphasized by Beadle & White (1968) for eucalypts. Choice of crop must depend, of course, not only on NUE at the level of tissues taken off-site, but also on the medium- and long-term effects of the plants on the soil.

INFLUENCE OF PLANTS ON SOIL FERTILITY

Restoration of soil fertility during a bush fallow is one of the best documented instances of plants affecting the nutrient-supplying power of the soil beneath them. Various aspects of this phenomenon are treated in the contributions by Juo & Kang, Nakano & Syahbuddin, Ramakrishnan and Trenbath in this volume. The effects of tree crops, as opposed to woody fallows, have been reviewed by Sanchez *et al.* (1985). It has often been thought that deeper-rooted plants, especially trees, play a critical role by 'pumping' phosphate and basic cations from the subsoil to the topsoil (cf. Nye & Greenland 1960). Now that the variable-charge phenomena of many tropical soils are beginning to be appreciated (Sollins *this volume*; Robertson *this volume*), we see the possibility of nitrate ions being retained in the subsoil after the cutting and burning of forest, and the possibility of their being brought to the surface by deeper-rooted plants of the fallow (Matson *et al.* 1987). A contrasting effect occurs where grasses come to dominate a site (often after burning). They tend to be shallower rooted than woody plants, and take up much less calcium per unit mass of shoot. In this way they may fail to counteract leaching of bases from the profile; the pH then falls, the concentration of available aluminium increases and with it the phosphate-binding power of the soil, and thus soil fertility is reduced (J. J. Ewel, personal communication).

A somewhat different perspective on the relative roles of tree and herb was provided by Bernhard-Reversat (1982), working in the Sahel. She showed that the soil under the scattered trees contained and released more nitrogen than that between the trees, but argued that this was mainly a result of greater growth of

herbs under the trees — in other words, an indirect effect of the trees. A more rad-
ical revision of the received view of the way in which trees affect soil fertility has
been provided by Kellman (1979, *this volume*), based on his studies of savanna in
Belize. Where various broadleaved trees have invaded savanna after the
cessation of burning, the soil is enriched in phosphate and bases, but apparently
not as a result of 'pumping' by deep roots or even by roots spreading far outside
the canopy as happens in the case of shrubs in semi-desert (Charley & West 1975).
Kellman emphasizes the fact that the soil (over granite) is so deeply weathered
that there is no especially rich source of phosphate and bases in the subsoil
awaiting transfer by roots of woody plants to the topsoil; Burnham (*this volume*)
has made essentially the same point for deeply weathered soils under forest in the
Far East. Juo & Kang (*this volume*) and Fölster (1986) emphasize how toxic a
highly acidic subsoil may be for root growth. All these observations force us to
think very carefully about Kellman's hypothesis that soil enrichment in his area
comes about essentially as a result of the trees capturing more effectively the
nutrients that fall in the rain. Critical measurements are certainly needed from a
number of areas.

Kellman (*this volume*) also points out the need to think about alternation of
forest and savanna as a result of climatic changes in the Quaternary, the
concomitant changes in soil fertility, and, particularly, the ability of some forest
trees tolerant of low soil fertility to invade savanna, change the soil and so
facilitate invasion by less tolerant species. As a background to such changes, we
have to think about the question of whether or not soils under tropical rain forest
are relentlessly losing their effective nutrient-supplying power as a result of
weathering and leaching over the millenia, even when they are not subject to pod-
zolization, paludification or formation of concretionary lateritic material. Rather
little seems to have been written about this question, and much hinges on the
extent to which losses to the sea from really old soils can be balanced by input in
rainfall.

Not only plants but also animals affect soil fertility. In addition to their
general role in speeding up nutrient cycling, not much discussed in this volume,
they can bring about massive changes in the spatial distribution of nutrients in a
system. Trapnell *et al.* (1976) have documented the impoverishment of the bulk
of the soil in a woodland in Zambia by termites, and the localized enrichment in
their nests.

PLANT–MICROBE AND PLANT–ANIMAL RELATIONS

Symbioses and mineral nutrition

Only a few remarks can be made here on this very important topic. Of the issues
raised by Alexander (*this volume*) in his paper on mycorrhiza, the most
outstanding to my mind is the question of competition between the vesicular-
arbuscular (VA) and sheathing types of mycorrhiza in the dipterocarp-dominated
forests of South-East Asia. How do so many species with VA mycorrhiza persist

in a forest where the most abundant and largest trees all have sheathing mycorrhiza?

The decrease in importance of trees with sheathing mycorrhiza found on passing from high-rainfall savannas to low-rainfall savannas, and the associated increase in importance of trees with dinitrogen-fixing nodules, is fascinating. The suggestion by Högberg (*this volume*) that this reflects a change from predominant phosphorus limitation to predominant nitrogen limitation is provocative, but not entirely convincing. For example, De Rham (1970) reported very low rates of nitrogen mineralization in the soils of high-rainfall savanna in the Ivory Coast. Moreover, in the Brazilian *cerrado*, where the soils are undeniably phosphate-poor (Lathwell & Grove 1986), some legumes are nodulated, e.g. species of *Dalbergia* and *Lonchocarpus* (J. I. Sprent, personal communication 1987). In the past it has been argued that where water is in very short supply (as it is for most of the time in low-rainfall savanna), nodulation is unlikely to be selected, and plants which 'invest' more of their carbon in gaining water rather than nitrogen will be favoured (Sprent 1985).

Symbioses between plants and ants have not been discussed in this Symposium, but for some plants they may be an important means of obtaining mineral nutrients (Huxley 1986). Insectivorous plants have also been missed out, despite their prominence in certain nutrient-poor tropical vegetation types (Richards 1952; Whitmore 1984).

Herbivory and plant defence

The major issue of whether or not losses to herbivores are relatively much greater in vegetation on nutrient-rich soils, as proposed by Janzen (1974), is another important issue not discussed. Proctor *et al.* (1983b) provided some strong evidence against the Janzen view.

Equally interesting is the question of the effectiveness of the different kinds of chemical defence described by Waterman & Mole (*this volume*), and the extent to which the chemical constitution of the parts of an individual plant change adaptively in response to shade, drought or reduced nutrient supply. Denslow *et al.* (1987) found that addition of nitrogen or phosphorus fertilizer to rooted cuttings of six shrub species did not induce the expected decrease in production of phenolics — nine out of ten significant differences were increases.

GENERAL COMMENTS AND NEEDS IN THE FUTURE

The following comments are based on my impressions of the talks and discussions at the Symposium.

1 There is still too little experimental work being done, with most reports still at the descriptive and correlative stage.

2 Definitions and hypotheses need to be thought through more rigorously, for example, in the case of 'nutrient-use efficiency'.

3 Rather little work involving new methods was reported; positive examples concerned denitrification, the variable-charge behaviour of soils, and the impact of addition of selected mineral nutrients on the growth of roots in intact forest.
4 Work done in the tropics needs to be seen less in isolation, and more in combination with the findings and ideas of those working in other regions, as is illustrated in the present contribution.
5 A positive attitude is needed with regard to the interactions between the effects of nutrients and the effects of other environmental factors, e.g. light and drought, not only on growth rate, but also on the production of defensive chemicals. Experimental work should be planned with the possible importance of interactions in mind.
6 The contributions concerned with nutrient supply and the roles of symbionts are very promising, but too little attention was paid to plant–animal and plant–disease relations.
7 More emphasis needs to be placed on potentially limiting nutrients other than nitrogen and phosphorus, and on the most deficient soils more work is needed on micro-nutrients.
8 Finally, in agreement with Murphy & Lugo (1986), Vitousek & Sanford (1986) and Whitmore (*this volume*), it is clear that more information is needed on (a) rain forests occupying the commonest types of soil rather than the extremes, (b) forests on all kinds of soil in dry climates, (c) savannas in high-rainfall areas, and (d) the various kinds of mixtures of different life forms now being used in experiments designed to provide for sustainable development in the tropics.

Despite these criticisms, it is clear that our understanding of the mineral nutrient relations of tropical forests and savannas has progressed greatly in the last 10 years, and that many exciting developments are just emerging.

CONCLUSION

The relationship between nutrient supply on the one hand and forest stature and physiognomy on the other is complex; commonly nutrient shortage is correlated with reduced stature, but there are notable exceptions — just as we find when looking for correlations between forest stature and water shortage or reduced temperatures. The question of whether or not nutrients are 'limiting growth' in a given community has to be asked both of the species present and those species found nearby but apparently unable to invade the community in question; species suited to inherently poor soils often respond rather little to additions above a very low level. Despite this complication, recent studies in montane forest have shown limitation by nitrogen, the element commonly supposed to be the first limiting nutrient in this type of vegetation. Recent experimental work in lowland rain forest has tended to emphasize limitation by elements other than nitrogen or phosphorus, notably calcium and magnesium. Much critical information is available for limitation by nitrogen and phosphorus in savanna in one low-rainfall area (the Sahel), but more is needed for a variety of savanna types in higher-rainfall areas, and for forests in tropical dry-climate regions.

Studies on nutrient-use efficiency in the tropics are in their infancy; care should be taken to see that appropriate measurements are made, and that comparisons allow for changes in NUE with plant and stand age and thus for different temporal and spatial patterns of regeneration in different communities. The counter-intuitive idea that plants of soils with a richer nutrient supply may accumulate more dry weight per unit of time and nutrient taken up, mainly by development of more stem tissue as a 'carbon sink', could prove to be widely applicable in forests and savannas.

Many of the exciting developments likely to occur in the immediate future concern the interactions between the effects of mineral nutrients and other environmental factors, the mechanisms whereby plants affect the fertility of the soil beneath them and the effects of nutrient supply on the interrelations between higher plants, their symbionts and the animals and disease organisms that prey on them — all vitally important in the production of viable development schemes for the tropics, as well as in the improvement of our understanding of natural communities.

ACKNOWLEDGEMENTS

I am indebted to J. R. Healey and Dr E. V. J. Tanner for discussions on their research, comments on a draft of this paper and permission to quote their unpublished results. I also thank Professors E. Medina and R. Herrera for arranging my visit to San Carlos de Rio Negro in 1982, and so enlarging enormously my experience of forests on strongly nutrient-deficient soils in the lowland tropics.

REFERENCES

Ågren, G.I. (1983). Nitrogen productivity of some conifers. *Canadian Journal of Forest Research*, **13**, 494–500.

Anderson, J.A.R. (1964). The structure and development of the peat swamps of Sarawak and Brunei. *Journal of Tropical Geography*, **18**, 7–16.

Armstrong, M.J. & Kirkby, E.A. (1979). Estimation of potassium recirculation in tomato plants by comparison of the rates of potassium and calcium accumulation in the tops with their fluxes in the xylem stream. *Plant Physiology*, **63**, 1143–1148.

Beadle, N.C.W. & White, G.J. (1968). The mineral content of the trunks of some Australian woody plants. *Proceedings of the Ecological Society of Australia*, **3**, 55–60.

Beard, J.S. (1955). The classification of tropical American vegetation-types. *Ecology*, **36**, 89–100.

Berendse, F. & Aerts, R. (1987). Nitrogen-use-efficiency: a biologically meaningful definition? *Functional Ecology*, **1**, 293–296.

Bernhard-Revarsat, F. (1982). Biogeochemical cycle of nitrogen in semi-arid savanna. *Oikos*, **38**, 321–332.

Bernhard-Reversat, F., Huttel, C. & Lemée, G. (1978). Structure and functioning of evergreen rain forest ecosystems of the Ivory Coast. *Tropical Forest Ecosystems* (Ed. by UNESCO, UNEP & FAO), pp. 557–574. UNESCO, Paris.

Boorman, L.A. (1982). Some growth patterns in relation to the sand dune habitat. *Journal of Ecology*, **70**, 607–614.

Bradshaw, A.D., Chadwick, M.J., Jowett, D., Lodge, R.W. & Snaydon, R.W. (1960). Experimental investigations into the mineral nutrition of several grass species. Part III. Phosphate level. *Journal of Ecology*, **48**, 631–637.

Bradshaw, A.D., Chadwick, M.J., Jowett, D. & Snaydon, R.W. (1964). Experimental investigations into the mineral nutrition of several grass species. Part IV. Nitrogen level. *Journal of Ecology*, **52**, 665–676.

Brown, R.H. (1978). A difference in N use efficiency in C3 and C4 plants and its implications in adaptation and evolution. *Crop Science*, **18**, 93–98.

Bruenig, E. (1969). On the seasonality of drought in the lowlands of Sarawak (Borneo). *Erdkunde*, **23**, 127–133.

Bruijnzeel, L.A. (1984). Immobilization of nutrients in plantation forests of *Pinus merkusii* and *Agathis dammara* growing on volcanic soils in central Java, Indonesia. *Proceedings of International Conference on Soils and Nutrition of Perennial Crops* (Ed. by A. Tajib & E. Pushparajah), pp. 19–29. Malaysian Soil Science Society, Kuala Lumpur.

Buckley, R.C., Corlett, R.T. & Grubb, P.J. (1980). Are the xeromorphic trees of tropical montane rainforests drought-resistant? *Biotropica*, **12**, 124–136.

Chapin, F.S., Vitousek, P.M. & Van Cleve, K. (1986). The nature of nutrient limitation in plant communities. *American Naturalist*, **127**, 48–58.

Charley, J.L. & West, N.E. (1975). Plant-induced soil chemical patterns in some shrub-dominated semi-desert ecosystems of Utah. *Journal of Ecology*, **63**, 945–963.

Cockayne, L. (1928). *The Vegetation of New Zealand*, 2nd edn. Engelmann, Leipzig.

Corner, E.J.H. (1966). *The Natural History of Palms*. Weidenfeld & Nicolson, London.

Cornforth, I.S. (1968). Relationship between soil volume used by roots and nutrient accessibility. *Journal of Soil Science*, **19**, 291–301.

Cuatrecasas, J. (1958). Aspectos de la vegetacion natural de Colombia. *Revista de la Academia de Ciencias Naturales de Colombia*, **10**, 221–264.

Cuevas, E. & Medina, E. (1983). Root production and organic matter decomposition in a terra firme forest of the upper Rio Negro basin. *International Symposium on Root Ecology and its Applications* (Ed. by L. Kutschera), pp. 653–666. Gumpenstein, Austria.

Cuevas, E. & Medina, E. (1986). Nutrient dynamics within Amazonian forest ecosystems. I. Nutrient flux in fine litter fall and efficiency of nutrient utilization. *Oecologia*, **68**, 466–472.

Denslow, J.S., Vitousek, P.M. & Schultz, J.C. (1987). Bioassays of nutrient limitation in a tropical rainforest soil. *Oecologia*, **74**, 370–376.

De Rham, P. (1970). L'azote dans quelques forêts, savanes et de terrains de culture d'Afrique tropicale humide (Côte d'Ivoire). *Veröffentlichungen des Geobotanischen Institutes, Zürich*, **45**, 1–127.

Edwards, P.J. (1982). Studies of mineral cycling in a montane rain forest in New Guinea. V. Rates of cycling in throughfall and litter fall. *Journal of Ecology*, **70**, 807–827.

Edwards, P.J. & Grubb, P.J. (1977). Studies of mineral cycling in a montane rainforest in New Guinea. I. The distribution of organic matter in the vegetation and soil. *Journal of Ecology*, **65**, 943–969.

Edwards, P.J. & Grubb, P.J. (1982). Studies of mineral cycling in a montane rain forest in New Guinea. IV. Soil characteristics and the division of mineral elements between the vegetation and soil. *Journal of Ecology*, **70**, 649–666.

Ellenberg, H. (1978). *Die Vegetation Mitteleuropas mit den Alpen*, 2nd edn. Ulmer, Stuttgart.

Fahey, T.J. & Knight, D.H. (1986). Lodgepole pine ecosystems. *BioScience*, **36**, 610–617.

Field, C. & Mooney, H.A. (1983). Leaf age and seasonal effects on light, water, and nitrogen use efficiency in a California shrub. *Oecologia*, **56**, 348–355.

Field, C. & Mooney, H.A. (1986). The photosynthesis–nitrogen relationship in wild plants. *On the Economy of Plant Form and Function* (Ed. by T.J. Givnish), pp. 25–55. Cambridge University Press, Cambridge.

Fölster, H. (1986). Forest–savanna dynamics and desertification processes in the Gran Sabana. *Interciencia, Caracas*, **11**, 311–316.

Garcia-Miragaya, J., San Jose, J.J. & Hernandez, J. (1983). Effect of added nitrogen, phosphorus and potassium on above-ground biomass production and nutrient content of *Trachypogon* savanna grasses. *Tropical Ecology*, **24**, 33–41.

Gay, P.E., Grubb, P.J. & Hudson, H.J. (1982). Seasonal changes in the concentrations of nitrogen, phosphorus and potassium, and in the density of mycorrhiza, in biennial and matrix-forming perennial species of closed chalkland turf. *Journal of Ecology*, **70**, 571–593.

Gerrish, G. & Bridges, K.W. (1984). A thinning and fertilizing experiment in *Metrosideros* dieback stands in Hawaii. *Hawaii Botanical Science Paper, Department of Botany, University of Hawaii*, **43**, i–iii & 1–107.

Gorham, E. (1953). The development of the humus layer in some woodlands of the English Lake District. *Journal of Ecology*, **41**, 123–152.

Gray, B. (1975). Size-composition and regeneration of *Araucaria* stands in New Guinea. *Journal of Ecology*, **63**, 273–289.

Gray, J.T. (1983). Nutrient use by evergreen and deciduous shrubs in southern California. I. Community nutrient cycling and nutrient-use efficiency. *Journal of Ecology*, **71**, 21–41.

Gregory, F.G. (1953). The control of growth and reproduction by external factors. *Report of the 13th International Horticultural Congress, 1952*, pp. 96–105.

Grubb, P.J. (1971). Interpretation of the 'Massenerhebung' effect on tropical mountains. *Nature (London)*, **229**, 44–45.

Grubb, P.J. (1977). Control of forest growth and distribution on wet tropical mountains: with special reference to mineral nutrition. *Annual Review of Ecology and Systematics*, **8**, 83–107.

Grubb, P.J. & Stevens, P.F. (1985). *The Forests of the Fatima Basin and Mt Kerigomna, Papua New Guinea with a Review of Montane and Subalpine Rainforests in Papuasia. Department of Biogeography and Geomorphology Publication BG/5*. Australian National University Press, Canberra.

Grubb, P.J. & Tanner, E.V.J. (1976). The montane forests and soils of Jamaica: a reassessment. *Journal of the Arnold Arboretum*, **57**, 313–368.

Hall, J.B. & Swaine, M.D. (1976). Classification and ecology of closed-canopy forest in Ghana. *Journal of Ecology*, **64**, 913–951.

Harcombe, P.A. (1977). The influence of fertilization on some aspects of succession in a humid tropical forest. *Ecology*, **58**, 1375–1383.

Hirose, T. (1971). Nitrogen turnover and dry matter production of a *Solidago altissima* population. *Japanese Journal of Ecology*, **21**, 18–32.

Hirose, T. (1975). Relations between turnover rate, resource utility and structure of some plant populations: a study in the matter budgets. *Journal of the Faculty of Science, University of Tokyo, Section 3, Botany*, **11**, 355–407.

Hirose, T. (1984). Nitrogen use efficiency in growth of *Polygonum cuspidatum* Sieb. et Zucc. *Annals of Botany*, **54**, 695–704.

Huxley, C.R. (1986). Evolution of benevolent ant–plant relationships. *Insects and the Plant Surface* (Ed. by B.E. Juniper & Sir Richard Southwood), pp. 257–282. Arnold, London.

Janzen, D.H. (1974). Tropical blackwater rivers, animals and mast fruiting by the Dipterocarpaceae. *Biotropica*, **6**, 69–103.

Kapos, V. & Tanner, E.V.J. (1985). Water relations of Jamaican upper montane rain forest trees. *Ecology*, **66**, 241–250.

Kellman, M. (1979). Soil enrichment by neotropical savanna trees. *Journal of Ecology*, **67**, 565–577.

Körner, C., Bannister, P. & Mark, A.F. (1986). Altitudinal variation in stomatal conductance, nitrogen content and leaf anatomy in different plant life forms in New Zealand. *Oecologia*, **69**, 577–588.

Körner, C. & Diemer, M. (1987). *In situ* photosynthetic responses to light, temperature and carbon dioxide in herbaceous plants from low and high altitude. *Functional Ecology*, **1**, 179–194.

Lambers, H. (1985). Respiration in intact plants and tissues: its regulation and dependence on environmental factors, metabolism and invaded organisms. *Encyclopaedia of Plant Physiology, Vol. 18. Higher Plant Cell Respiration* (Ed. by R. Douce & D.A. Day), pp. 418–473. Springer, Berlin.

Lathwell, D.J. & Grove, T.L. (1986). Soil–plant relationships in the tropics. *Annual Review of Ecology and Systematics*, **17**, 1–16.

Lawton, R.O. (1982). Wind stress and elfin stature in a montane rain forest tree: an adaptive explanation. *American Journal of Botany*, **69**, 1224–1230.

Lee, K.E. (1969). Some soils of the British Solomon Islands Protectorate. *Philosophical Transactions of the Royal Society of London, Series B*, **255**, 211–257.

Marrs, R.H., Proctor, J., Heaney, A. & Mountford, M.D. (1988). Changes in soil nitrogen-mineralization and nitrification along an altitudinal transect in tropical rainforest in Costa Rica. *Journal of Ecology*, **76**, 468–482.

Matson, P.A. & Vitousek, P.M. (1987). Cross-system comparison of soil nitrogen transformations and nitrous oxide fluxes in tropical forests. *Global Biogeochemical Cycles*, **1**, 163–170.

Matson, P.A., Vitousek, P.M., Ewel, J.J., Mazzarino, M.J. & Robertson, G.P. (1987). Nitrogen transformations following tropical forest felling and burning on a volcanic soil. *Ecology*, **68**, 491–502.

Medina, E., Sabrado, M. & Herrera, R. (1978). Significance of leaf orientation for leaf temperature in an Amazonian sclerophyll vegetation. *Radiation and Environmental Biophysics*, **15**, 131–140.

Miller, H.G. (1984). Dynamics of nutrient cycling in plantation ecosystems. *Nutrition of Plantation Forests* (Ed. by G.D. Bowen & E.K.S. Nambiar), pp. 53–78. Academic Press, London.

Mitchell, H.L. & Chandler, R.F. (1939). The nitrogen nutrition and growth of certain deciduous trees of northeastern United States. *Black Rock Forest Bulletin*, **11**, i–vii & 1–94.

Murphy, P.G. & Lugo, A.E. (1986). Ecology of tropical dry forest. *Annual Review of Ecology and Systematics*, **17**, 67–88.

Murray, D.B. & Nichols, R. (1966). Light, shade and growth of some tropical plants. *Light as an Ecological Factor* (Ed. by R. Bainbridge, G.C. Evans & O. Rackham), pp. 249–263. British Ecological Society Symposium 6. Blackwell Scientific Publications, Oxford.

Newman, E.I. (1978). Root microorganisms: their significance in the ecosystem. *Biological Reviews*, **53**, 511–554.

Nye, P.H. & Greenland, D.J. (1960). *The Soil Under Shifting Cultivation. Technical Communication 51.* Commonwealth Bureau of Soils, Harpenden, U.K.

Peace, W.J.H. & Grubb, P.J. (1982). Interaction of light and mineral nutrient supply in the growth of *Impatiens parviflora. New Phytologist*, **90**, 127–150.

Peace, W.J.H. & McDonald, F.D. (1981). An investigation of the leaf anatomy, foliar mineral levels, and water relations of a Sarawak forest. *Biotropica*, **13**, 100–109.

Pearcy, R.W. (1987). Photosyntnetic gas exchange responses of Australian tropical forest trees in canopy, gap and understory micro-environments. *Functional Ecology*, **1**, 169–178.

Penning de Vries, F.W.T. & Djiteye, M.A. (Eds.) (1982). *La Productivité des Pâturages Sahéliens— Une Étude des Sols, des Végétations et de l'Exploitation de Cette Ressource Naturelle.* Centre for Agricultural Publishing and Documentation, Wageningen.

Polak, B. (1948). Landbouw op Veengronden. *Landbouw Buitenzorg*, **20**, 1–50.

Proctor, J., Anderson, J.M., Chai, P. & Vallack, H.W. (1983a). Ecological studies in four contrasting lowland rain forests in Gunung Mulu National Park, Sarawak. I. Forest environment, structure and floristics. *Journal of Ecology*, **71**, 237–260.

Proctor, J., Anderson, J.M., Fogden, S.C.L. & Vallack, H.W. (1983b). Ecological studies in four contrasting lowland rain forests in Gunung Mulu National Park, Sarawak. II. Litterfall, litter standing crop and preliminary observations on herbivory. *Journal of Ecology*, **71**, 261–283.

Richards, P.W. (1952). *The Tropical Rain Forest.* Cambridge University Press, Cambridge.

Ritz, K. & Newman, E.I. (1985). Evidence for rapid cycling of phosphorus from dying roots to living plants. *Oikos*, **45**, 174–180.

Rozijn, N.A.M.G. (1984). *Adaptive strategies of some dune annuals.* PhD Thesis, Free University of Amsterdam.

Rundel, P.W. (1982). Nitrogen utilization efficiencies in Mediterranean-climate shrubs of California and Chile. *Oecologia*, **55**, 409–413.

Saker L.R., Clarkson, D.T. & Purves, J. (1988). Internal cycling of N and S in *Ricinus* (castr bean). *Long Ashton Annual Report for 1987.*

Sanchez, P.A., Palm, C.A., Davey, C.B., Szott, L.T. & Russell, C.E. (1985). Tree crops as soil improvers in the humid tropics? *Attributes of Trees as Crop Plants* (Ed. by M.G.R. Cannell & J.E. Jackson), pp. 327–359. Institute of Terrestrial Ecology, Monks Wood.

Sanford, R.L., Saldarriaga, J., Clark, K.E., Uhl, C. & Herrera, R. (1985). Amazon rain-forest fires. *Science*, **227**, 53–55.

Saverimuttu, A.M.T. (1987). *Physiological ecology of Arrhenatherum elatius and Bromus erectus on calcareous soils of differing fertility.* PhD Thesis, University of Cambridge.

Simpson, R.J., Lambers, H. & Dalling, M.J. (1982). Translocation of nitrogen in a vegetative wheat plant (*Triticum aestivum*). *Physiologia Plantarum*, **56**, 11–17.

Small, E. (1972). Photosynthetic rates in relation to nitrogen recycling as an adaptation to nutrient deficiency in peat bog plants. *Canadian Journal of Botany*, **50**, 2227–2233.

Southwick, E.E. (1984). Photosynthate allocation to floral nectar: a neglected energy investment. *Ecology*, **65**, 1775–1779.

Specht, R.L. & Rayson, P. (1957). Dark Island Heath. I. Definition of the ecosystem. *Australian Journal of Botany*, **5**, 52–85.

Sprent, J.I. (1985). Nitrogen fixation in arid environments. *Plants for Arid Lands* (Ed. G.E. Wickens, J.R. Goodin & D.V. Field), pp. 215–229. George, Allen & Unwin, London.

Sugden, A.M. (1986). The montane vegetation and flora of Margarita Island, Venezuela. *Journal of the Arnold Arboretum*, **67**, 187–232.

Switzer, G.L. & Nelson, L.E. (1972). Nutrient accumulation and cycling in loblolly pine (*Pinus taeda* L.) plantation ecosystems: the first twenty years. *Proceedings of the Soil Science Society of America*, **36**, 143–147.

Tanner, E.V.J. (1977). Four montane rain forests of Jamaica: a quantitative characterization of the floristics, the soils and the foliar mineral levels, and a discussion of the interrelations. *Journal of Ecology*, **65**, 883–918.

Tanner, E.V.J. (1980). Studies on the biomass and productivity in a series of montane rain forests in Jamaica. *Journal of Ecology*, **68**, 573–588.

Tanner, E.V.J. (1985). Jamaican montane forests: nutrient capital and cost of growth. *Journal of Ecology*, **73**, 553–568.

Tanner, E.V.J., Kapos, V., Freskos, S., Healey, J.R. & Theobald, A.M. (1989). Nitrogen and phosphorus fertilization of Jamaican montane forest trees. *Journal of Tropical Ecology*, **5**, in press.

Thurston, J.M. (1969). The effect of liming and fertilizers on the botanical composition of permanent grassland, and on the yield of hay. *Ecological Aspects of the Mineral Nutrition of Plants* (Ed. by I.H. Rorison), pp. 3–10. Symposium of the British Ecological Society 9. Blackwell Scientific Publications, Oxford.

Trapnell, C.G., Friend, M.T., Chamberlain, G.T. & Birch, H.F. (1976). The effects of fire and termites on a Zambian woodland soil. *Journal of Ecology*, **64**, 577–588.

Vitousek, P.M. (1982). Nutrient cycling and nutrient use efficiency. *American Naturalist*, **119**, 553–572.

Vitousek, P.M. (1984). Litterfall, nutrient cycling, and nutrient limitation in tropical forests. *Ecology*, **65**, 285–298.

Vitousek, P.M. & Denslow, J.S. (1986). Nitrogen and phosphorus availability in treefall gaps of a lowland tropical rainforest. *Journal of Ecology*, **74**, 1167–1178.

Vitousek, P.M., Matson, P.A. & Turner. D.R. (1988). Elevational and age gradients in Hawaiian montane rainforest: foliar and soil nutrients. *Oecologia*, **77**, 565–570.

Vitousek, P.M. & Sanford, R.L. (1986). Nutrient cycling in moist tropical forest. *Annual Review of Ecology and Systematics*, **17**, 137–167.

Vitousek, P.M., Walker, L.R., Whiteaker, D., Muller-Dombois, D. & Matson, P.A. (1987). Biological invasion by *Myrica faya* alters ecosystem development in Hawaii. *Science*, **238**, 802–804.

Webb, L.J. (1968). Environmental relationships of the structural types of Australian rain forest vegetation. *Ecology*, **49**, 296–311.

Whitmore, T.C. (1969). The vegetation of the Solomon Islands. *Philosophical Transactions of the Royal Society of London, Series B*, **255**, 259–270.

Whitmore, T.C. (1984). *Tropical Rain Forests of the Far East*, 2nd edn. Clarendon Press, Oxford.

Whitmore, T.C. & Burnham P.C. (1969). An altitudinal sequence of forests and soils on granite near Kuala Lumpur. *Malayan Nature Journal*, **22**, 99–118.

Williams, R.F. (1939). Physiological ontogeny in plants and its relation to nutrition. 6. Analysis of the unit leaf rate. *Australian Journal of Experimental Biology and Medical Science*, **17**, 132.

Note added in proof
Vitousek, Matson & Turner (1988) found a marked and significant decline in foliar nitrogen concentration in *Metrosideros polymorpha* with increase in altitude in Hawaii (cf. p. 421, *this volume*).

Mineral nutrients in tropical ecosystems: a soil scientist's view

A. WILD

Department of Soil Science, University of Reading,
Reading RG1 5AQ

SUMMARY

1 The requirements for rational land-use planning which leads to increased food production are (a) classification and characterization of soils and (b) development of stable systems of soil management.

2 Soil analysis for nutrients in tropical savannas and forests is often unsatisfactory because sampling is inadequate and the methods used are those developed for short-term availability to arable crops. It is recommended that measurements should be made of total nutrients and the rate of turnover of organically held nutrients.

3 Techniques that have been developed to measure the components of the nitrogen balance sheet need to be applied to tropical ecosystems.

4 Because of the diversity of soils, annual rainfall and its distribution, altitude and range of plant species, models which incorporate these variables are needed to describe the cycling of nutrients and their rates of net mineralization.

5 The processes of acidification are reviewed and reference is made to the effect of microbial activity on soil redox potential.

6 Soil scientists, ecologists and others need to collaborate more closely to improve our understanding of processes in tropical ecosystems so that any development for food production is put on a more secure basis.

INTRODUCTION

Land is perhaps the most important natural resource in tropical countries. Much of it is under forest and savanna vegetation which is being cleared for agricultural development. Some development has to take place quickly because more food needs to be produced, but it causes concern to ecologists, soil scientists and others. Important practical questions are whether we can distinguish those areas of land which might be used successfully for agriculture in the long term from those which cannot, and whether we can devise stable systems of cultivation that lead to increased food production. These are fundamental questions that involve more than the ecologist and the soil scientist and they cannot be dealt with adequately in a short paper.

Here, only three topics will be highlighted: nutrients and their sources, nutrient dynamics and acidification. The wider issues have been dealt with by Lal, Sanchez & Cummings (1986), and further useful information has been given by Nye & Greenland (1960), Sanchez (1976), Jordan (1985), Ewel (1986), Lathwell & Grove (1986) and Vitousek & Sanford (1986). Jones & Wild (1975) dealt with the management of soils of the West African savanna, and Lal (1987) has given a full account of the physical changes and erosion hazard when soils in the tropics are brought into cultivation. Attiwill & Leeper (1987) have recently described nutrient cycling in Australian forests.

Harsh experience has frequently demonstrated that soil management in the tropics should not simply mimic that which has been successful in temperate countries. Where scientific resources are short we can use what we know from elsewhere as long as we recognize that the physical, chemical, biological and socio-economic conditions will set limits on what can be achieved. We must also beware of over-simplification, because in the tropics, soils, annual rainfall and its distribution, altitude and range of natural plant species are very diverse.

NUTRIENTS AND THEIR SOURCES

According to the criteria of Arnon & Stout (1939), 13 nutrients are essential for the growth of higher plants: the major elements nitrogen, phosphorus and potassium, the secondary elements calcium, magnesium and sulphur, and the micro-nutrients boron, chlorine, copper, iron, manganese, molybdenum and zinc. In addition, cobalt, sodium and silicon are required for some processes in some plants. For animals there is a different list (Underwood 1977).

Nye & Greenland (1960) reported data from different sites of the annual increase of nutrients contained in the above-ground vegetation of African rain forest (Table 1). They represent net change, that is, gross uptake minus gross loss. From chemical analysis of the above-ground biomass of montane forests in Jamaica, Tanner (1985) has estimated the amounts of nutrients required for annual growth. More data are needed on this important aspect of nutrient cycling, and sulphur and micro-nutrients should be included.

Soil as a source of nutrients

The two sources of nutrients are the atmosphere and the regolith. The upper part of the regolith is the soil profile which, for the present purpose, will be taken to include litter. Through wet and dry deposition the atmosphere can provide many

TABLE 1. Mean annual increase of nutrients in the above-ground vegetation of tropical rain forests of Africa (Nye & Greenland 1960)

	N	P	K	Ca + Mg
			(kg ha^{-1})	
Over first 5 years	114	6.3	91	84
Over first 18 years	39	5.9	34	46
Over first 40 years	40	2.8	17	54

nutrient elements in chemically combined form, but nitrogen and sulphur are usually the most important (Jordan 1985). The amounts added to the ecosystem decrease roughly exponentially with distance from the source. The amount of dry deposition also depends on the height and nature of leaf surfaces.

In soil the solution acts as the immediate source of nutrients. Recent work has added to our understanding of the uptake process, which is now recognized to be less simple than was once thought. For example, depending on their nutritional status, plant roots can modify their environment (Marschner 1986). From well-mixed solutions roots can take up nutrients from very low concentrations, e.g. 0.4 μM phosphate and 1 μM potassium, and as long as the concentrations are maintained, the uptake rates are sufficient to allow the plants to achieve their potential growth rates (Wild, Jones & Macduff 1987).

In soils, because of uptake by the root, nutrient depletion often occurs close to the root surface, and the zone of depletion increases with time. This produces a concentration gradient which leads to the diffusion of nutrient to the root: the main process for the transport of potassium and phosphate (Nye & Tinker 1977). Another effect of depletion of the solution is that nutrients are desorbed from the surfaces of clays and organic matter. The soil solution is also replenished in nitrogen, phosphate and sulphate by the mineralization of organic matter. In addition to diffusion, convective flow of the soil solution carries nutrient to the root, the rate depending on the solution concentration and the rate of transpiration. These concepts are more fully described by Nye & Tinker (1977), Barber & Silberbush (1984) and Wild (1988). Mycorrhizal associations have an important role in nutrient uptake, especially for elements in low concentrations in the soil solution, and are discussed by Mikola (1980) and Harley & Smith (1983). Bowen (1984) has reviewed the growth and functioning of tree roots and the effect of mycorrhizas.

Ideally, we can describe nutrient uptake by roots in terms of nutrient concentration (strictly activity) in the soil solution, the exchangeable or easily desorbed nutrient, the rate of mineralization of organically held nutrients, the rate of transport through the soil, the mean distance between active roots, and the rate of plant growth, but there are too many unknowns for this to be practicable. Instead, the usual method is to measure the amount of nutrient released to a chemical extractant, of which there are several, which provides an index of availability commonly known as a soil test value. The concentration in the extract which is considered just sufficient to maintain the potential growth rate depends on the conditions for growth, the extractant used and many other variables. Sanchez (1976) discussed the interpretation of results obtained with soil extractants and rightly commented that soil test values are useful only when correlated with crop responses. They will rank soils according to the amount of nutrient they release to the extractant, but the amount does not itself establish whether or not there is a deficiency. With trees, correlations are difficult to obtain and soil test values are of little use.

Where time and resources permit, nutrient supplies can be characterized better than by soil test values. The method to be used depends on the nutrient under investigation. For nitrogen, there are well-known methods for measuring mineralization rates of organically held nitrogen under field and laboratory conditions (Hesse 1971), but predicting rates is still difficult. Characterization of the phosphate supply requires measurement of both the rate of mineralization of organically held phosphorus, a measurement that is required for natural ecosystems but is rarely made, and the amount of inorganic phosphate held on clay and oxide surfaces that can be easily desorbed. The desorbable phosphate can be measured using anion exchange resins (Page, Miller & Kenney 1982) and by ^{32}P (Le Mare 1982).

Over a short period of growth the quantity of potassium that can be taken up by plants is adequately assessed by conventional cation exchange methods, but over periods of more than a few weeks the release of non-exchangeable potassium becomes increasingly important. Quantification of the rate of release is not easy, but a good indication of its importance is given by the size distribution and identity of the soil minerals containing potassium (Munson 1985). The calcium and magnesium status of soils are satisfactorily assessed by cation exchange methods, but if weatherable minerals are present, total calcium and magnesium should also be measured. Sulphur resembles phosphorus in being a component of soil organic matter; in soils of dry tropical savannas it is often also present as gypsum and in acid soils sulphate is adsorbed on clay and oxide surfaces. Desorbable sulphate is usually measured by extraction with a phosphate solution (Page, Miller & Kenney 1982). The availability of micro-nutrients in general is difficult to assess except by soil test values.

Considering the longevity of trees and the amount of nutrients that accumulate in them, my conclusion is that more attention should be paid to characterizing the nutrient supplies in forest soils. Methods developed for arable crops will characterize the immediately available supplies, but total nutrients should also be measured. To characterize the rate of supply the method depends on the nutrient, but with nitrogen, phosphorus and sulphur, the rates of mineralization of organically held nutrient should be known.

Comment is also needed on the required intensity and depth of soil sampling. Most tree roots are in the top 50 cm of soil, and soil must be properly sampled to this depth. The intensity of sampling will depend on the purpose of the investigation and on the nature of the site, but at least 20 samples per hectare from each soil layer should be taken. Samples should be taken below 50 cm to the limit of root growth even though this may be difficult. The nutrient reserves in this greater depth of soil can be measured by total analysis. Although many soils of the humid tropics contain no, or few, weatherable minerals down to several metres (Burnham, *this volume*), this is not always so. From detailed mineralogical investigation of soils of southern Nigeria, Hughes (1981) reported muscovite, biotite, feldspar and hornblende as common or abundant in the fine sand fraction of B horizons of a few soils. Their presence was related to the local parent material and to colluvial processes. As would be expected from the mineral content, some of the soils contained large amounts of nutrient elements (Greenland 1981). Although it is not possible to measure directly the rate of release of nutrients from weatherable minerals, budgets obtained from watersheds (catchments) provide estimates (Likens *et al.* 1977).

Techniques for measuring components of the nitrogen balance sheet

Compared with the research support for temperate agricultural systems, that for natural ecosystems in the tropics is miniscule. It is greater, although still small, for cultivated ecosystems in the tropics and for temperate woodlands and tree plantations. The contrast is clearly shown by our lack of understanding of the components of the nitrogen balance sheet. Techniques have been developed which allow measurements to be made of these components including biological nitrogen fixation, denitrification, ammonia volatilization, nitrate leaching and nitrogen cycling within the soil. As yet there are no reliable balance sheets for nitrogen in the tropics.

Quantifying nitrogen balance sheets is itself difficult. One method is to use catchments, measure inputs in rainfall and outputs to rivers, and estimate biological fixation and gaseous losses by difference. Using this method, Salati & Vose (1984) estimated the nitrogen balance in the Amazon Basin as $+18.9$ kg ha^{-1} $year^{-1}$. The biggest annual input was attributed to biological fixation. The annual recycling of nitrogen in litter at three sites was given as 57, 106 and 141 kg ha^{-1}.

There are many publications on regional nitrogen cycles (Rosswall 1980; Clark & Rosswall 1981; Wetselaar, Simpson & Rosswall 1981; Robertson, Herrera & Rosswall 1982; Robertson & Rosswall 1986). A common theme is the lack of reliable data. Symbiotic and non-symbiotic nitrogen fixation are difficult to measure reliably under field conditions. Although there are methods based on acetylene reduction, isotope dilution and $^{15}N_2$ incorporation (Giller & Day 1985), estimates are generally inferred from changes of total nitrogen in the ecosystem. Values for West Africa (Table 2) from the review of Robertson & Rosswall (1986) give orders of magnitude. Little progress seems to be being made in identifying

TABLE 2. Nitrogen fixed in West African vegetation zones (Robertson & Rosswall 1986)

Vegetation zone		Fixation (kg ha^{-1} year^{-1})
Forests	Cultivated	6
	Early-successional	100
	Mid-successional	60
	Mature	15
Savanna	Cultivated	7
	Grazed, fallow	30
Sahel	Cultivated	7
	Grazed, fallow	12
Sub-desert	Grazed, unused	<1

the organisms responsible, or indeed the relative contributions by organisms in the phyllosphere and in the soil.

No measurements in the tropics other than on paddy rice appear to have been reported on losses by denitrification*. Measurement can be made of the production of nitrous oxide when the reduction to dinitrogen is blocked by acetylene, which can be done using soil cores (Ryden & Rolston 1983). Loss of gaseous ammonia from soils under forests is improbable, although there might be volatilization of ammonia and other reduced nitrogen compounds from leaves (Farquhar, Wetselaar & Weir 1983). When soil is brought into cultivation, nitrogen is lost when vegetation is burned. If the soil has a pH of 7 or above, ammonia may be volatilized, especially when the soil dries.

Nitrate leaching can always be expected if nitrate is present in the soil and there is substantially greater rainfall than transpiration. Salati & Vose (1984) gave a value of 4–6 kg NO_3-N ha^{-1} leached annually in the Amazon Basin. In 2 years after a forest fallow, mineralization of soil nitrogen exceeded crop uptake by 240 kg N ha^{-1}, and most was probably lost by leaching (Mueller-Harvey, Juo & Wild 1985). From uncropped and unfertilized monolith lysimeters at Onne near Port Harcourt, Nigeria (average rainfall 2420 mm $year^{-1}$) the annual leaching loss over 2 years was 154 kg N ha^{-1} (Wong, Wild & Juo 1987). Other values from a range of environments in West Africa have been summarized by Jones & Wild (1975) and Greenland (1980). The suggestion of Greenland that nitrate leaching might be retarded in acid soils of West Africa, as in other acid soils, has recently been confirmed (Wong *et al.* 1987). The consequences of nitrate leaching are that nitrogen is lost from the ecosystem, and basic cations are also lost.

NUTRIENT DYNAMICS

Of the inputs to the soil from vegetation (Jordan 1985), those from litterfall have been best described. Table 3 gives averaged data sets from Proctor (1984) and Cole & Rapp (1981) for tropical and temperate forests. The reported analyses do not include sulphur or micro-nutrients. Also included are the calculated ratios of C : N, C : P and N : P.

The data illustrate the point that litterfall in general has wide ratios of carbon (which provides the energy source for the organisms that decompose the litter) to nitrogen, phosphorus and presumably sulphur. These three elements are components of the complex polymers that constitute soil organic matter. In the organic matter of the A layers of soil the ratios are much narrower. The C : N ratio is usually between 10 and 14, the C : P ratio is about 80–120 and the C : S ratio is also about 100 (Dalal 1977; Wild 1988). In upland soils in which there is annual through-drainage, the ratios of C : N and C : S in the soil as a whole are about the same as in organic matter because this component contains most of the

---

*But see Robertson, G.P. & Tiedje J.M. (1988) *Nature,* **336**, 756–759 for recent measurements in Costa Rica.

TABLE 3. The amount of litterfall in tropical and temperate forests, the concentrations and amount of nutrient elements within it and its C : N, C : P and N : P ratios. The values are the means of the data collated by Cole & Rapp (1981) and Proctor (1984) and refer to dry matter; number of observations in parentheses.

Component	Temperate forests		Tropical forests	
	Concentration (%)	Amount (kg ha^{-1})	Concentration (%)	Amount (kg ha^{-1})
(Litterfall)		3047 (16)		8240 (137)
Nitrogen	1.48	45 (16)	1.16	95 (132)
Phosphorus	0.14	4.2 (16)	0.072	5.9 (128)
Potassium	0.45	14 (16)	0.36	30 (79)
Calcium	0.97	30 (16)	1.17	96 (81)
Magnesium	0.13	4 (16)	0.29	24 (71)
C : N ratio		34		43
C : P ratio		364		698
N : P ratio		11		16

soil nitrogen and sulphur. Some of the soil phosphorus is present in inorganic forms and the above value applies to the C : organic phosphorus ratio (Anderson 1980). Considerable amounts of carbon are evolved as CO_2 before these narrower ratios are achieved. The rates of litter decomposition, and hence of CO_2 evolution, have been reviewed by Anderson & Swift (1983) and only a few points will be made here.

The intense biological activity which results in net loss of carbon by respiration increases the soil biomass. By scavenging the mineral sources in the labile pool, organisms incorporate the nutrients they require into their tissues (biological immobilization). Immobilization persists as long as the readily available energy source exceeds the nutrient supply in the labile pool. Because of the variable nature of plant residues, there is no universal ratio below which there will be no appreciable immobilization of nutrients. As a guide, a C : N ratio of about 25 and a C : P ratio of 200–300 may be used to separate net mineralization from net immobilization. For sulphur the ratio is probably about the same as for phosphorus.

Using the data in Table 3, calculation can be made of the evolution of CO_2 that must occur in converting the litterfall of tropical forests into soil organic matter with a C : N ratio of 10 and a C : organic P ratio of 100. Assuming that half the mass of litterfall is carbon, the required carbon loss is 3170 kg ha^{-1} year^{-1} (4120–950) for nitrogen and 3530 kg ha^{-1} year^{-1} (4120–590) for phosphorus. This calculation indicates that net immobilization of phosphorus will last a little longer than net immobilization of nitrogen. Also important is that whereas carbon and nitrogen can be added by biological fixation processes and some sulphur will be absorbed from the atmosphere, the phosphorus content of soil is controlled by the parent material. Indeed, McGill & Cole (1981) argued that phosphorus is 'the ultimate control on organic matter cycling and accumulation'.

The high ratios of C : organic P in soils of Ghana under forest and savanna (Nye & Bertheux 1957) support this view.

The period during which there is net immobilization cannot be calculated with any certainty because of lack of reliable measurements of CO_2 evolution from litter. The range from tropical soils has been reported by Ewel *et al.* (1981) as 0.5–19.5 g CO_2-C m^{-2} day^{-1}, which includes respiration loss from roots. For illustration only, a rate of evolution of 2 g CO_2-C m^{-2} day^{-1} would need to continue for 159 days and 177 days to lower the C : N ratio to 10 and the C : P ratio to 100 in the example given above.

These calculations based on average data serve only to show the probable extent of biological immobilization from litterfall under forests. They are no substitute for through-the-year measurements of litterfall, CO_2 evolution from litter, C : N, C : organic P and C : organic S ratios. The succession of organisms during the decomposition of organic materials is itself worth investigation, as Anderson *et al.* (1985), Clarholm (1985) and Coleman (1985) and his associates have shown with other ecosystems.

The overall effect of immobilization can be great. A good illustration is that incorporation of phosphorus into soil organic matter limited the growth of grass on old soils in New Zealand (Walker & Syers 1976).

CHANGES UNDER CULTIVATION

The nutrient status of the soil changes quickly when land under forest or savanna vegetation is brought into cultivation. More nutrient is conserved if the vegetation is burned than if removed from the site (Sanchez 1976; Ewel *et al.* 1981; Greenland & Okigbo 1982). Most burning practices in forest clearance cause little loss of nutrients from the soil itself (Ewel *et al.* 1981).

When land is brought into cultivation, the fate of soil nitrogen, phosphorus and sulphur is largely dependent on changes in the content of soil organic matter. It has been shown that decomposition of plant debris and soil organic matter, as measured by carbon loss, needs to be described by multicompartment systems, each compartment having its own rate of loss (Jenkinson & Rayner 1977). For nitrogen the rate of net mineralization is less variable because it is conserved compared with carbon. The same relative constancy of mineralization is expected to apply to phosphorus and sulphur. A good account of the changes of soil nitrogen under shifting cultivation has been given by Sanchez (1982).

Several equations have been used to describe the rate of change of the content of nitrogen in soil (Bartholomew 1977; Campbell 1978). The equations may assume a constant rate of change, and therefore a size of change that is proportional to the content of nitrogen in the soil. When addition of nitrogen (A) in plant debris is made to soil containing an amount (N) of soil nitrogen, the rate of change is

$$dN/dt = -kN + A$$

where k is the decomposition constant. Integration over time t gives

$$N = N_0 e^{-kt} + A/k\,(1 - e^{-kt})$$

where N_0 is the nitrogen content at zero time. The values of k and t are usually considered on an annual basis. If the values of N_0, k and t are known, the value of N can be calculated for a succession of years t.

Greenland (1980) has shown from a collection of data from West Africa that apart from the first 2 years after clearance of forest and savanna vegetation, the rate of decrease of soil nitrogen conforms reasonably well with an annual mineralization constant of 0.02–0.06. Mueller-Harvey, Juo & Wild (1985, *this volume*) reported rates of decrease of carbon, nitrogen, organic phosphorus and organic sulphur after clearance of a 15-year-old forest at Ibadan, Nigeria on an Alfisol. During a 22-month period after clearance the mineralization constants (k) were 0.179 (carbon), 0.193 (nitrogen), 0.136 (phosphorus) and 0.262 (sulphur). As expected, the value of the mineralization constant k for nitrogen is higher than reported by Greenland (1980) for longer-term mineralization.

Measurements at the Ibadan site showed that during the first 2 years of cultivation there was mineralization of 622 kg ha^{-1} soil nitrogen and crop uptake (two crops per year) of 382 kg ha^{-1}. This indicates a large loss from the soil, and considering the excess rainfall, this was probably by leaching; hence a large part of the soil nitrogen built up under the forest fallow was wasted. Phosphorus is not lost from the soil because it is adsorbed on to oxide and clay surfaces. Sulphur, as SO_4^{2-}, is more weakly adsorbed and some leaching loss is expected.

It is worth considering whether the loss of nitrogen after a fallow can be reduced. Mineralization rates of organic matter are affected by soil pH, texture, water content, temperature, and under flood conditions, by the supply of oxygen. Temperature has a pronounced effect. For example, Jenkinson & Ayanaba (1977) found the decomposition rate of ^{14}C-labelled ryegrass (*Lolium perenne*) to be 4 times greater at Ibadan, Nigeria than at Rothamsted, England. The velocity coefficient at $(T+10)\,°C$ was between 2 and 3 times that at $T\,°C$, which is the usual observation (Campbell 1978). Because of the close relationship between the gross mineralization of organic carbon and the net mineralization of nitrogen, the same temperature effect will apply to nitrogen.

Soil temperature is lower and more nearly constant under forest than under cultivation. At 5 cm depth the soil temperature at Ibadan was about 10–15 °C lower than after clearing, and was also lower under a mulch of crop residues than in bare soil (Lal 1975). Curves B and C in Fig. 1 show the effect of the decomposition constant (k) on the rate of change of soil nitrogen. The difference between the curves might represent the effect of a forest canopy or an increase in altitude of about 2000 m. The mulch of crop residues such as cereal straw will itself contain nitrogen which will mineralize, but the effect is small (compare curves A and B) compared with the effect of temperature.

Based on the calculations used for Fig. 1, Table 4 gives the annual amounts of

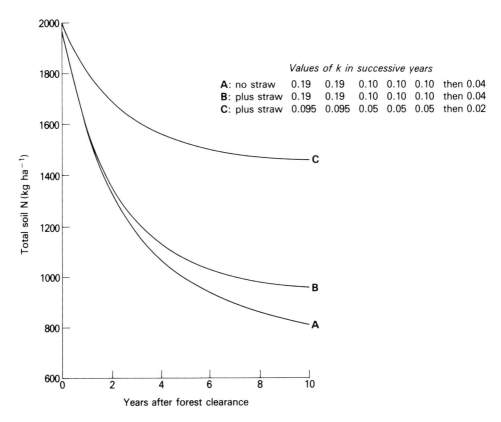

FIG. 1. Effect of decomposition constant k and addition of cereal straw on the nitrogen content of soil calculated from $\ln N_t/N_0 = kt$, where N_t is nitrogen content after time t (years) and N_0 is initial nitrogen content. A, no straw; B and C, with straw and allowing for its nitrogen content.

nitrogen mineralized in soil. Because of gaseous and leaching losses, not all the nitrogen released by mineralization is taken up by crops. The proportion of mineral nitrogen that is taken up is commonly about one-half, but varies widely depending on crop growth, the amount of mineral nitrogen in the soil and gaseous and leaching losses. The amounts of nitrogen that can be expected to be taken up

TABLE 4. Effect of soil temperature and mulch on annual mineralization rate of nitrogen in cropped soil, $\triangle N$ (kg ha^{-1}). System A, no mulch; B, mulch at 4 t ha^{-1} year^{-1} containing 0.5% N and at same temperature as A; C, mulch at temperature 10 °C lower than B

Years	System A		System B		System C	
	k	$\triangle N$	k	$\triangle N$	k	$\triangle N$
1	0.19	340	0.19	340	0.095	179
2	0.19	280	0.19	285	0.095	164
3	0.10	128	0.10	132	0.05	81
4	0.10	117	0.10	122	0.05	79
5	0.10	104	0.10	111	0.05	76
6–10	0.04	36	0.04	41	0.02	29

by crops can therefore be obtained by multiplying the values in Table 4 by a factor which is variable and therefore needs to be measured. The same calculations can be done for phosphorus and sulphur.

Calculations for the Ibadan site (Table 4) indicate that mineralization of organic matter after a forest fallow should produce enough nitrogen, phosphorus and sulphur to support yields of about 3 t maize grain per year for 4 years. A lower yield should be sustained, for a longer period, if the mineralization rate is reduced by protecting the soil surface from solar radiation.

The purpose in giving these calculations is to show that they could provide a basis for advising farmers on the use of fertilizers, which are required when the supply of nutrients is lower than is needed for the planned crop yield. It is particularly difficult to advise on the requirement for nitrogen fertilizer in the humid tropics because mineralization and leaching loss occur concurrently during the growing season. Modelling, based on reliable measurements at selected sites, could help to overcome this problem.

ACIDIFICATION

Soils under tropical forest are commonly, but not always, acid and the pH range is wide. To take two examples: the pH values (in water) of four soils from the Amazon Basin were in the range 3.7–4.7 (Salati & Vose 1984), and in five soils from Sarawak the pH was in the range 3.6–6.1 (Proctor et al. 1983). Soil pH influences several processes and reactions that affect nutrient supplies, in addition to effects on the animal and plant species in the ecosystem. The causes of change of pH therefore deserve some attention.

Van Breemen, Mulder & Driscoll (1983) listed 19 reactions which can increase or decrease soil pH. Examples are:

Nitrification

$$NH_4^+ + 4O \rightarrow NO_3^- + H_2O + 2H^+ \tag{1}$$

Oxidation of ferrous iron

$$4Fe^{2+} + 2O + 10H_2O \rightarrow 4Fe(OH)_3 + 8H^+ \tag{2}$$

Weathering of orthoclase to kaolinite

$$2KAlSi_3O_8 + 2H^+ + 9H_2O \rightarrow 2K^+ + Al_2Si_2O_5(OH)_4 + 4H_4SiO_4 \tag{3}$$

Reduction of ferric iron

$$4Fe(OH)_3 + 8H^+ \rightarrow 4Fe^{2+} + 2O + 10H_2O \tag{4}$$

Reactions (1) and (2) result in acidification. In reactions (3) and (4) protons are removed from solution, the pH increases and the process is sometimes described as alkalinization. Reactions (2) and (4) involve the oxidation and reduction of iron and are common processes in soils; they are examples of a redox system (Rowell 1988b) which is strongly influenced by microbial activity. Other examples of acidification processes are sulphide oxidation, and uptake of cations by plant roots in excess of the uptake of an equivalent of anions.

Rainwater is essentially a solution of carbonic acid which gives a pH of 5.65 at the atmospheric pressure of CO_2. The pH is lower in the presence of dissolved oxides of nitrogen and sulphur. Dry deposition of sulphur oxides and ammonia (after nitrification) also contributes to the acidification of soil from atmospheric sources. Unless carbonates or weatherable minerals are present, the usual effect is that freely-drained soils in high-rainfall areas become more acid with time. A fuller description of the chemistry of acidification has been given by Skeffington (1987).

The effect on the soil pH depends also on the buffer capacity of the soil. Soils are able to remove protons from solution by ion exchange on the surfaces of clays and organic matter, the protons in solution being replaced by basic cations (K^+, Na^+, Ca^{2+}, Mg^{2+}). This process is reversible. Below a pH of about 5.5 aluminium also acts as a buffer to a further decrease of pH. For example,

$$Al(OH)_3 + H^+ \rightarrow Al(OH)_2^+ + H_2O$$

although this is a simplification of a more complex process (Rowell 1988a).

A large perturbation of pH occurs when forested land is brought into cultivation. The ash left after a burn contains several salts, including carbonates, hydroxides and silicates, which raise the soil pH. Ewel *et al.* (1981) reported an ash deposit of 670 g m^{-2} after burning 8–9-year-old forest in Costa Rica which raised the pH of the soil (0–3 cm) from 5.0 to 6.2. Nitrification will increase acidity and, if there is throughflow of water, nitrate and other anions will be leached from the soil accompanied by an equivalent amount of cations. From cropped acid soil at Onne near Port Harcourt, Nigeria, which had received 1 t ha^{-1} of calcium hydroxide, the average amounts of calcium, magnesium, potassium and sodium leached in 1 year were 316, 27, 20 and 30 kg ha^{-1}, respectively (Wong 1985). Leaching of these basic cations will result in acidification.

AN OVERVIEW

The questions that were posed in the Introduction were: 'can we distinguish those areas of land which might be used successfully for agriculture in the long term from those which cannot, and can we devise stable systems of cultivation that lead to increased food production?' We need to be able to answer both questions in the affirmative wherever development for agricultural use is occurring or will occur. To provide affirmative answers for each area of land being considered for development there are certain prerequisites.

1 Land evaluation, land-use planning and soil surveys are required. Planning should include the decision to leave land undisturbed if development would lead to serious problems such as erosion or severe soil compaction, or would require expensive inputs that would make the development uneconomic.

2 Trials at research institutions should be directed towards the establishment of stable systems of soil management and these should be tested and adapted for other environments. This necessarily entails long-term research. Investigation of the use of mulches and interplanting of hedgerows of trees with annual crops (alley cropping) at the International Institute of Tropical Agriculture (Lal 1987; Juo & Kang *this volume*) are good examples of what is needed. The systems were developed on Alfisols at Ibadan and are being modified for use on more acid Oxisols near Port Harcourt.

A major problem with tropical soils is their diversity, which is probably the reason why there are so many half-truths about them. Generalizations describe tropical soils as 'acid', 'nutrient poor' and 'high phosphate fixing', all of which are often wrong. Such misconceptions can be avoided if we accept soil diversity as a fact. Although the language may seem strange, systems of soil classification (FAO/UNESCO 1974; Soil Survey Staff 1975), which continue to be improved, produce order from complexity and help to avoid misleading generalizations.

A lesson can also be learned from the way that the problem of diversity is tackled in temperate countries. Field experiments at research institutions located in the main ecological zones are used to identify problems and produce solutions. In order to extend these findings to other locations, we need to know what soil properties and what other conditions are required for good crop growth, and we need to understand processes. For example, field experiments might establish the optimum application of nitrogen fertilizer as an average over a period of years, but to extend this elsewhere, the growing conditions, rates of mineralization of organically held nitrogen, and rates of loss of mineral nitrogen need to be taken into account. Similarly, the Universal Soil Loss Equation (Smith & Wischmeier 1962), which is process-based, helps to predict the erosion hazard. Salinization and acidification can also be quantified with increasing confidence as the processes become better understood. Nutrient dynamics as described earlier fit into this context.

To summarize, much experimental work on soils is required in the tropics and to be successful it should: (i) use good soil and land-use surveys, (ii) include long-term field experiments, and (iii) be based on the soil/crop processes that determine crop growth. Lal (1985) has set out the requirements more fully.

The soil scientist needs to know more about soils at undisturbed sites in the tropics, partly because they are themselves of interest and partly because they provide the baseline from which the effects of cultivation can be assessed. For agricultural development there is need for collaboration between soil scientists, ecologists and others who are concerned about the future of these important ecosystems.

REFERENCES

Anderson, G. (1980). Assessing organic phosphorus in soils. *The Role of Phosphorus in Agriculture* (Ed. by F.E. Khasawneh, E.C. Sample & E.J. Kamprath), pp. 411–431. American Society of Agronomy, Madison, Wisconsin.

Anderson, J.M., Huish, S.A., Ineson, P., Leonard, M.A. & Splatt, P.R. (1985). Interactions of invertebrates, micro-organisms and tree roots in nitrogen and mineral element fluxes in deciduous woodland soils. *Ecological Interactions in Soil* (Ed. by A.H. Fitter), pp. 377–392. Blackwell Scientific Publications, Oxford.

Anderson, J.M. & Swift, M.J. (1983). Decomposition in tropical forests. *Tropical Rain Forest: Ecology and Management* (Ed. by S.L. Sutton, T.C. Whitmore & A.C. Chadwick), pp. 287–309. Blackwell Scientific Publications, Oxford.

Arnon, D.I. & Stout, P.R. (1939). The essentiality of certain elements in minute quantity for plants with special reference to copper. *Plant Physiology*, 14, 371–375.

Attiwill, P.M. & Leeper, G.W. (1987). *Forest Soils and Nutrient Cycles*. Melbourne University Press, Melbourne.

Barber, S.A. & Silberbush, M. (1984). *Roots, Nutrient and Water Flux and Plant Growth*. Wiley, Chichester.

Bartholomew, W.V. (1977). Soil nitrogen changes in farming systems in the humid tropics. *Biological Nitrogen Fixation in Farming Systems of the Tropics* (Ed. by A. Ayanaba & P.J. Dart), pp. 27–42. Wiley, Chichester.

Bowen, G.D. (1984). Tree roots and the use of nutrients. *Nutrition of Plantation Forests* (Ed. by G.D. Bowen & N.K.S. Nambiar), pp. 147–179. Academic Press, London.

Campbell, C.A. (1978). Soil organic carbon, nitrogen and fertility. *Soil Organic Matter* (Ed. by M Schnitzer & S.U. Khan), pp. 173–271. Elsevier, Amsterdam.

Clarholm, M. (1985). Possible roles for roots, bacteria, protozoa and fungi in supplying nitrogen to plants. *Ecological Interactions in Soil* (Ed. by A.H. Fitter), pp. 355–365. Blackwell Scientific Publications, Oxford.

Clark, F.E. & Rosswall, T. (Eds.) (1981). *Terrestrial Nitrogen Cycles. Ecological Bulletin (Stockholm) No. 33.*

Cole, D.W. & Rapp, M. (1981). Elemental cycling in forest ecosystems. *Dynamic Properties of Forest Ecosystems* (Ed. by S.E. Reichle), pp. 341–409. Cambridge University Press, Cambridge.

Coleman, D.C. (1985). Through a ped darkly: an ecological assessment of root–soil–microbial–faunal interactions. *Ecological Interactions in Soil* (Ed. by A.H. Fitter), pp 1–21. Blackwell Scientific Publications, Oxford.

Dalal, R.C. (1977). Soil organic phosphorus. *Advances in Agronomy*, 29, 83–117.

FAO/UNESCO (1974). *Soil Map of the World, Vol. 1. Legend.* FAO–UNESCO, Rome.

Ewel, J.J. (1986). Designing agricultural ecosystems for the humid tropics. *Annual Review of Ecology and Systematics*, 17, 245–271.

Ewel, J.J., Berish, C., Brown, B., Price, N. & Raich, J. (1981). Slash and burn impacts on a Costa Rican wet forest site. *Ecology*, 62, 816–829.

Farquhar, G.D., Wetselaar, R. & Weir, B. (1983). Gaseous nitrogen losses from plants. *Gaseous Loss of Nitrogen from Plant-Soil Systems* (Ed. by J.R. Freney & J.R. Simpson), pp. 159–194. Nijhoff/Junk, The Hague.

Giller, K.E. & Day, J.M. (1985). Nitrogen fixation in the rhizosphere: significance in natural and agricultural systems. *Ecological Interactions in Soil* (Ed. by A.H. Fitter), pp. 127–147. Blackwell Scientific Publications, Oxford.

Greenland, D.J. (1980). The nitrogen cycle in West Africa—agronomic considerations. *Nitrogen Cycling in West African Ecosystems* (Ed. by T. Rosswall), pp. 73–81. SCOPE/UNEP International Unit, Sweden.

Greenland, D.J. (Ed.) (1981). *Characterization of Soils in Relation to their Classification and Management for Crop Production: Examples from Areas of the Humid Tropics.* Clarendon Press, Oxford.

Greenland, D.J. & Okigbo, B.N. (1982). Crop production under shifting cultivation and maintenance of soil fertility. *Symposium on Potential Productivity of Field Crops*, pp. 505–524. International Rice Research Institute, Los Banos, Philippines.

Harley, J.L. & Smith, S.E. (1983). *Mycorrhizal Symbiosis.* Academic Press, London.

Hesse, P.R. (1971). *A Textbook of Soil Chemical Analysis.* Murray, London.

Hughes, J.C. (1981). Mineralogy. *Characterization of Soils in Relation to their Classification and Management for Crop Production: Examples from some Areas of the Humid Tropics* (Ed. by D.J. Greenland), pp. 30–48. Clarendon Press, Oxford.

Jenkinson, D.S. & Ayanaba, A. (1977). Decomposition of carbon-14 labelled plant material under tropical conditions. *Soil Science Society of America Journal,* **41**, 912–915.

Jenkinson, D.S. & Rayner, J.H. (1977). The turnover of soil organic matter in some of the Rothamsted classical experiments. *Soil Science,* **123**, 298–305.

Jones, M.J. & Wild, A. (1975). *Soils of the West African Savanna. Technical Communication No. 55.* Commonwealth Bureau of Soils, Harpenden.

Jordan, C.F. (1985). *Nutrient Cycling in Tropical Forest Ecosystems.* Wiley, Chichester.

Lal, R. (1975). *Role of Mulching Techniques in Tropical Soil and Water Management. Technical Bulletin No. 1.* International Institute of Tropical Agriculture, Ibadan, Nigeria.

Lal, R. (1985). Conversion of tropical rainforest: agronomic impact and ecological consequences. *Advances in Agronomy,* **39**, 173–264.

Lal, R. (1987). *Tropical Ecology and Physical Edaphology.* Wiley, Chichester.

Lal, R., Sanchez, P.A. & Cummings, R.W. (1986). *Land Clearing and Development in the Tropics.* Balkema, Boston.

Lathwell, D.J. & Grove, T.L. (1986). Soil–plant relationships in the tropics. *Annual Review of Ecology and Systematics,* **17**, 1–16.

Le Mare, P.H. (1982). Sorption of isotopically exchangeable and non-exchangeable phosphate by some soils of Colombia and Brazil, and comparisons with soils of southern Nigeria. *Journal of Soil Science,* **33**, 691–707.

Likens, G.E., Bormann, F.H., Pierce, R.S., Eaton, J.S. & Johnson, N.M. (1977). *Biogeochemistry of a Forested Ecosystem.* Springer, New York.

Marschner, H. (1986). *Mineral Nutrition of Higher Plants.* Academic Press, London.

McGill, W.B. & Cole, C.V. (1981). Comparative aspects of cycling of organic C, N, S, and P through soil organic matter. *Geoderma,* **26**, 267–286.

Mikola, P. (Ed.) (1980). *Tropical Mycorrhizal Research.* Clarendon Press, Oxford.

Mueller-Harvey, I., Juo, A.S.R. & Wild, A. (1985). Soil organic C, N, S, and P after forest clearance in Nigeria: mineralization rates and spatial variability. *Journal of Soil Science,* **36**, 585–591.

Munson, R.D. (Ed.) (1985). *Potassium in Agriculture.* American Society of Agronomy, Madison, Wisconsin.

Nye, P.H. & Bertheux, M.H. (1957). The distribution of phosphorus in forest and savannah soils of the Gold Coast and its agricultural significance. *Journal of Agricultural Science (Cambridge),* **49**, 141–159.

Nye, P.H. & Greenland, D.J. (1960). *The Soil Under Shifting Cultivation. Technical Communication No. 51.* Commonwealth Bureau of Soils, Harpenden.

Nye, P.H. & Tinker, P.B. (1977). *Solute Movement in the Soil-Root System.* Blackwell, Oxford.

Page, A.L., Miller, R.H. & Kenney, D.R. (Eds.) (1982). *Methods of Soil Analysis,* Part 2. American Society of Agronomy, Madison, Wisconsin.

Proctor, J. (1984). Tropical forest litterfall II: the data set. *Tropical Rain Forest: The Leeds Symposium* (Ed. by A.C. Chadwick & S.L. Sutton), pp. 83–113. Special publication of the Leeds Philosophical and Literary Society, Leeds.

Proctor, J., Anderson, J.M., Chai, P. & Vallack, H.W. (1983). Ecological studies in four contrasting lowland rain forests in Gunung Mulu National Park, Sarawak I. *Journal of Ecology,* **71**, 237–260.

Robertson, G.P., Herrera, R. & Rosswall, T. (Eds.) (1982). *Nitrogen Cycling in Ecosystems of Latin America and the Caribbean.* Nijhoff/Junk, The Hague.

Robertson, G.P. & Rosswall, T. (1986). Nitrogen in West Africa: the regional cycle. *Ecological Monographs,* **56**, 43–72.

Rosswall, T. (Ed.) (1980). *Nitrogen Cycling in West African Ecosystems.* SCOPE/UNEP International Unit, Sweden.

Rowell, D.J. (1988a). Soil acidity and alkalinity. *Russell's Soil Conditions and Plant Growth* (Ed. by A. Wild), pp. 844–898. Longman, London.

Rowell, D.J. (1988b). Flooded and poorly drained soils. *Russell's Soil Conditions and Plant Growth*

(Ed. by A. Wild), pp. 899–926. Longman, London.

Ryden, J.C. & Rolston, D.E. (1983). The measurement of denitrification. *Gaseous Loss of Nitrogen from Plant–Soil Systems* (Ed. by J.R. Freney & J.R. Simpson), pp. 91–132. Nijhoff/Junk, The Hague.

Salati, E. & Vose, P.B. (1984). Amazon Basin: a system in equilibrium. *Science*, **225**, 127–138.

Sanchez, P.A. (1976). *Properties and Management of Soils in the Tropics.* Wiley, New York.

Sanchez, P.A. (1982). Nitrogen in shifting cultivation systems of Latin America. *Plant and Soil*, **67**, 91–103.

Skeffington, R.A. (1987). Transport of acidity through ecosystems. *Pollutant Transport and Fate in Ecosystems* (Ed. by P.J. Coughtrey, M.H. Martin & M.H. Unsworth), pp. 139–154. Blackwell Scientific Publications, Oxford.

Smith, D.D. & Wischmeier, W.H. (1962). Rainfall erosion. *Advances in Agronomy*, **14**, 109–148.

Soil Survey Staff (1975). *Soil Taxonomy. Handbook No. 436.* U.S. Department of Agriculture, Washington.

Tanner, E.V.J. (1985). Jamaican montane forests: nutrient capital and cost of growth. *Journal of Ecology*, **73**, 553–568.

Underwood, E.J. (1977). *Trace Elements in Human and Animal Nutrition.* Academic Press, London.

Van Breemen, N., Mulder, J. & Driscoll, C.T. (1983). Acidification and alkalinization of soils. *Plant and Soil*, **75**, 283–308.

Vitousek, P.M. & Sanford, R.L. (1986). Nutrient cycling in moist tropical forest. *Annual Review of Ecology and Systematics*, **17**, 137–167.

Walker, T.W. & Syers, J.K. (1976). The fate of phosphorus during pedogenesis. *Geoderma*, **15**, 1–19.

Wetselaar, R., Simpson, J.R. & Rosswall, T. (Eds.) (1981). *Nitrogen Cycling in South-East Asian Wet Monsoonal Ecosystems.* Australian Academy of Science, Canberra.

Wild, A. (Ed.) (1988). *Russell's Soil Conditions and Plant Growth*, 11th edn. Longman, London.

Wild, A., Jones, L.H.P. & Macduff, J.H. (1987). Uptake of mineral nutrients and crop growth: the use of flowing nutrient solutions. *Advances in Agronomy*, **41**, 171–219.

Wong, M.T.F., Wild, A. & Juo, A.S.R. (1987). Retarded leaching of nitrate measured in monolith lysimeters in south-east Nigeria. *Journal of Soil Science*, **38**, 511–518.

Wong, M.T.F. (1985). *Crop uptake and leaching loss of nitrogen from ^{15}N labelled urea using monolith lysimeters in S.E. Nigeria.* PhD Thesis, Reading University, U.K.

Index

Index

Lightning Source UK Ltd.
Milton Keynes UK
UKHW041833040521
383143UK00001B/40